DIFCO MANUAL

DIFCO MANUAL

of

DEHYDRATED CULTURE MEDIA *and* REAGENTS

for

MICROBIOLOGICAL *and* CLINICAL LABORATORY PROCEDURES

NINTH EDITION

DIFCO LABORATORIES
INCORPORATED
DETROIT, MICHIGAN

First Edition	1927
Second Edition	1929
Third Edition	1931
Fourth Edition	1933
Fifth Edition	1935
Sixth Edition	1939
Seventh Edition	1943
Eighth Edition	1948
Ninth Edition	1953
Reprinted	1953
Reprinted	1956
Reprinted	1958
Reprinted	1960
Reprinted	1962
Reprinted	1963
Reprinted	1964
Reprinted	1965
Reprinted	1966
Reprinted	1967
Reprinted	1969
Reprinted	1971

APPRECIATION

Difco Laboratories desires hereby to acknowledge its indebtedness to the many microbiologists from whom it has so often sought advice and whose cooperation and assistance it has so frequently received in the development, improvement and standardization of these products.

Acknowledgment is also made of the use of published papers and textbooks as a source of much of the material in this book.

Foreword

THIS EDITION of the Difco Manual, the ninth published since 1927, has been completely revised and rewritten. The Ninth Edition is the first to include the reagents used in the preparation of media for in vitro propagation and maintenance of tissue cells.

When we first introduced prepared dehydrated culture media to the scientific world, they were regarded as laboratory curiosities. Today, Difco products are used in microbiological laboratories in all parts of the world. Difco products are not only being used by a continually increasing number of investigators, but are also constantly extending into new fields of microbiology. Bacto Dehydrated Culture Media and laboratory reagents are used in municipal and state health departments, water and sewage works, in dairies, in medical and technical colleges and the larger universities, in private diagnostic laboratories, hospitals, and commercial laboratories. Research laboratories maintained by the Federal Government are also users of Difco products.

Recommendation and approval have been extended to our products by the authors of many standard textbooks of bacteriology and by the committees on methods and procedures of scientific societies such as the American Public Health Association, the American Dairy Science Association and others.

Bacto Dehydrated Culture Media and laboratory reagents are prepared according to available standards or accepted formulae. Each ingredient is thoroughly tested and the final product is subjected to rigid examination and is standardized before being offered for distribution. The new section entitled Tissue Culture Media Reagents describes the products prepared in collaboration with the Tissue Culture Association and are tested and certified for tissue culture procedures.

The dehydrated media are stable and resist deterioration over long periods of time. They are readily and quickly prepared for use and yield uniform lots of media which provide identical nutritional conditions at all times. Aside from these readily apparent advantages, Bacto Dehydrated Culture Media are truly economical when actual cost comparisons are made.

Grateful acknowledgment is made of the support we have received from bacteriologists the world over. It is the desire of our organization to continue and to extend our services to the advancement of microbiology and related sciences.

Difco Laboratories

Table of Contents

Introduction

BACTERIOLOGY emerged as a definite branch of science as a result of the monumental and immortal researches of Pasteur and Koch. When in 1876 Robert Koch, for the first time in history, propagated a pathogenic bacterium in pure culture outside the body, he not only established *Bacillus anthracis* as the cause of a specific disease in cattle, but he inaugurated a method of investigation of disease in general which is still pursued with unabated vigor. The decade immediately following Koch's epoch-making introduction of solid culture media for the isolation and growth of bacteria ranks as one of the brightest in the history of medicine because of the number, variety, and brilliance of the discoveries made in that period. These discoveries, which, as Koch himself expressed it, came "as easily as ripe apples fall from a tree," were all dependent upon and resulted from the evolution of correct methods for the "in vitro" growth of bacteria.

The fundamental principles elaborated at that time, of which the most important was the introduction of the "poured plate" method for isolation of pure cultures, still constitute the foundation of bacteriological research. Nevertheless, it has become more and more apparent that a successful attack upon the problems still unsolved is closely related to, if not dependent upon, a thorough understanding of the minutiae influencing bacterial nutrition. With a suitable culture medium, properly used, advances in bacteriology are more readily made than when either the medium or method of use is inadequate. The bacteriologist of today is, therefore, largely concerned with the evolution of methods for the development and maintenance of growth of bacteria, upon which an understanding of the biological and biochemical phenomena resulting from bacterial activity must largely be dependent.

The chemical analyses of bacteria indicate that they are essentially water plants, the protoplasm of which contains chemical elements found in other types of plant protein (Ford). In order to build up the cells of bacteria in their anabolic phase, the protoplasmic elements must be found in the immediate environment. So vast is the problem of bacterial metabolism, and so numerous and diverse are the minutiae it includes, that a comprehensive discussion of its ramifications is precluded here. It is the purpose of this discussion to present briefly only some of the outstanding developments in this phase of bacteriology, especially as they concern the evolution of new methods for the cultivation and study of bacteria.

Almost without exception wherever bacteria occur in nature, and this is particularly true of the pathogenic forms, nitrogenous materials and carbohydrates are present. These are utilized in the maintenance of growth and for the furtherance of bacterial activities. So complex is the structure of many of these substances, however, that before they can be utilized by bacteria they must be broken down into simpler compounds. Such alterations are effected by processes of hydrolysis, oxidation, reduction, deamination, etc., and are the result of bacterial activities of primary and essential importance. These changes are ascribed to the activities of bacterial enzymes which, obviously, are both numerous and varied. The processes involved, as well as their end-products, are exceedingly complex; those of fermentation, for example, result in the production of such end products as acids, alcohols, ketones, and gases including hydrogen, carbon dioxide, methane, etc.

Abstract as such studies of bacterial metabolism may seem, their practical application is soon apparent. From these studies has come a better understanding of the nutritional needs of bacteria, and from this in turn has come the development of culture media productive of rapid and luxuriant growth—essential requisites for the isolation and study of specific organisms.

11

Studies to determine the forms of carbon, hydrogen, oxygen, and nitrogen which could most easily be utilized by bacteria for their development were originally carried on by Naegeli between 1868 and 1880, and were published by him[1] in the latter year. Naegeli's report covered the use of a large variety of substances including carbohydrates, alcohols, amino acids, organic nitrogen compounds, and inorganic nitrogen salts.

The first reference to the use of peptone for the cultivation of microorganisms is that made by Naegeli in the report referred to above, when in 1879 he compared peptone and ammonium tartrate. Because of its content of amino acids and other nitrogenous compounds which are readily utilized by bacteria, peptone soon became one of the most important constituents of culture media, as it still remains. In the light of our present knowledge, proteins are believed to be complex compounds of amino acids joined together mainly by means of the peptide linkage. When subjected to hydrolysis proteins yield metaproteins, proteoses, peptones, polypeptides, and finally the chemically simpler amino acids and their analogs. The intermediate products should be considered as classes of compounds, rather than individual substances, for there exist no sharp lines of demarcation between the various classes—one group shades by imperceptible degrees into the next. All bacteriological peptones, thus, are mixtures of various products of protein hydrolysis. Not all the products of protein decomposition are equally utilizable by all bacteria. In their relations to proteins, bacteria may be divided into two classes; those which decompose naturally occurring proteins, and those which require simpler nitrogenous compounds such as peptones and amino acids.

The relation of amino acids to bacterial metabolism, and the ability of bacteria to use these compounds, have been studied by many workers. Duval[2,3], for example, reports that cysteine and leucine are essential in the cultivation of *Mycobacterium leprae*. Kendall, Walker, and Day[4] and Long[5] report that the growth of *M. tuberculosis* is dependent upon the presence of amino acids. Many other workers have studied the relation of amino acids to the growth of other organisms, as for example, Hall, Campbell, and Hiles[6] to the meningococcus and streptococcus; Cole and Lloyd[7] and Cole and Onslow[8] to the gonococcus; and Jacoby and Frankenthal[9] to the influenza bacillus. Indispensable as amino acids are to the growth of many organisms, certain of them in sufficient concentration may exert an inhibitory effect upon bacterial development.

From the data thus far summarized, it is apparent that the problem of bacterial metabolism is indeed complicated, and that the phase concerned with bacterial growth and nutrition is of the utmost practical importance. It is not improbable that bacteriological discoveries of the greatest etiological value await merely the evolution of suitable culture media and methods of utilizing them, just as in the past important discoveries were long delayed because of a lack of similar requirements. Bacteriologists are therefore continuing to expend much energy on the elucidation of the minutiae of bacterial metabolism, and are continuing to seek methods of applying, in a practical way, the results of their studies.

While the importance of nitrogenous substances for bacterial growth was recognized early in the development of bacteriological technique, it was also realized, as has been indicated, that bacteria could not always obtain their nitrogen requirements directly from protein. It is highly desirable, in fact essential, to supply nitrogen in readily assimilable form, or in other words, to incorporate in media proteins which have already been partially broken down into their simpler and more readily utilizable components. Many laboratory methods, such as hydrolysis with alkali[10], acid[11,12,13], enzymatic digestion[14,8,15,16,17,18], partial digestion of plasma[19], et al., have been described for the preparation of protein hydrolysates.

The use of protein hydrolysates, particularly gelatin and casein, has stimulated a revival of interest in studies of the development of bacterial toxins and has opened entirely new fields of research such as the microbiological assay of vitamins and amino acids. The importance of these new paths of investigation can, as yet, only be estimated but it is already apparent that the knowledge which has been acquired is of essential value in an understanding of bacterial metabolism. Among studies in the first of these fields may be mentioned the work of Mueller and his associates[20,21,22,23,24,25] on the production of diphtheria toxin; that of Tamura et al.[26] of toxin of *Clostridium welchii;* that of Bunney and Loerber[27,28] on scarlet fever toxin, and of Favorite and Hammon[29] on staphylococcus enterotoxin. The work of Snell and Wright[30] may be mentioned as but one of many references to investigations on the assay of vitamins by means of microbiological methods. Closely associated with research of this nature are such studies as those of Mueller[31,32] on pimelic acid as a growth factor for *Corynebacterium diphtheriae,* and those of O'Kane[33] on synthesis of riboflavin by staphylococci.

In this brief discussion of certain phases of bacterial nutrition we have attempted to indicate the complexity of the subject and to emphasize the importance of continued study of bacterial nutrition. Difco Laboratories has been engaged in research closely allied to this problem in its broader aspects since 1914 when Bacto-Peptone was first introduced. Difco Dehydrated Culture Media, and ingredients of such media, have won universal acceptance as useful and dependable laboratory adjuncts in all fields of microbiology.

1 Sitz'ber, math.-physik. Klasse Akad. Wiss. Muenchen, 10:277:1880.
2 J. Exp. Med., 12:46:1910.
3 J. Exp. Med., 13:365:1911.
4 J. Infectious Diseases, 15:455:1914.
5 Am. Rev. Tuberculosis, 3:86:1919.
6 Brit. Med. J., 2:398:1918.
7 J. Path. Bact., 21:267:1917.
8 Lancet, II:9:1916.
9 Biochem. Zeit., 122:100:1921.
10 Centr. Bakt., I:29:617:1901.
11 Indian J. Med. Research, 5:408:1917-18.
12 Compt. rend. soc. biol., 78:261:1915.
13 J. Bact., 25:209:1933.
14 Ann. de l'Inst., Pasteur, 12:26:1898.
15 Indian J. Med. Research, 7:536:1920.
16 Sperimentale, 72:291:1918.
17 J. Med. Research, 43:61:1922.
18 Can. J. Pub. Health, 32:468:1941.
19 Centr. Bakt., I:77:108:1916.
20 J. Bact., 29:515:1935.
21 Brit. J. Exp. Path., 27:335:1936.
22 Brit. J. Exp. Path., 27:342:1936.
23 J. Bact., 36:499:1938.
24 J. Immunol., 37:103:1939.
25 J. Immunol., 40:21:1941.
26 Proc. Soc. Expl. Biol. Med., 47:284:1941.
27 J. Immunol., 40:449:1941.
28 J. Immunol., 40:459:1941.
29 J. Bact., 41:305:1941.
30 J. Biol. Chem., 139:675:1941.
31 J. Biol. Chem., 119:121:1937.
32 J. Bact., 34:163:1940.
33 J. Bact., 41:441:1941.

THE ORIGIN
of Dehydrated Culture Media

IT IS A PLEASURE to include, as a part of this book, the abstract given below which is believed to be the earliest reference to the preparation and use of dehydrated culture media, at least in this country. It is to be noted that Dr. Frost's arguments in favor of these preparations are just as forceful today as they were in 1909.

DESICCATED CULTURE MEDIA

W. D. FROST

University of Wisconsin

Abstract of Paper at Boston (1909) Meeting of the Society of American Bacteriologists. Science, 31:555: (Apr. 8) 1910.

In order to overcome the generally recognized faults of bacterial culture media, such as variation in composition of small batches, time consumed in preparation, rapidity with which it deteriorates, its unavailability in small institutions or private practice, the preparation of culture media in large batches in establishments especially equipped for it and then desiccated is suggested.

The author's work on this problem, covering nearly a decade of time, is considered and samples are submitted.

There is apparently no reason why the different culture media cannot be put on the market in the form which requires merely the addition of water and sterilization to make it ready for use. Not only the ordinary, but probably most of the special media, can be prepared in this way and could be put up where desired, in the form of tablets, these to be of such size that they could be put directly in test tubes and when the proper amount of water is added they would be ready for sterilization and use.

It is interesting to note that Doerr, in Kraus and Uhlenhut: Handbuch der Mikrobiologischen Technik, states he also prepared powdered culture media by drying on glass in 1909.

The practical application of the dehydration of culture media was initiated and pioneered by Difco in 1915, under the direction of Dr. J. W. M. Bunker.

GENERAL CONDITIONS
Pertaining to the Cultivation of Microorganisms

THE DEVELOPMENT of microorganisms upon culture media is dependent upon a number of very important factors:

(a) The proper food elements must be available.
(b) Oxygen must be available as required.
(c) A certain degree of moisture is necessary.
(d) The medium must be of the proper reaction.
(e) Proper temperature relations must prevail.
(f) The medium must be sterile.
(g) Contamination must be prevented.

A satisfactory microbiological culture medium must contain available sources of carbon, nitrogen, inorganic salts and, in certain cases, vitamins or other growth-promoting substances. These were originally supplied in the form of the meat infusions which were, and still are in certain cases, widely used in culture media. Beef extract frequently replaces meat infusions, but the preparation of this substance subjects it to the loss of its heat labile nutritive factors in much the same way as infusions are affected. The addition of peptone provides a readily available source of nitrogen and carbon.

Peptone is used in culture media to supply an available form of nitrogen since native proteins are not generally attacked by bacteria. Most organisms are capable of utilizing the amino acids and other simpler nitrogenous compounds present in peptone. Continued investigations in our laboratories indicate that for the isolation and propagation of many organisms the complicated infusion media can be replaced by simpler media prepared by using the proper peptones in place of the meat infusions heretofore employed.

Certain bacteria require additions of other food substances such as serum, blood, or ascites to the culture medium upon which they are to be propagated. Carbohydrates may also be desirable at times, and certain salts such as those of calcium, manganese, magnesium, sodium, and potassium seem to be required. Dyes may be added to media as indicators of metabolic activity or because of their selective inhibitory powers. Growth promoting substances of a vitamin-like nature are essential or assist greatly in the development of certain types of bacteria.

The consistency of a liquid medium may be modified by the addition of agar, gelatin or albumin in order to change it into a solid or semisolid state. Solid media, which were originally devised for the isolation of organisms in pure culture, are now universally used for almost all general cultural work. The semisolid media are used chiefly for carrying stock cultures or for propagating the anaerobes.

One of the principal landmarks in bacteriology was the preparation of a satisfactory medium by Hesse's introduction of agar as a solidifying agent for bacteriological culture media, Hueppe: Die Methoden der Bakterienforschung, 250: 1891. Previous to that time infusions of plant and animal tissues, solutions of organic compounds, and gelatin media only were employed. Until the introduction of gelatin media by Koch in 1881, the only method for obtaining pure cultures was the very unsatisfactory dilution procedure devised by Lister. The solid media used after the introduction of gelatin were only partially effective since many of the organisms under investigation would not develop satisfactorily at temperatures below the melting point of the gelatin, while others liquefied the gelatin. Bacteriology as a science began with the development of methods for the cultivation of bacteria, and the use of agar was a step of greatest importance.

Most bacteria are capable of growth under ordinary conditions of oxygen tension. Certain types, however, are capable of deriving their oxygen from their food substances. The aerobic organisms require the free admission of air, while the anaerobes grow only in the exclusion of atmospheric oxygen. Between these two groups are the microaerophiles which develop best under partial anaerobic conditions and the facultative aerobes and anaerobes which develop over a wide Eh range.

Anaerobic conditions for growth of microorganisms are obtained in a number of ways:

(a) Addition of small amounts of agar to liquid media.
(b) Addition of fresh tissue to the medium.
(c) Culturing in the presence of aerobic organisms.
(d) Addition of a reducing substance to the medium.
(e) Displacement of the air by carbon dioxide.
(f) Absorption of the oxygen by chemicals.
(g) Removal of oxygen by direct oxidation of readily oxidizable substances such as burning a candle, heating of palladiumized asbestos, copper, hydrogen, phosphorus or other readily oxidizable metals.
(h) Incubation in the presence of germinating grain or pieces of potato.
(i) Inoculation into the deeper layers of solid media, or under a layer of oil in liquid media.
(j) Combinations of these methods.

Methods of readily obtaining anaerobic conditions in the laboratory are discussed in detail on page 118. Swancara[1] describes a method of removing oxygen from individual tubes of culture media and also a method of supplying partial carbon dioxide tension. For anaerobic conditions a cotton plug is placed just above the culture medium in tubes and a gelatin capsule containing pyrogallic acid in a Durham fermentation tube is placed on top of this plug. A solution of sodium hydroxide is placed in the Durham fermentation tube and the culture tube then sealed with a rubber stopper or screw cap. The tube is then ready for incubation, the oxygen being removed by the action of the sodium hydroxide on the pyrogallic acid. He also describes a method of obtaining partial carbon dioxide tension in individual tubes by similarly placing a broken household match on a cotton plug just above the medium. Remove the percussion tip from the match prior to placing in the tube. Seal the culture tube with a rubber stopper or screw cap and ignite the match head by applying heat to the outside of the tube.

Proper moisture conditions must prevail in the culture media employed for the propagation of microorganisms. A moist medium and a moist atmosphere are necessary for the continued luxuriant growth of the vegetative cells.

The pH or reaction of the culture medium, expressing its hydrogen ion concentration, is extremely important for the growth of microorganisms. The majority of the microorganisms prefer culture media which are approximately neutral, while others may require a medium which is distinctly acid. The pH or reaction of the culture medium is determined by colorimetric or electrometric measurement of its hydrogen ion concentration. It should be noted that additions of acid or alkali which are insufficient to prevent the growth of bacteria in a medium may inhibit or prevent them from proceeding with the normal functions of their metabolic processes.

The usual range of temperature suitable for the growth of microorganisms lies between 15° and 43°C. Microorganisms have, however, been known to develop at 0°C., and others, such as the soil organisms, may grow at 80°C. The pathogenic organisms in general are limited by a comparatively narrow range of temperature around 37°C. while the saprophytes usually have a much broader latitude.

All organisms exhibit three cardinal points in their thermic relations:

(a) A minimum below which development ceases.
(b) An optimum at which growth is luxuriant.
(c) A maximum above which growth ceases and death occurs.

In addition to a suitable temperature for growth of microorganisms it is necessary to provide sufficient moisture in the atmosphere. Some organisms require a moist surface for growth. For example, media in plates inoculated with the gonococcus, may fail to show growth of the organism if placed in an ordinary incubater at 35–37°C. A duplicate inoculation, in contrast, in a sealed container in which is placed moist cotton or a wet towel to provide moisture, will show profuse growth. Incubators should have open containers filled with water at all times to provide sufficient moisture for growth and prevent drying of media. Growth of most microorganisms is obtained in the absence of light. Sunlight is to be avoided.

The media upon which microorganisms are grown must be sterile or free from all other forms whose development might influence or prevent the normal growth of the inoculated type. The usual method for immediate sterilization of culture media is by means of the autoclave in which steam under pressure is the sterilizing agent. The proper operation of the autoclave to insure sterilization of media requires careful manipulation.

Autoclave sterilization for 15 minutes at 15 pounds pressure (121°C.) is recommended for quantities of liquid media up to one liter. If larger volumes are to be sterilized in one container, and especially if the medium is not hot when placed in the autoclave, a longer period should be employed. The medium is prepared according to formula, distributed in tubes or flasks which are then plugged with nonabsorbent cotton or loosely capped and placed in the autoclave. Tubes should be placed in racks or packed loosely in baskets. Flasks should never be more than two-thirds full.

In the operation of the autoclave, all the enclosed air must be allowed to escape and must be completely replaced by steam. Pressure-temperature relations of a properly operated autoclave are shown in the table below.

Pressure-Temperature Relations in Autoclave

(Figures based upon complete replacement of air by steam.)

Pressure in Pounds	Temperature °C	°F
5	108	226
10	116	240
15	121	250
20	127	260
25	131	267
30	134	274

If all the air is not removed from the sterilizing chamber, which condition is best shown by use of a thermometer in the exhaust line of the autoclave, an entirely different pressure-temperature relationship exists. Through the courtesy of Dr. F. W. Tanner[2] we are able to reproduce the following chart which plainly shows the actual temperature in the autoclave when the air is not completely exhausted.

Effect of Entrapped Air on Temperature of Autoclave

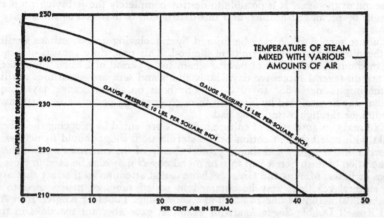

When the operator is assured that all the air is replaced by steam, which is best indicated by a thermometer placed in the exhaust line, the outlet valve of the autoclave is closed and the steam pressure is raised to 15 pounds. When the thermometer indicates a temperature of 121°C. heating is continued for 15 minutes. A maximum of 15 minutes is recommended for the sterilization of carbohydrate media in tubes to be used for fermentation studies. After the sterilization period has been completed, the source of steam is cut off and the autoclave is allowed to return to atmospheric pressure. Pressure should not drop too rapidly or the media will boil over, blowing the plugs from the tubes or flasks. Pressure should, however, drop rapidly enough to prevent excessive exposure of the media to heat after the sterilization period. Ordinarily about 8, and not more than 12, minutes should be required for the usual bacteriological laboratory autoclave to reach atmospheric pressure without danger of prolonged heating. The media should be removed from the autoclave shortly after sterilization and should not be permitted to remain in the autoclave for any appreciable length of time after the sterilization period.

For the sterilization of coagulable material such as serum, see the method given for Bacto-Loeffler Blood Serum, page 128.

Oversterilization or prolonged heating will change the composition of the medium. For example, in our laboratories we have shown that Phenol Red Lactose Broth which has been sterilized for 15 minutes at 15 pounds pressure (121°C.), or sterilized by filtration, produces no demonstrable amount of acid when inoculated with *Salmonella typhosa*. The same lot of medium sterilized for 30 or 45 minutes at 121°C. showed appreciable acid production under the same conditions of testing. This demonstrates that oversterilization resulted in a breakdown of the lactose.

Agar media on prolonged sterilization or heating are apt to show a precipitate.

Repeated melting of solidified agar, or long holding of melted agar at high temperature, may likewise cause a precipitate to form in the media. Media containing agar may also form a flocculent precipitate if the liquid medium is held in the water bath at 43 to 45°C. for longer than 30 minutes. This flocculent agar precipitate, however, may be dispersed by reheating the medium.

Excessive heating of media also results in an increase in acidity. The reaction of the media will become more acid as heating is prolonged. Some media which are acid, such as Wort Agar (pH 4.8) will, upon prolonged heating, cause destruction of the agar. It is possible to destroy completely the jellifying properties of agar by prolonged heating, and this destruction is hastened as the acidity increases.

Culture media which may be injured by autoclaving are sometimes sterilized by the discontinuous or intermittent method. This procedure consists of heating the medium in a chamber of flowing steam for a period of 20 or 30 minutes, or longer, on several successive days. Body fluids and sera are sometimes sterilized in the inspissator at 53° to 70°C. for one hour on six successive days. Liquid media may be sterilized by filtration through unglazed porcelain or earthenware candles, or through a sterilizing pad.

External contamination of culture media is prevented by plugging the tubes or flasks with nonabsorbent cotton before sterilization. Plugs should fit neither too loosely nor too tightly and should protect the lip of the container against the accumulation of dust. Screw cap tops or metal covers may also be used to close the tubes or flasks. Marcus and Greaves[3] have called attention to the fact that atypical cultural reactions may be obtained in sealed tubes of media used to test biochemical activities due to anaerobic conditions. Tubes of Kligler Iron Agar and Russell Double Sugar Agar, for example, gave aberrant reactions in tubes sealed with screw caps or rubber stoppers. The same medium with tubes loosely capped, or caps replaced with cotton plugs, showed typical reactions.

Media should always be stored in a cool moist atmosphere to prevent evaporation. Prolonged storage of sterile media cannot, however, be recommended. If tubes of media have been kept for any length of time they should be reheated just before use. Liquid media should be heated in a boiling water bath or in flowing steam for a few minutes, to drive off dissolved gases, and then cooled quickly in cold water without agitation just prior to inoculation. Agar tubes should be melted and allowed to solidify in order to secure a moist surface which is desired by most microorganisms. These precautions for both liquid and solid media are extremely important for the initiation of growth of highly parasitic organisms such as those encountered in blood culture work.

Blood or other body fluids to be cultured should always be taken prior to the administration of the therapeutic agent. If drugs have been administered their bactericidal effects should be neutralized, if possible. The addition of p-aminobenzoic acid (PAB) in 0.5 mg. per cent to the medium will assure the inactivation of any sulfa drug carried over with the inoculum. Bacto-Penase, a concentrated purified penicillinase, should be added to the sterile cooled medium used for blood culture if the patient is under penicillin therapy. Bacto-Brain Heart Infusion with P.A.B. and Agar with added Bacto-Penase is an ideal medium for blood culture work. The small amount of agar present will give all degrees of anaerobiosis, permitting the development of aerobes as well as the strictest anaerobes, the PAB will inactivate any sulfa drug, the added Bacto-Penase will inactivate any penicillin in the inoculum, while 100 ml. of the medium itself will inactivate up to 1000 units of streptomycin.

[1] Am. J. Med. Tech., 14:214:1948.
[2] Am. J. Pub. Health, 25:301:1935.
[3] J. Lab. Clin. Med., 36:134:1950.

THE PREPARATION
of Media from Dehydrated Culture Media, Difco

THE ADVANTAGES of dehydrated media and their efficiency for the cultivation of a large variety of saprophytic and pathogenic microorganisms have been recognized by the authors of many bacteriological texts, including "Standard Methods for the Examination of Water and Sewage," "Standard Methods for the Examination of Dairy Products" and "Diagnostic Procedures and Reagents" of the American Public Health Association.

The preparation of media from Bacto Dehydrated Culture Media is a time-saving and economical process by which large or small quantities of standard and uniform culture media are made available with the minimal expenditure of effort.

The composition of each medium is stated on the label of the bottle with the quantities of the ingredients present in one liter of the finished medium. All that is necessary to rehydrate the medium is to weigh accurately the dehydrated medium, dissolve the powder in freshly distilled water or boiled distilled water and sterilize the solution. For ease of preparation and for best results with Bacto Dehydrated Media, a discussion of these methods is given in detail.

Distilled water should be used in the rehydration of dehydrated culture media. Distilled water that has been stored at room temperature for any length of time is apt to absorb sufficient gases to actually alter the final reaction and composition of the medium. It is recommended that freshly distilled water or boiled distilled water at room temperature be used in the preparation of all media.

The quantity of dehydrated culture medium to use per liter is specified on each package. Amounts for small or large quantities may be easily calculated, and the desired amount weighed. Best results will be obtained by adding the powder to a dry flask, and then adding the freshly distilled water a little at a time with constant agitation to prevent the formation of lumps. A stirring rod may be used to secure an even mixture. The entire amount of distilled water is added when all of the powder is thoroughly wetted. Broth or liquid media are readily soluble in water at room temperature. Agar media must be heated to the boiling point for complete solution. This may be accomplished in several ways. For small quantities (up to 300 ml.) the best procedure is to heat the flask over a free flame, keeping the contents of the flask well agitated to prevent burning; for larger quantities, solution of the agar media may be more easily effected in flowing steam, stirring from time to time, or in the autoclave. Another satisfactory method, which reduces the heating period of the medium is to boil three-quarters of the distilled water over a free flame and suspend the dehydrated medium in the remaining cold distilled water, taking care that all of the medium is thoroughly wetted and evenly suspended. The suspension is then finally added to the boiling water and boiling continued until solution is complete. Gelatin media are best dissolved by heating to 50°C. in a water bath. Agar or gelatin media must be in complete solution before being dispensed into the containers in which they are to be sterilized.

Care should be exercised to avoid contamination of media during the rehydration process. Only chemically clean glassware should be used in dissolving the media, and for distribution in the final container. It has been shown that detergents used in washing glassware, if not satisfactorily removed by repeated rinsing, may be responsible for growth inhibition and changes in reaction. Three highly advertised soapless cleansers commonly employed for cleaning laboratory glassware were investigated and found quite bacteriostatic for many bacteria. Glassware on which two of the three cleansers were used required two thorough rinses, and that on which the third detergent was used required three complete rinses in cold water to remove the toxic effect of the cleanser for bacteria. Clean glassware is particularly required in media for microbiological assay procedures where extremely small amounts of material may give rise to erratic results. For example, in the assay of Vitamin B_{12}, as small a quantity as 0.01 millimicrogram will give rise to a definite growth response. The importance of clean glassware in the assay of this vitamin was stressed by the U.S. Pharmacopeia Vitamin B_{12} Study Panel, since they stated that glassware for this purpose required special handling, and as many as twelve rinses appeared to be necessary for satisfactory results.

Following rehydration, Difco culture media require no filtration. In some cases the medium contains a slight flocculent precipitate, such as, for example, Levine E.M.B. Agar and Bacto-Niacin Assay Medium. Removal of these precipitates will result in an inferior growth response. The filtration of any medium through cotton is especially to be avoided. Wright[1] showed that cotton-wool contained a material inhibitory to the growth of the pneumococcus. Drea[2] showed that absorbent cotton stoppers contained inhibitory material for the tubercle bacilli. Boyd and Casman[3] filtered 100 ml. quantities of Tryptose Agar through 10 gram portions of 15 different commercial brands of absorbent cotton and failed to obtain growth from a dilute inoculum of *Brucella abortus* while the unfiltered medium supported good growth of the test organism. They were able to extract a fatty acid-like substance from the cotton which completely inhibited growth when added to the medium in a concentration of 1 mg. per liter, as did unsaturated fatty acids from cottonseed oil. The addition of starch to the medium neutralized this toxic effect. The same observation was also made with centrifuged and cotton filtered Potato Infusion Agar for *B. abortus*. The centrifuged medium gave excellent growth while medium filtered through cotton was inferior.

Adjustment of the reaction of the medium is not required. The final reaction of the sterilized medium at 25°C. is shown on the label of each bottle. Temperature and method of standardization of the potentiometer in the determination of pH is important. The potentiometer should be standardized with a standard buffer solution, near the same reaction of the medium. The temperature of the standard buffer used in standardizing the instrument should be the same as the medium when making readings. The ionization constant increases with a rise in temperature. For example, the pH of distilled water free from carbon dioxide at 25°C. is practically pH 7.0, but at 40°C. is 6.7.

Uniform standardized media are readily prepared in large or small amounts from Bacto Dehydrated Culture Media. By the use of these products microbiologists are able to provide themselves daily with freshly prepared and wholly satisfactory media of known composition and definite reaction.

[1] J. Path. Bact., 38:499:1943.
[2] J. Bact., 44:149:1942.
[3] Public Health Reports, 66:44:1951.

Dehydrated Culture Media

GUIDES
for the Selection of Culture Media

THE TABLES on the following pages will assist in the selection of media for various purposes. The media listed are discussed in detail in this Manual and they are recommended as being those most generally employed for specific purposes. For the reason that media other than those listed may be preferred in some laboratories, we suggest that consideration also be given to similar media which are discussed in the same section of the manual.

Culture Media for the Examination of Water and Sewage
"Standard Methods" Procedures

Plate Counts	Presumptive	Tests for Coliform Organisms		
		Confirmed	Completed	
Nutrient Agar	Lactose Broth	Endo Agar	Nutrient Agar	
Nutrient Gelatin	Lauryl Tryptose	Levine E.M.B. Agar	Lactose Broth	
Tryptone Glucose Extract Agar	Broth	Brilliant Green Bile 2%		
		Formate Ricinoleate Broth		
		Lauryl Tryptose Broth		

Control of Water Filtration Plant Operation

Selective Broths	Selective Agars	Differential Test Media
Fuchsin Lactose Broth	MacConkey Agar	Bacto-Tryptone
Brilliant Green Bile 2%	Violet Red Bile Agar	M.R.-V.P. Medium
M.B.-B.C.P. Medium	Desoxycholate Lactose Agar	Koser Citrate Medium
Formate Ricinoleate Broth	Brilliant Green Bile Agar	
Crystal Violet Broth	Levine E.M.B. Agar	
Eijkman Lactose Medium		
E C Medium		
MacConkey Broth		

Culture Media for the Examination of Dairy and Other Food Products

PLATE COUNTS
  Tryptone Glucose Extract Agar
  Proteose Tryptone Agar
  Beef Lactose Agar
  Nutritive Caseinate Agar
  Heart Infusion Agar
BRUCELLA
  Tryptose Agar
LACTOBACILLI
  Tomato Juice Agar
  Trypsin Digest Agar
  Peptonized Milk
  Skim Milk
  Micro Assay Culture Agar
  Micro Inoculum Broth
  Snyder Test Agar
HEMOLYTIC STREPTOCOCCI
  Heart Infusion Agar

COLIFORM ORGANISMS
  Brilliant Green Bile 2%
  Formate Ricinoleate Broth
  Violet Red Bile Agar
  Desoxycholate Agar
  Desoxycholate Lactose Agar
  MacConkey Agar
  Lactose Broth
  Endo Agar
  Levine E.M.B. Agar
  Bacto-Tryptone
  M.R.-V.P. Medium
  Koser Citrate Medium
THERMOPHILES
  Dextrose Tryptone Agar
  Thermoacidurans Agar
MOLDS AND YEASTS
  Potato Dextrose Agar
  Malt Agar

Dehydrated Media for Cultivation of Pathogenic Bacteria

MICROORGANISM	ISOLATION	DIFFERENTIATION	PROPAGATION
Pneumococci Meningococci Streptococci (enterococci)	Brain Heart Infusion Media Tryptose Phosphate Broth Tryptose Blood Agar Base Blood Agar Base Heart Infusion Agar Dextrose Broth Mitis Salivarius Agar* Azide Blood Agar Base* Azide Dextrose Broth*	Blood Agar Base Media Phenol Red Carbohydrate Media Bacto-Oxgall Bacto-Bile Salts No. 3 Sodium Desoxycholate	Brain Heart Infusion Media Tryptose Phosphate Broth Dextrose Starch Agar Tryptose Agar Dextrose Broth Dextrose Agar AC Medium
Staphylococci	Brain Heart Infusion Media Tryptose Phosphate Broth Blood Agar Base Media Mannitol Salt Agar Staphylococcus Medium No. 110 Chapman Stone Medium Azide Blood Agar Base	Blood Agar Base Media Phenol Red Carbohydrate Media Loeffler Blood Serum Staphylococcus Medium No. 110 Chapman Stone Medium Nutrient Gelatin Coagulase Plasma	Brain Heart Infusion Media Tryptose Phosphate Broth Dextrose Starch Agar Tryptose Agar
Neisseria	GC Medium Base or Proteose No. 3 Agar enriched, with Bacto-Hemoglobin and Bacto-Supplement A or Bacto-Supplement B	Phenol Red Carbohydrate Media Mueller Hinton Medium	Dextrose Starch Agar GC Medium Base or Proteose No. 3 Agar enriched with Bacto-Supplement B
Corynebacterium	Loeffler Blood Serum Dextrose Proteose No. 3 Agar with Bacto-Tellurite Blood Solution Mueller Tellurite Base with Mueller Tellurite Serum	Dextrose Proteose No. 3 Agar with Bacto Tellurite-Blood Solution Phenol Red Carbohydrate Media	Loeffler Blood Serum
Brucella	Tryptose Agar Tryptose Agar with Crystal Violet Tryptose Broth	Tryptose Agar with Thionin or Basic Fuchsin	Tryptose Agar

* Recommended for streptococci only.

Organism			
Pasteurella and *Listeria*	Bacto-Tryptose Agar Cystine Heart Agar with Bacto-Hemoglobin and Bacto-Supplement B		Tryptose Agar Cystine Heart Agar with Bacto-Hemoglobin
Hemophilus	Bordet Gengou Agar Base with fresh blood Proteose No. 3 Agar with Bacto-Hemoglobin and Bacto-Supplement A or Bacto-Supplement B Brain Heart Infusion with Bacto-Supplement B Thio Medium with Bacto-Supplement B		Proteose No. 3 Agar with Bacto-Hemoglobin and Bacto-Supplement A or Bacto-Supplement B Brain Heart Infusion with Bacto-Supplement B Bordet Gengou Agar Base with fresh blood Dextrose Agar with fresh blood
Clostridia	AC Medium Veal Infusion Medium Egg Meat Medium Cooked Meat Medium Brewer Anaerobic Agar	Cooked Meat Medium Loeffler Blood Serum Nutrient Gelatin Peptone Colloid Medium Tryptone	AC Medium Veal Infusion Medium Egg Meat Medium Cooked Meat Medium
Mycobacterium tuberculosis	Petragnani Medium Lowenstein-Jensen Medium Bovine TB Medium Peizer TB Medium Dubos Oleic Agar		Dubos Media Long's Asparagin Medium Petragnani Medium Lowenstein-Jensen Medium Bovine TB Medium Dorset Medium Peizer TB Medium
Fungi	Sabouraud Maltose Agar Littman Oxgall Agar Brain Heart Infusion Agar Malt Agar Potato Dextrose Agar	Corn Meal Agar Sabouraud Dextrose Agar Sabouraud Maltose Agar	Sabouraud Maltose Agar Littman Oxgall Agar Brain Heart Infusion Agar
Endamoeba histolytica	Endamoeba Medium with Horse Serum Saline 1:6 and Rice Powder		Endamoeba Medium with Horse Serum Saline 1:6 and Rice Powder

Gram Negative Enteric Bacteria

MICROORGANISM	ENRICHMENT	ISOLATION	DIFFERENTIATION	PROPAGATION
Coliform group		Violet Red Bile Agar Levine E.M.B. Agar Endo Agar MacConkey Agar Desoxycholate Agar Tergitol 7 Agar Desoxycholate Lactose Agar	Levine E.M.B. Agar Koser Citrate Medium M.R.-V.P. Medium Simmons Citrate Agar Malonate Broth Urea Agar	Nutrient Agar Nutrient Broth Cooked Meat Medium
Salmonella typhosa	Tetrathionate Broth Selenite Broth	MacConkey Agar S.S. Agar Bismuth Sulfite Agar Bacto-E.M.B. Agar Desoxycholate Agar Desoxycholate Citrate Agar	Russell Double Sugar Agar Kligler Iron Agar Triple Sugar Iron Agar Urea Broth and Agar S.I.M. Medium Friewer–Shaughnessy Medium Phenol Red Tartrate Agar Purple Carbohydrate Media	Same as above
Salmonella, other than *S. typhosa*	Same as above	MacConkey Agar Bismuth Sulfite Agar S.S. Agar Brilliant Green Agar Bacto-E.M.B. Agar Desoxycholate Agar Desoxycholate Citrate Agar	Same as above	Same as above
Shigella		MacConkey Agar S.S. Agar Bacto-E.M.B. Agar Desoxycholate Agar Desoxycholate Citrate Agar	Same as above	Same as above

MEDIA FOR THE EXAMINATION OF WATER AND SEWAGE

THE DEHYDRATED CULTURE MEDIA listed in this section conform to the formulae given in "Standard Methods for the Examination of Water and Sewage," Ninth Edition, 1946, of the American Public Health Association and the American Water Works Association. Carefully selected standardized ingredients are used in the exact proportions specified in the "Standard Methods" formulae. The reaction of each medium is carefully adjusted so that the final reaction will fall within the range of pH recommended in "Standard Methods."

The American Public Health Association has permitted the use of dehydrated media of "Standard Methods" composition continuously since 1923 in every edition of its "Standard Methods for the Examination of Water and Sewage," including the current Ninth Edition.

The U. S. Public Health Service Drinking Water Standards[1] specify that the procedures recommended in "Standard Methods of Water Analysis" of the American Public Health Association be followed in all details, including the culture media. It is, therefore, permissible for Bacto Dehydrated Culture Media to be used in the testing of the potability of water according to the U. S. Public Health Service Drinking Water Standards.

A guide for the selection of culture media listed in this section is given on page 25.

[1] Public Health Reports, 61:376:1946
(Reprint No. 2697).

"STANDARD METHODS" MEDIA

THE MEDIA listed in this section are used for the bacteriological examination of water in accordance with the procedures of "Standard Methods for the Examination of Water and Sewage."

BACTO
NUTRIENT BROTH (B3)
DEHYDRATED

Bacto-Beef Extract .... 3 g.
Bacto-Peptone .... 5 g.

Bacto-Nutrient Broth is a peptone meat extract liquid medium recommended for general laboratory use for the cultivation of the microorganisms that are not exacting in food requirements. Bacto-Nutrient Broth is prepared in accordance with the formula specified by the American Public Health Association and American Water Works Association's "Standard Methods for the Examination of Water and Sewage"[1] and "Standard Methods for the Examination of Dairy Products"[2] this medium has been prepared to give to bacteriologists an Extract Broth of approved and standard formula. It is also recommended as a base to which a variety of materials may be added, for the preparation of a large number of differential, selective, and enriched media requiring only the addition of dyes, salts, carbohydrates, tissues, or serous fluids. An enriched medium such as Rosenow[3] described for the isolation of streptococci from infected teeth, was prepared by adding dextrose, pieces of sterile brain tissue, and marble chips to Nutrient Broth.

Bouillon or Beef Broth as suggested by Loeffler was one of the earliest media used in bacteriology. An infusion of meat and a peptone constituted the nutriments of this medium. Later it was shown that for many routine purposes beef extract could satisfactorily replace the infusion of fresh meat and had the decided advantage of ease of preparation, uniformity, and economy. The American Public Health Association recognized the advantage of beef extract in standard culture media and in 1917 discontinued the use of infusion of beef in standard media. Bacto-Nutrient Broth has been prepared to duplicate the formula approved by the American Public Health Association and since 1927 our label has carried a statement to this effect.

Bacto-Nutrient Broth is recommended for use in the tube dilution method of testing the sensitivity of microorganisms to antibiotics. Waisbren, Carr and Dunnett[4] showed that Bacto-Nutrient Broth, Bacto-Dextrose Broth or Bacto-Tryptose Phosphate Broth were suitable media for comparative sensitivity test studies while a Tryptic soy medium inhibited the action of Neomycin, Aureomycin, Terramycin and Polymyxin against the test organism.

To rehydrate the medium, dissolve 8 grams of Bacto-Nutrient Broth in 1000 ml. of distilled water. Distribute in tubes and sterilize in the autoclave for 15 minutes at 15 pounds pressure (121°C.). The final reaction of the medium will be pH 6.8.

One pound of Bacto-Nutrient Broth will make 56.7 liters of medium.

[1] Standard Methods for the Examination of Water and Sewage, 9th Edition: 185:1946.
[3] Standard Methods for the Examination of Dairy Products, 9th Edition: 166:1948.
[8] J. Dental Research, 1:205:1919.
[4] Am. J. Clin. Path., 21:884:1951.

BACTO
LACTOSE BROTH   (B4)
DEHYDRATED

Bacto-Beef Extract	3 g.
Bacto-Peptone	5 g.
Bacto-Lactose	5 g.

Bacto-Lactose Broth is recommended for use in the presumptive test for members of the coliform (*Escherichia-Aerobacter*) group from water and other materials. This medium is prepared according to the formula specified in "Standard Methods for the Examination of Water and Sewage,"[1] and in "Standard Methods for the Examination of Dairy Products."[2]

In the determination of the potability of drinking water one of the most important tests is the detection of possible fecal contamination. The presence of *Escherichia coli* is generally considered to be an indication of fecal pollution of the water.

The demonstration of the presence of coliform bacteria in water has been reduced to a relatively simple process as outlined in "Standard Methods." Since 1917 the recommended procedure has been:

1. The determination of gas production in Lactose Broth resulting from the direct inoculation of water (presumptive test).
2. The inoculation of differential or selective media from tubes of fermented Lactose Broth (confirmed test).

3. The identification of Gram negative, non-sporulating, aerobic organisms capable of producing gas when reinoculated into Lactose Broth (completed test).

Since 1917 "Standard Methods of Water Analysis," in the interests of greater uniformity, has recommended the use of a Beef Extract Lactose Broth in place of the infusion medium formerly employed. Bacto-Lactose Broth is prepared from the ingredients recommended in "Standard Methods" and requires only solution in distilled water and sterilization. No adjustment of reaction is required.

Bacto-Lactose Broth prepared in the normal concentration contains 0.5 per cent each of Bacto-Lactose and Bacto-Peptone together with 0.3 per cent Bacto-Beef Extract. This concentration of sugar and of peptone yields an optimum growth of the organisms of the coli-aerogenes group.[3] "Standard Methods"[1] specify that when using inocula greater than 1 ml., multiple strength Lactose Broth shall be prepared to maintain the concentration of nutriments as given in the formula (1 ml. or less of sample may be added to 10 ml. of single strength medium).

"Standard Methods" procedures apply to the U.S.P.H.S. Drinking Water Standards[4] in all details of technique in the bacteriological examination, including apparatus and media. These specifications provide for the use of 10 ml. and 100 ml. as standard portions of water for the bacteriological test. They recommend standard dilution water bottles of 160 to 180 ml. capacity as containers for the presumptive test where 100 ml. water samples are to be tested; and also authorize the use of either the ordinary inverted vial or a Cowles[5] tube for collection of gas produced in the medium. The inverted vial or Cowles tube must be of sufficient length so that it will be in at least a 45° angle to the base of the bottle. For convenience it is recommended that the bottles used for the test be marked at the volume of medium to be used and also at the total volume of the medium plus the water sample. For instance, if it is desired to use regularly 35 ml. of concentrated medium for each 100 ml. of water sample the bottle can be marked at the 35 ml. and the 135 ml. points.

In order to maintain a constant final concentration of nutriments in all tests, it is suggested that the medium be prepared in the concentrations given in the table below.

To rehydrate the medium, dissolve 13 grams, or other specified quantity, of Bacto-Lactose Broth in 1000 ml. of distilled water, distribute into test tubes or bottles with fermentation vials and sterilize in an autoclave for 15 minutes at 15 pounds pressure (121° C.). The final reaction of the medium will be pH 6.7.

One pound of Bacto-Lactose Broth will make 34.9 liters of medium.

Concentrations of Dehydrated Medium Required
to Maintain the Proper Concentration of Ingredients

Inoculum	Amount Medium in Tube	Vol. Medium and Inoculum	Bacto-Lactose Broth used per 1000 ml.
1 ml.	10 ml. or more	11 ml. or more	13 g.
10 ml.	30 ml.	40 ml.	17.3 g.
10 ml.	20 ml.	30 ml.	19.5 g.
100 ml.	50 ml.	150 ml.	39 g.
100 ml.	35 ml.	135 ml.	49.4 g.
100 ml.	20 ml.	120 ml.	78 g.

[1] Standard Methods for the Examination of Water and Sewage, 9th Edition: 186:1946.
[2] Standard Methods for the Examination of Dairy Products, 9th Edition: 133:1948.
[3] Public Health Reports, 44:2865:1929.
[4] Public Health Reports, 61:376:1946 (Reprint No. 2697).
[5] J. Bact., 38:677:1939.

BACTO
NUTRIENT GELATIN   (B11)
DEHYDRATED

Bacto-Beef Extract	3 g.
Bacto-Peptone	5 g.
Bacto-Gelatin	120 g.

Bacto-Nutrient Gelatin is recommended for the 20°C. plate count of water according to "Standard Methods for the Examination of Water and Sewage"[1] of the American Public Health Association and the American Water Works Association. It is also recommended for the determination of gelatin liquefaction in the identification of anaerobes and other microorganisms.

Gelatin was one of the first solidification agents used in the science of bacteriology, enabling the direct plate count to be used rather than the dilution method for determination of bacterial populations, and for the isolation of pure cultures. However, there are certain limitations to the use of gelatin in plating and isolation procedures, as incubation must be carried out at approximately 20°C., a temperature lower than the optimum for many organisms. Further, many organisms have the ability to attack and liquefy the gelatin. Although Nutrient Gelatin is still used in the plate count of water with incubation at 19–21°C., plating procedures now most generally utilize media containing agar as a solidifying agent. The chief use of Nutrient Gelatin is for the detection of proteolysis (the elaboration of gelatinolytic enzymes) as evidenced by the liquefaction of gelatin.

Bacto-Nutrient Gelatin is prepared according to the formula specified in "Standard Methods" and since 1925 our label has carried a statement to that effect. Plates are incubated at 19–21°C. for 48 hours and the colonies counted. In determining gelatin liquefaction of pure cultures in this medium, tubes are incubated for at least five days at 19–21°C. If the optimum temperature for the organism in question is above 20°C., incubate at the desired temperature and after incubation cool the tubes to 20°C., to determine if the gelatin has been liquefied.

To rehydrate the medium, suspend 128 grams of Bacto-Nutrient Gelatin in 1000 ml. of cold distilled water and warm to about 50°C. to dissolve the medium completely. Distribute in tubes and sterilize in the autoclave for 15 minutes at 15 pounds pressure (121°C.). The final reaction of the medium will be pH 6.8.

One pound of Bacto-Nutrient Gelatin will make 3.5 liters of medium.

[1] Standard Methods for the Examination of Water and Sewage, 9th Edition:186:1946.

BACTO
NUTRIENT AGAR   (B1)
DEHYDRATED

Bacto-Beef Extract	3 g.
Bacto-Peptone	5 g.
Bacto-Agar	15 g.

Bacto-Nutrient Agar is recommended for the examination of water according to "Standard Methods for the Examination of Water and Sewage"[1] of the American Public Health Association and the American Water Works Association. It is also recommended as a general culture medium for the cultivation of the majority of the less fastidious microorganisms, as well as a base to which a variety of materials are added to give selective, differential, or enriched media.

Infusions of meat were first generally employed together with peptone as nutriments in culture media. Later it was found that for many routine procedures beef extract gave fully as good results and had the decided advantages of greater ease of preparation, greater uniformity, and economy. A simple medium composed of beef extract, peptone, and agar has been one of the most generally used media in bacteriological procedures. It is used for the ordinary routine examinations of water, sewage, and food products; for the carrying of stock cultures; for the preliminary cultivation of samples submitted for bacteriological examination; and for isolating organisms in pure culture.

Bacto-Nutrient Agar was originally prepared to duplicate an extract agar of approved and standard formula. The American Public Health Association in its earliest reports on methods for water analysis emphasized the necessity of the universal use of a standard medium, and since the Third Edition of "Standard Methods of Water Analysis" in 1917[2] has recommended the use of beef extract rather than infusion of meat in the preparation of Nutrient Agar. In the Fifth Edition of "Standard Methods of Water Analysis," 1923,[3] and the Fourth Edition of "Standard Methods of Milk Analysis," 1923,[4] the use of dehydrated media of "Standard Methods" composition has been permitted for the bacteriological examination of water and milk. In the Fifth Edition of "Standard Methods of Milk Analysis," 1927,[5] the use of Bacto dehydrated media was approved as being on a par with laboratory-made media for the bacteriological plate count of milk, and in this connection the work of Norton and Seymour[6] was cited. Bacto-Nutrient Agar is prepared in accordance with the formula specified in "Standard Methods of Water Analysis"[7] and since 1924 our label has stated "Conforms to Standard Methods Formula." The "Standard Methods for the Examination of Dairy Products" Ninth Edition[8] specifies a medium known as Tryptone Glucose Extract Milk Agar, as discussed on page 57, to take the place of Nutrient Agar in the bacteriological examination of dairy products.

To rehydrate the medium, suspend 23 grams of Bacto-Nutrient Agar in 1000 ml. of cold distilled water and heat to boiling to dissolve the medium completely. In preparing large volumes of the medium the heating period required to effect complete solution may be reduced by boiling about three-fourths of the distilled water over a free flame and suspending the dehydrated medium in the remaining cold distilled water, taking care that all particles of the medium are thoroughly wetted and evenly suspended. The suspension is then slowly added to the boiling water and boiling continued for a minute or two to complete solution. The medium is distributed in tubes or flasks and sterilized in the autoclave for 15 minutes at 15 pounds pressure (121°C.). The final reaction of the medium will be pH 6.8.

One pound of Bacto Nutrient Agar will make 19.7 liters of medium.

[1] Standard Methods for the Examination of Water and Sewage, 9th Edition: 186:1946.
[2] Standard Methods of Water Analysis, 3rd Edition: 99:1917.
[3] Standard Methods of Water Analysis, 5th Edition: 97:1923.
[4] Standard Methods of Milk Analysis, 4th Edition: 4:1923.
[5] Standard Methods of Milk Analysis, 5th Edition: 7:1927.
[6] Am. J. Pub. Health, 16:35:1926.
[7] Standard Methods of Water Analysis, 8th Edition: 201:1936.
[8] Standard Methods for the Examination of Dairy Products, 9th Edition:93:1948.

BACTO
TRYPTONE GLUCOSE EXTRACT AGAR
DEHYDRATED

The option of using Bacto-Tryptone Glucose Extract Agar as discussed on page 57 for plate counts of water is permissible in following "Standard Methods" procedures in laboratories where both milk and water counts are made, so that two different media need not be carried in stock. In "Standard Methods for the Examination of Water and Sewage," Ninth Edition, 1946, page 191, it is stated that experimental data indicate Bacto-Tryptone Glucose Extract Agar and Bacto-Nutrient Agar give practically the same counts with water samples, and that colonies are larger and more easily counted when the former medium is used.

BACTO

ENDO AGAR (B6)

DEHYDRATED

Bacto-Peptone	10 g.
Bacto-Lactose	10 g.
Dipotassium Phosphate	3.5 g.
Bacto-Agar	15 g.
Sodium Sulfite	2.5 g.
Bacto-Basic Fuchsin	0.4 g.

Bacto-Endo Agar is recommended for the confirmation of the presumptive test for members of the coliform group in the bacteriological examination of water, milk, and other dairy products, according to "Standard Methods for the Examination of Water and Sewage"[1] and "Standard Methods for the Examination of Dairy Products."[2]

Endo[3] originally described a medium using a fuchsin sulfite indicator to differentiate lactose fermenting and lactose non-fermenting organisms of the intestinal tract. Upon plates of this medium, in which the fuchsin has been decolorized by sodium sulfite, typhoid and other lactose non-fermenting organisms appear as clear, colorless, glistening drops against the faint pink background of the medium. Coliform organisms fermenting lactose become red and color the surrounding medium. The typical reactions of this medium are not caused by acid production but by the intermediate product acetaldehyde, which is fixed by the sodium sulfite as was shown by Margolena and Hansen[4] and Neuberg and Nord.[5]

Endo's original formula has been subjected to many modifications, due largely to variations in the available dyes and sulfites and to new uses of the medium advocated by individual investigators. The result has been a multiplicity of variations of the formula. Harris[6] investigated the problem of Endo Agar, studying various ingredients, reaction, and available dyes. He reported that by using Levine's modification[7] several sources of error were eliminated and that Bacto-Peptone as recommended by Levine gave satisfactory results. In this modification Dr. Harris found that a basic fuchsin composed of almost equal parts of rosanilin and pararosanilin gave color reactions which were exceedingly sensitive and consistent. Bacto-Endo Agar was developed in cooperation with Dr. Harris, conforming to the Levine modification with the dye combination proposed by Harris.

Endo Agar was originally developed for the isolation of typhoid bacilli. Since that time more satisfactory media have been developed for this problem and Endo Agar has proved of most value in the bacteriological examination of water. Endo Agar and Levine Eosin Methylene Blue Agar are the two solid media specified in the Ninth Edition of "Standard Methods for the Examination of Water and Sewage" for the confirmation of the presence of coliform organisms in Lactose Broth tubes giving a positive presumptive test. The formula used in the preparation of Bacto-Endo Agar is identical with Formula II of "Standard Methods for the Examination of Water and Sewage,"[8] and since 1932 our label has carried a statement to this effect. For the isolation of members of the *Salmonella* and *Shigella* group see Bacto-Bismuth Sulfite Agar, page 139; Bacto-S S Agar, page 134; Bacto-MacConkey Agar, page 131; Bacto-Tetrathionate

Broth Base, page 157; Bacto-Selenite Broth, page 158; Bacto-Brilliant Green Agar, page 144.

Endo Agar inoculated the same day as rehydrated may be used without autoclave sterilization. Under these conditions the medium need be heated only to boiling to dissolve it completely before pouring into plates.

To rehydrate the medium, suspend 41.5 grams of Bacto-Endo Agar in 1000 ml. of cold distilled water and heat to boiling to dissolve the medium completely. Distribute in tubes or flasks and sterilize in the autoclave for 15 minutes at 15 pounds pressure (121°C.). The characteristic flocculant precipitate present in the medium following autoclaving may be evenly dispersed by twirling or gently shaking the flask just prior to pouring into sterile petri dishes. The final reaction of the medium will be pH 7.5.

One pound of Bacto-Endo Agar will make 10.9 liters of medium.

r. Standard Methods for the Examination of Water and Sewage, 9th Edition: 195:1946.
2 Standard Methods for the Examination of Dairy Products, 9th Edition: 33:1948.
3 Centr. Bakt., Abt. I, Orig., 35:109:1904.
4 Stain Tech., 8:131:1933.
5 Biochem. Zeit., 96:133:1919.
6 Military Surgeon, 57:280:1925.
7 Abst. Bact., 2:13:1918.
8 Standard Methods for the Examination of Water and Sewage, 9th Edition: 187:1946.

BACTO

LEVINE E.M.B. AGAR (B5)

DEHYDRATED

Bacto-Peptone	10 g.
Bacto-Lactose	10 g.
Dipotassium Phosphate	2 g.
Bacto-Agar	15 g.
Bacto-Eosin Y	0.4 g.
Bacto-Methylene Blue	0.065 g.

Levine Eosin Methylene Blue Agar is recommended for the confirmation of presumptive tests of members of the coliform group in the bacteriological examination of water, milk, and other dairy products according to "Standard Methods for the Examination of Water and Sewage"[1] and "Standard Methods for the Examination of Dairy Products."[2] It may also be used for differential plate count as mentioned in Appendix I of "Standard Methods for the Examination of Water and Sewage."[3] While pathogens concerned in enteric fevers caused by members of the *Salmonella* and *Shigella* group will develop on this medium, forming translucent, colorless colonies which are readily differentiated from lactose-fermenters, its principal function is to demonstrate the presence of coliform bacteria from water and milk samples.

Levine[4] developed an Eosin Methylene Blue Agar which gave excellent differentiation of *Escherichia coli* and *Aerobacter aerogenes*. The colon colonies usually show a dark center and have a greenish metallic sheen, but occasionally variants have been observed similar to the type described but having no sheen. Another variant grows effusely in colonies somewhat larger than the typical growth and has a distinct metallic sheen. Colonies of *A. aerogenes* are usually much larger than typical *E. coli* and tend to run together. The centers are usually brown in color and not as dark as *E. coli*. The metallic sheen is only occasionally observed. A more detailed differentiation is indicated in the accompanying table.

To obtain the most satisfactory reactions, especially in the differentiation of *E. coli* and *A. aerogenes,* it is very important that particular care be taken in the choice of the dyes and a meticulous determination be made of their proper proportions. The Bacto dyes in this medium are selected to satisfy the extreme delicacy of the medium. Levine recommends that the reaction should not be

DIFFERENTIATION OF *Bact. coli* AND *Bact. aerogenes* ON

LEVINE E.M.B. AGAR

(*Levine, Bull. 62, Iowa Eng. Exp. Sta., 1921*)

	Bact. coli[1]	*Bact. aerogenes*[2]
SIZE	Well isolated colonies are 2–3 mm. in diameter.	Well isolated colonies are larger than coli; usually 4–6 mm. in diameter or more.
CONFLUENCE	Neighboring colonies show little tendency to run together.	Neighboring colonies run together quickly.
ELEVATION	Colonies slightly raised; surface flat or slightly concave, rarely convex.	Colonies considerably raised and markedly convex; occasionally the center drops precipitately.
APPEARANCE BY TRANSMITTED LIGHT	Dark, almost black centers which extend more than ¾ across the diameter of the colony; internal structure of central dark portion difficult to discern.	Centers deep brown; not as dark as *Bact. coli* and smaller in proportion to the rest of the colony. Striated internal structure often observed in young colonies.
APPEARANCE BY REFLECTED LIGHT	Colonies dark, button-like, often concentrically ringed with a greenish metallic sheen.	Much lighter than *Bact. coli*, metallic sheen not observed except occasionally in depressed center when such is present.

[1] Two other types have been occasionally encountered. One resembles the type described, except that there is no metallic sheen, the colonies being wine colored. The other type of colony is somewhat larger (4 mm.), grows effusely, and has a marked crenated or irregular edge, the central portion showing a very distinct metallic sheen. These two varieties constitute about 2 or 3 per cent of the colonies observed.

[2] A small type of aerogenes colony, about the size of the colon colonies, which shows no tendency to coalesce, has been occasionally encountered.

adjusted and the medium should not be filtered. The medium is relatively stable and may be stored for short periods of time. It is usually used in petri dishes; however, some laboratories have found tubes to be convenient. The tubes should be prepared with long slants and no butts.

Levine E.M.B. Agar is prepared according to the formula specified in "Standard Methods for the Examination of Water and Sewage"[5] and since 1926 our label has carried a statement to this effect.

The "Standard Methods for the Examination of Water and Sewage" in the Ninth Edition permits the use of either Endo or Eosin Methylene Blue Agar as solid media for confirming tubes of Lactose Broth showing positive presumptive tests.

Taft and Daly[6] prepared a selective medium for the primary isolation of pathogenic intestinal bacteria by adding normal sodium hydroxide solution (generally 1.5 ml. per liter medium) to Bacto-Levine E.M.B. Agar. This selective medium gave superior results to that obtained with Desoxycholate Citrate Agar, and gave uniformly good results as did S S Agar in the examination of stools. The authors suggest that the selective Levine E.M.B. Agar be supplemented by an enrichment such as Tetrathionate Broth in laboratories doing routine stool examination.

Levine-E.M.B. Agar inoculated the same day as rehydrated may be used without autoclave sterilization. Under these conditions the medium need be heated only to boiling to dissolve it completely before pouring into plates.

To rehydrate the medium, suspend 37.5 grams of Levine E.M.B. Agar in 1000 ml. of cold distilled water and heat to boiling to dissolve the medium completely. Distribute in tubes or flasks and sterilize in the autoclave for 15 minutes at 15 pounds pressure (121°C.). The characteristic flocculant precipitate present in the medium following autoclaving may be evenly dispersed by gently twirling or shaking the flask just prior to pouring into sterile petri dishes. The final reaction of the medium will be pH 7.1.

One pound of Levine E.M.B. Agar will make 12 liters of medium.

[3] Standard Methods for the Examination of Water and Sewage, 9th Edition: 195:1946.
[3] Standard Methods for the Examination of Dairy Products, 9th Edition: 134:1948.
[6] Standard Methods for the Examination of Water and Sewage, 9th Edition: 228:1946.
[4] Bull. 62, Iowa Eng. Exp. Sta., 1921.
[5] Standard Methods for the Examination of Water and Sewage, 9th Edition: 187:1946.
[6] Am. J. Clin. Path., 17:561:1947.

BACTO

BRILLIANT GREEN BILE 2% (B7)

DEHYDRATED

Bacto-Peptone	10 g.
Bacto-Lactose	10 g.
Bacto-Oxgall	20 g
Bacto-Brilliant Green	0.0133 g.

Bacto-Brilliant Green Bile 2% is recommended for the confirmation of presumptive tests for members of the coliform group in the bacteriological examination of water according to "Standard Methods for the Examination of Water and Sewage"[1] and for the detection of members of the coliform (*Escherichia-Aerobacter*) group in milk and dairy products as specified in "Standard Methods for the Examination of Dairy Products."[2] This medium may also be used in the control of water filtration plant operation as described in Appendix I of "Standard Methods for the Examination of Water and Sewage"[3].

The development of a selective medium which would inhibit organisms other than members of the coliform group has long been of interest to sanitary bacteriologists. The principal interest has been in media containing bile and brilliant green. The American Water Works Association made extensive studies of this problem through its Committee No. 1 on "Standard Methods of Water Analysis." Dunham and Schoenlein[4] have recorded their investigations of the proportions of bile and brilliant green giving optimum results. They reported that, under the conditions of their investigations, a reduced bile content and a dilution of dye higher than that originally suggested by Muer and Harris[5], improved conditions for the development of *Escherichia coli*. The necessity of maintaining the proper concentration of ingredients after the water sample is added was emphasized. Jordan[6] indicated in his report that this medium is slightly superior to Lactose Broth and to the more concentrated bile medium in the detection of the coliform group in water. McCrady and Langevin[7] reported that Bacto-Brilliant Green Bile 2% is satisfactory for the detection of the coliform group in controlling the pasteurization of milk. McCrady[8] in studies on media for the detection of the presence of coliform organisms in water, found that while selective media were not as satisfactory as Lactose Broth for the presumptive test, they could be recommended for confirmation of the presumptive test and that for this purpose Brilliant Green Bile 2% was most satisfactory.

Bacto-Brilliant Green Bile 2% is prepared according to the formula specified in "Standard Methods for the Examination of Water and Sewage"[9] and "Standard Methods for the Examination of Dairy Products"[2], and since 1933 our label has carried a statement to that effect.

When the medium is to be used in water purification plant control where the inoculum is greater than 1 ml., particular care must be taken to preserve the correct concentration of dye and bile in the medium after dilution with the sample. The table given below indicates the quantity of dehydrated medium to use per 1000 ml. distilled water to maintain the correct concentrations of dye and bile.

In the presumptive test for members of the coliform group in the examination of dairy products a series of tubes of Brilliant Green Bile 2% are inoculated with appropriate dilutions of the sample. Use 5 tubes of each solution. Select dilutions to provide at least one positive and one negative tube in the series inoculated. Incubate tubes for 48 hours at 35–37°C. Gas formation constitutes a positive presumptive test.

To rehydrate the medium, dissolve 40 grams of Bacto-Brilliant Green Bile 2% in 1000 ml. of distilled water. The medium is distributed in fermentation tubes and sterilized by autoclaving for 15 minutes at 15 pounds pressure (121°C.). The final reaction of the medium will be pH 7.2.

One pound of Bacto-Brilliant Green Bile 2% will make 11.3 liters of medium.

Concentrations of Dehydrated Medium Required to Maintain the Proper Concentration of Ingredients

Inoculum	Volume Medium in Tube	Volume Medium and Inoculum	Bacto-Brilliant Green Bile 2% used per 1000 ml.
1 ml. or less	10 ml.	10 ml.	40 g.
10 ml.	20 ml.	30 ml.	60 g.
10 ml.	30 ml.	40 ml.	53 g.

[1] Standard Methods for the Examination of Water and Sewage, 9th Edition: 194:1946.
[2] Standard Methods for the Examination of Dairy Products, 9th Edition: 152:1948.
[3] Standard Methods for the Examination of Water and Sewage, 9th Edition: 226:1946.
[4] Stain Tech., 1:129:1926.
[5] Am. J. Pub. Health, 10:874:1920.
[6] J. Am. Water Works Assoc., 18:337:1927.
[7] J. Dairy Science, 15:321:1932.
[8] Am. J. Pub. Health, 27:1243:1937.
[9] Standard Methods for the Examination of Water and Sewage, 9th Edition: 188:1946.

BACTO
FORMATE RICINOLEATE BROTH
DEHYDRATED

Bacto-Formate Ricinoleate Broth is used in the confirmed and completed tests for the presence of members of the coliform group in water and sewage examination and for the detection (presumptive) test of members of the coliform group, as given in the "Standard Methods for the Examination of Dairy Products," Ninth Edition, page 131, 1948. Its use is confined to the study of the possible presence of spore-forming lactose-fermenting organisms as given in "Standard Methods for the Examination of Water and Sewage," Ninth Edition, 1946, pages 196 and 197. This selective broth may also be used in parallel planting with Lactose Broth in the control of water filtration plant operations as described in Appendix I of the Ninth Edition, page 226. A complete discussion of this medium is given on page 60.

BACTO
LAURYL TRYPTOSE BROTH (B241)
DEHYDRATED

Bacto-Tryptose	20 g.
Bacto-Lactose	5 g.
Dipotassium Phosphate	2.75 g.
Monopotassium Phosphate	2.75 g.
Sodium Chloride	5 g.
Sodium Lauryl Sulfate	0.1 g.

Bacto-Lauryl Tryptose Broth is prepared according to the formula of Mallmann and Darby[1] and is recommended for use in the standard tests for the coliform group as specified in "Standard Methods for the Examination of Water and Sewage"[2].

The fermentation of lactose with the production of gas has been used as an indicator of the potability of water for many years. The formation of gas from Lactose Broth constitutes a presumptive test for the coliform group (this term includes all aerobic and facultative anaerobic Gram-negative non-spore-forming bacilli which are capable of producing gas from lactose)[2]. Cowls[3] showed that the addition of sodium lauryl sulfate to Lactose Broth gave a medium selective for the coliform group. Darby and Mallmann[4] demonstrated the value of Bacto-Tryptose in the detection of coliform organisms. In a 2 per cent concentration of Bacto Tryptose the rate of reproduction during the early logarithmic growth phase was increased over that obtained with Bacto-Peptone. The addition of phosphate buffer to the Bacto-Tryptose medium caused a greater growth in the late logarithmic phase and slightly greater increase during the lag phase than did the non-buffered medium. When sodium chloride was added to the medium a marked increase in the rate of reproduction during the lag and early growth phases was observed. Their final medium permitted the so-called "slow lactose fermenters" to produce gas in greater quantities in a shorter period of time. The medium consisted of 2 per cent Bacto-Tryptose, 0.5 per cent lactose, 0.4 per cent dipotassium phosphate, 0.15 per cent monopotassium phosphate, and 0.5 per cent sodium chloride, and had a final reaction of pH 6.8.

In an attempt to improve the methods used to demonstrate members of the coliform group from water, Mallmann and Darby[1] investigated a large number of wetting agents, and showed that sodium lauryl sulfate gave best results as a non-inhibitive selective agent for members of the coliform group. Optimum results were obtained by the addition of 1:10,000 sodium lauryl sulfate to the buffered Tryptose Lactose Broth. In their comparative study in the checking of various types of water it was shown that the Lauryl Sulfate Tryptose Broth (Bacto-Lauryl Tryptose Broth) gave a higher colon index than did the confirmatory "Standard Methods" media, and that gas production in the Lauryl Tryptose Broth served not only as a presumptive test, but was also confirmatory of the presence of the coliform group for routine testing of water.

In a study of the coliform bacteria from chlorinated waters Levine[5] compared Lactose Broth and Lauryl Tryptose Broth. The latter medium gave fewer false positive presumptive tests than did Lactose Broth and suppressed the spore forming aerogenic bacteria. However, organisms showing a delayed fermentation of lactose were not eliminated by Lauryl Tryptose Broth.

Bacto-Lauryl Tryptose Broth was studied by 17 collaborating laboratories situated throughout the United States and Canada. The results of this comparative survey are reported by McCrady[6]. The study comprised the use of different types of water and embraced different methods of treatment of samples. The results showed that the substitution of Lauryl Tryptose Broth for "Standard Methods" Lactose Broth would result in a reduction in the number of primary gas positives to be confirmed, and an increase in the number of positive coliforms. It was recommended that further study be made by different laboratories with particular reference to use of the medium in the examination of finished waters.

Perry and Hajna[7] in a comparative study of E C Medium and Lauryl Tryptose Broth reported both media to be highly sensitive and specific for coliform bacteria from water, shellfish and sewage. A positive presumptive test with either medium was more dependable than the usual "confirmed" or "completed" test.

The Ninth Edition of "Standard Methods for the Examination of Water and Sewage" permits the substitution of Lauryl Tryptose Broth for Lactose Broth in the standard tests for members of the coliform group in the examination of all waters except final filtered, treated and filter-treated waters: "It may be substituted for lactose broth also in the examination of final filtered, treated and filtered-treated waters provided the laboratory worker has amply demonstrated by correlation of positive completed tests (isolations of coliform organisms) secured through the use of lauryl sulfate tryptose broth with those secured through the use of lactose broth, in the examination of such waters, that the substitution results in no reduction from the density of coliform organisms indicated by the standard procedure using lactose broth"[2].

Bacto-Lauryl Tryptose Broth duplicates the formula described by Mallmann and Darby[1] and specified in "Standard Methods for the Examination of Water and Sewage," Ninth Edition[2]. It may be prepared in single strength when examining 1 ml. or less of water as an inoculum. For inocula of 10 ml. consult the table given below.

Concentration of Dehydrated Medium Required to Maintain the Proper Concentration of Ingredients

Inoculum	Amt. Medium in Tube	Vol. Medium and Inoculum	Bacto-Lauryl Tryptose Broth used per 1000 ml.
1 ml. or less	10 ml.	10 ml.	35.6 g.
10 ml.	20 ml.	30 ml.	53.4 g.
10 ml.	30 ml.	40 ml.	47.3 g.

To rehydrate the medium, dissolve 35.6 grams of Bacto-Lauryl Tryptose Broth in 1000 ml. distilled water. Distribute into fermentation tubes and sterilize in the autoclave for 15 minutes at 15 pounds pressure (121°C.). The final reaction of the medium will be pH 6.8.

One pound of Bacto-Lauryl Tryptose Broth is sufficient for 12.7 liters single strength medium.

[1] Am. J. Pub. Health, 31:127:1941.
[2] Standard Methods for the Examination of Water and Sewage, 9th Edition: 193:1946.
[3] J. Am. Water Works Assoc., 30:979:1938.
[4] J. Am. Water Works Assoc., 31:689:1939.
[5] Am. J. Pub. Health, 31:351:1941.
[6] Am. J. Pub. Health, 33:1199:1943.
[7] Am. J. Pub. Health, 34:735:1944.

SUPPLEMENTARY MEDIA
for Water and Sewage Examination

The media in this section are listed in Appendix I of "Standard Methods for the Examination of Water and Sewage," Ninth Edition, 1946, or have been used for a long period of time in the examination of water and sewage.

In addition to the media discussed in detail in this section, other media described elsewhere in the Manual are also used in Appendix I procedures. A complete discussion of these media is given as indicated in the following listing.

Brilliant Green Bile 2%
Formate Ricinoleate Broth
MacConkey Agar
Violet Red Bile Agar
Desoxycholate Lactose Agar
Levine E.M.B. Agar

BACTO
FUCHSIN LACTOSE BROTH (B10)
DEHYDRATED

Bacto-Beef Extract	3 g.
Bacto-Peptone	5 g.
Bacto-Lactose	5 g.
Bacto-Basic Fuchsin	0.015 g.

Bacto-Fuchsin Lactose Broth is a selective medium which may be used in parallel planting with Lactose Broth in the control of water filtration plant operation as described in Appendix I of "Standard Methods for the Examination of Water and Sewage"[1].

As a result of investigations of media to reduce the number of false positives occurring in examination of waters for *Escherichia coli*, Ritter[2] devised a medium composed of Lactose Broth with the addition of basic fuchsin. The dye is present in the medium in a concentration which has been found to inhibit satisfactorily Gram-positive organisms and other bacteria which may be responsible for false positive tests for *E. coli*. McCrady,[3] in his study on procedures for the detection of the presence of coliform organisms in water, found that Fuchsin Lactose Broth, although satisfactory for some waters as a direct presumptive medium, could not be used as satisfactorily as Lactose Broth with all waters, and, therefore, recommended that it be used as a confirmatory medium. Bacto-Fuchsin Lactose Broth is prepared according to the formula specified in "Standard Methods for the Examination of Water and Sewage"[4] and since 1936 our label has carried a statement to that effect.

To rehydrate the medium, dissolve 13 grams of Bacto-Fuchsin Lactose Broth in 1000 ml. of distilled water. The medium is distributed in fermentation tubes and sterilized by autoclaving for 15 minutes at 15 pounds pressure (121°C.). The final reaction of the medium will be pH 6.8.

For water filtration plant control work, where the inoculum is greater than 1 ml., particular care must be taken to preserve the correct concentration of the ingredients after dilution with the sample. For example, if 10 ml. of water are to be added to 10 ml. of medium, the medium should be prepared in double strength.

One pound of Bacto-Fuchsin Lactose Broth will make 34.8 liters of medium.

[1] Standard Methods for the Examination of Water and Sewage, 9th Edition: 226:1946.
[2] J. Am. Water Works Assoc., 24:413:1932.
[3] Am. J. Pub. Health, 27:1243:1937.
[4] Standard Methods for the Examination of Water and Sewage, 8th Edition: 204:1936.

BACTO
M.B.-B.C.P. MEDIUM   (B21)
DEHYDRATED

Bacto-Beef Extract	5 g.
Bacto-Peptone	7.8 g.
Bacto-Lactose	4.7 g.
Dipotassium Phosphate	1.7 g.
Monopotassium Phosphate	0.3 g.
Bacto-Erythrosin (L-D)	0.0064 g.
Bacto-Methylene Blue (L-D)	0.064 g.
Bacto-Brom Cresol Purple	0.01 g.

Bacto-M.B.-B.C.P. Medium has been suggested for the detection of coliform bacteria in water supplies and is included in Appendix I of "Standard Methods for the Examination of Water and Sewage"[1] for use in parallel planting with Lactose Broth in the control of water filtration plant operations. It is prepared according to a modification of the original formula of Dominick and Lauter and varies slightly from the formula in "Standard Methods for the Examination of Water and Sewage."[3]

Dominick and Lauter[2] devised the M.B.-B.C.P. Medium so as to decrease the length of time required for determining the presence of coliform bacteria in water. Their medium is essentially a buffered Lactose Broth to which a combination of dyes has been added. The test depends upon reduction of methylene blue by coliform organisms so that when the dye has been reduced the acid (yellow) color of the brom cresol purple is brought to view. The dyes employed inhibit lactose fermenting organisms which are not members of the coliform group. A positive test is generally assured within 24 hours incubation and a heavy contamination will yield a positive test within 12 hours. The incubation of tubes for 48 hours is recommended when they are not definitely positive after 24 hours. The production of gas without the characteristic color change or, conversely, a color change without gas production is regarded as a negative test. In the positive test there must be gas accompanied by a typical color reaction. Bartram and Black[4] found Bacto-M.B.-B.C.P. Medium to be the most productive of the selective media used in their study of strains of *Escherichia, Aerobacter,* and intermediates which had been recently isolated from raw milk.

To rehydrate the medium, dissolve 19.6 grams of Bacto-M.B.-B.C.P. Medium in 1000 ml. of distilled water. Dispense into fermentation tubes in 10 ml. quantities. Sterilize in the autoclave for 15 minutes at 15 pounds pressure (121°C.). The final reaction of the medium will be pH 6.9.

For water filtration plant control work or other procedures where the inoculum is greater than a loop or 1 ml., particular care must be taken to preserve the correct concentration of the ingredients after dilution with the sample. For example, if 10 ml. of water are to be added to 10 ml. of medium, the medium should be prepared in double strength.

One pound of Bacto-M.B.-B.C.P. Medium will make 23.1 liters of medium.

[1] Standard Methods for the Examination of Water and Sewage, 9th Edition: 226:1946.
[2] J. Am. Water Works Assoc., 21:1067:1929.
[3] Standard Methods for the Examination of Water and Sewage, 8th Edition: 261:1936.
[4] J. Bact., 37:371:1939.

BACTO

CRYSTAL VIOLET LACTOSE BROTH (B8)

DEHYDRATED

Bacto-Peptone	5 g.
Bacto-Lactose	5 g.
Dipotassium Phosphate	5 g.
Monopotassium Phosphate	1 g.
Bacto-Crystal Violet	0.00143 g.

Bacto-Crystal Violet Lactose Broth is a selective medium used in parallel planting with Lactose Broth in the control of water filtration plant operations as described in Appendix I of "Standard Methods for the Examination of Water and Sewage"[1] It is prepared according to the formula suggested by Salle.[2]

Crystal Violet Lactose Broth is a buffered Lactose Broth containing crystal violet (gentian violet) in a concentration sufficient to inhibit Gram-positive organisms and other bacteria which may be responsible for false positive tests. The concentration of this bacteriostatic agent in the medium is not sufficient to affect the growth of members of the coliform group. Salle[2] suggested that such a medium be employed in the bacteriological examination of water, and McCrady[3] in studies on media for the detection of the presence of coliform organisms in water, found that while selective media were not as satisfactory as Lactose Broth for the presumptive test, they could be recommended for confirmation of the presumptive test, and that for this purpose Crystal Violet Lactose Broth could be recommended.

The Ninth Edition of "Standard Methods"[4] permits the use of Crystal Violet Lactose Broth as an alternate medium for the confirmed test for the presence of members of the coliform group when it has been shown to yield a maximum number of coliform organisms as indicated by a series of completed tests. Bacto-Crystal Violet Lactose Broth is prepared according to the formula specified in "Standard Methods for the Examination of Water and Sewage,"[5] and since 1936 our label has carried a statement to that effect.

To rehydrate the medium, dissolve 16 grams of Bacto-Crystal Violet Lactose Broth in 1000 ml. of distilled water. The medium is distributed in fermentation tubes and sterilized by autoclaving for 15 minutes at 15 pounds pressure (121°C.). The final reaction of the medium will be pH 7.4.

For water filtration plant control work, where the inoculum is greater than 1 ml., particular care must be taken to preserve the correct concentrations of the ingredients after dilution with the sample. For example, if 10 ml. of water are to be added to 10 ml. of medium, the medium should be prepared in double strength.

One pound of Bacto-Crystal Violet Lactose Broth will make 28.3 liters of medium.

[1] Standard Methods for the Examination of Water and Sewage, 9th Edition: 226:1946.
[2] J. Bact., 20:381:1930.
[3] Am. J. Pub. Health, 27:1243:1937.

[4] Standard Methods for the Examination of Water and Sewage, 9th Edition: 195:1946.
[5] Standard Methods for the Examination of Water and Sewage, 8th Edition: 203:1936.

BACTO
EIJKMAN LACTOSE MEDIUM   (B17)
DEHYDRATED

Bacto-Tryptose	15 g.
Bacto-Lactose	3 g.
Dipotassium Phosphate	4 g.
Monopotassium Phosphate	1.5 g.
Sodium Chloride	5 g.

Bacto-Eijkman Lactose Medium is used in the differentiation of *Escherichia coli* from other coliform bacteria. This medium may also be used in parallel planting with Lactose Broth in the control of water filtration plant operations. Its use is suggested in Appendix I of the Ninth Edition of "Standard Methods for the Examination of Water and Sewage"[1] for this purpose.

In 1904 Eijkman[2] described a method of separating the strains of coli originating from the feces of warm-blooded animals from the strains characteristic of cold-blooded animals. His method consisted essentially in placing the water under investigation in fermentation tubes or flasks and adding one-eighth its volume of a sterile solution containing 10 per cent dextrose, 10 per cent peptone, and 5 per cent sodium chloride. This mixture was then incubated at 46°C. The presence of a uniform turbidity and gas production was considered indicative of the presence of fecal colon strains. Many investigators have studied this method with water samples and pure cultures with varying results. One of the factors limiting the value of this method was the inability to obtain growth of transplants from positive tubes incubated at 46°C. Undoubtedly, the acidity at the relatively high temperature of incubation was responsible for the death of the culture within 24 to 48 hours.

Perry and Hajna[3] modified Eijkman's original method of decreasing the carbohydrate content and adding a phosphate buffer. Their study demonstrated that with 0.3 per cent dextrose and a potassium phosphate buffer the reaction of the medium, after inoculation with *E. coli* and incubation, was pH 5.6, while under the conditions described by Eijkman the reaction of the medium was pH 4.5. As a result, they were able to culture *E. coli* in every instance after incubation at 46°C. for 96 hours and for longer periods.

Perry[4] in 1939 reported on the use of a modified Eijkman Medium using 0.3 per cent lactose. This medium had been used successfully and routinely for the isolation of *E. coli* for a number of years. In a personal communication, Dr. Perry[5] recommended that Bacto-Tryptose replace Bacto-Peptone in this formula. The specificity of this medium for the detection of *E. coli* of fecal origin requires that the composition of the medium be uniform and exact, and that the incubation temperature be properly controlled at 45.5 to 46°C. at all times. The formula for Bacto-Eijkman Lactose Medium conforms to the formula for Eijkman Broth as specified in Appendix I, "Standard Methods for the Examination of Water and Sewage."[6]

To rehydrate the medium, dissolve 28.5 grams of Bacto-Eijkman Lactose Medium in 1000 ml. of distilled water and dispense in fermentation tubes. Sterilize in the autoclave for 15 minutes at 15 pounds pressure (121°C.). The final reaction of the medium will be pH 6.8.

When the medium is to be used in water filtration plant control work where the inoculum is greater than 1 ml., particular care must be taken to preserve the correct concentration of the ingredients after dilution with the sample. For example, if 10 ml. of water are to be added to 10 ml. of medium, the medium should be prepared in double strength.

One pound of Bacto-Eijkman Lactose Medium will make 15.9 liters of medium.

[1] Standard Methods for the Examination of Water and Sewage, 9th Edition:226:1946.
[2] Centr. Bakt., II. Abt., 37:742:1904.
[3] J. Bact., 26:419:1933.
[4] Food Research, 4:381:1939.
[5] Personal Communication, 1939.
[6] Standard Methods for the Examination of Water and Sewage, 9th Edition:232:1946.

BACTO
E C MEDIUM (B314)
DEHYDRATED

Bacto-Tryptose	20 g.
Bacto-Lactose	5 g.
Bacto-Bile Salts No. 3	1.5 g.
Dipotassium Phosphate	4 g.
Monopotassium Phosphate	1.5 g.
Sodium Chloride	5 g.

Bacto-E C Medium conforms to the formula given by Hajna and Perry[1] for the medium described for the detection of coliform bacteria at 37°C. and of *Escherichia coli* at 45.5°C. It can be used either as a primary medium for the growth of *E. coli* or as a satisfactory secondary medium for *E. coli* confirmation. This selective broth may be used in parallel planting with Lactose Broth in the control of water filtration plant operation as described in Appendix I of "Standard Methods for the Examination of Water and Sewage."[2]

In an effort to improve further the methods for the detection of members of the coliform group and *E. coli* Hajna and Perry[1] developed E C Medium. This medium consisted of a buffered Lactose Broth to which was added 0.15 per cent of Bacto-Bile Salts No. 3. Growth of spore formers and fecal streptococci was inhibited by the bile salts while growth of coli was enhanced by its presence. The medium can be used at 37°C. for the detection of coliform organisms or at 45.5°C. for the isolation of *E. coli*. In a further evaluation study of the E C Medium and Lauryl Tryptose Broth, Perry and Hajna[3] reported the results obtained from eleven different laboratories examining a variety of waters, milk, and shellfish. The results indicated that these media were highly specific for coliform bacteria. A presumptive test reading with the E C Medium or Lauryl Tryptose Broth seemed more dependable than the usual "confirmed" or "completed" test for coliform bacteria.

To rehydrate the medium, dissolve 37 grams Bacto-E C Medium in 1000 ml. of distilled water. Sterilize in the autoclave for 15 minutes at 15 pounds pressure (121°C.). Final reaction of the medium will be pH 6.9.

For water filtration plant control work, where the inoculum is greater than 1 ml., particular care must be taken to preserve the correct concentration of the ingredients after dilution with the sample. For example, if 10 ml. of water are to be added to 10 ml. of medium, the medium should be prepared in double strength.

One pound of Bacto-E C Medium will make 12.2 liters of medium.

[1] Am. J. Pub. Health, 33:550:1943.
[2] Standard Methods for the Examination of Water and Sewage, 9th Edition:236:1946.
[3] Am. J. Pub. Health, 34:735:1944.

BACTO

H D BROTH   (B443)

DEHYDRATED

Bacto-Tryptose	20 g.
Bacto-Lactose	5 g.
Sodium Desoxycholate	0.1 g.
Dipotassium Phosphate	4 g.
Monopotassium Phosphate	1.5 g.
Sodium Chloride	5 g.

Bacto-H D Broth (Hajna Desoxycholate Broth) is recommended as a presumptive and confirmatory medium for coliform bacteria from drinking water, swimming pools, sewage, urine, shell fish and dairy products. This medium is prepared according to the formula given by Hajna,[1] using sodium desoxycholate as a selective agent.

The coliform group as defined by the "Standard Methods for the Examination of Water and Sewage"[2] includes all aerobic and facultative anaerobic Gram-negative non-spore-forming bacilli which ferment lactose with gas formation. Leifson[3] suggested the use of sodium desoxycholate in Lactose Broth for the detection of coliform bacteria. Hajna[1] determined that 0.1 g. sodium desoxycholate per liter of Buffered Tryptose Lactose Broth to be optimum for the development of coliforms. This medium proved to be equal or superior to standard Lactose Broth as a presumptive medium and equal or superior to Brilliant Green Bile 2% as a confirmatory medium.

In comparing the efficiency of the Desoxycholate Broth and standard Lactose Broth using a variety of specimens including market oysters, crab meat, cottage cheese, water samples of all types, swimming pool water samples, milk and urine, 2460 tubes showed gas in the H D Broth, all of which confirmed as members of the coliform group; 2811 showed gas in standard Lactose Broth tubes with 2421 confirming as coliform by the Brilliant Green Lactose Bile 2% method.[1] As a confirmatory medium from 7669 presumptive Lactose Broth tubes, H D Broth gave 7499 confirmations for coliform against 7263 with Brilliant Green Bile 2%.[1]

To rehydrate the medium, dissolve 35.6 grams of Bacto-H D Broth in 1000 ml. distilled water. Distribute in tubes with fermentation vials and sterilize in the autoclave for 15 minutes at 10 pounds pressure (116°C.). Sterilization at 121°C. is not recommended. Final reaction of the medium will be pH 6.9.

When the inoculum is larger than 1 ml. per 10 ml. of medium, particular care must be taken to preserve the correct concentration of the ingredients after dilution with the sample. For example if 10 ml. of water are to be added to 10 ml. of medium, the medium should be prepared in double strength.

One pound of Bacto-H D Broth will make 12.7 liters of medium.

[1] Pub. Health Lab., 9:77:1951.   Water and Sewage, 9th Edition:193:1946.
[2] Standard Methods for the Examination of   [3] J. Path. Bact., 40:581:1935.

BACTO

S F MEDIUM   (B315)

DEHYDRATED

Bacto-Tryptone	20 g.
Bacto-Dextrose	5 g.
Dipotassium Phosphate	4 g.
Monopotassium Phosphate	1.5 g.
Sodium Azide	0.5 g.
Sodium Chloride	5 g.
Bacto-Brom Cresol Purple	0.032 g.

Bacto-S F Medium is recommended as a selective liquid medium for the detection of fecal streptococci from milk, water, swimming pools, sewage and feces. In this medium coliform and other Gram-negative organisms are inhibited. Bacto-S F Medium is prepared according to the formula of Hajna and Perry[1].

Sodium azide has been employed as a selective agent in media for the isolation of streptococci by a number of investigators. Snyder and Lichstein[2] and Lichstein and Snyder[3] reported that 0.01 per cent sodium azide in Blood Agar prevented swarming of proteus and permitted the isolation of streptococci from stools and other infected material without overgrowth by Gram-negative organisms. Mallmann[4] used 1:5000 sodium azide in a buffered Tryptose broth for the examination of sewage and reported that streptococci grew while coliform organisms were inhibited. This method made possible an easy procedure for routine laboratory detection of streptococci. Packer[5,6] used sodium azide and crystal violet in the preparation of a selective Blood Agar for streptococci and *Erysipelothrix rhusiopathiae*. Hajna and Perry[1] devised a selective medium containing 0.05 per cent sodium azide, dextrose and the indicator, brom cresol purple, for the detection of fecal streptococci in swimming pools, water samples and milk. They specified 45.5°C. as the incubation temperature, and reported that growth accompanied with an acid reaction, as shown by the change in color of the medium, was almost complete evidence of the presence of fecal streptococci.

To rehydrate the medium dissolve 36 grams Bacto-S F Medium in 1000 ml. distilled water. Distribute in tubes and sterilize in the autoclave for 15 minutes at 15 pounds pressure (121°C.). Final reaction of the medium will be pH 6.9.

When the inoculum is greater than 1 ml., particular care must be taken to preserve the correct concentration of the ingredients after dilution with the sample. For example, if 10 ml. of water are to be added to 10 ml. of medium, the medium should be prepared in double strength.

One pound of Bacto-S F Medium will make 12.6 liters of medium.

[1] Am. J. Pub. Health, 33:550:1943.
[2] J. Infectious Diseases, 67:113:1940.
[3] J. Bact., 42:653:1941.
[4] Sewage Works J., 12:875:1940.
[5] J. Bact., 42:137:1941.
[6] J. Bact., 46:343:1943.

BACTO
B A G G BROTH (B442)
DEHYDRATED

Bacto-Tryptose	20 g.
Bacto-Dextrose (Glucose)	5 g.
Dipotassium Phosphate	4 g.
Monopotassium Phosphate	1.5 g.
Sodium Chloride	.5 g.
Sodium Azide	0.5 g.
Bacto-Brom Cresol Purple	0.015 g.

Bacto-B A G G Broth (Buffered Azide Glucose Glycerol Broth) is a selective liquid medium for the detection of fecal streptococci from all types of specimens. It is prepared according to the formula given by Hajna[1] and is a modification of SF Medium as described by Hajna and Perry.[2] Coliform and other Gram negative organisms and buccal streptococci are inhibited on this medium as they are on SF Medium while fecal streptococci develop unrestricted.

In using SF Medium for the detection and isolation of fecal streptococci, particularly *Streptococcus fecalis,* Hajna noted that acid production in the medium was much more rapid when the inoculum consisted of a stool received in buffered glycerol saline. Investigation of this observation showed that glycerol facilitated the fermentation of dextrose by members of Streptococcus Group D and Hajna[1] described the addition of glycerol to SF Medium to give the same rapid acid production with pure cultures of *S. fecalis* as with stool specimens. The concentration of Brom Cresol Purple was decreased to detect more readily the color change from purple to yellow within 24 hours incubation.

Hajna[1] reported that growth with acid production is almost definite evidence of the presence of fecal streptococci. *Streptococcus zymogenes, durans* and *liquefaciens* develop at 37°C. or 45°C. *Streptococcus lactis* does not grow at 45°C. making possible a differentiation of these organisms using this incubation temperature. An incubation temperature of 37°C. is suggested for the detection of fecal streptococci from swimming pools, water samples, food products such as oysters and crab meat and from pathological material such as catheterized urine and exudates.

To rehydrate the medium, dissolve 36 grams Bacto-B A G G Broth in 1000 ml. of distilled water containing 5 ml. Bacto-Glycerol. Distribute in tubes in 10 ml. amounts and sterilize in the autoclave for 15 minutes at 10 pounds pressure (116°C.). Sterilization at 121°C. is not recommended. Final reaction of the medium will be pH 6.9.

When the inoculum is larger than 1 ml., particular care must be taken to preserve the correct concentration of the ingredients after dilution with the sample. For example, if 10 ml. of water are to be added to 10 ml. of medium, the medium should be prepared in double strength.

One pound of Bacto-B A G G Broth will make 12.6 liters of medium.

[1] Pub. Health Lab., 9:80:1951.   [2] Am. J. Pub. Health, 33:550:1943.

BACTO
AZIDE DEXTROSE BROTH   (B387)
DEHYDRATED

Bacto-Beef Extract	4.5 g.
Bacto-Tryptone	15 g.
Bacto-Dextrose	7.5 g.
Sodium Chloride	7.5 g.
Sodium Azide	0.2 g.

Bacto-Azide Dextrose Broth is a liquid medium selective for streptococci, and is recommended for use in the detection of these organisms from milk, water, swimming pools, sewage, feces and other specimens. This medium is prepared according to a formula given by Rothe[1] as emanating from the laboratory of the Illinois State Health Department.

The use of sodium azide as an inhibitor of Gram-negative organisms in an attempt to detect streptococci has been pointed out by a number of investigators. Edwards[2] in 1933 used a liquid medium containing crystal violet and sodium azide as a selective broth in the isolation of mastitis streptococci. Hartman[3] reported the value of sodium azide as a selective agent for the isolation of streptococci causing mastitis. Bryan, Devereux, Hirschey and Corbett[4] reported that sodium azide in a concentration of 1:5000 was a better selective preservative for milk cultures and gave more accurate results for the microscopic and Hotis tests for *Streptococcus mastitis* than 1:50,000 brilliant green.

Mallmann, Botwright and Churchill[5] in studying the selective bacteriostatic effect of slow oxidizing agents reported that sodium azide exerted a bacteriostatic effect on Gram-negative bacteria and permitted the growth of Gram-positive organisms. Hajna and Perry[6] used this principle in designing a selective medium for the detection of fecal streptococci. Their medium, Bacto-S F Medium, is described in detail on page 46 of the Manual. Ritter and Treece[7] also used 0.02 per cent sodium azide in a broth containing 2 per cent Proteose Peptone No. 3, 0.1 per cent dextrose and 0.5 per cent sodium chloride for the detection of cocci in swimming pools. The selectivity of this medium was later increased by the addition of crystal violet to this medium by Ritter.[8]

In a comparative study of media for the detection of streptococci in water and sewage Mallmann and Seligmann[9] used Bacto-Azide Dextrose Broth. They reported the medium offered a new means of measuring the presence of streptococci in water, sewage, shellfish and other materials in which sewage pollution is suspected.

To rehydrate the medium dissolve 34.7 grams Bacto-Azide Dextrose Broth in 1000 ml. distilled water. Distribute in tubes and sterilize in the autoclave for 15 minutes at 15 pounds pressure (121°C.). Inocula of 1 loop or 1 ml. may be added to 10 ml. or more of medium. The medium should be prepared in multiple strength for larger inocula to preserve the correct concentration of ingredients. For example, if 10 ml. of inoculum is to be added to 10 ml. of medium, the medium should be prepared in double strength. Final reaction of the medium will be pH 7.2.

One pound of Bacto-Azide Dextrose Broth will make 13.1 liters single strength medium.

[1] Rothe, Personal Communication, 1948.
[2] J. Comp. Path. Therap., 46:211:1933.
[3] Milchw. Forsch., 18:116:1936.
[4] North Am. Vet., 20:424:1939.
[5] J. Infectious Diseases, 69:215:1941.
[6] Am. J. Pub. Health, 33:550:1943.
[7] Am. J. Pub. Health, 38:1532:1948.
[8] Ritter, Personal Communication, 1949.
[9] Am. J. Pub. Health, 40:286:1950.

BACTO
BORIC ACID BROTH (B439)
DEHYDRATED

Proteose Peptone, Difco	10 g.
Bacto-Lactose	5 g.
Dipotassium Phosphate	12.2 g.
Monopotassium Phosphate	4.1 g.
Boric Acid	3.25 g.

Bacto-Boric Acid Broth is a liquid medium for the enrichment and presumptive identification of *Escherichia coli* from water and food, as indicated by growth and gas production at 42.5°–43.5°C. This medium is prepared according to the formula of Vaughn, Levine and Smith [1]

The presence of *E. coli* is considered by many to be a reliable index of human or animal fecal contamination, and for some food products the presence of coliform bacteria may not be a true indication of the sanitary quality of the food. Thus a method which would permit the selective enrichment and identification of *E. coli* would be of decided value in the determination of the sanitary significance of the various coliform bacteria found in foods. Many methods have been devised for this purpose. Bacto-E C Medium as described on page 45 is a modification of the Eijkman test designed to detect *E. coli* at an incubation temperature of 45.5°C. Boric acid has been added to lactose media to favor the growth of *E. coli* as described by Levine[2,4] and Levine, Epstein and Vaughn.[3] Bartram and Black[5] and Wolford and Berry[6] reported boric acid to be of value in the detection and differentiation of *E. coli* from other coliform bacteria. Vaughn, Levine and Smith[1] made a study of the various ingredients, reaction, concentration, and incubation temperature and presented data to show that their medium is useful both for primary enrichment and rapid presumptive identification of *E. coli*. They stressed that all conditions of the test must be adhered to or the medium is of little value. The concentration of boric acid must be maintained at 3.25 g. per liter. Multiple strength medium must be prepared when inocula greater than 1 ml. per 20 ml. of medium are used. The temperature of the medium must be constantly kept between 42.5°–43.5°C., and experience has shown that an oil bath with adequate stirring device to insure even distribution of heat is required. They report that the use of ordinary or water jacketed air incubators and water baths have re-emphasized the desirability of an oil bath. Maximum inhibition of the boric acid resistant members of the *Aerobacter* and *E. freundii* groups are obtained only under these conditions, permitting the growth and development of gas by only *E. coli* in 48 hours. The productivity of Boric Acid Broth was investigated by the authors. They were able, in pure culture studies, to demonstrate gas production in every combination of *E. coli* and other coliforms, including a boric acid resistant *Aerobacter aerogenes* strain when *E. coli* was present in the mixture. In the absence of this organism no gas was formed in 48 hours. The detection of *E. coli* from water samples was compared using Lactose Broth at 35°C. and the Boric Acid Broth at 42.5°–43.5°C. The results of this series of experiments showed that the boric acid medium could be considered more reliable than Lactose Broth for enriching and recovering *E. coli* from contaminated water. Similar results have been obtained using food samples.

Bacto-Boric Acid Broth duplicates the formula described by Vaughn, Levine and Smith[1]. They stated that their medium might be prepared with the addition of Andrade or other suitable indicator, if desired. Similarly any desired indicator may be added in preparing the medium from Bacto-Boric Acid Broth.

To rehydrate the medium, dissolve 34.6 grams in 1000 ml. distilled water. Distribute in tubes in 20 ml. amounts with inverted fermentation vials and sterilize in the autoclave for 15 minutes at 15 pounds pressure (121°C.). If inocula greater than 1 ml. is used the medium must be prepared in multiple strength to maintain the correct concentration of the ingredients. Final reaction of the medium will be pH 7.0.

One pound of Bacto-Boric Acid Broth will make 13.1 liters single strength medium.

[1] Food Research, 16:10:1951.
[2] Am. J. Pub. Health, 11:21:1921.
[3] Am. J. Pub. Health, 24:505:1934.
[4] J. Bact., 29:24:1935.
[5] J. Bact., 31:24:1936.
[6] Food Research, 13:172:1948.

BACTO
ENTEROCOCCI PRESUMPTIVE BROTH   (B300)
DEHYDRATED

Bacto-Tryptone	5 g.
Bacto-Yeast Extract	5 g.
Bacto-Dextrose	5 g.
Sodium Azide	0.4 g.
Bacto-Brom Thymol Blue	0.032 g.

These Enterococci media are prepared according to the formulae given by Sandholzer and Winter[1] for the detection of Enterococci in water supplies, swimming pools, sewage or other specimens suspected of containing these organisms. The procedure, as described, consists of a presumptive test in which the production of acid and turbidity (growth) in an azide presumptive broth after incubation at 45°C. is considered positive presumptive evidence for the presence of Enterococci. The positive presumptive tests are then confirmed by inoculating a slant-broth combination prepared with an azide agar medium overlaid with a salt-azide-penicillin broth. Pinpoint colonies on the slant, growth sediment in the broth, the presence of Gram-positive ovoid streptococci in the broth, and a negative catalase test is considered confirmed positive evidence of the presence of Enterococci.

To rehydrate the medium (single strength) dissolve 15.4 grams Bacto-Enterococci Presumptive Broth in 1000 ml. of distilled water. Tube in 8 ml. amounts and sterilize in the autoclave for 15 minutes at 15 pounds pressure (121°C.). The concentrated or 5 strength presumptive enrichment broth is prepared by dissolving 77 grams of Bacto-Enterococci Presumptive Broth in 1000 ml. distilled water. Inocula of 1 loop to 2 ml. are used for 8 ml. tube of the single strength medium. The 5 times strength medium is distributed in 2 ml. amounts and following sterilization as above, is inoculated with 10 ml. of sample per tube. The final reaction of the medium is pH 8.4.

One pound of Bacto-Enterococci Presumptive Broth will make 29.4 liters of medium.

[1] Commercial Fisheries Leaflet TL2, November, 1946.

BACTO

ENTEROCOCCI CONFIRMATORY AGAR (B301)

DEHYDRATED

Bacto-Tryptone	5 g.
Bacto-Yeast Extract	5 g.
Bacto-Dextrose	5 g.
Sodium Azide	0.4 g.
Bacto-Agar	15 g.
Bacto-Methylene Blue	0.01 g.

A discussion of the use of this medium is given above under Bacto-Enterococci Presumptive Broth.

To rehydrate the medium, suspend 30.4 grams Bacto-Enterococci Confirmatory Agar in 1000 ml. of cold distilled water. Heat to boiling to dissolve the medium completely and distribute in tubes. Sterilize in the autoclave for 15 minutes at 15 pounds pressure (121°C.). The medium is allowed to cool in a slanted position. The final reaction of the medium is pH 8.0.

One pound of Bacto-Enterococci Confirmatory Agar will make 14.9 liters of medium.

BACTO
ENTEROCOCCI CONFIRMATORY BROTH   (B302)
DEHYDRATED

Bacto-Tryptone	5 g.
Bacto-Yeast Extract	5 g.
Bacto-Dextrose	5 g.
Sodium Azide	0.4 g.
Sodium Chloride	65 g.
Bacto-Methylene Blue	0.01 g.

A discussion of the use of this medium is given above under Bacto-Enterococci Presumptive Broth.

To rehydrate the medium, dissolve 80.4 grams Bacto-Enterococci Confirmatory Broth in 1000 ml. of distilled water. Distribute in flasks in 100 ml. quantities and sterilize in the autoclave for 15 minues at 15 pounds pressure (121°C.). Final reaction of the medium will be pH 8.0. When cooled to room temperature and just prior to use, add 65 units of penicillin to each 100 ml. of medium. Enough Enterococci Confirmatory Broth containing penicillin is added to each Enterococci Confirmatory Agar slant to cover approximately one-half the surface of the slant.

One pound of Bacto-Enterococci Confirmatory Broth will make 5.6 liters of medium.

BACTO
BRILLIANT GREEN BILE AGAR   (B14)
DEHYDRATED

Bacto-Peptone	8.25 g.
Bacto-Lactose	1.9 g.
Bacto-Oxgall	0.00295 g.
Sodium Sulfite	0.205 g.
Ferric Chloride	0.0295 g.
Monopotassium Phosphate	0.0153 g.
Special Agar (Noble)	10.15 g.
Erioglaucine	0.0649 g.
Bacto-Basic Fuchsin	0.0776 g.
Bacto-Brilliant Green	0.0000295 g.

Bacto-Brilliant Green Bile Agar duplicates the medium described by Noble and Tonney[1] for determining the relative density of coliform bacteria in water and sewage. This medium is not recommended for the determination of the absolute density of coliform organisms in water samples, but rather as an indication of the degree of contamination of the sample. It is suggested as a selective agar medium for this purpose in Appendix I of "Standard Methods for the Examination of Water and Sewage."[2]

In the enumeration of coliform bacteria using Bacto-Brilliant Green Bile Agar plates should be poured in dilutions which will show not less than ten colonies of coliform organisms per plate and it is, therefore, suggested that several dilutions be plated from each sample. When 10 ml. quantities of water are to be plated an equal quantity of double strength medium should be employed. Inoculated plates are incubated at 37°C. for 17 hours and for not longer than 19 hours. Colonies of coliform bacteria are deep red at the center with a pink halo sharply outlined against a uniformly blue background. The colonies vary from 0.4 to 0.8 mm. in diameter.

The medium is rather sensitive to light, particularly direct sunlight, which produces a decrease in the productivity of the medium and change in color from deep blue to purple or red. It is recommended that the medium be prepared just prior to use and when necessary to store the medium, it should be kept in the dark.

To rehydrate the medium, suspend 20.6 grams of Bacto-Brilliant Green Bile Agar in 1000 ml. of cold distilled water and heat to boiling to dissolve the medium completely. Distribute in tubes or flasks and sterilize in the autoclave for 15 minutes at 15 pounds pressure (121°C.).The final reaction of the medium will be pH 6.9.

One pound of Bacto-Brilliant Green Bile Agar will make 22 liters of medium.

[1] J. Am. Water Works Assoc., 27:108:1935.   [2] Standard Methods for the Examination of Water and Sewage, 9th Edition:228:1946.

BACTO
TRYPTONE (B123)
DEHYDRATED

Bacto-Tryptone in a 1 per cent concentration is specified in "Standard Methods for the Examination of Water and Sewage"[1] for the performance of the indole test, and is also specified in "Standard Methods for the Examination of Dairy Products,"[2] for use in preparing media for the standard plate count.

A complete discussion of Bacto-Tryptone, and other uses of this peptone, is given on page 260.

The test for indole recommended in "Standard Methods" is that of Kovacs[3] which is also recommended in "Diagnostic Procedures and Reagents"[4] of the American Public Health Association. This test is performed by adding 0.2 to 0.3 ml. of Kovacs' reagent to 5 ml. of a 24-hour culture of the organism under investigation. A dark red color in the surface layer constitutes a positive test; the original yellow color of the solution is a negative test when this reagent is used for indole detection. Kovacs' reagent is made by dissolving 5 grams of p-dimethyl-aminobenzaldehyde in 75 ml. of amyl alcohol and adding 25 ml. of concentrated hydrochloric acid.

Among the many other tests for the detection of indole, particular mention may be made here of the Ehrlich-Boehme[5] procedure, the Goré[6] modification of this reaction, and the Gnezda[7] technique.

For the Ehrlich-Boehme test two solutions are necessary. Solution I consists of 1 gram p-dimethylaminobenzaldehyde in 95 ml. of ethyl alcohol (95 per cent) and 20 ml. of concentrated hydrochloric acid. Solution II is a saturated aqueous solution of potassium persulfate. To about 10 ml. of the culture showing good growth of the organism 5 ml. of Solution I are added, then 5 ml. of Solution II are added, and the mixture is shaken well. A red color developing in five minutes indicates a positive test for the presence of indole. Pure Culture Study of Bacteria[8] states that this test may be performed by first shaking up the culture with ethyl ether and then adding Solution I, dropping it down the side of the tube so that it spreads out as a layer between the ether and the culture fluid. The formation of a purplish red color at the interface of the two liquids within 5 minutes indicates indole production.

For the Goré test the same solutions used for the Ehrlich-Boehme test are employed. The cotton plug, which must be of white absorbent cotton, used for plugging the culture tube is moistened with four to six drops of Solution II and then with the same amount of Solution I. The plug is replaced in the tube and is pushed down until it is about one inch above the surface of the medium. The tube is heated in a boiling water bath for 15 minutes without allowing the medium to touch the plug. The appearance of a red color on the plug indicates the presence of indole.

The Gnezda test is carried out as follows: A strip of filter paper is dipped into a warm saturated solution of oxalic acid and is then dried thoroughly. The strip is bent at an angle and is inserted into the culture tube in such a manner that it presses against the sides and remains immediately below the cotton plug. Although it is not necessary to sterilize the paper, aseptic precautions should be observed when it is placed in the tube. The cotton plug is reinserted into the tube which is then incubated at 37°C. Development of a pink color on the paper indicates the formation of indole.

[1] Standard Methods for the Examination of Water and Sewage, 9th Edition:230:1946.
[2] Standard Methods for the Examination of Dairy Products, 9th Edition:92:1948.
[3] Zeit. Immunitaetsf. Exper. Therap., 55:311:1928.
[4] Diagnostic Procedures and Reagents, 2nd Edition:53:1945.
[5] Centr. Bakt. I Abt. Orig., 40:129:1905.
[6] Indian J. Med. Research, 8:505:1921.
[7] Compt. rend. acad. sci., 128:1584:1899.
[8] Manual of Methods of Pure Culture Study of Bacteria, 7th Edition: Leaflet V, page 9, 1939.

BACTO

M.R.-V.P. MEDIUM (B16)

DEHYDRATED

Buffered Peptone		7 g.
Bacto-Dextrose		5 g.
Dipotassium Phosphate		5 g.

Bacto-M.R.-V.P. Medium is recommended for the performance of the Methyl Red and Voges-Proskauer Tests in differentiation of the coli-aerogenes group. The use of this medium is recommended in Appendix I of "Standard Methods for the Examination of Water and Sewage"[1] for this purpose.

Clark and Lubs[2] first pointed out that in a suitable medium coli organisms produced a high acidity which was constant, while the aerogenes group produced a much less acid reaction, and on continued incubation became more alkaline. This difference in the acidity produced in the cultivation of coli or aerogenes could be recognized by the addition of the indicator methyl red. This Clark and Lubs test has become known as the Methyl Red Reaction.

Closely associated with the Methyl Red Reaction is the test described by Voges and Proskauer,[3] who noted that a color reaction took place if certain cultures in a suitable medium were treated with potassium hydroxide and allowed to stand for some time. This color reaction develops particularly in that part of the medium exposed to the air, and is very similar to that of a dilute alcoholic solution of eosin. The development of the color reaction upon treatment of cultures with potassium hydroxide was found to be due to the presence of acetyl-methylcarbinol, (3-hydroxy-2-butanone). Levine[4] recommended that the term "Voges-Proskauer Reaction" be restricted to designate the formation of acetyl-methylcarbinol from dextrose.

Bacto-M.R.-V.P. Medium was developed as a simple and reliable medium for use in the performance of the Methyl Red and Voges-Proskauer Tests. Ruchhoft, Kallas, Chinn, and Coulter[5] reported that Bacto-M.R.-V.P. Medium is uniform and superior to laboratory-made media for these tests.

For performance of the Methyl Red and Voges-Proskauer Tests, each tube should be inoculated with a pure culture.

The Methyl Red Test is performed after 5 days incubation at 30°C. as recommended by Vaughn, Mitchell and Levine[6] and "Standard Methods."[1] For the Voges-Proskauer Test the culture should be incubated for 24 to 48 hours at 30°C.[1,5]

Methyl Red Test

To 5 ml. of culture add 5 drops of methyl red solution. A positive reaction is indicated by a distinct red color, showing the presence of acid. A negative reaction is indicated by a yellow color. The indicator solution is prepared by dissolving 0.1 gram Bacto-Methyl Red in 300 ml. of 95 per cent alcohol and diluting to 500 ml. with distilled water.

Voges-Proskauer Test

To 5 ml. of culture add 5 ml. of a 10 per cent solution of potassium hydroxide, mix well, allow to stand exposed to the air, and observe at intervals of 2, 12, and 24 hours. A positive test is indicated by the development of an eosin pink color. This is the test as originally described.[2]

Various other tests have been suggested as being excellently adapted to the demonstration of the development of acetyl-methyl-carbinol, chief among which are those of Werkman,[7] O'Meara,[8] Levine, Epstein and Vaughn[9] and Vaughn, Mitchell and Levine.[6]

Werkman's test[7] consists of the addition of 2 drops of a 2 per cent solution of ferric chloride to 5 ml. of culture, followed by 5 ml. of 10 per cent sodium hydroxide, and shaking the tube well to mix. A stable copper color appearing in a few minutes is indicative of a positive test.

O'Meara[8] recommends the addition of approximately 25 mg. of solid creatine to 5 ml. of culture and then adding 5 ml. concentrated (at least 40 per cent) sodium hydroxide. The development of a red color in a few minutes, after thorough agitation of the tube, is a positive test. Levine, Epstein and Vaughn[9] modified the O'Meara technique by dissolving the creatine in a concentrated solution of potassium hydroxide.

"Standard Methods"[1] specifies the use of the Barritt[10] method as recommended by Vaughn, Mitchell and Levine[6] for the performance of this test. The test is made by adding 0.6 ml. of 5 per cent alpha-naphthol in absolute ethyl alcohol and 0.2 ml. of 40 per cent potassium hydroxide to 1 ml. of culture.

To rehydrate the medium, dissolve 17 grams of Bacto-M.R.-V.P. Medium in 1000 ml. of distilled water. Distribute in 10 ml. quantities in test tubes. Sterilize in the autoclave for 15 minutes at 15 pounds pressure (121°C.). The final reaction of the medium will be pH 6.9.

One pound of Bacto-M.R.-V.P. Medium will make 26.7 liters of medium.

[1] Standard Methods for the Examination of Water and Sewage, 9th Edition.130.1946.
[2] J. Infectious Diseases, 17:160:1915.
[3] Zeit. Hyg., 28:20:1898.
[4] J. Bact., 1:153:1916.
[5] J. Bact., 22:125:1931.
[6] J. Am. Water Works Assoc., 31:993:1939.
[7] J. Bact., 10:12:11:1930.
[8] J. Path. Bact., 34:401:1931.
[9] Am. J. Pub. Health, 24:505:1934.
[10] J. Path. Bact., 42:441:1936.

BACTO
KOSER CITRATE MEDIUM (B15)
DEHYDRATED

Sodium Ammonium Phosphate ..... 1.5 g.
Monopotassium Phosphate .... 1 g.
Magnesium Sulfate .... 0.2 g.
Sodium Citrate .... 3 g.

Bacto-Koser Citrate Medium is a liquid medium recommended for the differentiation of *Escherichia coli and Aerobacter aerogenes*. It conforms to the formula specified in Appendix I of "Standard Methods for the Examination of Water and Sewage"[1] for this purpose. In this medium an ammonium salt serves as the sole source of nitrogen, and sodium citrate as the only source of carbon.

The desirability for a means of differentiating coli-aerogenes organisms in sanitary studies has long been recognized and a wide variety of media have been devised to accomplish the same. Koser[2] showed that either citric acid or its sodium salt, when employed in a synthetic medium as the only source of carbon, is readily utilized by *A. aerogenes,* while *E. coli* fail to develop. This property was quite constant and not quickly acquired or lost.

In using this medium, coli-like colonies from Endo or Eosin Methylene Blue Agar plates are inoculated into tubes of Koser Citrate Medium and, after 24 to 48 hours incubation, tubes showing marked turbidity mav be assumed to contain organisms of the aerogenes group. Inasmuch as coli-type organisms fail to grow in this medium all tubes inoculated from coli-like colonies on Endo or Eosin Methylene Blue Agar plates and remaining clear after 36 hours incubation may be considered as coli.

Bacto-Koser Citrate Medium is prepared according to Koser's[2] original formula. Chemically pure salts are used in the preparation of the medium and it is carefully tested to be sure that no sources of carbon, other than the citrate radical, or nitrogen other than ammonium salts, are present.

To rehydrate the medium, dissolve 5.7 grams of Bacto-Koser Citrate Medium in 1000 ml. of distilled water. The medium is distributed in tubes and sterilized by autoclaving for 15 minutes at 15 pounds pressure (121°C.). The final reaction of the medium will be pH 6.7.

One pound of Bacto-Koser Citrate Medium will make 79.6 liters of medium.

[1] Standard Methods for the Examination   [2] J. Bact., 8:493:1923.
of Water and Sewage, 9th Edition:231:1946.

BACTO
MacCONKEY BROTH   (B20)
DEHYDRATED

Bacto-Peptone	20 g.
Bacto-Lactose	10 g.
Bacto-Oxgall	5 g.
Bacto-Brom Cresol Purple	0.01 g.

Bacto-MacConkey Broth is prepared according to a modification of the bile salt broth recommended by MacConkey[1] which contained 0.5 per cent sodium taurocholate and litmus as an indicator. In later publications[2,3] MacConkey suggested other variants of this medium and employed neutral red instead of litmus as an indicator.

In recent investigations of the original formula, taking into consideration its probable use as a presumptive medium in the detection of the coliform group in water and milk examination, it was demonstrated that Bacto-Oxgall was well adapted for use in this medium instead of sodium taurocholate. Medium prepared from Bacto-MacConkey Broth is clear and does not require filtration or adjustment of the reaction. Bacto-MacConkey Broth is now prepared with the sulfonephthalein indicator Bacto-Brom Cresol Purple. The color of the uninoculated medium is the same as when the indicator litmus was used, but after incubation, acid is demonstrated by the color of the medium changing to yellow.

To rehydrate the medium, dissolve 35 grams of Bacto-MacConkey Broth in

1000 ml. of distilled water and distribute in 10 ml. quantities in fermentation tubes. Sterilize by autoclaving for 15 minutes at 15 pounds pressure (121°C.). The final reaction of the medium will be pH 7.3.

When the medium is to be used with inocula greater than 1 ml., particular care must be taken to preserve the correct concentration of the ingredients after dilution with the sample. For example, if 10 ml. of water are to be added to 10 ml. of medium, the medium should be prepared in double strength.

One pound of Bacto-MacConkey Broth will make 12.9 liters of medium.

[1] Centr. Bakt., 29:740:1901.   [3] J. Hyg., 8:322:1908.
[2] J. Hyg., 5:333:1905.

MEDIA FOR THE EXAMINATION OF DAIRY AND OTHER FOOD PRODUCTS

THE DEHYDRATED CULTURE MEDIA listed in this section are recommended for the examination of milk and other dairy products. In many cases the formulae conform to those in "Standard Methods of the Examination of Dairy Products" of the American Public Health Association and the Association of Official Agricultural Chemists, Ninth Edition 1948, and "Methods and Standards for the Production of Certified Milk," 1950, of the American Association of Medical Milk Commissions, or other official procedures.

Carefully selected standardized ingredients are used in the exact proportions specified in the "Standard Methods" formulae. The reaction of each medium is adjusted so that the final reaction of each preparation made from the dehydrated product will fall within the range of pH recommended in "Standard Methods."

The American Public Health Association has permitted the use of dehydrated media of "Standard Methods" composition continuously since 1923 in every edition of its "Standard Methods of Milk Analysis," including the current Ninth Edition of "Standard Methods for the Examination of Dairy Products."

A guide for the selection of culture media listed in this section is given on page 25.

"STANDARD METHODS" MEDIA

THE MEDIA listed in this section conform to the specifications for the examination of milk and other dairy products as outlined in the "Standard Methods for the Examination of Dairy Products," Ninth Edition.

BACTO
TRYPTONE GLUCOSE EXTRACT AGAR (B2)
DEHYDRATED

Bacto-Beef Extract	3 g.
Bacto-Tryptone	5 g.
Bacto-Dextrose (d-glucose)	1 g.
Bacto-Agar	15 g.

Bacto-Tryptone Glucose Extract Agar is recommended for use in determining the standard plate count of milk and other dairy products according to the methods specified in "Standard Methods for the Examination of Dairy Products."[1] In determining the total bacterial counts of certified milk the use of Tryptone Glucose Extract Milk Agar is approved by the Committee on Methods and Standards for the Production of Certified Milk.[2] The Ninth Edition of "Standard Methods for the Examination of Water and Sewage"[3] permits the use of Tryptone Glucose Extract Agar in place of Nutrient Agar for standard plate counts of water.

Bacto-Tryptone Glucose Extract Agar is a modification of the Tryptone Glucose Skim Milk Agar of Bowers and Hucker.[4] Extensive investigations in many widely separated laboratories established the superiority of their medium over Nutrient Agar for estimations of bacteria in milk and other dairy products. This work has been ably summarized by Yale[5] in his report on the use of the medium. Robertson[6] has employed this medium in a study of the bacterial count of ice cream, and Dennis and Weiser[7] employed it in their study of the influence of the incubation temperature on bacterial counts of milk. Prickett[8] used a Glucose Agar containing Bacto-Tryptone in his study of the thermophilic bacteria in milk which was described in the Sixth Edition of "Standard Methods of Milk Analysis"[9] and was prepared in the dehydrated form as Bacto-Yeast Dextrose Agar. "Standard Methods for the Examination of Dairy Products"[10] presently recommends the use of Tryptone Glucose Extract Agar for the detection of thermophilic bacteria. Media similar to that used by Prickett were recommended by Downs, Hammer, Cordes, and Macy[11] in their report on the bacteriological methods for the analysis of dairy products.

A committee on Standard Methods for the Examination of Dairy Products evaluated, comparatively, the modified medium of Bowers and Hucker to determine whether it was superior to the then standard Nutrient Agar for the plate count of milk. As a result of these studies the committee[12,13] recommended the adoption of Tryptone Glucose Extract Milk Agar as the standard medium for the bacteriological plate count of milk. Details of the "Standard Methods" committee's studies are reported by Abele.[14]

Dilutions of the sample are plated according to Standard Methods procedures on this medium and the plates incubated for 48 hours ± 3 hours, at 32°C. or 35°C. Comparison of total counts with Tryptone Glucose Extract Milk Agar and the former standard Nutrient Agar have indicated greatest differences in low grade milk and milk products. Certified milk and other high grade milks have shown little difference in final counts.

The dehydrated medium does not contain skim milk since the "Standard Methods" committee has recommended that skim milk be added to the medium only when the dilution of the specimen is greater than 1 to 10. Bacto-Skim Milk, as discussed on page 74, is recommended for the preparation of a standardized skim milk solution to be used with Bacto-Tryptone Glucose Extract Agar in the preparation of the skim milk medium.

To rehydrate the medium, suspend 24 grams of Bacto-Tryptone Glucose Extract Agar in 1000 ml. of cold distilled water. Tap water, or unsatisfactory distilled water, may give a precipitate in the final medium. Heat to boiling to dissolve the medium completely. Distribute in tubes or flasks and sterilize in the autoclave for 15 minutes at 15 pounds pressure (121°C.). The final reaction of the medium will be pH 7.0. When the medium is to be prepared with skim milk, 10 ml. of skim milk are added to one liter of medium just before sterilization.

If directions for the preparation of the medium are not followed carefully, or if the medium is subjected to excessive heat before, during or after the sterilization period, a precipitation may occur. The following recommendations to overcome difficulties in the preparation of the medium are suggested.

It is necessary to stir the suspended medium during the heating period to prevent the medium from settling out and burning on the bottom of the flask. In the preparation of large quantities of medium (500 ml. or more) about three-fourths of the water may be heated to boiling. The dehydrated medium is evenly suspended in the remaining unheated distilled water, and this suspension is promptly added to the boiling distilled water. The medium should be boiled for several minutes to effect complete solution.

Not all samples of fresh skim milk are satisfactory for the preparation of the medium. For that reason we recommend the addition of 10 ml. of a 10 per cent solution of Bacto-Skim Milk per liter of Tryptone Glucose Extract Agar after the medium is in complete solution.

The use of Pyrex or other hard glass containers is recommended for sterilization.

Do not overheat medium in the autoclave. Care should be taken that the autoclave reaches 15 pounds pressure (121°C.) promptly and be maintained there for 15 minutes after which the steam supply is cut off and the autoclave allowed to come to atmospheric pressure without unnecessary delay. Not more than thirty to forty minutes for the complete operation should be required. The medium should not be allowed to cool or solidify in the autoclave, but should be removed promptly after sterilization.

Do not hold melted agar at 45°C. for over 30 minutes. Tryptone Glucose Extract Milk Agar will flocculate if held at 43 to 45°C. for longer than 30 minutes. This flocculation can be dispersed by re-heating the medium. The flocculation will not develop if the medium is held at 48 to 50°C.

If it is not practical to follow the above directions in detail, and a troublesome precipitate persists, the complete medium may be prepared by the addition of sterile skim milk to sterile liquid Tryptone Glucose Extract Agar under aseptic conditions, just prior to pouring plates.

One pound of Bacto-Tryptone Glucose Extract Agar will make 18.9 liters of medium.

[1] Standard Methods for the Examination of Dairy Products, 9th Edition:93:1948.
[2] Methods and Standards for the Production of Certified Milk, 21:1950.
[3] Standard Methods for the Examination of Water and Sewage, 9th Edition:191:1946.
[4] Tech. Bull. 228, N. Y. State Agr. Exp. Sta., 1935.
[5] Am. J. Pub. Health, 28:148:1938.
[6] Proc. 36th Cong. Intern. Assoc. Ice Cream Manufacturers, 9:189:1936.
[7] J. Dairy Science, 20:445:1937.
[8] Tech. Bull. 147, N. Y. State Agr. Exp. Sta., 1928.
[9] Standard Methods of Milk Analysis, 6th Edition:60:1934.
[10] Standard Methods for the Examination of Dairy Products, 9th Edition:343:1948.
[11] J. Dairy Science, 18:647:1935.
[12] Am. J. Pub. Health, 28:1447:1938.
[13] Ninth Annual Year Book (1938–39) p. 79, Suppl., Am. J. Pub. Health, 29:No. 2:1939.
[14] Am. J. Pub. Health, 29:821:1939.

BACTO
BRILLIANT GREEN BILE 2%
DEHYDRATED

A complete discussion of this medium as used in the presumptive test for coliform organisms in milk and other dairy products is given under Bacto-Brilliant Green Bile 2%, page 37. This medium has also been referred to as Brilliant Green Lactose Peptone Bile, and similar variations.

BACTO
FORMATE RICINOLEATE BROTH (B9)
DEHYDRATED

Bacto-Peptone	5 g.
Bacto-Lactose	5 g.
Sodium Formate	5 g.
Sodium Ricinoleate	1 g.

Bacto-Formate Ricinoleate Broth is prepared according to the formula speci-fied in "Standard Methods for the Examination of Dairy Products"[1] and "Standard Methods for the Examination of Water and Sewage."[2] It is used for the presumptive test for the members of the coliform group in the bacteriological examination of milk according to "Standard Methods."[3] The procedure for use of this medium in water examination is discussed on page 39.

In research on the development of a medium which would be sufficiently selective, yet at the same time not inhibitive to any member of the coliform group which might be present in the water or milk sample, Stark and England[4] devised Formate Ricinoleate Broth. The sodium formate present in the medium accelerates growth and gas production of coli and related organisms, while sodium ricinoleate inhibits the development of Gram-positive bacteria and other organisms which give positive presumptive tests that do not confirm. It is inter-esting to note that gas production appears earlier in this medium than in other media under the same conditions, and that it is present in larger proportions at the completion of the test. The buffer action of the medium, due largely to the destruction of the sodium formate, maintains a more constant reaction, as shown by the fact that, even after 48 hours incubation with coli, the reaction of the medium is rarely more acid than pH 6.0. Noble and White,[5] in their report on the relative productivity of various fermentation media, state that media pre-pared from Bacto-Formate Ricinoleate Broth had a higher productivity rating than other media with which they were compared.

Tiedeman and Smith,[6] in a comparison of several methods for the detection of coliform organisms in pasteurized milk stated that in a survey of 896 samples of pasteurized milk, showing no fermentation in Formate Ricinoleate Broth, 821 or 91.6 per cent gave no colonies on Desoxycholate Agar. An additional 56 or 6.2 per cent gave a count of between 1 and 3 colonies per ml. A total of 97.8 per cent negative fermentation tests gave less than 3 colonies on the plating medium, which was considered good correlation. They further state that the Formate Ricinoleate Broth fermentation test is a critical one but does not give information as to the number of coliforms present as does the use of Violet Red Bile Agar or Desoxycholate Agar.

In the presumptive test for members of the coliform group in the examination of dairy products a series of tubes of Formate Ricinoleate Broth are inoculated with appropriate dilutions of the sample. Use 5 tubes of each dilution. Select dilutions to provide at least one positive and one negative tube in the series inoculated. Incubate tubes for 48 hours at 35–37°C. Gas formation constitutes a positive presumptive test.

When the medium is to be used in water filtration plant control work[7] where the inoculum is greater than 1 ml., particular care must be taken to preserve the correct concentration of the ingredients after dilution with the sample. The table given below indicates the quantity of dehydrated medium to use per 1000 ml.

To rehydrate the medium, dissolve 16 grams of Bacto-Formate Ricinoleate Broth in 1000 ml. of distilled water. The medium is distributed in fermentation tubes and sterilized by autoclaving for 15 minutes at 15 pounds pressure (121°C.). The final reaction of the medium will be pH 7.4.

One pound of Bacto-Formate Ricinoleate Broth will make 28.3 liters of medium.

Concentrations of Dehydrated Medium Required to Maintain the Proper Concentration of Ingredients

Inoculum	Amt. Medium in Tube	Vol. Medium and Inoculum	Bacto-Formate Ricinoleate Broth used per 1000 ml.
Loop or 0.1 ml.	10 ml. or more	10 ml. or more	16 g.
1 ml.	5 ml.	6 ml.	19.2 g.
10 ml.	10 ml.	20 ml.	32 g.
10 ml.	15 ml.	25 ml.	26.6 g.
10 ml.	20 ml.	30 ml.	24 g.
10 ml.	30 ml.	40 ml.	21.3 g.

[1] Standard Methods for the Examination of Dairy Products, 9th Edition:131:1948.
[2] Standard Methods for the Examination of Water and Sewage, 9th Edition:188:1946.
[3] Standard Methods for the Examination of Dairy Products, 9th Edition:133:1948.
[4] J. Bact., 29:26:1935.
[5] J. Bact., 29:23:1935.
[6] J. Milk Tech., 8:323:1945.
[7] Standard Methods for the Examination of Water and Sewage, 9th Edition:226:1946.

BACTO
VIOLET RED BILE AGAR (B12)
DEHYDRATED

Bacto-Yeast Extract .... 3 g.
Bacto-Peptone .... 7 g.
Bacto-Bile Salts No. 3 .... 1.5 g.
Bacto-Lactose .... 10 g.
Sodium Chloride .... 5 g.
Bacto-Agar .... 15 g.
Bacto-Neutral Red .... 0.03 g.
Bacto-Crystal Violet .... 0.002 g.

Bacto-Violet Red Bile Agar is recommended for the direct plate count of coliform bacteria in water, milk, dairy and other food products. "Standard Methods for the Examination of Dairy Products"[1] recommends the use of Violet Red Bile Agar for the ml. coliform count in milk and other dairy products. In Appendix I of "Standard Methods for the Examination of Water and Sewage"[2] this medium is suggested as a selective agar medium for direct plating of water for members of the coliform group.

The original work by Difco Laboratories on the development of a solid selective medium for the quantitative estimation of the number of viable coliform organisms in water, milk, dairy and other food products was undertaken in 1932 in cooperation with M. H. McCrady, at that time sub-referee of the committee on Standard Methods of Milk Analysis of the American Public Health Association. The formula adopted had exhaustive trials in our laboratories and was also used extensively by others in the determination of the presence and numbers of coliform organisms in milk and dairy products. The use of Bacto-Bile Salts No. 3 in place of Bacto-Bile Salts originally employed resulted in an improved medium.

Bacto-Violet Red Bile Agar is especially applicable to the control of pasteurization of milk and cream. The use of this medium makes it possible to determine quantitatively the coliform count of the milk at any stage of the process. Therefore, it is possible to determine the cleanliness of apparatus and the efficiency of the process as well as to detect sources of contamination at various stages.

Bartram and Black[3] in an investigation of media for the isolation of the coliform group from raw, pasteurized, and certified milk, found Bacto-Violet Red Bile Agar to be the most satisfactory solid medium for this work. Babel and Parfitt[4] studying media for the detection of *Escherichia-Aerobacter* in ice cream, used Bacto-Violet Red Bile Agar and reported its superiority over other solid media recommended for such work. Yale[5,7] reported the use of Bacto-Violet Red Bile Agar in making coli counts of ice cream and pasteurized milk. Fabian and Hook[6] used Bacto-Violet Red Bile Agar in establishing the count of *Escherichia-Aerobacter* in a study of sanitary conditions of ice cream as served at the fountain. Miller and Prickett[8] published a note on the use of this medium in a practical case concerning recontamination of milk. The Violet Red Bile Agar counts were completed within 24 hours after plating. This is a considerable saving in time in comparison with the confirmed Brilliant Green Bile procedure which requires a minimum period of 48 hours. Quinn and Garnatz[9] used Bacto-Violet Red Bile Agar for the coli-aerogenes count of frozen eggs.

Bacto-Violet Red Bile Agar is a poured plate medium. It is recommended that 15–20 ml. of medium and not more than 1 ml. of milk be used per petri dish of 100 mm. diameter..After pouring the plates, the medium is allowed to solidify. Many investigators prefer to cover the solidified agar with 3–4 ml. of melted medium as recommended by "Standard Methods for the Examination of Dairy Products."[10] Plates are then incubated at 37°C. for 18–24 hours and at the end of this time are examined by transmitted light. Organisms of the coliform group, due to their ability to ferment lactose, form purplish red subsurface colonies, 1 to 2 mm. in diameter and are generally surrounded by a reddish zone of precipitated bile. The plates should not be incubated longer than 24 hours, inasmuch as the organisms whose growth has been suppressed may develop and confuse the count. Best results are obtained if plates are not too heavily seeded —the inoculum being diluted so that not more than 150 colonies will develop per plate.

In using this selective medium best results will be obtained if it is not subjected to autoclave sterilization since organisms, not killed by the boiling required to dissolve the medium, will not form colonies during the 24-hour incubation period. Following boiling to dissolve the medium completely, it is ready for use.

Saccharose in 1 per cent concentration may be added to isolation media, such as Bacto-Violet Red Bile Agar to permit the detection of certain members of the coliform group which ferment saccharose more readily than lactose. This principle was described by Holt-Harris and Teague[11] and has been employed by many other bacteriologists.

To rehydrate the medium, suspend 41.5 grams of Bacto-Violet Red Bile Agar in 1000 ml. of cold distilled water and heat to boiling to dissolve the medium completely. Cool to 40–44°C. and pour into plates containing the inoculum. After solidification of the medium a cover layer may be added, if desired. The final reaction of the medium will be pH 7.4.

One pound of Bacto-Violet Red Bile Agar will make 11 liters of medium.

[1] Standard Methods for the Examination of Dairy Products, 9th Edition:132:1948.
[2] Standard Methods for the Examination of Water and Sewage, 9th Edition:228:1946.
[3] Food Research, 1:551:1936.
[4] J. Dairy Science, 19:497:1936.
[5] Proc. Intern. Assoc. Ice Cream Manufacturers, 2:17:1936.
[6] Proc. Intern. Assoc. Ice Cream Manufacturers, 2:30:1936.
[7] Am. J. Pub. Health, 27:564:1937.
[8] J. Dairy Science, 21:559:1936.
[9] J. Bact., 45:49:1943.
[10] Standard Methods for the Examination of Dairy Products, 9th Edition:135:1948.
[11] J. Infectious Diseases, 18:596:1916.

BACTO
DESOXYCHOLATE AGAR (B273)
DEHYDRATED

Bacto-Peptone	10 g.
Bacto-Lactose	10 g.
Sodium Desoxycholate	1 g.
Sodium Chloride	5 g.
Dipotassium Phosphate	2 g.
Ferric Citrate	1 g.
Sodium Citrate	1 g.
Bacto-Agar	15 g.
Bacto-Neutral Red	0.03 g.

Bacto-Desoxycholate Agar is used for the direct enumeration of coliform bacteria in dairy products as specified in "Standard Methods for the Examination of Dairy Products."[1] It may also be employed as a non-selective primary plating medium for the isolation of enteric pathogens. The formula of Bacto-Desoxycholate Agar is essentially that described by Leifson[2] and is recommended for all procedures specifying the use of a Desoxycholate Agar.

For presumptive determination of coliforms in dairy products a poured plate of Desoxycholate Agar is prepared. After the medium has solidified, many investigators prefer to add a thin cover layer of uninoculated medium. Plates are incubated at 37°C. for 18–24 hours. Organisms other than those of the enteric group are inhibited. Coliform colonies are red in contrast to light colorless colonies produced by enteric organisms not capable of attacking lactose.

For the isolation of enteric pathogens streak or smear plates are prepared. Plates should be dry before inoculation for best results. On this medium coliform organisms are not inhibited and develop red opaque colonies. Colonies of *Salmonella* are colorless and raised with margins varying from smooth to irregular. *Shigella* colonies are colorless or opaque presenting somewhat of a ground glass appearance.

Saccharose in 1 per cent concentration may be added to isolation media, such as Bacto-Desoxycholate Agar to permit the detection of certain members of the coliform group which ferment saccharose more readily than lactose. This principle was described by Holt-Harris and Teague[3] and has been employed by many other bacteriologists. In some laboratories pathogenic significance is assigned to these organisms, and under such conditions, saccharose should not be added to the medium.

To rehydrate the medium, suspend 45 grams of Bacto-Desoxycholate Agar in 1000 ml. of cold distilled water and heat to boiling to dissolve the medium completely. Do not sterilize in the autoclave. Cool the dissolved liquid medium to 45–50°C. before using it in making poured plates for the coliform count. After the inoculated medium in the petri dish has solidified, cover the surface with a thin layer of the medium cooled to 45–50°C. The final reaction of the medium will be pH 7.3.

One pound of Bacto-Desoxycholate Agar will make 10 liters of medium.

[1] Standard Methods for the Examination of Dairy Products, 9th Edition: 132:1948.

[2] J. Path. Bact., 40:581:1935.
[3] J. Infectious Diseases, 18:596:1916.

BACTO
DESOXYCHOLATE LACTOSE AGAR   (B420)
DEHYDRATED

Bacto-Peptone	10 g.
Bacto-Lactose	10 g.
Sodium Desoxycholate	0.5 g.
Sodium Chloride	5.0 g.
Sodium Citrate	2.0 g.
Bacto-Agar	15 g.
Bacto-Neutral Red	0.03 g.

Bacto-Desoxycholate Lactose Agar is used for the direct enumeration of coliform organisms in milk, water and other materials. It is a modification of the medium described by Leifson,[1] and is prepared according to the formula specified for Desoxycholate Lactose Agar in "Standard Methods for the Examination of Water and Sewage"[2] and "Methods and Standards for the Production of Certified Milk."[3]

Counts of coliform organisms may be made directly using Desoxycholate Lactose Agar. Gram-positive cocci and rods including the spore-forming bacilli are generally inhibited. Lactose fermenting coliform organisms grow unrestricted and form typical red subsurface colonies, surrounded by a zone of precipitated bile and indicator. Incubation periods should be 24 hours or less since other organisms may develop, on longer incubation causing confusion.

A thin layer of sterile medium may be used as a cover, thus having only subsurface colonies. Following solidification of the inoculated plate a small amount of sterile medium (about 4–5 ml. per 95 mm. plate) is added and allowed to solidify forming a thin cover layer.

Bacto-Desoxycholate Lactose Agar differs from Bacto-Desoxycholate Agar essentially in that it contains less sodium desoxycholate, and is accordingly slightly less selective against Gram-positive organisms. It is suggested that the medium be sterilized in the autoclave if not used immediately following heating to boiling to effect complete solution.

To rehydrate the medium suspend 42.5 grams Bacto-Desoxycholate Lactose Agar in 1000 ml. of cold distilled water and heat to boiling to dissolve the medium completely. The medium requires no further sterilization if used at once. If it is to be stored, distribute in tubes or flasks and sterilize in the autoclave for 15 minutes at 15 pounds pressure (121°C.). Avoid overheating of the medium. Final reaction of the medium will be pH 7.1.

One pound of Bacto-Desoxycholate Lactose Agar will make 10.7 liters of medium.

[1] J. Path. Bact., 40:581:1935.
[2] Standard Methods for the Examination of Water and Sewage, 9th Edition:228:1946.

[3] Methods and Standards for the Production of Certified Milk, 26:1953–1954.

BACTO
POTATO DEXTROSE AGAR   (B13)
DEHYDRATED

Potatoes, Infusion from	200 g.
Bacto-Dextrose	20 g.
Bacto-Agar	15 g.

Bacto-Potato Dextrose Agar is recommended for the determination of yeasts and molds in butter and in frozen dessert ingredients according to the procedure of "Standard Methods for the Examination of Dairy Products." [1,2] This medium is also used for the isolation and cultivation of yeasts and molds in other dairy and food products. "Standard Methods for the Examination of Dairy Products"[2] specifies a reaction of pH 4.5 for Potato Dextrose Agar in determining the mold content of dried milk.

In a study of comparative methods and media used in the microbiological examination of creamery butter, Shadwick[3] investigated a number of media and found that Bacto-Potato Dextrose Agar gave the most consistent and highest count of yeasts and molds in salted and unsalted butter.

To rehydrate the medium, suspend 39 grams of Bacto-Potato Dextrose Agar in 1000 ml. of cold distilled water and heat to boiling to dissolve the medium completely. Distribute in tubes or flasks and sterilize by autoclaving for 15 minutes at 15 pounds pressure (121°C.). The medium will have a final reaction of pH 5.6.

It is frequently desirable in making yeast and mold counts to inhibit bacterial growth by acidifying the medium, and "Standard Methods" recommends that the reaction of the medium be reduced to pH 3.5±0.1 subsequent to sterilization. The label of each package of Bacto-Potato Dextrose Agar specifies the quantity of sterile tartaric acid (10 per cent solution) that should be added to each 100 ml. of the sterile melted medium to adjust the reaction to pH 3.5. After the tartaric acid has been added to the medium, it is mixed well and poured plates are prepared as usual. The medium should never be heated after the acid is added inasmuch as heating in the acid state will hydrolyze the agar, destroying its solidifying properties.

One pound of Bacto-Potato Dextrose Agar will make 11.3 liters of medium.

[1] Standard Methods for the Examination of Dairy Products, 9th Edition: 157:1948.

[2] Standard Methods for the Examination of Dairy Products, 9th Edition: 181:1948.

[3] Food Research, 3:287:1938.

BACTO
TRYPTOSE AGAR
DEHYDRATED

"Standard Methods for the Examination of Dairy Products," Ninth Edition recommends the use of Bacto-Tryptose Agar for the detection of *Brucella* organisms in milk. A complete discussion of Bacto-Tryptose Agar is given on page 111.

BACTO
MALT AGAR (B24)
DEHYDRATED

Malt Extract, Difco	30 g.
Bacto-Agar	15 g.

Bacto-Malt Agar is recommended for the detection and isolation of yeasts and molds from dairy products, food, and other materials. For the mold count of dry milk "Standard Methods for the Examination of Dairy Products"[1] specifies the use of dehydrated Bacto-Malt Agar or Bacto-Potato Dextrose Agar. This medium is also recommended for carrying stock cultures of yeast and molds used in microbiological assay procedures.

Malt media for yeasts and molds have been in use for many years. Reddish[2] in

1919 prepared a satisfactory substitute for beer wort from malt extract. His medium was used by Thom and Church[3] in their studies of the *Aspergilli*. A Malt Agar was also employed by Fullmer and Grimes[4] for their studies of the growth of yeasts on synthetic media.

The increasing importance of dairy sanitation has already brought milk under strict microbiological control, and this control has now been extended to include other dairy products, such as butter, cheese, concentrated and dried milk. Malt media are readily adapted to the cultivation of fungi encountered in dairy sanitation. Butter and cheese manufacturers have recognized the yeast and mold content of their products as an index of their sanitary classification. The damaging effects of certain molds, which are of tremendous importance, particularly in butter, may be greatly reduced through eradicating the sources of contamination by means of strict sanitary control and frequent checking by routine microbiological examination. Test samples may be taken at each step of the manufacturing process to indicate the sources of contamination.

Hood and White[5] have reported their extensive studies of media commonly employed for counting molds and yeasts in butter, and evolved a tentative procedure for making these determinations, recommending Bacto-Malt Agar acidified with lactic acid U.S.P. to a reaction of pH 3.5 just prior to pouring of plates. This more acid reaction inhibits the growth of bacteria which would otherwise form colonies that would be confused with colonies of molds and yeasts.

The committee of the American Dairy Science Association[6,7] recommended the use of Bacto-Malt Agar in its 1930 and 1933 reports on the microbiological analysis of butter. Parfitt[8] has also recommended Bacto-Malt Agar in order to secure comparative mold and yeast counts of butter. As mentioned above, "Standard Methods"[1] suggest the use of dehydrated Bacto-Malt Agar for mold count of dry milk. For this purpose the reaction of the medium should be adjusted to pH 4.5.

Bacto-Malt Agar is recommended for carrying stock cultures of yeast and molds used in microbiological assays. The American Association of Cereal Chemists[9] specifies the use of Bacto-Malt Agar in carrying cultures of *Saccharomyces carlsbergensis* in stock and also for the preparation of the inoculum in the assay of pantothenic acid and Vitamin B_6 complex. Miller and Golding[10] used Bacto-Malt Agar in their study of the oxygen requirements of molds.

Heating processes during the rehydration and sterilization should be completed in as short a period as possible. Excessive exposure to heat causes partial hydrolysis of the agar with resultant inability to solidify properly when cooled. Normally, a medium prepared from Bacto-Malt Agar is slightly soft and is ideal for plating purposes. However, if the medium is desired for streaking, use 54 grams of Bacto-Malt Agar per 1000 ml. distilled water, or include 5 grams Bacto-Agar with the 45 grams of Bacto-Malt Agar per liter.

To rehydrate the medium, suspend 45 grams of Bacto-Malt Agar in 1000 ml. of cold distilled water and heat to boiling to dissolve the medium completely. Distribute in tubes or flasks and sterilize in the autoclave for 15 minutes at 15 pounds pressure (121°C.). The final reaction of the medium will be pH 5.5.

Frequently, in establishing the yeast and mold count, it is desired to avoid confusion from bacterial growth by acidifying the medium to pH 4.5 or 3.5. On the label of each package of Bacto-Malt Agar there is specified the amount of lactic acid U.S.P. (85 per cent) which should be added to 100 ml. of sterile melted Bacto-Malt Agar to adjust the reaction to pH 4.5 or 3.5. After the acid has been well mixed with the Malt Agar, plates are poured as usual, allowed to harden, and incubated for 5 days at 25°C. before counts of yeast and mold colonies are made. The medium should never be heated after the acid is added, as heating in the acid state will hydrolyze the agar, reducing its solidifying properties so that the resulting medium will be soft or mushy.

One pound of Bacto-Malt Agar will make 10 liters of medium.

[1] Standard Methods for the Examination of Dairy Products, 9th Edition:181:1948.
[2] Abs. Bact., 3:6:1919.
[3] Thom and Church: The Aspergilli, 1926.
[4] J. Bact., 8:586:1923.
[5] Can. Dept. Agr. Pamphlet, 92-N.S.

[6] J. Dairy Science, 13:394:1930.
[7] J. Dairy Science, 16:289:1933.
[8] J. Dairy Science, 16:141:1933.
[9] Cereal Laboratory Methods, 5th Edition: 132,135:1947.
[10] J. Dairy Science, 32:101,1949.

BACTO

DEXTROSE TRYPTONE AGAR (B80)

DEHYDRATED

Bacto-Tryptone	10 g.
Bacto-Dextrose	5 g.
Bacto-Agar	15 g.
Bacto-Brom Cresol Purple	0.04 g.

Bacto-Dextrose Tryptone Agar is recommended for the determination of thermophilic "flat sour" organisms associated with the spoilage of food products. It was developed in collaboration with the research laboratories of the National Canners Association and is recommended for that purpose in their "Bacterial Standards for Sugar."[1] For plate count of mesophilic or thermophilic aerobes in sweetening agents used in frozen desserts, "Standard Methods for the Examination of Dairy Products"[2] recommend the use of Bacto-Dextrose Tryptone Agar.

Bacto-Dextrose Tryptone Agar is primarily used as a plating medium and when employed for determining thermophiles, it should be incubated at 55°C. for 36–48 hours in an incubator sufficiently humid to prevent drying of the medium.

To rehydrate the medium, suspend 30 grams of Bacto-Dextrose Tryptone Agar in 1000 ml. of cold distilled water and heat to boiling to dissolve the medium completely. Distribute in tubes or flasks and sterilize in the autoclave for 15 minutes at 15 pounds pressure (121°C.). The final reaction of the medium will be pH 6.7.

One pound of Bacto-Dextrose Tryptone Agar will make 15.1 liters of medium.

[1] Pub. of National Canners Association, 1933.   [2] Standard Methods for the Examination of Dairy Products, 9th Edition:185:1948.

ADDITIONAL MEDIA

Media as used in "Standard Methods for the Examination of Dairy Products" procedures are listed below. Complete discussions of these media will be found on the pages indicated.

SUPPLEMENTARY MEDIA
for Dairy and Other Food Products

THE ROUTINE bacteriological examination of dairy and other food products may usually be performed upon the standard media listed in the previous section. Special examinations including visual sanitation tests, however, require media for specific purposes. Propagation of pure cultures, and the maintenance of stock cultures also require special media, and the dehydrated culture media listed in this section are prepared for such uses.

BACTO
PROTEOSE TRYPTONE AGAR (B23)
DEHYDRATED

Bacto-Beef Extract	3 g.
Proteose Peptone, Difco	5 g.
Bacto-Tryptone	5 g.
Sodium Chloride	5 g.
Bacto-Dextrose	1 g.
Bacto-Agar	15 g.

Bacto-Proteose Tryptone Agar is recommended for determining the bacterial plate count of certified milk. This medium is prepared according to the formula specified in "Methods and Standards for the Production of Certified Milk"[1] of the American Association of Medical Milk Commissions, Incorporated.

The combination of Proteose Peptone, Difco, and Bacto-Tryptone in place of a single peptone is excellently suited for the cultivation of bacteria ordinarily encountered in milk. The larger size of the colonies which develop on Proteose Tryptone Agar during the usual incubation period facilitates counting of the plate. Comparative study of Bacto-Proteose Tryptone Agar by the Committee on Methods and Standards has indicated that this dehydrated medium is satisfactory for determining total counts of bacteria in certified milk. Plate counts are made according to the usual procedure with 0.1 ml. and 0.01 ml. (1 ml. of 1 to 10 and 1 to 100 dilution) of certified milk and the plates incubated for 48 hours at 35–37°C. For the bacterial count of milk according to "Standard Methods for the Examination of Dairy Products," Bacto-Tryptone Glucose Extract Agar, as discussed on page 57, should be employed.

Proteose Tryptone Agar has also been used as a plating medium to determine total counts of food products. Quinn and Garnatz[2] used Bacto-Proteose Tryptone Agar for total bacterial count of whole eggs in their study of methods of thawing frozen eggs.

To rehydrate the medium, suspend 34 grams of Bacto-Proteose Tryptone Agar in 1000 ml. of cold distilled water and heat to boiling to dissolve the medium completely. Distribute in tubes or flasks and sterilize in the autoclave for 15 minutes at 15 pounds pressure (121°C.). The final reaction of the medium will be pH 7.0.

One pound of Bacto-Proteose Tryptone Agar will make 13.3 liters of medium.

[1] Methods and Standards for the Production of Certified Milk, 26:1953-1954.   [2] J. Bact., 45:49:1943.

BACTO
HEART INFUSION AGAR
DEHYDRATED

This medium is recommended in "Methods and Standards for the Production of Certified Milk" for the preparation of Blood Agar plates for the recognition and differentiation of hemolytic streptococci. Such Blood Agar plates may also be used for the total bacterial count of certified milk. A complete discussion of Bacto-Heart Infusion Agar is given on page 87.

BACTO
BEEF LACTOSE AGAR   (B25)
DEHYDRATED

Beef Heart, Infusion from	450 g.
Proteose Peptone, Difco	5 g.
Bacto-Lactose	10 g.
Bacto-Agar	15 g.

Bacto-Beef Lactose Agar is prepared according to the formula for Beef Infusion Lactose Agar recommended by the subcommittee on Microbiological Methods for Examining Butter[1] of the American Dairy Science Association for determining the total bacterial count in the microbiological analysis of butter. This medium, with 0.5 ml. of sterile skim milk added to each plate at the time of pouring, may be used for the detection of proteolytic colonies.

While much of the spoilage in butter is due to the presence of molds and yeasts, bacteria are also capable of causing extensive losses due to the production of undesirable flavors. The subcommittee on Microbiological Methods for Examining Butter of the American Dairy Science Association in its report has included methods for the bacterial count and the detection of proteolytic and lipolytic bacteria as well as for determination of yeasts and molds. In this report the medium recommended for the total bacterial count is Beef Infusion Lactose Agar.

To rehydrate the medium, suspend 45 grams of Bacto-Beef Lactose Agar in 1000 ml. of cold distilled water and heat to boiling to dissolve the medium completely. Distribute in tubes or flasks and sterilize in the autoclave for 15 minutes at 15 pounds pressure (121°C.). The final reaction of the medium will be pH 6.8.

One pound of Bacto-Beef Lactose Agar will make 10 liters of medium.

[1] J. Dairy Science, 16:289:1933.

BACTO
NUTRITIVE CASEINATE AGAR   (B27)
DEHYDRATED

Bacto-Peptonized Milk	7 g.
Bacto-Isoelectric Casein	3 g.
Special Agar	12 g.

Bacto-Nutritive Caseinate Agar is recommended for the differential plate count of milk. On poured plates of this medium inoculated with dilutions of milk and other dairy products, strong and weak acid forming colonies and peptonizing colonies may be readily differentiated from one another.

Ayers and Mudge[1] devised a differential medium for milk control which was essentially Nutrient Extract Agar, containing skim milk powder extractives. The medium gave high counts when compared with Nutrient Agar because it was well adapted for the growth of lactic acid bacteria. Black, Prouty, and Graham,[2] and Prouty[3] gave a detailed method for the practical use of Bacto-Nutritive Caseinate Agar and modified the medium by adding the brom cresol purple indicator to the medium prior to sterilization, using 8 ml. of the indicator solution per 1000 ml. of Nutritive Caseinate Agar.

Bacto-Nutritive Caseinate Agar was developed in our laboratories to duplicate the medium of Ayers and Mudge. Modifications of the original formula were necessary, but the dehydrated culture medium yields results comparable with the original. Peptonizers and acid formers are readily distinguished, which together with the total count, give a more complete sanitary knowledge of the milk sample under investigation than is possible with plain agar media. In determining the differential count, the plates are incubated for 48 hours, and then a total count of all colonies is made. Next the strong acid forming colonies are counted, these being distinguished by a white zone of precipitated casein surrounding the colonies. The plate is then flooded with brom cresol purple indicator solution (0.4 gram Bacto-Brom Cresol Purple, 7.4 ml. of N/10 sodium hydroxide and 92.6 ml. distilled water) for five minutes, and a count made of all acid forming colonies which are yellow against the purple background of the medium. To determine the number of weak acid formers, the number of strong acid formers is subtracted from the number of total acid forming colonies. The plate is then flooded with dilute acetic acid (5 per cent solution), and the peptonizing colonies, which are surrounded by a clear zone are counted.

To rehydrate the medium, suspend 22 grams of Bacto-Nutritive Caseinate Agar in 1000 ml. cold distilled water and heat to boiling to dissolve the medium completely. Distribute in tubes or flasks and sterilize in the autoclave for 15 minutes at 15 pounds pressure (121°C.). The reaction of the medium will be pH 6.5.

One pound of Bacto-Nutritive Caseinate Agar will make 20.6 liters of medium.

[1] J. Bact., 5:565:1920.　　　　　　　　　[3] J. Dairy Science, 17:115:1934.
[2] J. Dairy Science, 15:99:1932.

BACTO

THERMOACIDURANS AGAR (B303)
DEHYDRATED

Bacto-Yeast Extract	5 g.
Proteose Peptone, Difco	5 g.
Bacto-Dextrose	5 g.
Dipotassium Phosphate	4 g.
Bacto-Agar	20 g.

Bacto-Thermoacidurans Agar is recommended for the cultivation of *Bacillus thermoacidurans* (*Bacillus coagulans*), the organism causing "flat sour" spoilage of tomato juice. It is prepared according to the formula described by Stern, Hegarty and Williams[1] for the isolation of this organism, and for its cultivation in pure culture.

For the detection of *B. thermoacidurans* Stern, Hegarty and Williams[1] recommend the plating of 1 ml. of tomato juice per 20 ml. of agar medium. They observed that larger quantities of tomato juice exhibited an inhibitory effect on the growth of the organism. Plates are poured with the sterile melted agar at 45–55°C. and, following solidification, incubated at 55°C. for 48 hours.

To rehydrate the medium, suspend 39 grams of Bacto-Thermoacidurans Agar in 1000 ml. of cold distilled water. Heat to boiling to dissolve the medium completely. Distribute in tubes or flasks and sterilize in the autoclave for 15 minutes at 15 pounds pressure (121°C.). Since this is an acid medium, overheating during the sterilization period or holding in the melted state should be avoided or a soft medium will result. The final reaction of the medium will be pH 5.0.

One pound of Bacto-Thermoacidurans Agar will make 11.6 liters of medium.

ᴬ Food Research, 7:186:1942.

BACTO
NEUTRALIZING BUFFER (B362)
DEHYDRATED

Monopotassium Phosphate	0.0425 g.
Sodium Thiosulfate	0.16 g.
Tamol-N	5.0 g.
Sodium Hydroxide	0.008 g.

Bacto-Neutralizing Buffer is designed for use in the Sterility Tests for Dairy Equipment as specified in Standard Methods for the Examination of Dairy Products[1] by the swab contact method, and for the bacteriological examination of food utensils according to the method presented by the Subcommittee on Food Utensil Sanitation[2] of the American Public Health Association. It is a modification of the "Standard Methods" buffered distilled water. Bacto-Neutralizing Buffer has the ability to inactivate the bactericidal and bacteriostatic effect of chlorine as well as quaternary ammonium compounds, as shown by laboratory and field tests using mixed flora as well as a large variety of pure cultures of organisms, including a *Sarcina* particularly sensitive to quaternary ammonium compounds.[8] Bacto-Neutralizing Buffer is used in conjunction with Bacto-Tryptone Glucose Extract Agar for the performance of such viability, sanitation or sterility tests.

Bacto-Neutralizing Buffer is not toxic for microorganisms. Plate counts made at intervals up to 5 hours on a suspension of organisms in the Neutralizing Buffer solution showed no reduction in numbers. This permits transfer of rinse water or swabs to the laboratory without danger of loss of viable organisms. Bacto-Neutralizing Buffer may be safely used in a concentration of 10 times the single strength in procedures requiring multiple strength solutions without danger of toxicity.

In using Bacto-Neutralizing Buffer in Sterility Tests for dairy Equipment, it is suggested that the procedure as given in "Standard Methods for the Examination of Dairy Products"[1] be closely followed

Bacto-Neutralizing Buffer is also recommended in Swab Test Procedures or Visual Sanitation Tests. Under these conditions it is often desired to examine more than one individual utensil as a unit. When so employed, the Neutralizing Buffer is distributed in screw cap tubes or screw cap swab bottles (cotton stoppers are not suitable) so that after autoclaving there will be 1 ml. of Neutralizing Buffer for each surface or utensil to be examined. If four similar utensils are to be examined as a unit, 4 ml. should be present in the tube. For the examination of food utensils the following procedure may be employed:

1. Dip a sterile swab into the tube of sterile Neutralizing Buffer.

2. Remove from the solution and squeeze the swab against the inside of the tube so as to remove the excess solution leaving the swab moist but not wet. One swab may be used for each group of four or more similar utensils.

3. Rub the swab slowly and firmly three times over the significant surfaces of the utensil to be examined, reversing the direction of the swab each time.

The significant surfaces of utensils are generally considered as the upper half inch of the inner and outer rims of glasses and cups and the entire inner and outer surfaces of the bowls of the spoons. In the examination of forks and knives the inner and outer tines of the fork and both sides of the blade of the knife should be swabbed. Plates and bowls should be swabbed on the inner and outer surfaces.

After swabbing each utensil return the swab to the Neutralizing Buffer solution, rotate well and press free from excess solution, before swabbing the next utensil in the group with the moist swab.

4. When the last utensil, generally four or more, has been swabbed, replace the swab in the Neutralizing Buffer, and shake vigorously. If separate swabs were used, break off each swab in the container under aseptic conditions.

5. Keep Neutralizing Buffer containing swabs at 0–6°C. until plated in the laboratory.

6. For procedures requiring a plate count, break the stick of the swab just above the cotton with sterile forceps, if this has not already been done as indicated above. Shake the swab in the Neutralizing Buffer thoroughly to disintegrate the cotton swabs. Plate 1 ml. or desired quantity using Bacto-Tryptone Glucose Extract Agar as the plating medium. Incubate at 32 or 35°C. for 48 hours before making the count.

If desired, a Visual Sanitation Test may be run by following the above directions through Step 4, except that in Step 4 the swab is not broken but following the swabbing of the last utensil, it is immersed in the Neutralizing Buffer, shaken vigorously, squeezed to remove excess moisture and then smeared directly on the surface of a slant of Bacto-Tryptone Glucose Extract Agar. Inoculation may be made by moving the moist swab across the surface of the slant from top to bottom horizontally and then vertically. The swab is rotated while being streaked across the surface of the medium. The inoculated medium is then incubated as desired.

To rehydrate Bacto-Neutralizing Buffer, dissolve 5.2 grams in 1000 ml. of cold distilled water. Distribute in screw cap containers and sterilize in the autoclave for 15 minutes at 15 pounds pressure (121°C.). Final reaction will be pH 7.2.

One hundred grams of Bacto-Neutralizing Buffer will make 19.2 liters.

[1] Standard Methods for the Examination of Dairy Products, 9th Edition:216:1948.

[2] Ann. Year Book 1947–48. Suppl. Am. J. Pub. Health, 5:68:1948.
[3] J. Milk Food Tech., 12:224:1949.

MEDIA FOR LACTOBACILLI

THE MEDIA listed in this section are useful for the cultivation, enumeration and study of *Lactobacilli,* particularly those concerned with the manufacture of dairy products.

BACTO
TOMATO JUICE AGAR (B31)
DEHYDRATED

Tomato Juice (400 ml.) .... 20 g.
Bacto-Peptone .... 10 g.
Bacto-Peptonized Milk .... 10 g.
Bacto-Agar .... 11 g.

Bacto-Tomato Juice Agar is recommended for the direct plate count and cultivation of *Lactobacilli*. It is an excellent plate medium for determining the relative numbers of organisms in acidophilus products and for estimating the degree of intestinal implantation.

The *Lactobacilli* grow poorly on ordinary culture media and require special nutrients. Mickle and Breed[1] reported the use of tomato juice in culture media for *Lactobacilli*, and Kulp,[2] while investigating the use of tomato juice on bacterial development, found that the growth of *L. acidophilus* was enhanced in media containing this material. Colonies on plates of this new medium were large and more characteristic than on other media. Later Kulp and White[3] described a modification of the original medium which gave them relatively high quantitative counts.

Bacto-Tomato Juice Agar is prepared according to Kulp and White's modification and contains Bacto-Peptone and Bacto-Peptonized Milk. The dehydrated medium is excellently suited for the cultivation of members of the *Lactobacillus* group.

To rehydrate the medium, suspend 51 grams of Bacto-Tomato Juice Agar in 1000 ml. of cold distilled water and heat to boiling to dissolve the medium completely. Distribute in tubes or flasks and sterilize in the autoclave for 15 minutes at 15 pounds pressure (121°C.). The final reaction of the medium will be pH 6.1.

One pound of Bacto-Tomato Juice Agar will make 8.9 liters of medium.

[1] Tech. Bull. 110, N. Y. State Agr.
Exp. Sta., 1925.
[2] Science, 66:512:1927.
[3] Science, 76:17:1932.

BACTO
TOMATO JUICE AGAR SPECIAL (B389)
DEHYDRATED

Tomato Juice (400 ml.) .... 20 g.
Bacto-Peptone .... 10 g.
Bacto-Peptonized Milk .... 10 g.
Bacto-Agar .... 20 g.

Bacto-Tomato Juice Agar Special is recommended for the direct plate count of the *Lactobacilli* from saliva and for the cultivation of other acidophilic microorganisms. It is prepared according to the formula suggested by Jay.[1,2] The number of *Lactobacilli* in saliva is an index of predisposition to dental caries as described by Jay.[1,2] Many dentists prefer to use the direct count of *Lactobacilli* for the diagnosis of caries rather than the colorimetric method using Bacto-Snyder Test Agar, as described on page 190.

The reaction of Bacto-Tomato Juice Agar Special is adjusted to pH 5.0 so as to encourage the growth of *Lactobacilli* and at the same time inhibit the growth of many commensal bacteria that may be encountered in saliva. This is a slightly more selective medium for *Lactobacilli* than is Bacto-Tomato Juice Agar or Bacto-Trypsin Digest Agar described on page 74.

To rehydrate the medium, suspend 60 grams Bacto-Tomato Juice Agar Special in 1000 ml. cold distilled water. Heat to boiling to dissolve the medium completely. Distribute in tubes or flasks and sterilize in the autoclave for 15 minutes at 15 pounds pressure (121°C.). Overheating of this acid medium is to be avoided to prevent hydrolysis of the agar giving a soft medium. Final reaction will be pH 5.0.

One pound of Bacto-Tomato Juice Agar Special will make 7.5 liters of medium.

[1] Bacteriology and Immunology of Dental Caries and Dental Science and Dental Art, 1938.   [2] Dentistry in Public Health, 1949.

BACTO
TRYPSIN DIGEST AGAR   (B30)
DEHYDRATED

Trypsinized Milk (800 ml.)	20 g.
Tomato Juice (200 ml.)	10 g.
Bacto-Peptone	8 g.
Bacto-Dextrose	4 g.
Dextrin, Difco	4 g.
Bacto-Agar	13 g.

Bacto-Trypsin Digest Agar is recommended for the plate count and cultivation of *Lactobacillus acidophilus*. By using a tryptic digest of milk, to which tomato juice and other nutriments were added, Dr. H. A. Cheplin was able to secure excellent growth of *L. acidophilus*.

Bacto-Trypsin Digest Agar readily lends itself to use in isolating strains of *L. acidophilus* as well as for carrying them in stock. It is an excellent plate medium for determining the relative numbers of organisms in acidophilus products and for estimating the degree of intestinal implantation.

Bacto-Trypsin Digest Agar is prepared according to the formula specified by Dr. Cheplin. Results obtained with this dehydrated medium when it is made up for use are comparable to those secured when the medium is prepared from ingredients.

To rehydrate the medium, suspend 59 grams of Bacto-Trypsin Digest Agar in 1000 ml. of cold distilled water and heat to boiling to dissolve the medium completely. Distribute in tubes or flasks and sterilize in the autoclave for 15 minutes at 15 pounds pressure (121°C.). The final reaction of the medium will be pH 6.1.

One pound of Bacto-Trypsin Digest Agar will make 7.6 liters of medium.

BACTO
SKIM MILK   (B32)
DEHYDRATED

Bacto-Skim Milk is high grade skim milk reduced to powder by the spray process. It is readily soluble and is easily prepared for use. Bacto-Skim Milk is recommended for use with Bacto-Tryptone Glucose Extract Agar in the preparation of the Tryptone Glucose Extract Milk Agar according to "Standard Methods for the Examination of Dairy Products."[1] It is also recommended for the preparation of skim milk solutions used in the propagation of organisms occurring in milk products, and to demonstrate coagulation and proteolysis of casein.

Bacto-Skim Milk may be used in media for the detection of proteolyzers, and as an ingredient in the preparation of media for the cultivation of such organisms as *Mycobacterium tuberculosis* and *Corynebacterium diphtheria*. A solution of Bacto-Skim Milk containing litmus is a widely used medium for determining acid production in milk and also the ability to peptonize or coagulate milk in the identification of microorganisms. Skim Milk is used to detect the so-called "stormy fermentation" of *Clostridium perfringens*.

Nungester and Ellingson[2] have suggested the addition of 0.1 per cent agar and iron, either in the form of filings or freshly pickled strips, to adjust the oxygen tension of the medium and permit more rapid development of organisms in the "stormy fermentation" test.

To rehydrate Bacto-Skim Milk to obtain the equivalent of fresh skim milk, dissolve 100 grams in 1000 ml. of cold distilled water. Distribute in tubes and sterilize in the autoclave for 15 minutes at 15 pounds pressure (121°C.). Overheating during sterilization results in the carmelization of the milk sugar. This is to be avoided since the resulting discoloration may give an atypical appearance of the sterile medium and may be further reflected in the appearance of growing cultures. The final reaction will be pH 6.4.

One pound of Bacto-Skim Milk will make 4.5 liters of skim milk.

[1] Standard Methods for the Examination of Dairy Products, 9th Edition:93:1948.

[2] Personal Communication.

BACTO
PEPTONIZED MILK (B35)
DEHYDRATED

Bacto-Peptonized Milk is used alone or as an ingredient in media for isolation and cultivation of the *Lactobacilli* and organisms encountered in the bacteriological examination of milk and dairy products.

As early as 1894 Kayser[1] used Peptonized Milk in his studies on lactic fermentation. Orla-Jensen[2] found Peptonized Milk to be exceptionally satisfactory in the cultivation of lactic acid forming organisms. Bacto-peptonized Milk was developed in our laboratories to provide a simple medium with readily available nitrogen for the cultivation of organisms of the *Lactobacillus* group. It contains the degradation products of the proteins, albumins, and globulins of milk, and therefore its nitrogen is more readily available for bacterial assimilation than the native proteins of milk. Rapid and luxuriant growth of *Lactobacilli* is readily obtained in solutions of Bacto-Peptonized Milk. For carrying stock cultures of lactic organisms, it is recommended that 0.1 per cent of Bacto-Agar be added to the medium. Kulp and White[3] used Bacto-Peptonized Milk with excellent results in their Tomato Juice Agar for *Lactobacillus acidophilus*. Devereux[4] employed Bacto-Peptonized Milk in his modification of the Cooledge Medium for testing the quality of milk. Weiss and Rettger[5] used Bacto-Peptonized Milk in their tomato juice media for *L. bifidus*.

To rehydrate the medium, dissolve 15 grams of Bacto-Peptonized Milk in 1000 ml. of cold distilled water. Distribute in tubes and sterilize in the autoclave for 15 minutes at 15 pounds pressure (121°C.). The final reaction of the medium will be pH 6.5.

One pound of Bacto-Peptonized Milk will make 30.2 liters of medium.

[1] Ann. inst. Pasteur, 8:737:1894.
[2] Centr. Bakt., II Abt., 4:96:1898.
[3] Science, 76:17:1932.
[4] Am. J. Pub. Health, 22:1291:1932.
[5] J. Bact., 28:501:1934.

BACTO
MICRO ASSAY CULTURE AGAR
DEHYDRATED

BACTO
MICRO INOCULUM BROTH
DEHYDRATED

Bacto-Micro Assay Culture Agar and Bacto-Micro Inoculum Broth have been developed for the cultivation of *Lactobacilli* in microbiological assays. These media are also recommended for the cultivation of other *Lactobacilli*. A complete discussion of Bacto-Micro Assay Culture Agar and Bacto-Micro Inoculum Broth is given on pages 212 and 213.

ADDITIONAL MEDIA

The media listed below have been rather extensively employed in the past for "Standard Methods" and supplementary procedures in the examination of water and milk. Other media have been developed which are considered superior and serve the purpose more adequately. For the present we will continue to carry these media in stock for those laboratories where they have been in routine use, or where it is desired to continue them for comparative purposes.

PRESENT RECOMMENDATIONS

Bacto-Yeast Dextrose Agar ....Bacto-Tryptone Glucose Extract Agar, page 57
Bacto-Brilliant Green Bile 5% ....Bacto-Brilliant Green Bile 2%, page 37
Bacto-Lactose Peptone Bile
Bacto-Purple Bile Salt Agar ....Bacto-Violet Red Bile Agar, page 61
Bacto-Gentian Violet Lactose Bile ......Bacto-Brilliant Green Bile 2%, page 37
Bacto-Formate Ricinoleate Broth, page 60
Bacto-Galactose Whey Agar ....Bacto-Tomato Juice Agar, page 73
Bacto-Whey Agar .....Bacto-Trypsin Digest Agar, page 74
Bacto-Peptonized Milk Agar
Bacto-Galactose Peptonized Milk ......Bacto-Peptonized Milk, page 75
Bacto-Whey Broth
Bacto-Purple Milk ....Bacto-Litmus Milk, page 192
Bacto-Ulrich Milk, page 193
Bacto-Neutral Red Medium
Bacto-Cooledge Broth

MEDIA FOR CULTIVATION OF PATHOGENIC MICROORGANISMS

INFUSION MEDIA

DEHYDRATED infusion media, Difco, are prepared under controlled conditions from large quantities of fresh tissue. Variations due to differences in meat are thereby minimized, thus assuring greater uniformity of the final medium than can be obtained when the medium is prepared in small lots from market meat. Infusions of meat have long been considered an essential part of media for the cultivation of many pathogenic organisms. Through years of practical use, Difco infusion media have demonstrated their suitability for the cultivation of fastidious streptococci, pneumococci, meningococci, and other pathogenic microorganisms.

Peptones now have been developed which in a 2 per cent concentration satisfactorily replace the infusion and peptone portion of infusion media for many of the fastidious pathogens. These peptone media will be discussed in the section, Peptone Media, Without Infusions, on pages 99–130.

A guide for the selection of culture media listed in this section is given on pages 26, 27 and 28.

BACTO
BRAIN HEART INFUSION (B37)
DEHYDRATED

Calf Brains, Infusion from	200 g.
Beef Heart, Infusion from	250 g.
Proteose Peptone, Difco	10 g.
Bacto-Dextrose	2 g.
Sodium Chloride	5 g.
Disodium Phosphate	2.5 g.

Bacto-Brain Heart Infusion is a liquid infusion medium recommended for the cultivation of streptococci, pneumococci, meningococci, and other organisms generally considered difficult to cultivate. Virulence, antigenicity, and other serological characteristics of organisms are quite uniformly maintained when grown on Bacto-Brain Heart Infusion. This medium is especially adapted for blood culture work. Bacto-Brain Heart Infusion, solidified with agar is recommended for the isolation of pathogenic fungi, and this medium is discussed in detail on page 90.

Rosenow[1] devised an excellent culture medium for the streptococci by adding pieces of brain tissue to Dextrose Broth. In this medium he was able to secure excellent results in culturing organisms from focal infections in the teeth or other tissues. Hayden,[2] using the same procedure as Rosenow, but adding crushed marble to the medium, reported that this medium was favorable for the growth of organisms from infections of the teeth, especially those showing a close relationship with eye infections.

Bacto-Brain Heart Infusion is prepared to duplicate the results obtained by Rosenow and Hayden. It contains the essential nutriments of their medium and possesses the advantage of yielding an easily prepared clear medium. An infusion of brains has replaced the nutritive value of the brain tissue, disodium phosphate replaced the buffer calcium carbonate, and if desired 0.1 per cent agar may be added to the medium giving conditions of oxygen tension similar to those produced by the tissue. The addition of a small amount of agar (0.1–0.2 per cent) to Brain Heart Infusion is particularly recommended for the growth and isolation of pathogenic microorganisms especially their primary isolation from blood and other specimen material.

The advantages of a medium with a low agar concentration and its influence on the development of bacteria, particularly the anaerobes, has been described by Hitchens.[3] In a broth, to which 0.1 per cent agar has been added, there is a clear upper zone well suited for aerobic growth; below this the flocculent agar develops variable degrees of anaerobiosis. This condition makes the medium suitable for the growth of either aerobic or anaerobic bacteria. Falk, Bucca, and Simmons[4] pointed out the advantages of the use of small quantities of agar (0.06 to 0.25 per cent) in the detection of contaminants in testing the sterility of biologicals. They demonstrated that the growth of even common forms, such as the hay bacillus and staphylococci, ordinarily considered easy to cultivate, was aided by the presence of a small quantity of agar. They also showed that growth is initiated in a much shorter incubation period in such media. They used 0.1 per cent agar in their routine tests. Bacto-Brain Heart Infusion with PAB and Agar, as discussed below, contains 0.1 per cent agar.

Dance and Murray[5] used Bacto-Brain Heart Infusion with 0.1 per cent added agar for the cultivation of hemolytic streptococci in their study of hemolytic properties on various Blood Agars. Berens, Nilson and Chapman[6] added 3 grams calf brain to 10 ml. of Brain Heart Infusion for the growth of bacteria from patients with certain inflammatory eye diseases. Chapman, Stiles, and Berens[7] and Chapman[8] used Bacto-Brain Heart Infusion in their test for pathogenicity of streptococci. Reitzel and Kohl[9] added 30–50 per cent sterile ascitic fluid to Bacto-Brain Heart Infusion and stated that some of the gonococci grew more readily in this medium than in a Hormone Brain Broth containing sterile pieces of brain. They also used Bacto-Brain Heart Infusion in combination with Bacto-Brain Veal Agar and Bacto-Hemoglobin for the isolation of the gonococcus. A detailed discussion of these products is given on pages 94 and 271.

The coagulation of plasma is one of the characteristics of pathogenic staphylococci. Brain Heart Infusion is especially well suited for the growth of staphylococci or for the preparation of the suspension of the organism used in the performance of the Coagulase Test, as described by Chapman.[10] A complete discussion of the performance of this test is given under Bacto-Coagulase Plasma, page 330. Newman,[11] in a study of the detection of food poisoning attributable to dairy products, used staphylococci grown in Brain Heart Infusion for the performance of the coagulase test.

Neter [12,13] added Bacto-Supplement B to Brain Heart Infusion and demonstrated that *Hemophilus influenzae* could be cultivated on this medium through serial transfers. He also used this enriched Brain Heart Infusion in tests designed to determine the streptomycin sensitivity of strains of *H. influenzae.*

Bacto-Brain Heart Infusion has been used in the preparation of media for the isolation of pathogenic fungi. Roseburg, Epps and Clark[14] found that Bacto-Brain Heart Infusion, containing 2 per cent agar, was more satisfactory than Dextrose Infusion Agar, for the isolation and cultivation of *Actinomyces israeli.* Incubation in a 5 per cent carbon dioxide atmosphere was required for best results. The addition of sheep blood to the medium was not an advantage. Howell[15] used Bacto-Brain Heart Infusion to which was added 2 per cent Bacto-Agar and 10 per cent sterile defibrinated horse blood for the cultivation of *Histoplasma capsulatum.* A selective medium for this microorganism was prepared by adding 40 units of streptomycin and 20 units penicillin per ml. of medium. In comparison with a Blood Agar similarly prepared from Potato Dextrose Agar, the Brain Heart Infusion medium gave a greater number of positive isolations. Incubation at room temperature was more efficient than at 37°C. Colonies isolated on the Brain Heart Infusion Blood Agar must be transferred to a medium such as Potato Dextrose Agar to obtain the characteristic tuberculate chlamydospores typical of *H. capsulatum.* Conant[16] recommended that a plate of Bacto-Brain Heart Infusion Agar be streaked and incubated at 37°C. under anaerobic conditions with the addition of 5 per cent carbon dioxide to obtain growth of the microaerophilic *Actinomyces bovis* in culturing this organism from infected mucous membranes, skin and subcutaneous tissues.

For blood culture work a procedure frequently used is to add as much as 10 ml. of blood specimen to 150 ml. of sterile Brain Heart Infusion contained in a 300 ml. Erlenmeyer flask or bottle. This is incubated at 37°C. and transfers are made to Blood Agar or other media for the isolation and identification of the organisms. Blood for blood culturing should always be taken prior to the administration of the therapeutic agent. If drugs have been administered their bacteriostatic effects should be neutralized. For example the addition of *p*-aminobenzoic acid (PAB) in 5 mg. per cent to the medium will assure the inactivation of any sulfa drug carried over with the inoculum. Bacto-Penase, a concentrated purified penicillinase, should be added to the sterile cooled medium used for blood culture if the patient is under penicillin therapy. Bacto-Brain Heart Infusion with PAB and Agar with added Bacto-Penase is an ideal medium for blood culture work. The small amount of agar present will give all degrees of anaerobiosis, permitting the development of the obligate anaerobes and microaerophiles as well as the aerobes. The PAB will inactivate any sulfa drug, the added Bacto-Penase will inactivate any penicillin in the inoculum, while 100 ml. of the medium itself will inactivate up to 1000 units of streptomycin.

For the detection of organisms from the blood of patients known to be under sulfonamide therapy, Bacto-Brain Heart Infusion with PAB or Bacto-Brain Heart Infusion with PAB and Agar are recommended. These media contain 5 mg. per cent of PAB which neutralizes the bacteriostatic effect of the sulfonamide present in the blood specimen.

To rehydrate the medium, dissolve 37 grams of Bacto-Brain Heart Infusion in 1000 ml. distilled water. Distribute in tubes or flasks and sterilize in the autoclave for 15 minutes at 15 pounds pressure (121°C.). The final reaction of the medium will be pH 7.4.

If the medium is not used the same day as prepared and sterilized, heat at 100°C. for several minutes to remove absorbed oxygen, and cool quickly without agitation, just prior to inoculation.

One pound of Bacto-Brain Heart Infusion will make 12.2 liters of medium.

[1] J. Dental Research, 1:205:1919.
[2] Arch. Internal Med., 32:828:1923.
[3] J. Infectious Diseases, 29:390:1921.
[4] J. Bact., 37:121:1939.
[5] J. Infectious Diseases, 63:122:1938.
[6] Am. J. Ophthalmol., 19:1060:1936.
[7] Am. J. Clin. Path., 9:1939: Tech. Suppl., 3:20:1939.
[8] Am. J. Digestive Diseases, 13:105:1946.

[9] J. Am. Med. Assoc., 110:1095:1938.
[10] Trans. N.Y. Academy Sciences, 9:52:1946.
[11] J. Milk and Food Tech., 13:226:1950.
[12] Science, 106:350:1947.
[13] J. Bact., 54:70:1947.
[14] J. Infectious Diseases, 74:131:1944.
[15] Public Health Reports, 63:173:1948.
[16] Diagnostic Procedures and Reagents, 3rd Edition: 452:1950.

BACTO

BACTO

BRAIN HEART INFUSION
with PAB   (B37A)
DEHYDRATED

BRAIN HEART INFUSION
with PAB and Agar   (B37B)
DEHYDRATED

Two modifications of Bacto-Brain Heart Infusion widely used in blood culture procedures are now available in dehydrated form. These media are especially recommended for the detection of organisms in the blood of patients under sulfonamide therapy there has been included in the formula sufficient *p*-aminobenzoic acid (PAB) to give a final concentration of 5 mg. per cent. This will neutralize the maximum amount of sulfonamide that might be carried over into the medium with the blood inoculum, and thereby exert an inhibitory effect upon pathogens inoculated into the medium.

The formula for Bacto-Brain Heart Infusion with PAB is identical with that of Bacto-Brain Heart Infusion except for the addition of 0.05 gram of *p*-aminobenzoic acid per liter. To rehydrate the medium dissolve 37 grams of Bacto-Brain Heart Infusion with PAB in 1000 ml. of distilled water.

The formula for Bacto-Brain Heart Infusion with PAB and Agar is identical with Bacto-Brain Heart Infusion except for the addition of 0.05 gram of p-aminobenzoic acid and 1 gram of Bacto-Agar per liter. The addition of this small amount of agar to the medium provides optimum conditions for the rapid luxuriant development of obligate anaerobes, micro-aerophiles and aerobes. To rehydrate the medium suspend 38 grams of Bacto-Brain Heart Infusion with PAB and Agar in 1000 ml. distilled water and heat to boiling to dissolve the medium completely.

Both of these media are distributed in tubes or flasks and sterilized in the autoclave for 15 minutes at 15 pounds pressure (121°C.) Final reaction of the media is pH 7.4.

BACTO
HEART INFUSION BROTH (B38)
DEHYDRATED

Beef Heart, Infusion from	500 g.
Bacto-Tryptose	10 g.
Sodium Chloride	5 g.

Bacto-Heart Infusion Broth is a liquid medium containing the extractives from fresh beef heart. It is recommended as a general laboratory medium for pathogenic as well as non-pathogenic bacteria. A liquid medium, prepared from an infusion of beef heart, is recommended in "Diagnostic Procedures and Reagents"[1] of the American Public Health Association for blood culturing the meningococcus and for other purposes. The "Standard Methods for the Examination of Dairy Products"[2] specify the use of a Heart Infusion Broth for their study of pathogenic streptococci.

Bouillon, or a liquid medium containing an infusion of meat, was one of the first media used for cultivation of bacteria. Many modifications of this medium have been used from time to time for a wide variety of purposes. Huntoon[3] using fresh beef heart and Bacto-Peptone, prepared a "hormone" broth in a special manner, to retain the growth-promoting substances. In order to have such a liquid infusion medium readily available, Bacto-Heart Infusion Broth was developed. Bacto-Tryptose, as employed in this medium, is better suited for the nutritional requirements of pathogenic bacteria than is Bacto-Peptone which was used by Huntoon in the preparation of his "hormone" media.

The cultural value of Bacto-Heart Infusion Broth is greatly increased by the addition of 0.1–0.2 per cent Bacto-Agar as discussed on page 77 under Bacto-Brain Heart Infusion. Many other modifications of the medium may also be made, such as the addition of dextrose, blood, or other ingredients to give an unlimited number of media for a variety of purposes.

To rehydrate the medium, dissolve 25 grams of Bacto-Heart Infusion Broth in 1000 ml. distilled water, distribute in tubes and sterilize in the autoclave for 15 minutes at 15 pounds pressure (121°C.). The final reaction of the medium is pH 7.4.

For best results, the medium should be freshly prepared. If it is not used the same day as sterilized, heat in boiling water or flowing steam for several minutes to remove absorbed oxygen and cool quickly without agitation, just prior to inoculation.

One pound of Bacto-Heart Infusion Broth will make 18.1 liters of medium.

[1] Diagnostic Procedures and Reagents, 3rd Edition: 13: 1950.

[2] Standard Methods for the Examination of Dairy Products, 9th Edition: 141: 1948.

[3] J. Infectious Diseases, 23: 169: 1918.

BACTO
VEAL INFUSION MEDIUM (B40)
DEHYDRATED

Veal, Infusion from	500 g.
Proteose Peptone, Difco	10 g.
Bacto-Agar	1 g.

Bacto-Veal Infusion Medium is prepared from selected lean veal, and is recommended as a liquid medium for the growth of anaerobes as well as many other bacteria generally considered difficult to cultivate. The medium contains 0.1 per cent agar which provides, in freshly heated media, various degrees of oxygen tension making possible the growth of anaerobes without special conditions.

The advantages of a medium with a low agar concentration, and its influence on the development of bacteria, particularly the anaerobes, has been described by Hitchens[1]. In a broth, to which 0.1 per cent agar has been added, there is a clear upper zone well suited for aerobic growth; below this the flocculent agar develops variable degrees of oxygen tension. This condition makes the medium suitable for the growth of either aerobic or anaerobic bacteria. Falk, Bucca, and Simmons[2] point out the advantages of the use of small quantities of agar (0.06–0.25 per cent) in the detection of contaminants in the sterility testing of biologicals. They show that the growth of even common forms, such as the hay bacillus and staphylococci, ordinarily considered easy to cultivate, was aided by the presence of a small quantity of agar, and that growth is initiated in a much shorter incubation period in such media. Since their experiments showed little difference between 0.1 and 0.25 per cent agar, they used 0.1 per cent agar in their routine tests, which is the quantity employed in Bacto-Veal Infusion Medium. In the report on culture media for non-acid products, Cameron[3], as associate referee, recommended Bacto-Veal Infusion Medium for use in the examination of canned meat. He reported this medium to be excellent as an enrichment for the propagation of anaerobes.

To rehydrate the medium, suspend 23 grams of Bacto-Veal Infusion Medium in 1000 ml. of cold distilled water and heat to boiling to dissolve the medium completely. Distribute in tubes and sterilize in the autoclave for 15 minutes at 15 pounds pressure (121°C.). The final reaction of the medium will be pH 7.3.

For best results, Bacto-Veal Infusion Medium should be freshly prepared. If the medium is not used the same day as sterilized, heat in boiling water or flowing steam for a few minutes to remove absorbed oxygen and then cool quickly without agitation, just prior to inoculation.

One pound of Bacto-Veal Infusion Medium will make 19.7 liters of medium.

[1] J. Infectious Diseases, 29:390:1921. [2] Assoc. Official Agr. Chem., 20:429:1937
[3] J. Bact., 37:121:1939.

BACTO
VEAL INFUSION BROTH (B344)
DEHYDRATED

Bacto-Veal Infusion Broth is identical to Bacto-Veal Infusion Medium except the small concentration of agar has been omitted. This infusion medium is suited for the cultivation of fastidious pathogenic microorganisms. "Standard Methods for the Examination of Dairy Products"[1] describe a Veal Infusion Broth, prepared from finely ground veal and 0.5 per cent Bacto-Tryptone, for the cultivation of pathogenic streptococci.

To rehydrate the medium dissolve 22 grams of Bacto-Veal Infusion Broth in 1000 ml. distilled water. Distribute in tubes and sterilize in the autoclave for 15 minutes at 15 pounds pressure (121°C.). The final reaction of the medium will be pH 7.3.

One pound of Bacto-Veal Infusion Broth will make 20.6 liters of medium.

¹ Standard Methods for the Examination of Dairy Products, 9th Edition:141:1948.

BACTO
PPLO ENRICHMENT BROTH (B410)
DEHYDRATED

Beef Heart, Infusion from	50 g.
Bacto-Peptone	10 g.
Sodium Chloride	5 g.
Bacto-Crystal Violet	0.01 g.

Bacto-PPLO Enrichment Broth is prepared according to the formula suggested by Morton, Smith, Williams, and Eickenberg,¹ for the selective enrichment of pleuropneumonia-like organisms (PPLO). This medium is designed to facilitate the isolation of PPLO from clinical specimens. It is also useful as an aid in the purification of PPLO colonies contaminated with other microorganisms. The growth of both Gram-positive and Gram-negative organisms is suppressed, while pleuropneumonia-like organisms develop. Following inoculation with clinical specimens or with bacterial contaminated agar block colonies of PPLO, incubate at 37°C. for 36–72 hours and then plate on PPLO Agar, containing 1 per cent Bacto-PPLO Serum Fraction, or 25 per cent Bacto-Ascitic Fluid. Inoculation of the plates is accomplished by transferring a drop of the enriched culture to the plate and spreading it uniformly over the surface of the medium.

To rehydrate the medium, suspend 21 grams of Bacto-PPLO Enrichment Broth in 1000 ml. of distilled water. Sterilize in the autoclave 15 minutes at 15 pounds pressure (121°C.). To each liter add 2.85 ml. of Bacto-Chapman Tellurite Solution to give a concentration of 1–35,000 of potassium tellurite. Add 25 per cent Bacto-Ascitic Fluid and tube in sterile tubes under aseptic conditions. The final reaction of the unenriched medium will be pH 7.8.

One pound of Bacto-PPLO Enrichment Broth will make 21.6 liters of unenriched medium.

¹ J. Dental Research, 30:415:1951.

BACTO
THIOL MEDIUM (B307)
DEHYDRATED

Proteose Peptone No. 3, Difco	10 g.
Bacto-Yeast Extract	5 g.
Bacto-Dextrose	1 g.
Sodium Chloride	5 g.
Thiol Complex	8 g.
Bacto-Agar	1 g.
p-Aminobenzoic Acid	0.05 g.

Bacto-Thiol Medium is recommended for culturing organisms from body fluids and other materials containing penicillin, streptomycin and sulfa drugs.

This medium does not contain thermolabile factors and accordingly may be sterilized in the autoclave. Bacto-Thiol Medium has the ability to inactivate penicillin, streptomycin and sulfa drugs. Luxuriant growth of staphylococci and other test organisms will be obtained from dilute inocula in 24 hours in 10 ml. of Bacto-Thiol Medium to which has been added 100 to 1000 units of penicillin, 1000 to 10,000 units of streptomycin, or sulfonamides. Bacto-Thiol Medium contains 0.1 per cent Bacto-Agar to maintain an OR potential conducive to growth of the strictest anaerobes, microaerophiles, and aerobic microorganisms, without special seal.

The medium should be distributed in tubes or containers to give a depth of at least 60 mm. for neutralization of penicillin. For the neutralization of streptomycin, the medium may be employed in tubes or in shallow layers in flasks. Neutralization of antibiotics and cultural response with Bacto-Thiol Medium is best when freshly prepared, or less than 4 days old.

Bacto-Thiol Medium enriched with 1 per cent Bacto-Supplement B has proven an especially valuable medium for blood culture. Broom[1] reported excellent results with the enriched Thiol Medium in the isolation of *Hemophilus influenzae* and meningococci. Huddleson[2] reported this medium satisfactory for the isolation, cultivation and maintenance of stock cultures of *Vibrio fetus*. Cultures remained viable in Thiol Medium for at least 150 days without transfer.

To rehydrate the medium, suspend 30 grams of Bacto-Thiol Medium in 1000 ml. freshly distilled water. Heat to boiling to dissolve the medium completely. Distribute in tubes or flasks as indicated above and sterilize in the autoclave for 15 minutes at 15 pounds pressure (121°C.). The final reaction of the medium will be pH 7.2.

[1] Personal Communication, 1948.   [2] J. Bact., 56:508:1948.

BACTO
THIOL BROTH (B434)
DEHYDRATED

Bacto-Thiol Broth has the same composition as Bacto-Thiol Medium except it contains no agar. It is prepared for laboratories requiring a medium having the properties of Thiol Medium except without agar. In rehydrating Bacto-Thiol Broth 29 grams are used per liter.

The final reaction of the medium will be pH 7.2.

BACTO
KRACKE BLOOD CULTURE MEDIUM (B41)
DEHYDRATED

Beef Heart	165 g.
Beef Brain	55 g.
Proteose Peptone, Difco	10 g.
Bacto-Dextrose	10 g.
Sodium Chloride	4 g.
Sodium Citrate	1 g.
Disodium Phosphate	2 g.

Bacto-Kracke Blood Culture Medium is recommended for the culturing of organisms from the blood in bacteriemias. The medium may also be used for maintaining cultures isolated from the blood and for carrying stock cultures.

Kracke and Teasley[1] made an exhaustive study of the methods of blood culturing and described a new medium which yielded relatively higher percentages of positive cultures than other methods commonly employed. In their medium the finely divided particles of brain and heart tissue aid in fixing the complement and in removing immune bodies from the blood specimen. The sodium citrate prevents the blood from clotting and also aids in fixing the complement. They used their medium in 50 ml. quantities in flasks and added 10 to 15 ml. of blood specimen. Cultures were incubated for 18 hours at 37°C., and if negative at that time, reincubated for 3 weeks, with frequent observations for growth, before being considered negative.

Since the publication of their paper, Dr. Kracke has made a revision of the formula (personal communication) resulting in a medium which would give more satisfactory results. Bacto-Kracke Blood Culture Medium is prepared according to this revision.

Feder[2] gave in detail a new and simplified technique for blood culturing. He recommended the use of Bacto-Kracke Blood Culture Medium.

Bacto-Kracke Blood Culture Medium when properly prepared, contains about 50 per cent solid meat particles. The supernatant liquid is frequently quite turbid due to the presence of some of this very finely divided tissue. In blood culture work it may be necessary to prepare smears or make a transfer to another medium in order to determine the presence of organisms. Bacto-Brain Heart Infusion with PAB and Agar as discussed on page 79, can be recommended as a clear liquid medium for blood culture work.

To rehydrate the medium, suspend 3.75 grams of Bacto-Kracke Blood Culture Medium in 50 ml. of distilled water. The suspension, with frequent agitation, is allowed to stand for at least 15 minutes or until all the particles are thoroughy wetted. It is essential that this step be adhered to closely, since the final medium will not be sterile unless all the meat particles are thoroughly wetted before heating. Maintain an even suspension of the meat particles if distributed in tubes. The medium is then sterilized in the autoclave for 15 minutes at 15 pounds pressure (121°C.).

Special precautions must be taken to prevent too quick a decrease in pressure at the end of the sterilization period, since a too rapid cooling of the autoclave produces a vigorous boiling of the medium which results in excessive turbidity of the supernatant liquid and may even occasionally blow the medium and plugs from the flasks. The final reaction of the medium will be pH 7.4.

For best results, this medium should be freshly prepared, or if not used the same day as sterilized, heat in boiling water or flowing steam for a few minutes and cool quickly without agitation, just prior to inoculation.

One pound of Bacto-Kracke Blood Culture Medium will make 6 liters of medium.

[1] J. Lab. Clin. Med., 16:169:1930.   [2] J. Lab. Clin. Med., 22:846:1937.

BACTO

EGG MEAT MEDIUM (B42)

DEHYDRATED

Beef Muscle .... 454 g.
Egg White from .... 6 eggs
Calcium Carbonate .... 5 g.

Bacto-Egg Meat Medium is a liquid medium containing particles of meat, egg white and calcium carbonate in suspension. It is recommended for the determination of proteolytic activity of organisms, and for carrying stock cultures of anaerobes.

The use of a combination of meat and egg white as a culture medium was reported by Rettger[1] in his studies on *Escherichia coli* and *Aerobacter aerogenes*. Later he[2] described the use of this medium in studies of intestinal putrefaction. In 1923, Reddish and Rettger[3] used it in their detailed study of *Clostridium putrificum*, and in the following year they[4] employed it in a study of other spore-forming anaerobes.

The medium is prepared from fresh meat and egg white, retaining the coagulated portion of the meat and egg white as a part of the medium. The experiments of Reddish and Rettger, using twelve different spore-forming anaerobes, indicate that a final reaction of pH 7.0 is satisfactory for the organisms, and that the range of pH 7.0–7.4 favors abundant growth and consistent development of typical morphological forms.

Bacto-Egg Meat Medium was developed with the cooperation of Dr. Reddish. The use of this dehydrated medium eliminates a tedious and disagreeable task that confronted the bacteriologist interested in the study of anaerobes. This medium is of particular value in studies of morphology and the proteolytic properties, as demonstrated by the digestion of meat, of these organisms. Bacto-Egg Meat Medium is recommended for carrying stock cultures of anaerobes, since even when the medium has evaporated to a practically water-free consistency the organisms still retain their original pathogenicity, morphological, cultural and biochemical characteristics to a remarkable degree.

To rehydrate the medium, suspend 15 grams of Bacto-Egg Meat Medium in 100 ml. distilled water. The suspension is allowed to stand, with frequent agitation, for at least 15 minutes or until all the particles are thoroughy wetted. It is essential that this step be adhered to closely, since the final medium will not be sterile unless all the meat particles are thoroughly wetted before heating. An even suspension of the particles should be maintained while dispensing into tubes. The medium is then sterilized in the autoclave for 15 minutes at 15 pounds pressure (121°C.). Special precautions must be taken to prevent too quick a decrease in pressure at the end of the sterilization period, since a too rapid cooling of the autoclave produces a vigorous boiling of the medium which results in excessive turbidity of the supernatant liquid and may even occasionally blow the medium and plugs from the tubes. The final reaction of the medium will be pH 7.2.

If not used immediately after sterilization, the tubes should be heated in a boiling water bath or flowing steam for a few minutes and cooled without agitation, just prior to inoculation.

One pound of Bacto-Egg Meat Medium will make 3 liters of medium.

[1] Am. J. Physiol., 8:284:1903.
[2] J. Biol. Chem., 2:71:1906.
[3] J. Bact., 8:375:1923.
[4] J. Bact., 9:13:1924.

BACTO
COOKED MEAT MEDIUM (B267)
DEHYDRATED

Beef Heart	454 g.
Proteose Peptone, Difco	20 g.
Bacto-Dextrose	2 g.
Sodium Chloride	5 g.

Bacto-Cooked Meat Medium was developed for studies of contaminated wounds carried on by investigators working under contract with the Office of

Scientific Research and Development. It is recommended for use as a general culture medium for both aerobic and anaerobic bacteria. It has proved especially valuable as a primary medium for culturing pathological specimens and as a stock culture medium on which to carry most laboratory cultures. This medium, containing solid meat particles, has the unusual capacity for initiating growth of bacteria from minute inocula and for maintaining the viability of cultures over long periods of time.

Theobald Smith[1] first made use of fresh unheated animal tissue for cultivating anaerobic organisms. Tarozzi[2] confirmed Smith's findings on the value of unheated tissue in broths for anaerobic culture, and discovered further that he could heat the meat-broth to 104–105°C. for 15 minutes without destroying its capacity to support anaerobic growth. A steam sterilized emulsion of brain tissue in water was employed by von Hibler[3,4] for cultivating anaerobic bacilli, and found to be particularly valuable in culturing and classifying these organisms. It was further noted by von Hibler that organisms growing in the cooked brain mash were less susceptible to the harmful effects of toxic metabolic products than were those cultured in milk or carbohydrate serum media. Robertson[5] carefully analyzed von Hibler's results and substituted beef heart for the brain tissue. She found the Cooked Meat Medium to be equally as satisfactory as the Cooked Brain Medium. Henry[6] employed the Cooked Meat Medium successfully for culturing the anaerobes and recommended it for differentiating between various putrefactive and saccharolytic species. Holman[7] used Cooked Meat Medium for general culture purposes and commented: "Perhaps the most favorable characteristic of the medium, after its general growth stimulating influence, is that the products of growth do not rapidly destroy the various forms, and of all media in common use it is to the meat medium that one can constantly return to reisolate bacteria which have died out or have become hopelessly overgrown in other media. The meat is the best single medium we have for studying the anaerobes from war wounds, the reactions are useful for rapid differentiation of groups, as well as for individual identification, and no other medium we have can so readily indicate the presence of anaerobes in mixed cultures where they are often not expected. The cooked meat medium is the most useful medium we have at present for obtaining growth of both anaerobic and aerobic bacteria, for storing mixed cultures for later isolation, as well as pure cultures for further investigation. "Standard Methods for the Examination of Dairy Products"[8] specifies the use of Holman's Alkaline Cooked Meat Medium for use in the examination of frozen dessert ingredients and "Diagnostic Procedures and Reagents"[9] describes a Ground Meat Medium for the cultivation of anaerobes.

The capacity of Cooked Meat Medium to initiate growth of minute inocula of both aerobic and anaerobic microorganisms makes it especially valuable for use in the primary culture of clinical specimens wherein the causative agent may be present in such small numbers that enrichment is necessary. In such primary cultures, even though more than one organism be present, the slower growing organisms continue to proliferate without great danger of overgrowth by the faster growing organisms, as is true in case of many other culture media.

Bacto-Cooked Meat Medium is also an excellent stock culture medium in which to carry laboratory cultures of most microorganisms. Experience indicates that in this medium strains of the *Clostridia,* such as *tetani, novyi, septicum, botulinum, sporogenes, putrificum, bifermentans, perfringens,* and *histolyticum* have remained viable as long as ten years. The Gram-negative enteric bacteria, including *Shigella, Salmonella, Proteus,* and the coliforms, all remained viable for more than five years; staphylococci, *Corynebacteria* and *Lactobacilli* have persisted for more than six months.

To rehydrate the medium, suspend 12.5 grams of Bacto-Cooked Meat

Medium in 100 ml. cold distilled water. Mix thoroughly and allow to stand for 15 minutes until all the particles are thoroughly wetted, and while maintaining an even suspension distribute into tubes. The medium may also be rehydrated by distributing 1.25 grams into test tubes, adding 10 ml. cold distilled water, and mixing thoroughly, allowing to stand to insure thorough wetting of all particles. Sterilize in the autoclave for 15 minutes at 15 pounds pressure (121°C.). To prevent blowing of medium, avoid rapid release of pressure in the autoclave after sterilization. Properly prepared tubes of Bacto-Cooked Meat Medium should have a well defined layer of meat particles overlaid by a clear, amber-colored supernatant liquid. As soon as the sterile medium has cooled to 37°C. it is inoculated by loop or pipette, introducing the inoculum well into the meat layer. The final reaction of the medium will be pH 7.2.

Tubes of Cooked Meat Medium not used the day they are prepared should be placed in a boiling water bath or flowing steam for a few minutes to drive out dissolved oxygen, then cooled to 37°C. and inoculated.

One pound of Bacto-Cooked Meat Medium will make 3.6 liters of medium.

[1] Centr. Bakt., 7:509:1890.
[2] Centr. Bakt., 38:619:1905.
[3] Centr. Bakt., 25:513:1899.
[4] Von Hibler: Untersuchungen ueber die Pathogen Anaeroben, 1908.
[5] J. Path. Bact., 20:327:1916.

[6] J. Path. Bact., 21:344:1917.
[7] J. Bact., 4:149:1919.
[8] Standard Methods for the Examination of Dairy Products, 9th Edition:192:1948.
[9] Diagnostic Procedures and Reagents, 3rd Edition:17:1950.

BACTO

HEART INFUSION AGAR (B44)

DEHYDRATED

Beef Heart, Infusion from	500 g.
Bacto-Tryptose	10 g.
Sodium Chloride	5 g.
Bacto-Agar	15 g.

Bacto-Heart Infusion Agar is a solid infusion medium recommended for general laboratory use for the cultivation of many pathogenic bacteria. It can be used as a base to which a large variety of materials, such as blood or carbohydrates, may be added, giving media for many special purposes. It is a satisfactory medium for mass culture of organisms, making it valuable in the preparation of vaccines. Bacto-Heart Infusion Agar is recommended by the American Association of Medical Milk Commissions[1] for preparation of Blood Agar for the recognition and differentiation of streptococci in the examination of certified milk.

Like infusion broth, a solid medium prepared with the extractives of fresh meat and containing agar was used almost from the beginning of bacteriology. Huntoon[2] was one among the many to show that highly pathogenic organisms, such as the meningococcus and pneumococcus, could be grown on an infusion medium without enrichment. Bacto-Tryptose, as employed in this formula, is better suited to the nutritional requirements of pathogenic bacteria than is Bacto-Peptone which was used by Huntoon in the preparation of his "hormone" agar. The blood culture method of Castaneda, as described in detail on page 113 under Tryptose Agar may be used with this medium.

To rehydrate the medium, suspend 40 grams of Bacto-Heart Infusion Agar in 1000 ml. of cold distilled water and heat to boiling to dissolve the medium completely. Distribute in tubes or flasks and sterilize in the autoclave for 15 minutes at 15 pounds pressure (121°C.). The final reaction of the medium will be pH 7.4.

If Blood Agar is to be prepared immediately, the sterile medium is cooled at once to 45-50°C. and while still liquid 5 per cent sterile defibrinated blood is added aseptically with thorough mixing, avoiding incorporation of air bubbles, and distributing in sterile tubes or plates as desired. Blood Agar for study of cultural characteristics of colonies should be incubated to insure sterility before use.

Since most microorganisms prefer a fresh medium with a moist surface, it is recommended that the Heart Infusion Agar be prepared as required, or melted and re-solidified just prior to use. Blood Agar from this medium should be prepared as required.

One pound of Bacto-Heart Infusion Agar will make 11.3 liters of medium.

[1] Methods and Standards for the Production   [2] J. Infectious Diseases, 23:169:1918.
of Certified Milk, 28:1953-1954.

BACTO
BLOOD AGAR BASE (B45)
DEHYDRATED

Beef Heart, Infusion from	500 g.
Bacto-Tryptose	10 g.
Sodium Chloride	5 g.
Bacto-Agar	15 g.

Bacto-Blood Agar Base is recommended as a base to which blood may be added for use in the isolation and cultivation of many fastidious pathogenic microorganisms. The slightly acid reaction of this medium is conducive to the preservation of red blood cells. Without the addition of blood, this medium can be recommended as a slightly acid agar medium for general laboratory work. Many microorganisms produce earlier and more abundant growth on Blood Agar with a slightly alkaline reaction, and therefore the use of this same medium at pH 7.4, Bacto-Heart Infusion Agar as discussed immediately above or Bacto-Tryptose Blood Agar Base discussed on page 115, is preferred.

Colonies of bacteria upon a Meat Infusion Blood Agar usually grow luxuriantly, and the hemolytic types exhibit clear distinct degrees of hemolysis. Norton[1] has recommended the use of such a medium with a reaction of pH 6.8 as being distinctly advantageous in culturing the pneumococcus and streptococcus groups. This slightly acid reaction seems to permit the development of clearer zones of hemolysis than does an alkaline reaction. Bacto-Blood Agar Base is a medium containing the extractives from fresh beef heart with Bacto-Tryptose. This medium, which contains no added carbohydrate, is especially recommended for use in the preparation of Blood Agar to study the hemolytic characteristics of colonies. It is also recommended for isolation of organisms directly from the blood. Bacto-Blood Agar base is mentioned in "Diagnostic Procedures and Reagents"[2] as an excellent basal medium for plate cultures for the pneumococci. The use of 1 ml. of venipuncture blood in a sterile petri dish to which is added the sterile cooled medium is recommended. The blood culture method of Castaneda, as described in detail on page 113 under Tryptose Agar may be used with this medium.

Tarshis and Frisch[3] investigated the addition of bank blood to various media for the cultivation of tubercle bacilli in pure culture and directly from sputa under routine diagnostic conditions. Three standard tuberculosis media were used in the comparative study. They recommended the addition of 25 per cent bank blood to Bacto-Blood Agar Base or Bacto-Bordet Gengou Agar Base with 1 per cent glycerol added since media of this type grew tubercle bacilli from small inocula producing colonies that were readily recognized. These media were easily prepared and in addition were economical. They were also satisfactorily employed in streptomycin sensitivity tests.

To rehydrate the medium, suspend 40 grams of Bacto-Blood Agar Base in 1000 ml. of cold distilled water and heat to boiling to dissolve the medium completely. Distribute in tubes or flasks and sterilize in the autoclave for 15 minutes at 15 pounds pressure (121°C.). The final reaction of the medium, before adding blood, will be pH 6.8.

If Blood Agar is to be prepared immediately, the sterile medium is cooled at once to 45–50°C., and, while still liquid, 5 per cent sterile defibrinated blood is added aseptically with thorough mixing, avoiding incorporation of air bubbles, and distributing in sterile tubes or plates as desired. Blood Agar should be incubated before use to insure sterility.

Since most microorganisms prefer a fresh medium with a moist surface it is recommended that Blood Agar Base be prepared as required, or melted and re-solidified just prior to use. Blood Agar from this medium should be prepared as required.

One pound of Bacto-Blood Agar Base will make 11.3 liters of the finished medium.

[1] J. Lab. Clin. Med., 17:558:1932.
[2] Diagnostic Procedures and Reagents, 3rd   Edition:70:1950.   [3] Am. J. Clin. Path., 21:101:1951.

BACTO
VEAL INFUSION AGAR (B343)
DEHYDRATED

Veal Heart, Infusion from	500 g.
Proteose Peptone, No. 3, Difco	10 g.
Sodium Chloride	5 g.
Bacto-Agar	15 g.

Bacto-Veal Infusion Agar is prepared from select lean veal and is recommended as a solid medium for the cultivation of fastidious pathogenic bacteria. It is also a suitable basal medium for enrichment by the addition of blood, ascitic fluid, serum or other enrichments.

To rehydrate the medium suspend 40 grams Bacto-Veal Infusion Agar in 1000 ml. cold distilled water and heat to boiling to dissolve the medium completely. Distribute in tubes or flasks and sterilize in the autoclave for 15 minutes at 15 pounds pressure (121°C.).

Since most organisms prefer a fresh medium with a moist surface, it is suggested that the medium be prepared as required or melted and re-solidified just prior to use. The final reaction of the medium will be pH 7.4.

One pound of Bacto-Veal Infusion Agar will make 11.3 liters of medium.

BACTO
PPLO AGAR (B412)
DEHYDRATED

Bacto-Beef Heart for Infusions,	
Infusion from	50 g.
Bacto-Peptone	10 g.
Sodium Chloride	5 g.
Bacto-Agar	14 g.

Bacto-PPLO Agar is a base used in preparing a solid medium for the isolation and cultivation of pleuropneumonia-like organisms (PPLO), as described by Morton, Smith and Leberman.[1] These authors found that Bacto-Peptone, Bacto-Tryptose and Bacto-Yeast Extract were satisfactory peptones in a medium for the cultivation of these organisms. Bacto-Peptone in the presence of an infusion of Bacto-Beef Heart for Infusions gave best results. Bacto-PPLO Agar duplicates their recommended formula.

Bacto-PPLO Agar, enriched with Bacto-Ascitic Fluid or Bacto-PPLO Serum Fraction will permit the development of colonies of PPLO visible microscopically, after 48 hours or longer aerobic incubation at 37°C. After 48 hours incubation inverted plates are examined under the low power of the microscope, focusing through the medium to its surface for the presence of surface colonies on the medium. Cultures should be examined daily after 48 hours for a period of one week before the plate is considered negative. PPLO colonies are round with a dense center and a less dense periphery, giving the appearance of a fried egg. They vary from 10 to 500 microns in diameter (0.01–0.5 mm.) and grow into the medium. Individual organisms are not resolved, so there is little evidence at this magnification of any cellular organization. Vacuoles are seen in the periphery of some of the colonies. They are the large bodies characteristic of the pleuropneumonia group.

To rehydrate the medium, suspend 34 grams of Bacto-PPLO Agar in 1000 ml. of cold distilled water and heat to boiling to dissolve the medium completely. Distribute in flasks and sterilize in the autoclave for 15 minutes at 15 pounds pressure (121°C.). After the medium has been cooled to 45–60°C., add 1 per cent Bacto-PPLO Serum Fraction or 25 per cent Bacto-Ascitic Fluid. Mix thoroughly and pour into sterile petri dishes. The reaction of the unenriched medium will be pH 7.8.

One pound of Bacto-PPLO Agar will make 13.3 liters unenriched medium.

[1] Am. J. Syphilis Gonorrh. Venereal Diseases, 35:361:1951.

BACTO
BRAIN HEART INFUSION AGAR (B418)
DEHYDRATED

Calf Brains, Infusion from	200 g.
Beef Heart, Infusion from	250 g.
Proteose Peptone, Difco	10 g.
Bacto-Dextrose	2 g.
Sodium Chloride	5 g.
Disodium Phosphate	2.5 g.
Bacto-Agar	15 g.

Bacto-Brain Heart Infusion Agar is recommended as a solid medium for the cultivation of fastidious pathogenic bacteria and fungi. A selective medium for fungi may be prepared by adding penicillin and streptomycin to the sterile medium.

The liquid medium, Bacto-Brain Heart Infusion, has for many years been the medium of choice for the cultivation of streptococci, pneumococci, meningococci and many other organisms considered difficult to cultivate, and has been especially valuable in blood culture work. This medium, solidified with agar to give Bacto-Brain Heart Infusion Agar, is a satisfactory solid medium for the cultivation of these organisms. In addition, the solid medium has been especially valuable as a neutral or slightly alkaline medium for the cultivation of pathogenic fungi. Selective media for fungi may be prepared by adding antibiotics or other selective agents. Roseburg, Epps and Clark[1] reported that Bacto-Brain Heart Infusion with 2 per cent agar was more satisfactory than 1 per cent Dextrose Infusion Agar for the isolation and cultivation of *Actinomyces israeli*. Incubation in an atmosphere of 5 per cent carbon dioxide was required for best results. The addition of sheep blood to the medium offered no growth advantage. Howell[2] used Bacto-Brain Heart Infusion to which was added 2 per cent Bacto-Agar and 10 per cent sterile defibrinated horse blood for the cultivation of *Histoplasma capsulatum*. A selective medium for the isolation of this organism was prepared by adding 40 micrograms streptomycin and 20 units penicillin per ml. of medium. In comparison with a Blood Agar similarly prepared from Potato Dextrose Agar, the Brain Heart Infusion Agar gave a greater number of positive isolations. Incubation at room temperature was more efficient than at 37°C. Colonies of *H. capsulatum* isolated on Brain Heart Infusion Agar must be transferred to a medium such as Potato Dextrose Agar to obtain the characteristic tuberculate chlamydospores typical of this fungus. Conant[3] recommended that a plate of Bacto-Brain Heart Infusion Agar be streaked and incubated at 37°C. under anaerobic conditions with the addition of 5 per cent carbon dioxide to obtain growth of the microaerophilic *A. bovis* in culturing this organism from infected mucous membranes and subcutaneous tissues.

Kotcher, Robinson and Miller[4] compared various media for the isolation of *H. capsulatum* from tissues of experimentally infected mice. Their results showed that Brain Heart Infusion Blood Agar gave the highest percentage recovery of *H. capsulatum* from the tissues of the infected mice.

Bacto-Brain Heart Infusion Agar contains 0.2 per cent Bacto-Dextrose, making it unsatisfactory for the determination of typical hemolytic reactions when enriched with blood. Bacto-Heart Infusion Agar, Bacto-Tryptose Blood Agar Base or Bacto-Blood Agar Base, as discussed on pages 87, 115 and 88, should be used in preparing Blood Agar for the determination of typical hemolytic reactions.

To rehydrate the medium, suspend 52 grams Bacto-Brain Heart Infusion Agar in 1000 ml. cold distilled water. Heat to boiling to dissolve the medium completely. Distribute in tubes or flasks and sterilize in the autoclave for 15 minutes at 15 pounds pressure (121°C.).

A selective medium for fungi is prepared by adding 20 units penicillin and 40 micrograms streptomycin per ml. sterile liquid medium, at 50–55°C. Final reaction of the medium will be pH 7.4.

One pound of Bacto-Brain Heart Infusion Agar will make 8.7 liters of medium.

[1] J. Infectious Diseases, 74:131:1944.
[2] Public Health Reports, 63:173:1948.
[3] Diagnostic Procedures and Reagents, 3rd Edition:452:1950.
[4] J. Bact., 62:613:1951.

BACTO

CYSTINE HEART AGAR (B47)

DEHYDRATED

Beef Heart, Infusion from	500 g.
Proteose Peptone, Difco	10 g.
Bacto-Dextrose	10 g.
Sodium Chloride	5 g.
l-Cystine, Difco	1 g.
Bacto-Agar	15 g.

Bacto-Cystine Heart Agar, enriched with Bacto-Hemoglobin, is recommended for the cultivation of *Pasteurella tularensis*. The use of this medium is suggested for this purpose by "Diagnostic Procedures and Reagents"[1] of the American Public Health Association. Bacto-Cystine Heart Agar without enrichment supports excellent growth of Gram-negative cocci and other pathogenic microorganisms.

Since *P. tularensis* was first isolated by McCoy and Chapin,[2] many media have been described for its cultivation. A large number of the media first employed were difficult to prepare and contained egg or serum. Francis[3] reported Blood Dextrose Cystine Agar in his later investigation as being a satisfactory medium for cultivating this fastidious organism. Shaw[4] added 0.05 per cent cystine and 1 per cent dextrose to Bacto-Heart Infusion Agar for the cultivation of *P. tularensis*. Shaw[5] also showed that the amount of destruction of cystine in the autoclave at 15 pounds pressure for 15 minutes would be small or negligible as far as the bacteriological culture medium was concerned.

Rhamy[6] found Francis' Blood Dextrose Cystine Agar to be excellent but often it became contaminated due to the difficulties attendant to its preparation. In his experience an autoclaved solution of Bacto-Hemoglobin added to Bacto-Cystine Heart Agar proved to be entirely satisfactory for the cultivation of *P. tularensis*. In three or four days the growth is sufficient for the preparation of bacterial antigens. Because of its nutritional value, this medium may also be used for cultivating many other organisms ordinarily difficult to grow.

Bacto-Cystine Heart Agar was originally developed in collaboration with Rhamy. As mentioned in the paper by Rhamy, referred to above, W. M. Simpson found this formula, with a reaction of pH 6.8, a most satisfactory medium for the cultivation of this organism. Also cooperating in these preliminary trial studies of the medium, Francis found a culture medium made with Bacto-Cystine Heart Agar and Bacto-Hemoglobin entirely satisfactory for growing *P. tularensis*.

When used with Bacto-Hemoglobin, the medium is prepared for use as follows:

A. Suspend 10.2 grams Bacto-Cystine Heart Agar in 100 ml. cold distilled water and heat to boiling to dissolve the medium completely. Sterilize in the autoclave for 15 minutes at 15 pounds pressure (121°C.).

B. Place 2 grams Bacto-Hemoglobin in a dry flask and add 100 ml. cold distilled water, while the flask is being agitated vigorously. The hemoglobin suspension is shaken intermittently for 10–15 minutes to break up all aggregates and effect complete solution and sterilized in the autoclave for 15 minutes at 15 pounds pressure (121°C.).

C. Both solutions are cooled to 50–60°C., mixed and poured into sterile petri dishes or tubes.

When a plain Cystine Dextrose Agar, without hemoglobin, is desired, the medium is rehydrated by suspending 51 grams of Bacto-Cystine Heart Agar in 1000 ml. cold distilled water and heating to boiling to dissolve the medium completely. Distribute in tubes or flasks and sterilize in the autoclave for 15 minutes at 15 pounds pressure (121°C.). The final medium will have a reaction of pH 6.8.

One pound of Bacto-Cystine Heart Agar will make 8.9 liters of the enriched, or plain, medium.

[1] Diagnostic Procedures and Reagents, 3rd Edition:259:1950.
[2] J. Infectious Diseases, 10:61:1912.
[3] J. Am. Med. Assoc., 91:1155:1928.
[4] Zentr. Bakt. I Abt. Orig., 118:216:1930.
[5] J. Lab. Clin. Med., 16:294:1930.
[6] Am. J. Clin. Path., 3:121:1933.

BACTO
MUELLER HINTON MEDIUM (B252)
DEHYDRATED

Beef, Infusion from	300 g.
Bacto-Casamino Acids, Technical	17.5 g.
Starch	1.5 g.
Bacto-Agar	17 g.

Bacto-Mueller Hinton Medium duplicates the formula recommended by Mueller and Hinton[1] for the primary isolation of the gonococcus and meningococcus. Sulfonamide resistance of gonococci and other microorganisms may also be determined on this medium.

In an attempt to develop a simple transparent medium containing no heat-labile materials and capable of withstanding autoclaving, Mueller and Hinton selected what they considered the most suitable complete medium available, and attempted to break it into its essential components. The medium chosen for study was the complex Gordon and Hine[2] Pea Meal Extract Agar, which, in the opinion of the senior author, had proved to be satisfactory for the primary isolation of the meningococcus and the gonococcus. As a result of the fractionation of the pea extract, it was found that the active portion was starch and not a protein. Additional work showed that starch could replace the growth-promoting properties of the pea extract and that the starch probably acts as a "protective colloid" against toxic materials present in the medium. In addition, they found that the tryptic digest of meat could be replaced by Bacto-Casamino Acids, Technical. Growth of the gonococcus and meningococcus on the developed medium was highly satisfactory and colonies were usually large and easily recognizable, especially with the aid of the oxidase reagent.

Goodale et al.[3] used the Mueller Hinton Medium to identify sulfonamide resistant strains of the gonococcus. Nelson[4] used Bacto-Mueller Hinton Medium in correlating sulfonamide resistance with the clinical picture in gonorrhoea. In "Diagnostic Procedures and Reagents"[5] of the American Public Health Association, the Mueller and Hinton Medium is suggested for the isolation and transportation of the meningococcus in the field or whenever blood is unobtainable.

For the cultivation of the gonococcus, it is imperative to have the incubation atmosphere saturated with moisture. Satisfactory conditions can be obained if the plates of Mueller Hinton Medium are incubated in a closed container, which contains cotton, a towel or a sponge saturated with water. A can with a suitable cover, Novy jar, desiccator or any other convenient sized container capable of retaining the moisture is entirely satisfactory. About 200 ml. of water added in this manner is ample for a container of one or two gallons capacity. Plates incubated under these conditions will give a luxuriant growth of many gonococci when identically inoculated plates incubated in the ordinary manner in the incubator show no growth. If the culture requires carbon dioxide for growth this may be supplied as indicated under Bacto-Proteose No. 3 Agar, page 116. Carbon dioxide is recommended for isolation, but is not generally necessary, in the presence of abundant moisture, for growth of isolated strains.

To rehydrate the medium, suspend 38 grams of Bacto-Mueller Hinton Medium in 1000 ml. of cold distilled water and heat to boiling to dissolve the medium completely. Distribute in tubes or flasks and sterilize for 10 minutes at 10 pounds pressure (116°C.). The final reaction of the medium will be pH 7.4.

It is recommended that the dissolved medium be distributed into test tubes in 5 ml. quantities for slants or into 120–200 ml. flasks in 20 ml. quantities for pouring plates. This medium must not be heated more than the sterilization period specified. The flasks can be used to pour plates at once and tubes may be melted in boiling water and used as needed.

One pound of Bacto-Mueller Hinton Medium is sufficient to prepare 11.9 liters of medium.

[1] Proc. Soc. Exp. Biol. Med., 48:330:1941.
[2] Brit. Med. J., 2:678:1916.
[3] J. Am. Med. Assoc., 123:547:1943.
[4] Personal Communication.
[5] Diagnostic Procedures and Reagents, 3rd Edition:192:1950.

BACTO

BRAIN VEAL AGAR (B49)

DEHYDRATED

Calf Brain, Infusion from	250 g.
Veal, Infusion from	375 g.
Proteose Peptone, Difco	10 g.
Monosodium Phosphate	1.25 g.
Sodium Chloride	3.75 g.
Bacto-Agar	15 g.

Bacto-Brain Veal Agar is a medium containing extractives of fresh calf brain and veal. It was developed primarily for the cultivation of the gonococcus. This medium also supports good growth of streptococci, pneumococci, meningococci, and other microorganisms generally considered difficult to cultivate.

Pelouze and Viteri,[1] following a study of the cultural requirements of the gonococcus, devised a simple medium, Brain Veal Agar, upon which this diplococcus grew luxuriantly. Bacto-Brain Veal Agar is prepared according to their formula and gives results comparable to the medium prepared by them. In addition, it is an excellent medium for other highly fastidious microorganisms. Bacto-Brain Veal Agar is a satisfactory medium for the preparation of bacterial antigens and vaccines.

For the cultivation of the gonococcus for complement-fixation work Garcia[2] reported that Bacto-Brain Veal Agar gave good growth. Saccone[3] used Bacto-Brain Veal Agar for the isolation of the gonococcus. Reitzel and Kohl,[4] in their modification of the McLeod method for the isolation of the gonocccus, employed a medium more adaptable for use in small laboratories. Their medium was prepared by using a combination of Bacto-Brain Heart Infusion as discussed on page 77 and Bacto-Brain Veal Agar which, when mixed with an equal quantity of Bacto-Hemoglobin as discussed on page 271, would give a final concentration of 1.2 per cent agar. Shaw[5] added 0.5 per cent cystine and 1 per cent dextrose to Bacto-Brain Veal Agar for the cultivation of *Pasteurella tularensis* with excellent results. Foshay[6] also used Bacto-Brain Veal Agar with Nutrose (sodium caseinate), dextrose, cystine, inorganic salts and serous enrichments for the propagation of *P. tularensis*.

Although Bacto-Brain Veal Agar will support good growth of the gonococcus, media prepared without infusions from meat have been developed, giving much better growth of these discriminating organisms. For isolation of the gonococcus we recommend a Chocolate Agar prepared from Bacto-Proteose No. 3 Agar and Bacto-Hemoglobin, enriched with Bacto-Supplement A or Bacto-Supplement B, or Bacto-G. C. Medium Base similarly enriched. The procedure is given in detail on pages 116 and 122. For cultivation of the gonococcus in pure culture we recommend Bacto-Dextrose Starch Agar as discussed on page 124.

To rehydrate the medium, suspend 53 grams of Bacto-Brain Veal Agar in 1000 ml. cold distilled water and heat to boiling to dissolve the medium completely. Distribute in tubes or flasks and autoclave for 15 minutes at 15 pounds pressure (121°C.). The final reaction of the medium will be pH 7.6.

Since best results are obtained with solid media having a moist surface, Brain Veal Agar should be used the same day it is prepared or, if not used at once, the medium should be melted and allowed to re-solidify. A moist surface is particularly important for the cultivation of the gonococcus, and for that reason it is recommended that sterile rubber stoppers be substituted for the cotton plugs as soon as the slants have cooled.

One pound of Bacto-Brain Veal Agar will make 8.5 liters of medium.

⁴ J. Am. Med. Assoc., 86:684:1926.
³ Rev. Med. Malaga, Nov. 6, 1930.
¹ Rinascenza Medica, 14:No. 17:1936, XIII.

⁴ J. Am. Med. Assoc., 110:1095:1938.
⁵ Zentr. Bakt., I Abt., Orig., 118:216:1930.
⁶ Am. J. Clin. Path., 3:379:1933.

BACTO
POTATO INFUSION AGAR (B51)
DEHYDRATED

Potatoes, Infusion from	250 g.
Bacto-Beef Extract	5 g.
Proteose Peptone, Difco	10 g.
Sodium Chloride	5 g.
Bacto-Dextrose	10 g.
Bacto-Agar	15 g.

Bacto-Potato Infusion Agar is prepared according to the formula used by Stockman and MacFadyean for the isolation of *Brucella abortus*. This medium permits a luxuriant growth of characteristic colonies of *B. abortus* from infected materials and may be used with excellent results in mass cultivation of the organism in the preparation of vaccines and antigens. Bacto-Tryptose Agar, which does not contain an infusion, as discussed on page 111, is recommended as being far more satisfactory than Bacto-Potato Infusion Agar for the isolation and cultivation of the *Brucella*.

To rehydrate the medium suspend 49 grams of Bacto-Potato Infusion Agar in 1000 ml. of a 2 per cent solution of glycerol in distilled water and heat to boiling to dissolve the medium completely. Distribute in tubes or flasks and sterilize in the autoclave for 15 minutes at 15 pounds pressure (121°C.). The final medium will have a reaction of pH 6.8 and will contain a slight precipitate which settles rapidly. The presence of this precipitate in no way interferes with the use of the medium.

Best results are obtained on freshly prepared media with a moist surface. It is suggested if the medium is not used the day it is prepared that the agar be melted and allowed to re-solidify in order to provide most satisfactory conditions for growth.

One pound of Bacto-Potato Infusion Agar will make 0 liters of medium.

BACTO
BORDET GENGOU AGAR BASE (B48)
DEHYDRATED

Potatoes, Infusion from	125 g.
Sodium Chloride	5.5 g.
Bacto-Agar	20 g.

Bacto-Bordet Gengou Agar Base, enriched with 15 to 20 per cent blood, is recommended for use in the "cough plate" method for the detection and isolation of

Hemophilus pertussis in the diagnosis of whooping cough. This is a modification of the medium originally described by Bordet and Gengou[1] in 1906 for the cultivation of *H. pertussis* and is prepared according to the formula recommended in Diagnostic Procedures and Reagents[2] of the American Public Health Association for the isolation of this organism. The addition of 1 per cent Proteose Peptone to the medium is suggested if employed for mass culture of *H. pertussis* as in vaccine production.

The "cough plate" method for the diagnosis of whooping cough was originally reported by Chievitz and Meyer[3] in 1916. Lawson and Mueller[4] in 1927 and Sauer and Hambrecht[5] in 1930 used modifications of the Bordet Gengou Medium to demonstrate the value of the cultural diagnosis of this disease. This method has been applied routinely as a diagnostic procedure for public health laboratories as a result of the thorough and painstaking investigations of Kendrick and her associates. Kendrick and Eldering[6] first used a modified Bordet Gengou Medium for the isolation and propagation of *H. pertussis*. Eldering and Kendrick[7] reported that the addition of 1 per cent of Proteose Peptone or Neopeptone increased the growth of *H. pertussis* thereby increasing the yield for vaccine.

With this modification of the Bordet Gengou Medium, enriched with 15 to 20 per cent blood, the appearance of colonies of *H. pertussis* is typical, being smooth, raised, glistening and not over 1 mm. in diameter. They are of a pearly, almost transparent appearance, and are surrounded by a characteristic zone of hemolysis which is not sharply defined, but which merges diffusely into the medium. The zone of hemolysis usually is absent if 30 per cent or more blood is added to the medium. Sterile sheep, rabbit or human blood may be used in preparing the medium. Horse blood should not be used in preparing vaccine.

Kendrick, Miller and Lawson[7] and Kendrick, Lawson and Miller[8] recommended that, after exposure, cough plates prepared from the modified Bordet Gengou Blood Agar should be incubated at 37°C. During the first 48 hours incubation they are examined for contamination by molds and spreaders, which are cut aseptically from the medium. The plates are then examined twice daily, using a hand lens, until typical colonies of *H. pertussis* are found or until discarded after 6 days of incubation.

Maclean[9] used Bacto-Bordet Gengou Agar Base and reported it to be efficient in the isolation of *H. pertussis*. He further reported that this medium was a valuable standard for the comparison of various lots of media prepared from ingredients.

Tarshis and Frisch[10] investigated the addition of bank blood to various media for the cultivation of tubercle bacilli in pure culture and directly from sputa under routine diagnostic conditions. Three standard tuberculosis media were used in the comparative study. They recommended the addition of 25 per cent bank blood to Bacto-Bordet Gengou Agar Base or Bacto-Blood Agar Base with 1 per cent glycerol added since media of this type grew tubercle bacilli from small inocula producing colonies that were readily recognized. These media were easily prepared and in addition were economical. They were also satisfactorily employed in streptomycin sensitivity tests.

To rehydrate the medium, suspend 3 grams of Bacto-Bordet Gengou Agar Base in 100 ml. of a 1 per cent solution of glycerol in distilled water and heat to boiling to dissolve the medium completely. Distribute in flasks and sterilize in the autoclave for 15 minutes at 15 pounds pressure (121°C.). It is cooled to 45 to 50°C. and aseptically enriched with 15 to 20 per cent sterile sheep, rabbit, or human blood[2] and is poured into sterile petri dishes. The blood should be used when fresh, never more than 72 hours after it has been obtained. Satisfactory plates should be bright cherry red in color and free from bubbles and lumps of agar. Plates may be used as long as they remain moist and red, usually two or three weeks if kept in the cold room. For mass cultivation of *H. pertussis* as in vaccine production dissolve 1 gram of Proteose Peptone in 100 ml. of glycerol solution used to rehydrate the medium.

One pound of Bacto-Bordet Gengou Agar Base is sufficient for 15 liters of medium.

[1] Am. inst. Pasteur, 20:731:1906.
[2] Diagnostic Procedures and Reagents, 3rd Edition:141:1950.
[3] Ann. inst. Pasteur, 30:503:1916.
[4] J. Am. Med. Assoc., 89:275:1927.
[5] J. Am. Med. Assoc., 95:263:1930.
[6] Am. J. Pub. Health, 24:309:1934.
[7] Am. J. Pub. Health, 26:506:1936.
[8] Sixth Annual Year Book (1935–36), p. 200, Suppl., Am. J. Pub. Health, 26:No. 3:1936.
[9] J. Path. Bact., 45:472:1937.
[10] Am. J. Clin. Path., 21:101:1951.

BACTO
ENDAMOEBA MEDIUM (B53)
DEHYDRATED

Beef Liver, Infusion from	272 g.
Proteose Peptone, Difco	5.5 g.
Disodium Phosphate	3 g.
Sodium Chloride	2.7 g.
Bacto-Agar	11 g.

Bacto-Endamoeba Medium is a Liver Infusion Agar prepared especially for the cultivation of *Endamoeba histolytica* from specimens. The formula corresponds to that recommended by Cleveland and Sanders[1] and Cleveland and Collier.[2]

Cleveland and his associates made a comprehensive study of the cultivation of *E. histolytica.* They used egg, serum and various other materials for cultivating the amoeba and state[1]: "We feel however, that we really did not cultivate *Entamoeba histolytica* until we grew it on slants of liver infusion agar covered with fresh horse serum-saline 1–6 and containing rice flour." They used about half strength Bacto-Liver Infusion Agar in this study. Bacto-Endamoeba Medium has been prepared to duplicate the modified Liver Infusion Agar described by Cleveland and his co-workers.

This medium, furthermore, is reported by them to be almost specific for *E. histolytica,* as far as the intestinal amoebae of man are concerned. They attempted to cultivate *Endolimax nana, Dientamoeba fragilis,* and *E. coli* and failed, while *E. histolytica* grew abundantly. In a committee report Spector,[3] referee, states that the method of Cleveland and Collier using Bacto-Liver Infusion Agar overlaid with sterile serum-saline 1–6 was one of the best for practical diagnostic purposes and that Wassermann-negative human inactivated serum, horse, or rabbit serum may be used. This report also mentions that other intestinal amoebae do not grow as readily in this culture medium as does *E. histolytica.*

To rehydrate the medium, suspend 33 grams of Bacto-Endamoeba Medium in 1000 ml. cold distilled water and heat to boiling to dissolve the medium completely. Distribute in tubes and sterilize in the autoclave for 15 minutes at 15 pounds pressure (121°C.). The final reaction of the medium will be pH 7.0. The tubes are allowed to solidify in a slanted position. For the cultivation of *E. histolytica* the slants are covered with Bacto-Horse Serum Saline 1–6 and a loopful of sterilized Bacto-Rice Powder is added. Bacto-Rice Powder is sterilized in a dry heat oven at 160°C. for one hour. Scorching must be prevented. These enrichments are discussed in detail on pages 273 and 300.

One pound of Bacto-Endamoeba Medium will make 13.7 liters of medium.

[1] Arch. Protiskenkunde, 70:223:1930.
[2] Am. J. Hyg., 12:606:1930.
[3] Sixth Annual Year Book (1935–36), p. 130, Suppl., Am. J. Pub. Health, 26:No. 3:1936.

BACTO
STOCK CULTURE AGAR   (B54)
DEHYDRATED

Beef Heart, Infusion from	500 g.
Proteose Peptone, Difco	10 g.
Bacto-Gelatin	10 g.
Bacto-Dextrose	0.5 g.
Bacto-Isoelectric Casein	5 g.
Disodium Phosphate	4 g.
Sodium Citrate	3 g.
Bacto-Agar	7.5 g.

Bacto-Stock Culture Agar is recommended for the maintenance of cultures of streptococci and other organisms. It is a soft, almost semisolid medium.

Ayers and Johnson[1] described a medium that gave luxuriant growth and long life of streptococci. Their medium was developed from a formula originally given them by Supplee. The success of their medium probably lies in the fact that the medium has a semisolid consistency, contains casein, is well buffered and contains a small quantity of dextrose which serves as a readily available source of energy. They reported that pathogenic streptococci remained viable for at least four months at room temperature (24°C.) in their medium. Organisms other than streptococci, such as pneumococci, human tubercle bacilli and others grew well on their Stock Culture Agar.

Bacto-Stock Culture Agar is prepared to duplicate the medium described by Ayers and Johnson. This medium, likewise, will support luxuriant growth of many pathogenic bacteria and preserve their viability over a long period of time.

Bacto-Cooked Meat Medium, as discussed on page 85, is also recommended as a medium for carrying cultures in stock. For carrying cultures of gonococcus, meningococcus, and other organisms not capable of splitting starch, the infusion free Bacto-Dextrose Starch Agar, in half concentration, is recommended as discussed on page 125.

To rehydrate the medium, suspend 50 grams of Bacto-Stock Culture Agar in 1000 ml. of cold distilled water and heat to boiling to dissolve the medium completely. Distribute in tubes and sterilize in the autoclave for 15 minutes at 15 pounds pressure (121°C.). The final reaction of the medium will be pH 7.5.

One pound of Bacto-Stock Culture Agar will make 9 liters of medium.

[1] J. Bact., 9:111:1924.

BACTO
LIVER VEAL AGAR   (B59)
DEHYDRATED

Bacto-Liver, Infusion from	50 g.
Veal, Infusion from	500 g.
Proteose Peptone, Difco	20 g.
Neopeptone, Difco	1.3 g.
Bacto-Tryptone	1.3 g.
Bacto-Dextrose	5 g.
Soluble Starch, Difco	10 g.
Bacto-Isoelectric Casein	2 g.
Sodium Chloride	5 g.
Sodium Nitrate	2 g.
Bacto-Gelatin	20 g.
Bacto-Agar	15 g.

Bacto-Liver Veal Agar is especially well suited for the isolation and cultivation of anaerobes. The medium may be used in anaerobic culture dishes or in deep tube culture.

Numerous methods for the cultivation of anaerobes have been devised and many media have been proposed for this purpose. The use of the anaerobic culture dish as described by Spray[1,2] is one of the procedures suggested for the propagation of these organisms. Medium prepared from Bacto-Liver Veal Agar is identical with the medium described by Spray[3,4] for use in his anaerobic culture dishes for cultivation of anaerobes.

Bacto-Liver Veal Agar gives excellent growth of the sporulating anaerobes. In a personal communication Spray reported the usefulness of this medium for isolation purposes since *Clostridium perfringens* colonies were fished within 6 hours from time of inoculation and *C. tetani* within 8 hours. Gas production is inhibited when the medium is inoculated sparingly. With proper dilution giving 10–15 colonies per plate, primary isolations of pure cultures are readily obtained. The medium may also be used in deep tube cultures of the sporulating anaerobes. Bacto-Liver Veal Agar is also suitable for the routine isolation and cultivation of many aerobes.

To rehydrate the medium, suspend 97 grams of Bacto-Liver Veal Agar in 1000 ml. cold distilled water and heat to boiling to dissolve the medium completely. Distribute in tubes or flasks and sterilize in the autoclave for 15 minutes at 15 pounds pressure (121°C.). The final reaction of the medium will be pH 7.3.

When it is used in the anaerobic dish, Spray[3] recommends that unless taken directly from the sterilizer, the medium should be boiled for 10 minutes and then cooled to 50°C. without agitation. Serial inoculations are then made and the medium is poured into the dishes. After solidification, 5 ml. sterile Liver Veal Agar is poured over the medium as a cover layer to prevent the spreading of surface colonies.

One pound of Bacto-Liver Veal Agar will make 4.6 liters of medium.

[1] J. Lab. Clin. Med., 16:203:1930.
[2] J. Bact., 21:23:1931.
[3] Personal Communication.
[4] J. Bact., 32:135:1936.

PEPTONE MEDIA
(*Without Infusions*)

INFUSIONS of meat with added peptone have been employed consistently as culture media for bacteria. Extractives from fresh meat have been considered essential in media for all but the most common organisms. In many cases, due to ease of preparation and demand for greater uniformity in media, beef extract has replaced the infusion of fresh meat. Media containing peptone without meat extractives have been used for the routine cultivation of some of the more hardy laboratory strains, or for routine tests such as the production of indole, methyl red test, etc. Peptones have been used in semi-synthetic broths for the production of diphtheria and scarlet fever toxin.

The opportunities for variation in media prepared from fresh meat are obvious. The freshness of the meat used in the infusion influences the amount of muscle sugar present in the final medium. The age of the animal, the cut of the meat, amount of trimming, time and conditions of infusion are further factors contributing to variability of the final media. Likewise, the infusion of meat is laborious, time consuming and costly. These conditions were recognized by the

Standard Methods Committee of the American Public Health Association, when in 1917[1] they specified the use of beef extract rather than infusion of fresh meat for use in the preparation of media for the examination of water. In 1921 "Standard Methods for Milk Analysis,"[2] in the interests of greater uniformity, specified the use of beef extract rather than infusions of beef for media used in plate counts of milk. A standard medium must be uniform in composition and easily prepared. Any procedure that simplifies the preparation and maintains greater uniformity of composition of media is a definite advance in technical bacteriology.

For isolation or cultivation of strains of many highly pathogenic organisms such as the *Brucella,* streptococci, pneumococci, gonococci, meningococci and others, it has generally been considered necessary to have infusions of fresh meat in the medium. Bateriological peptones have been pioneered and developed by Difco Laboratories that make the addition of infusions of fresh meat unnecessary for the cultivation of many organisms, including even the discriminating gonococci, meningococci, pneumococci, streptococci, *Brucella* and others. For example, Bacto-Tryptose Agar, developed and prepared in 1938, proved more satisfactory for the isolation and cultivation of *Brucella,* streptococci and pneumococci than previously employed infusion media. Bacto-Proteose No. 3 Agar and Bacto-Dextrose Starch Agar also developed in 1938 for the isolation and cultivation of the gonococci, simplified the cultural diagnosis of gonorrhoea so as to make it a routine test even for the smallest laboratory. These media contain specially prepared bacteriological peptones without infusions and have proven in many years of practical use to be superior to previously recommended complicated infusion and enriched media used for the cultivation of these organisms. A 2 per cent solution of Bacto-Tryptose or Proteose Peptone No. 3 will satisfactorily replace the peptone-infusion portion of media previously employed for the isolation and propagation of streptococci, pneumococci, meningococci, gonococci and other fastidious microorganisms. In the discussion of Meat Infusion Broths in "Diagnostic Procedures and Reagents"[3] of the American Public Health Association, the referee states that in his laboratory a broth with 2 per cent pancreatic digest of casein and 0.5 per cent yeast extract has been substituted for infusion broth and the growth of the more fastidious organisms has been heavier than that obtained in infusion media.

The simplicity of preparation and uniformity of composition, combined with the ability to grow the organisms, make the Peptone Media listed in this secton of practical value and interest.

It is a well recognized fact that infusion media contain varying amounts of muscle sugar. In preparing media from peptones this variability can be controlled by the addition of a known and definite quantity of dextrose. A small quantity of dextrose (0.025–0.05 per cent) in peptone media assists materially in the initiation of growth of many bacteria.

[1] Standard Methods of Water Analysis, 3rd Edition:93:1917.
[2] Standard Methods of Milk Analysis, 3rd Edition:7:1921.
[3] Diagnostic Procedures and Reagents, 3rd Edition:13:1950.

BACTO
TRYPTOSE PHOSPHATE BROTH   (B60)
DEHYDRATED

Bacto-Tryptose .... 20 g.
Bacto-Dextrose .... 2 g.
Sodium Chloride .... 5 g.
Disodium Phosphate .... 2.5 g.

Bacto-Tryptose Phosphate Broth is a liquid peptone medium prepared without an infusion of meat, recommended for the cultivation of streptococci, pneumococci, meningococci and other organisms generally considered difficult to cultivate. This medium is especially adapted for blood culture work. A procedure frequently used for this purpose is to add as much as 10 ml. blood specimen to 150 ml. of sterile Tryptose Phosphate Broth contained in a 300 ml. Erlenmeyer flask or bottle. Inoculated flasks are incubated at 37°C. and are observed at intervals for bacterial growth. When growth occurs in the flasks, transfers are made to Blood Agar or other suitable media for isolation and identification, according to usual practice.

The addition of 0.1–0.2 per cent Bacto-Agar to Tryptose Phosphate Broth improves the productivity of the medium for most purposes. The advantages of a medium with a low agar concentration is discussed fully under Bacto-Brain Heart Infusion, page 77. In the "Standard Methods for the Examination of Dairy Products,"[1] 0.1 per cent agar is included in the formula for Tryptose Phosphate Agar Broth as used in the isolation of pathogenic bacteria from cheese. "Diagnostic Procedures and Reagents"[2] of the American Public Health Association include the addition of 0.1–0.2 per cent agar in the formula of Tryptose Phosphate Broth.

Newman[3] in a study of the detection of food poisoning attributable to dairy products, used Tryptose Phosphate Broth to which was added 0.1 per cent agar and 1:2500 sodium azide for the cultivation of streptococci. An incubation temperature of 37°C. was used with this medium. Bacto-Tryptose Phosphate Broth is recommended for use in the tube dilution method of testing the sensitivity of microorganisms to antibiotics. Waisbren, Carr and Dunnett[4] showed that Bacto-Tryptose Phosphate Broth, Bacto-Dextrose Broth or Bacto-Nutrient Broth were suitable media for comparative sensitivity test studies while a medium containing a soy bean peptone inhibited the action of Neomycin, Aureomycin, Terramycin and Polymyxin against the test organism.

To rehydrate the medium, dissolve 29.5 grams of Bacto-Tryptose Phosphate Broth in 1000 ml. distilled water. Distribute in tubes or flasks. For blood culture work dispense in 150 ml. quantities in 300 ml. Erlenmeyer flasks or bottles. The medium is sterilized in the autoclave for 15 minutes at 15 pounds pressure (121°C.). The final reaction of the medium will be pH 7.3.

If the medium is not used immediately after preparation, it should be heated in the autoclave or in a boiling water bath in order to drive off dissolved oxygen, and should then be cooled to 37°C. without agitation, just prior to inoculation.

One pound of Bacto-Tryptose Phosphate Broth will make 15.3 liters of medium.

[1] Standard Methods for the Examination of Dairy Products, 9th Edition:165:1948.
[2] Diagnostic Procedures and Reagents, 3rd Edition:16:1950.
[3] J. Milk and Food Tech., 13:226:1950.
[4] Am. J. Clin. Path., 21:884:1951.

BACTO
DEXTROSE BROTH (B63)
DEHYDRATED

Bacto-Beef Extract	....	3 g.
Bacto-Tryptose	....	10 g.
Bacto-Dextrose	....	5 g.
Sodium Chloride	....	5 g.

Bacto-Dextrose Broth is recommended as a liquid enrichment medium for the isolation of many bacteria. It is a superior medium for the cultivation of organisms such as streptococci, pneumococci, meningococci and other microorganisms.

The fact that dextrose (*d*-glucose) is a readily available source of energy, utilized by a large number of organisms, makes Dextrose Broth an important medium in any laboratory. Dextrose Broth can be recommended to give rapid growth and hasten the early development of attenuated forms. A liquid medium containing dextrose is especially adapted to primary culture in the isolation of pathogenic bacteria. Bacto-Dextrose Broth contains 0.5 per cent dextrose along with Bacto-Tryptose. This medium is superior to most Infusion-Peptone Dextrose Broths for the cultivation of a large variety of bacteria, including the pathogenic cocci, and has the further advantage of greater uniformity. Bacto-Dextrose Broth is especially suited for use in the preparation of Rosenow's Dextrose Brain Broth[1] as described for the isolation of streptococci. The value of Bacto-Dextrose Broth is greatly increased for the cultivation of organisms like streptococci, pneumococci, meningococci, gonococci, etc., if 0.1 per cent agar be incorporated in the medium as discussed on page 77 under Bacto-Brain Heart Infusion.

Bacto-Dextrose Broth is recommended for use in the tube dilution method of testing the sensitivity of microorganisms to antibiotics. Waisbren, Carr and Dunnett[2] showed that Bacto-Dextrose Broth, Bacto-Tryptose Phosphate Broth or Bacto-Nutrient Broth were suitable media for comparative sensitivity test studies while a medium containing a soy bean peptone inhibited the action of Neomycin, Aureomycin, Terramycin and Polymyxin against the test organism.

To rehydrate the medium, dissolve 23 grams of Bacto-Dextrose Broth in 1000 ml. of distilled water. Distribute in tubes and sterilize in the autoclave for 15 minutes at 15 pounds pressure (121°C.). Final reaction of the medium will be pH 7.2.

For best results Bacto-Dextrose Broth should be freshly prepared. If the medium is not used the same day as sterilized, heat in boiling water or flowing steam for a few minutes to remove absorbed oxygen, and cool quickly without agitation, just prior to inoculation.

One pound of Bacto-Dextrose Broth will make 19.7 liters of medium.

[1] J. Dental Research, 1:205:1919.   [2] Am. J. Clin. Path., 21:884:1951.

BACTO
TRYPTOSE BROTH (B62)
DEHYDRATED

Bacto-Tryptose	20 g.
Sodium Chloride	5 g.
Bacto-Dextrose	1 g.
Thiamine Hydrochloride	0.005 g.

Bacto-Tryptose Broth is prepared without extract or infusion of meat and is recommended as a general laboratory medium for the cultivation of discriminating pathogenic as well as saprophytic bacteria. Huddleson[1] used a broth containing 2 per cent Bacto-Tryptose as an enrichment medium in the isolation of *Brucella* from man. McCullough, Mills, Herbst, Roessler and Brewer[2] reported that the addition of thiamine, dextrose and iron salts increased the growth of *B. suis*. Sanders and Huddleson[3] showed that the addition of dextrose and thiamine hydrochloride to the medium resulted in the stimulation of the growth of all species of *Brucella*. Bacto-Tryptose Broth is prepared according to the formula of Tryptose Dextrose Vitamin B Broth as given in the "Diagnostic Procedures and Reagents"[4] of the American Public Health Association and is particularly recommended as a blood enrichment medium, with the addition of sodium citrate, for isolation of *Brucella* from febrile and afebrile patients according to the method of Huddleson[1] and as given in "Diagnostic Procedures and Reagents."[5]

In the past, it has been considered necessary to have meat extract or meat infusions in culture media for the cultivation of bacteria, except possibly for some of the more easily cultivated strains. It has been shown that many fastidious pathogenic organisms can be isolated and cultivated in media prepared without meat extract, infusions of meat or other enrichment if a suitable peptone is employed. Bacto-Tryptose, in 2 per cent concentration, satisfactorily replaces the usual infusion-peptone portion of many media. Huddleson[1] pointed out that the probability of isolating Brucella from human blood is hastened and more certain if the blood be incubated in Bacto-Tryptose Broth. Sodium Citrate in 1 per cent concentration added to the medium serves as an anticoagulant and assists in fixing the complement of the blood specimen.

The procedure in detail for the isolation of Brucella from human blood is given in the discussion of Bacto-Tryptose Agar on page 111. In a personal communication Huddleson recommended that the Tryptose Broth blood culture be incubated in 10 per cent carbon dioxide, rather than 25 per cent as originally specified.

The addition of 0.1 per cent of agar to Tryptose Broth is highly recommended, if the use of this small amount of agar is not objectionable. Diagnostic Procedures and Reagents[5] prefers the use of the Tryptose Broth with the addition of 0.05–0.1 per cent agar for culturing Brucella from whole blood. Growth of aerobes and anaerobes in liquid media is greatly increased by the addition of 0.1 per cent of agar, as was demonstrated by Hitchens[6] and by Falk, Bucca, and Simmons.[7] Borman and West[5] stated that the addition of 0.05–0.1 per cent of agar to the Tryptose Broth was preferable in primary blood culture for Brucella.

Schuhardt, Rode, Foster and Oglesby,[8] by special techniques, demonstrated that a few of the numerous samples of Bacto-Tryptose which had been in his laboratory exhibited some toxicity for certain Brucella abortus strains used in his laboratory. The particular samples of Bacto-Tryptose possessing this characteristic had absorbed moisture and had undergone chemical change. Schuhardt[9] in a discussion of this observation stated that "the ease of neutralization of this toxic factor by blood, serum, agar and other substances tends to make the practical significance of the toxicity relatively minor. We probably would not have encountered it had we not been doing extensive tests on the in vitro effect of sulfonamides on Brucella using decimal dilution inocula". The high productivity of Bacto-Tryptose Agar, and Bacto-Tryptose used clinically for the isolation and cultivation of Brucella attests to its value for the primary cultivation of Brucella as well as other fastidious organisms.

To rehydrate the medium, dissolve 25 grams of Bacto-Tryptose Broth in 1000 ml. of distilled water. Distribute in tubes, bottles or flasks and sterilize in the autoclave for 15 minutes at 15 pounds pressure (121°C.). The final reaction of the medium will be pH 7.2.

For best results Bacto-Tryptose Broth should be freshly prepared. If not used the same day as sterilized, heat in boiling water or flowing steam to remove absorbed oxygen and cool quickly without agitation, just prior to inoculation.

One pound of Bacto-Tryptose Broth will make 18.1 liters of medium.

[1] Huddleson: Brucellosis in Man and Animals, 14:1939.
[2] J. Bact., 53:5:1947.
[3] J. Vet. Research, 11:70:1950.
[4] Diagnostic Procedures and Reagents, 3rd Edition:17:1951.
[5] Diagnostic Procedures and Reagents, 3rd Edition:246:1951.
[6] J. Infectious Diseases, 29:390:1921.
[7] J. Bact., 37:121:1939.
[8] J. Bact., 57:1:1949.
[9] Personal Communication, 1949.

PEPTONE COLLOID MEDIUM (B61)
DEHYDRATED

Bacto-Tryptose	20 g.
Sodium Chloride	5 g.
Bacto-Agar	1 g.

Bacto-Peptone Colloid Medium, containing 0.1 per cent agar, is a liquid medium recommended for the cultivation of anaerobes, and also for many aerobes generally considered difficult to cultivate. This medium was developed as a basal medium to which carbohydrate and other test materials could be added for studying the physiological properties of anaerobes and other microorganisms.

The preparation of the usual peptone-infusion medium employed for pathogenic bacteria, is a costly, laborious, time-consuming task, resulting in media that vary from time to time depending on the age of the meat, condition of infusion and a number of other factors. In Bacto-Peptone Colloid Medium, a 2 per cent concentration of Bacto-Tryptose satisfactorily replaces the peptone infusion portion of infusion media. This medium will support excellent growth of the anaerobes and is also equally well suited for the propagation of meningococci, streptococci, pneumococci and other microorganisms that are generally considered difficult to cultivate. For many organisms, especially the anaerobes, Bacto-Peptone Colloid Medium will be improved by the addition of a small quantity of dextrose as a source of readily available energy. An added 0.025 to 0.05 per cent dextrose is sufficient to initiate growth and still not enough to produce gas or to give rise to appreciable acid production. The above mentioned quantities of dextrose are well within the limits of muscle sugar normally obtained in infusion media. It is not practical to include the indicator in the medium for fermentation studies with anaerobes, since these organisms reduce the indicators to their leuco bases. Solutions of indicator should be added to the culture after incubation to detect changes in hydrogen ion concentration.

The advantages of a medium with a low agar concentration and its influence on the development of bacteria, particularly the anaerobes, has been described by Hitchens.[1] In a broth, to which 0.1 per cent agar has been added, there is a clear upper zone well suited for aerobic growth; below this the flocculent agar develops all degrees of anaerobiosis. This condition makes the medium suitable for the growth of either aerobic or anaerobic bacteria. Falk, Bucca, and Simmons[2] point out the advantages of the use of small quantities of agar (0.06 to 0.25 per cent) in the detection of contaminants in testing the sterility of biologicals. They show that the growth of even common forms, such as the hay bacillus and staphylococci, ordinarily considered easy to cultivate, were aided by the addition of a small quantity of agar. They also showed that growth is initiated in a much shorter incubation period in such media. In their routine tests they used 0.1 per cent agar which is the amount present in Bacto-Peptone Colloid Medium.

To rehydrate the medium, suspend 26 grams of Bacto-Peptone Colloid Medium in 1000 ml. of cold distilled water and heat to boiling to dissolve the medium completely. Distribute in tubes and sterilize in the autoclave for 15 minutes at 15 pounds pressure (121°C.). The final reaction of the medium will be pH 7.3.

For best results Bacto-Peptone Colloid Medium should be freshly prepared. If the medium is not used the same day as sterilized, heat in boiling water or flowing steam for a few minutes to remove absorbed oxygen, cool quickly without agitation, just prior to inoculation.

One pound of Bacto-Peptone Colloid Medium will make 17.4 liters of medium.

[1] J. Infectious Diseases, 29:390:1921.　　　　　[2] J. Bact., 37:121:1939.

BACTO

DUBOS BROTH BASE (B385)
DEHYDRATED

Bacto-Asparagine	2 g.
Bacto-Casitone	0.5 g.
Disodium Phosphate	2.5 g.
Monopotassium Phosphate	1 g.
Ferric Ammonium Citrate	50 mg.
Magnesium Sulfate	10 mg.
Calcium Chloride	0.5 mg.
Zinc Sulfate	0.1 mg.
Copper Sulfate	0.1 mg.
Tween 80	0.2 g.

Bacto-Dubos Broth Base is recommended for the preparation of a liquid medium for the rapid cultivation of pure cultures of *Mycobacterium tuberculosis*. It is prepared in accordance with the formula given by Dubos, Fenner and Pierce.[1] This is a modification of the original medium described by Dubos and Davis[2] and Dubos and Middlebrook.[3]

Liquid media have been used for the cultivation of tubercle bacilli for many years. Generally the growth on these media appeared as a surface pellicle. Dubos[4] reported rapid and submerged growth of *M. tuberculosis* in Long's Synthetic Medium to which was added soya bean phosphatide and a polyoxyalkylene derivative of sorbitan monostearate (Tween 60). Dubos and Davis,[2] in a study of factors influencing the growth of *M. tuberculosis* described, among other media, a liquid medium containing Tween 80, an oleic acid ester, and albumin (serum fraction V). In this liquid medium growth of the tubercle bacillus was obtained in 3–5 days from dilute inocula. The addition of the albumin fraction V to the medium facilitated the growth of tubercle bacilli from small inocula but did not increase markedly the total amount of growth produced. Less pure preparations of the protein increased the amount of growth as well as initiated growth from minute inocula.[4,5] The character of the growth obtained on this medium was different from that obtained on liquid media previously described. Subsurface, readily dispersible growth was obtained, and pellicle formation occurred only in old cultures. This type of growth was particularly valuable in obtaining an even suspension of tubercle bacilli for use in mouse and guinea pig infection tests and for other techniques requiring an even suspension of organisms.

Dubos and Davis[2] obtained typical diffuse cultures of acid-fast bacilli from sodium hydroxide treated human sputa, and avian bacilli from animals experimentally infected. Even though the medium was capable of supporting growth of tubercle bacilli from pathological material, they cautioned against its indiscriminate use in diagnostic work. Foley[6,7] reported that a liquid medium similar to that described by Dubos could be used successfully for the isolation of tubercle bacilli from various pathologic materials, and that a combination of rapid culture in this medium and guinea pig confirmation should result in a shorter period of time required for diagnosis of tuberculosis. Goldie[8] used the liquid medium for the cultivation of tubercle bacilli from sputa treated with ammonium carbonate and penicillin. Other laboratories,[9] after thorough comparative study, reported that the liquid medium as described by Dubos could not be recommended for the clinical diagnosis of tuberculosis, confirming the statement of Dubos.

Media similar to the one described by Dubos have been used by numerous investigators for various pure culture studies of the tubercle bacillus, as, for example, the work of Middlebrook[10] and others. Such a medium is excellent for carrying stock cultures of *M. tuberculosis,* as organisms maintain their viability without change in phase of virulence for long periods of time. It also offers a suitable means of running chemotherapeutic screening tests and the testing of the sensitivity of the tubercle bacillus to antibiotics and other materials.

Wolinsky and Steenken[11] and Bernstein, D'Esapo and Steenken[12] used Dubos Medium and modifications of this liquid medium in testing the resistance of tubercle bacilli to streptomycin. Wong, Hambly and Anderson[13] used a modification of the Dubos and Davis medium to demonstrate sensitivity of *M. tuberculosis* to subtilin. Beattie[14] compared hydrochloric acid and trisodium phosphate treatment of sputa, followed by culturing on the fluid medium of Dubos and on Petragnani medium. Her results indicated no superiority of either method of treatment of sputa, however, the evidence suggested that the use of trisodium phosphate may adversely affect the growth of the tubercle bacilli. Both the liquid and solid medium were equally effective in the cultivation of *M. tuberculosis* in this study.

Mollov, Hill and Oshinsky used Dubos[15] medium for the routine isolation and cultivation of *M. tuberculosis.* They added 10 units of penicillin per ml. of the Dubos liquid medium as a selective agent. Types of specimens examined were sputum, gastric contents, pleural fluid, spinal fluid and urine. The necessity of making smears to determine the presence of the tubercle bacillus was stressed and they streaked on Petrick's medium to detect tubercle bacilli and show typical colony characteristics. These authors also found the Dubos liquid medium to be helpful in the determination of sensitivity and resistance of the tubercle bacilli to streptomycin.

Bacto-Dubos Broth Base enriched with Bacto-Dubos Medium Albumin or Bacto-Dubos Medium Serum will give growth in from 3–5 days from a 10^{-8} mg inoculation of *M. tuberculosis* and in 10–15 days using 10^{-7} mg inoculum. The medium prepared with Bacto-Dubos Medium Serum will generally give a more luxuriant growth and initiate growth from a smaller inoculum than that enriched with Bacto-Dubos Medium Albumin. Growth is generally more diffuse in media prepared with the Albumin enrichment, while with the Serum enrichment the growth is granular. Bacto-Dubos Medium Albumin is a 5.0 per cent solution of albumin fraction V from bovine plasma in normal saline and contains 7.5 per cent Bacto-Dextrose. Bacto-Dubos Medium Serum is beef serum with 7.5 per cent Bacto-Dextrose. Both solutions are filter sterilized.

The early and luxuriant growth of tubercle bacilli in media prepared with Dubos Broth Base and Dubos Medium Serum make it ideal for the cultivation and study of pure cultures of these organisms. It is also recommended for culturing spinal, pleural and peritoneal fluids likely to harbor the tubercle bacillus in pure culture. Growth is readily visible. In sensitivity tests where the presence or absence of growth is the determining factor, the medium prepared with Bacto-Dubos Medium Serum may be recommended. For tests requiring turbidimetric determinations for quantitative growth, mouse or guinea pig inoculation work or other techniques requiring a readily dispersible growth, the medium should be prepared with Bacto-Dubos Medium Albumin.

The microscopic appearance of tubercle bacilli, when viewed with a 16 mm. objective, is quite typical on this medium. The organisms appear in irregular clumps or tangled filaments rather than as individual cells. Edges of these clumps, examined with the oil immersion lens, show typical acid-fast bacilli. If it is desired to grow tubercle bacilli from concentrated sputa or other pathological material it is difficult to distinguish macroscopically between tubercular granules and debris, or possible growth from extraneous organisms. It is necessary to determine the presence of tubercle bacilli microscopically. Even though the medium, inoculated with treated specimens, shows obvious contaminants, a microscopic examination will often show that the tubercle bacilli have multiplied even in the presence of the contaminants.

The medium may be prepared with or without glycerol. The addition of glycerol enhances the growth of human strains of tubercle bacilli, and is not required by bovine or avian strains. Glycerol may be added to the distilled water at the time of rehydrating the medium. The use of Bacto-Glycerol is recommended since it has been tested bacteriologically to insure freedom from toxic principles and for suitability for use in this medium.

To rehydrate the medium dissolve 1.3 grams Bacto-Dubos Broth Base in 180 ml. distilled water or 170 ml. distilled water containing 10 ml. Bacto-Glycerol. Sterilize in the autoclave for 15 minutes at 15 pounds pressure (121°C.). Cool to below 50°C. and add the contents of one tube Bacto-Dubos Medium Albumin (20 ml.) or Bacto-Dubos Medium Serum (20 ml.) under aseptic conditions. Mix thoroughly and distribute in 16–20 mm. diameter sterile test tubes in 5–7 ml. amounts. Incubate for 24 hours to test sterility. The medium is then ready for inoculation.

One pound of Bacto-Dubos Broth Base will make 69.8 liters of medium.

[1] Am. Rev. Tuberculosis, 61:66:1950.
[2] J. Expl. Med., 83:409:1946.
[3] Am. Rev. Tuberculosis, 56:334:1947.
[4] Proc. Soc. Exp. Biol. Med., 58:361:1945.
[5] J. Exp. Med., 85:9:1947.
[6] Proc. Soc. Exp. Biol. Med., 62:298:1946.
[7] J. Lab. Clin. Med., 32:842:1947.
[8] Proc. Soc. Exp. Biol. Med., 65:210:1947.
[9] Personal Communications, 1947–48.
[10] Proc. N.Y. State Assoc. Pub. Health Lab., 27:28:1947.
[11] Am. Rev. Tuberculosis, 55:281:1947.
[12] Am. Rev. Tuberculosis, 58:344:1948.
[13] J. Lab. Clin. Med., 32:837:1947.
[14] J. Lab. Clin.. Med., 34:733:1949.
[15] Am. J. Clin. Path., 20:1085:1950.

BACTO
DUBOS BROTH BASE (B435)
without Tween 80
DEHYDRATED

Bacto-Dubos Broth Base without Tween 80 has the same formula as Bacto-Dubos Broth Base except Tween 80 has been omitted. In certain tests to determine the sensitivity of tubercle bacilli to various antibiotics or other bactericidal agents it may be desirable to omit the Tween 80. There is a possibility that this material present in the medium may influence the sensitivity of the tubercle bacilli to the test substance.

BACTO
DUBOS OLEIC AGAR BASE (B373)
DEHYDRATED

Bacto-Casitone	0.5 g.
Bacto-Asparagine	1 g.
Disodium Phosphate	2.5 g.
Monopotassium Phosphate	1 g.
Ferric Ammonium Citrate	50 mg.
Magnesium Sulfate	10 mg.
Calcium Chloride	0.5 mg.
Zinc Sulfate	0.1 mg.
Copper Sulfate	0.1 mg.
Bacto-Agar	15 g.

Bacto-Dubos Oleic Agar Base is recommended for the preparation of a solid medium for the isolation of *Mycobacterium tuberculosis*. It is prepared according to the formula described by Dubos and Middlebrook.[1] Bacto-Dubos Oleic Agar Base enriched with Bacto-Dubos Oleic Albumin Complex may also be used as a basal medium on which to test the sensitivity of *M. tuberculosis* to chemotherapeutic agents.

Dubos and Middlebrook in a discussion of media for the cultivation of tubercle bacilli described an agar medium suitable for diagnostic primary isolations and also for studies of colony morphology. This medium is prepared without glycerol or dextrose in order to discourage the growth of commensal organisms that might not have been killed during the concentration process. Asparagine likewise is added in minimal quantities to provide maximum selectivity. The basal agar is enriched with Bacto-Dubos Oleic Albumin Complex, (page 275). The sterile base is cooled to 50–55°C., and oleic acid albumin complex and penicillin as selective agent are added. The medium is mixed and distributed in sterile tubes or plates as desired. About 15 ml. of medium is used per 95 mm. dish and following solidification two drops of an adequately diluted suspension of the tubercle bacilli or of pathological material are used as an inoculum. Roberts, Wallace and Erlich[2] in a study of methods of isolation of the tubercle bacilli reported that Dubos Oleic Albumin Agar Medium gave better results than other media, even superior to guinea pig inoculations. Byham,[3] comparing different media for primary isolation work, reported best results with Middlebrook's medium.[4] Commensal organism contamination was reduced by the penicillin and early growth of the tubercle bacilli was obtained. Foley,[5] in a limited survey, too small to permit analysis reported that four strains grew on the solid Dubos medium, but failed to develop in the liquid Dubos medium. He pointed out that colonial morphology is strikingly different on the Dubos Agar than on coagulated egg media.

To rehydrate the medium suspend 4.2 grams Bacto-Dubos Oleic Agar Base in 180 ml. of cold distilled water. Heat to boiling to dissolve the medium completely. Sterilize in the autoclave for 15 minutes at 15 pounds pressure (121°C.). Cool to 50–55°C. and add the contents of one tube of Bacto-Dubos Oleic Albumin Complex (20 ml.) and 5,000 to 10,000 units of penicillin (25 to 50 units per ml.), under aseptic conditions. Mix thoroughly and distribute in sterile tubes or plates as desired. Keep uninoculated medium in the refrigerator.

One pound of Bacto-Dubos Oleic Agar Base will make 21.6 liters of medium.

[1] Am. Rev. Tuberculosis, 56:334:1942.
[2] Am. Rev. Tuberculosis, 61:563:1950.
[3] Am. J. Clin. Path., 20:678:1950.
[4] Proc. N.Y. State Assoc. of Pub. Health Lab., 27:28:1947.
[5] J. Lab. Clin. Med., 32:842:1947.

BACTO
TB BROTH BASE (B291)
DEHYDRATED

Bacto-Yeast Extract	2 g.
Proteose Peptone No. 3, Difco	2 g.
Bacto-Casitone	2 g.
Disodium Phosphate	2.5 g.
Monopotassium Phosphate	1 g.
Sodium Citrate	1.5 g.
Magnesium Sulfate	0.6 g.
Tween 80	0.5 g.

Bacto-TB Broth Base is a modification of the medium described by Dubos and Davis[1] and is recommended for the preparation of a liquid medium for the rapid cultivation of *Mycobacterium tuberculosis*. This modification was prepared since we considered it to give earlier and more rapid growth than the original Dubos formula, as well as the initiation of growth from inocula containing fewer organisms. This base, when enriched with Bacto-Dubos Medium Serum, will support luxuriant growth of tubercle bacilli from dilute inocula after a short incubation period (within 7–10 days). *M. tuberculosis* produces a granular growth, settling to the bottom of the tube in this medium. When the base is enriched with Bacto-Dubos Medium Albumin a readily dispersible or diffuse growth is obtained.

A discussion of liquid media for the cultivation of the tubercle bacilli is given in the description of the medium, Bacto-Dubos Broth Base, (page 105). Media prepared from Bacto-TB Broth Base are recommended for the cultivation and propagation of pure cultures of *M. tuberculosis,* and for culturing pathological specimens such as spinal, pleural and peritoneal fluids likely to contain the tubercle bacillus in pure culture. It is also employed for determining the sensitivity of *M. tuberculosis* to antibiotics and other chemotherapeutic agents. Generally, solid media have proven more satisfactory for initial propagation of the organism from specimens.

The medium may be prepared with or without glycerol. The addition of glycerol enhances the growth of human strains of tubercle bacilli and is not required by bovine or avian strains. Glycerol may be added to the distilled water at the time of rehydrating the medium. The use of Bacto-Glycerol is recommended since it has been tested bacteriologically to insure freedom from toxic principles and for suitability for use in this medium.

To rehydrate the medium, dissolve 2.4 grams Bacto-TB Broth Base in 180 ml. of distilled water or 170 ml. of distilled water containing 10 ml. Bacto-Glycerol. Sterilize in the autoclave for 15 minutes at 15 pounds pressure (121°C.). Cool to below 50°C. and add the contents of one tube Bacto-Dubos Medium Serum (20 ml.) or one tube Bacto-Dubos Medium Albumin (20 ml.) under aseptic conditions. The medium is mixed thoroughly and distributed under aseptic conditions in 16–20 mm. diameter test tubes in 5–7 ml. amounts. The medium is then ready for inoculation. Final reaction of the base and medium prepared as above will be pH 7.0.

One pound of Bacto-TB Broth Base will make 37.8 liters of medium.

[1] J. Exp. Med., 83:409:1946.

BACTO
TB BROTH BASE (B374)
without Tween 80
DEHYDRATED

Bacto-TB Broth Base without Tween 80 has the same formula as Bacto-TB Broth Base except Tween 80 has been omitted. In certain tests to determine the sensitivity of tubercle bacilli to various antibiotics or other bactericidal agents, it may be desirable to omit the Tween 80. There is a possibility that this material present in the medium may influence the sensitivity of the tubercle bacilli to the test substance.

BACTO
PEIZER TB MEDIUM BASE   (B400)
DEHYDRATED

Bacto-Beef Extract	3 g.
Bacto-Casamino Acids	10 g.
Bacto-Asparagine	3 g.
Potato Starch	15 g.
Ferric Ammonium Citrate	0.1 g.
Magnesium Sulfate	0.015 g.
Dipotassium Phosphate	3.5 g.
Citric Acid	0.1 g.
Bacto-Agar	15 g.

Bacto-Peizer TB Medium Base with Bacto-Peizer TB Medium **Enrichment** is recommended for the isolation and cultivation of *Mycobacterium tuberculosis,* and for the determination of sensitivity of this organism to therapeutic agents. This base and enrichment are prepared according to the formulae described by Peizer and Schecter.[1]

Media prepared with coagulated egg or egg yolk have generally been considered most satisfactory for the isolation and cultivation of the tubercle bacilli. Peizer and Schecter[1] described an agar medium enriched with egg yolk, which gave comparable results with coagulated egg yolk media for initial cultivation of the tubercle bacilli from specimens. The medium also gave an early and luxuriant growth with satisfactory inhibition of commensal organisms. The medium consists of an agar base to which is added an enrichment composed of egg yolk, glycerol, and dextrose and with malachite green as a selective agent. The basal medium has been prepared in dehydrated form and the enrichment supplied ready for addition to the sterile rehydrated agar base.

The ease of preparation of the complete medium from Bacto-Peizer TB Medium Base and Bacto-Peizer TB Medium Enrichment in amounts as required, its high nutritional value and its selectivity make it ideally suited for the isolation of the tubercle bacilli from clinical specimens. In addition, the medium may be used for determining the sensitivity of the tubercle bacillus to therapeutic agents. When used for sensitivity testing, the complete medium is poured either into sterile petri dishes or wide-mouth bottles and allowed to solidify. The medium is heavily inoculated by smearing a suspension of the organism over the surface to produce a mass growth. Treated specimens showing a Gaffky of III or more may also be smeared in a similar manner for testing the sensitivity of the organisms from primary culture. Bacto-Sensitivity Disks containing 1, 10 and 100 mcg. dihydrostreptomycin are then placed on the inoculated medium. The plates or bottles are sealed and incubated. Observations are made for growth of the organism and size of the zone of inhibition of growth around the disks. See Bacto-Sensitivity Disks (p. 335) for complete discussion of this technique.

Peizer, Widelock and Schecter[2] used this basal medium in testing the sensitivity of the tubercle bacillus to streptomycin. In their method the streptomycin was included in the enrichment.

To rehydrate the medium suspend 49.8 grams Bacto-Peizer TB Medium Base in 1000 ml. cold distilled water. Heat to boiling to dissolve the medium completely. Distribute in 100 ml. amounts and sterilize in the autoclave for 15 minutes at 15 pounds pressure (121°C.). Cool to 45–50°C. and add the contents of one bottle of Bacto-Peizer TB Medium Enrichment to 100 ml. of the sterile medium. Mix well, avoiding the formation of bubbles. Distribute in sterile tubes or plates as desired, under aseptic conditions. Tubes are slanted in the desired position and medium allowed to solidify.

One pound of Bacto-Peizer TB Medium Base will make 11.8 liters of medium.

[1] Am. J. Clin. Path., 20:682:1950.   [2] Am. J. Clin. Path., 21:982:1951.

BACTO
TRYPTOSE AGAR (B64)
DEHYDRATED

Bacto-Tryptose	20 g.
Bacto-Dextrose	1 g.
Sodium Chloride	5 g.
Bacto-Agar	15 g.
Thiamine Hydrochloride	0.005 g.

Bacto-Tryptose Agar is recommended for the isolation, cultivation and differentiation of the *Brucella*. "Standard Methods for the Examination of Dairy Products"[1] and "Diagnostic Procedures and Reagents"[2] of the American Public Health Association, recommend this medium for this purpose. Bacto-Tryptose Agar is also recommended as a general medium for the cultivation of a large variety of pathogenic organisms, especially the streptococci.

Isolation or cultivation of organisms of the *Brucella* group was originally accomplished by means of Liver Infusion Agar as recommended by Stafseth,[3] and Huddleson, Hasley and Torrey.[4] Completely satisfactory results were not consistently obtained on this medium due to variations of the infusions from liver tissue. Because of these irregular results on Liver Infusion Agar, an extensive investigation of media for the propagation of *Brucella* was undertaken in our laboratories in cooperation with Dr. Huddleson. This investigation led to the development of a new medium[5] which is excellently adapted to the nutritional requirements of the *Brucella*, and which is satisfactory for both primary isolation and routine propagation of these organisms.[6] This medium is prepared with Bacto-Tryptose as the sole source of nitrogen. The suitability of this peptone for cultivation of the *Brucella* is demonstrated by the fact that, in a 2 per cent solution of Bacto-Tryptose containing 0.5 per cent sodium chloride and 0.1 per cent Bacto-Dextrose, growth is obtained from small inocula in 24 hours, while a much larger inoculum and an incubation period of 7–10 days are required to obtain similar growth in Liver Broth.

For isolation of *Brucella* strains from infected milk, where Gram-positive contaminants are present, crystal violet (gentian violet) is used in a final concentration of 1 to 700,000 in Tryptose Agar. This amount of dye is sufficient to suppress practically all Gram-positive organisms which might otherwise interfere. To secure the proper concentration, 1.4 ml. of a one-tenth per cent solution of Bacto-Crystal Violet should be added to each liter of Tryptose Agar before sterilization of the medium. The sterile medium is poured into sterile petri dishes, solidified and then inoculated. Each plate receives 0.1–0.2 ml. gravity cream spread upon the surface of the medium by means of a sterile glass rod with a right angle bend. The spreading of the inoculum is readily accomplished by rotating the plate in a horizontal plane.

The inoculated plates are incubated for 5 days at 37°C. in an atmosphere of 10 per cent carbon dioxide. At the end of this period *Brucella* generally appear as purplish, smooth, hemispherical colonies about 1–5 mm. in diameter, and are transparent to transmitted light. Occasionally the colonies may be flat instead of convex. Streptococci, which are the usual interfering contaminants, form large, opaque, spreading, rough colonies slightly purple in color and not at all to be confused with those of the *Brucella*.

If the original plate contains colonies of other bacteria or molds, typical *Brucella* colonies should be purified by transfer to Tryptose Agar slants or to another plate of the crystal violet medium. The organisms should be properly identified and the species determined. If aerobic types of *Brucella* such as *suis* or *melitensis*, are present in the milk, their growth will not be inhibited by incubating the inoculated plates in an atmosphere of 10 per cent carbon dioxide.

Bacto-Tryptose and Bacto-Tryptose Agar are also particularly well suited to the isolation of *Brucella* from the blood. During 1937, Huddleson[5] had an opportunity to study the use of Bacto-Tryptose in an enrichment medium, and Bacto-Tryptose Agar in the isolation of *Brucella melitensis* from 55 cases of undulant fever on the Island of Malta. Of the total number of cases, 38 were febrile and 17 were afebrile at the time the blood was cultured. Positive cultures were obtained in 32 cases of the former group and 5 of the latter. Growth appeared within 4 days in 23 of the cultures. One culture required 18 days of incubation before a positive subculture was obtained.

Briefly, the procedure recommended by Huddleson[5] is as follows: An enrichment broth, composed of 2 per cent Bacto-Tryptose, 0.5 per cent sodium chloride and 1 per cent sodium citrate, or Bacto-Tryptose Broth, page 102, with 1 per cent sodium citrate added, is prepared and distributed in 20 ml. amounts in 50 ml. serum vials closed with rubber diaphragm stoppers. The vials are then autoclaved for 15 minutes at 15 pounds pressure (121°C.). The air in the vial is replaced with carbon dioxide by puncturing the diaphragm with a 23-gauge needle, removing the air and replacing it with carbon dioxide before introducing the blood. In a personal communication Huddleson recommended the use of 10 per cent carbon dioxide rather than the 25 per cent originally specified. Immediately after collection from the patient, the medium is inoculated with 2 to 5 ml. of blood by puncturing the stopper with the same needle used in collecting the blood sample. The vial is shaken vigorously to prevent clotting.

The vials are then incubated at 37°C. At the end of every fourth day the culture is mixed by shaking, and 0.5 ml. of the contents is removed by means of a sterile 1 ml. syringe and needle and inoculated on a petri plate of Tryptose Agar. The plate is incubated under 10 per cent carbon dioxide for 4 days. If no growth is obtained from the blood culture within 20 days, it may be discarded.

A convenient method for establishing an atmosphere of 10 per cent carbon dioxide is that described by Thompson[7] in which a solution of sodium bicarbonate is mixed with sulfuric acid directly in the container. When a molar solution (84 grams per liter) of sodium bicarbonate is mixed in equal parts with dilute sulfuric acid (1 ml. concentrated acid in 29 ml. distilled water), 22.4 ml. carbon dioxide are liberated for each milliliter of bicarbonate solution. Calculation of the cubic contents of the container in which the cultures are incubated will indicate the quantity of each solution required to create a carbon dioxide concentration of approximately 10 per cent. For example, for a container having a net volume of 1000 ml., one would use 4.5 ml. of each reagent. The solutions are preferably introduced separately into the container and are mixed after it has been sealed. A similar procedure is also described in detail by Shaughnessy.[8]

A satisfactory carbon dioxide tension can also be supplied by one of the following procedures:

1. Replace about 10 per cent of the air in the container with the gas from a tank of liquid carbon dioxide.

2. Place a lighted smokeless candle near the top of the container with the plates, and seal the container.

Another method for isolation of *Brucella* by blood culture is the double medium method as described by Castaneda.[9] This method may also be used in culturing other organisms from the blood. His method consisted of preparing a medium containing 2 per cent Bacto-Tryptose, 0.5 per cent sodium chloride, 0.5 per cent sodium citrate and 3.0 per cent agar. This medium is sterilized in 15 ml. amounts in 100 ml. flat-sided rectangular bottles. The bottles are placed on their side so that the agar medium solidifies on one of the narrow side walls forming an even, transparent layer. To each bottle are then added under aseptic conditions 10 ml. of sterile broth containing 2 per cent Bacto-Tryptose and 2 per cent sodium citrate. The air in the bottles is then replaced by the desired mixtures of carbon dioxide and air by a suitable mechanical device. The double medium is incubated at 35–37°C. for 3 or 4 days to test sterility, during which time the surface of the agar is wetted with the broth by tilting the bottle at 24 hour intervals. The sterile double medium is then inoculated with 10 ml. of the patient's blood and the mixture of broth and blood washed over the surface of the agar. Incubation is at 36°C. with the bottle in an upright position. The medium is examined at daily intervals, and every other day the blood-broth mixture is allowed to flow over the agar layer. Castaneda reported that if colonies developed in the agar layer in 24 to 48 hours it was likely that the culture had been contaminated. When colonies appear 24 to 48 hours after the second inoculation the cultivated organism was usually found to be a *Salmonella*, less frequently a staphylococcus or a streptococcus. It may be a *Brucella;* however, colonies of these organisms are more generally encountered after the sixth day of incubation, that is after the third inoculation of the Tryptose Agar with the blood-broth mixture. The culture is discarded as negative after 20 days incubation. There are many modifications of this method in routine practical use. The quantity of media, size of bottle, amount of inoculum varying in the various laboratories. Marvin[10] also described a blood culture bottle utilizing a Tryptose Agar and a Tryptose Phosphate Broth combination as being a practical method for blood culture work.

Huddleson[11,12] has established the differentiation of *Brucella* types by their behavior in the presence of certain bacteriostatic dyes. Bacto-Tryptose Agar is employed effectively as a base for the thionin and basic fuchsin media used by Huddleson. Bacto-Thionin is employed in 1:100,000 dilution (1 ml. 1 per cent solution of Bacto-Thionin per liter), and basic fuchsin in 1:100,000 dilution (1 ml. 1 per cent solution of Bacto-Basic Fuchsin). The plates should be inoculated within 24 hours after pouring, as the dyes become reduced in the medium on standing. The bacteriostatic action of the dyes in these concentrations in Tryptose Agar is in every way comparable with that previously described by Huddleson. *B. melitensis* and *B. suis* will grow on Tryptose Agar containing thionin, while *B. abortus* is inhibited; *B. melitensis* and *B. abortus* develop on Tryptose Agar containing basic fuchsin and *B. suis* is inhibited.

For the differentiation of the *Brucella* types on the basis of hydrogen sulfide production it is recommended that Bacto-Tryptose Agar be dissolved in an infusion prepared from Bacto-Liver (page 289). Differentiation of the three *Brucella* species by means of their hydrogen sulfide production is not clearly defined when distilled water alone is used in preparing the medium.

When voluminous growth of organisms is desired, as in the preparation of *Brucella* antigens, it is recommended that a seed culture be prepared first by propagating the organisms in Bacto-Tryptose Broth. An incubation period of 24 hours at 35–37°C. is generally sufficient to produce a heavy growth. The seed culture is then spread upon the surface of the medium. A medium prepared by dissolving Bacto-Tryptose Agar in an infusion of Bacto-Liver (page

289) will yield a somewhat heavier growth on prolonged incubation than will a medium prepared with distilled water.

Schubert[13] reported that the rapidity and amount of growth of some recently isolated fastidious strains of B. abortus was markedly improved on Bacto-Tryptose Agar in the presence of a specially prepared liver extract demonstrating strong catalase activity.

Bacto-Tryptose Agar is also recommended as a general solid medium for the cultivation of pathogenic organisms, being an excellent medium, without enrichment, for streptococci, pneumococci, meningococci and others. Blood Agar may be prepared by adding 5 per cent sterile defibrinated blood to melted sterile Tryptose Agar at 50°C. Bacto-Tryptose Agar contains 0.1 per cent dextrose, probably slightly more than is present in the average meat infusion medium in the form of muscle sugar. Ruediger,[14] Brown[15] and Fuller and Maxted[16] have all demonstrated that the presence of dextrose, or a reducing sugar, inhibits hemolysin production by streptococci, giving rise to false reactions. For that reason hemolytic reactions may be atypical on Bacto-Tryptose Agar and should be confirmed on Blood Agar prepared from Bacto-Tryptose Blood Agar Base, Bacto-Blood Agar Base, Bacto-Heart Infusion Agar or on a medium prepared with 2.0 per cent Bacto-Tryptose, 0.5 per cent sodium chloride and 1.5 per cent Bacto-Agar (Tryptose Agar without dextrose).

Chapman, Stiles, and Berens[17] in their study of the isolation and "in vitro" testing of pathogenic types of non-exotoxic streptococci, used Bacto-Tryptose Agar as a base for Blood Agar because it gave more luxuriant growth of streptococci than other base media. Cultures of Pasteurella multocida were cultivated on Tryptose Agar by Carter.[18] He reported that it was not necessary to freeze dry cultures for storage when grown on Tryptose Agar. By adding 5 per cent saccharose to the medium he was able to identify readily blue, intermediate and fluorescent colonies of the organism. Silverman and Elberg[19] in their study of Brucella antigens used Tryptose Agar for the cultivation of their strains of B. abortus, B. suis and B. melitensis. Boyd and Casman[20] reported that Tryptose Agar filtered through absorbent cotton became toxic for a fastidious strain of B. abortus. The toxic factors extracted from the cotton were characterized as fatty acids. This toxicity could be nullified by the simple addition of 0.03–0.1 per cent corn starch to the medium, bearing a similarity to the report of Ley and Mueller[21] demonstrating the ability of starch to neutralize toxic factors found in samples of some agar using the gonococcus as a test organism.

Gray, Stafseth, Thorp, Sholl and Riley[22] described a new technique for the isolation of Listeria monocytogenes from infected brain by grinding the medulla in a mortar with about 10 ml. of Tryptose Broth and then emulsifying with glass beads in a shaking machine for about 20 minutes. About 0.3 ml. of the suspension is then plated on Bacto-Tryptose Agar and incubated at 37°C. for 24 hours. The colonies of Listeria are light green with a finely textured surface when viewed with a dissecting microscope and sufficiently characteristic that they can be identified even in cases of extreme contamination. Storage of the brain suspension in the refrigerator for 24 hours seemed to increase the number of Listeria developing on the medium. Gray, Stafseth and Thorp[23] added potassium tellurite in 0.1 to 0.05 per cent concentration to Bacto-Tryptose Agar as a selective medium for the isolation of Listeria. The Listeria colonies were black, as are other organisms developing on the medium but showed the characteristic green color at the periphery of the colony when viewed by reflected light with a dissecting microscope. Gray, Stafseth and Thorp[24] showed the value of this method for isolation of L. monocytogenes from 36 sheep and 31 cattle over a four year period.

Schuhardt, Rode, Foster and Oglesby,[25] by special techniques, demonstrated that a few of the numerous samples of Bacto-Tryptose which had been in his laboratory exhibited some toxicity for certain *Brucella abortus* strains used in his laboratory. The particular samples of Bacto-Tryptose possessing this characteristic had absorbed moisture and had undergone chemical change. Schuhardt[26] in a discussion of this observation stated that "the ease of neutralization of this toxic factor by blood, serum, agar and other substances tends to make the practical significance of the toxicity relatively minor. We probably would not have encountered it had we not been doing extensive tests on the *in vitro* effect of sulfonamides on *Brucella* using decimal dilution inocula". The high productivity of Bacto-Tryptose Agar and Bacto-Tryptose used clinically for the isolation and cultivation of *Brucella* attests to its value for the primary cultivation of *Brucella* as well as other fastidious organisms.

To rehydrate the medium, suspend 41 grams of Bacto-Tryptose Agar in 1000 ml. of cold distilled water and heat to boiling to dissolve the medium completely. Distribute in tubes or flasks and sterilize in the autoclave for 15 minutes at 15 pounds pressure (121°C.). The final reaction of the medium will be pH 7.2.

Since most microorganisms prefer a fresh medium with a moist surface, it is recommended that Bacto-Tryptose Agar be prepared as required, or melted and re-solidified just prior to use.

One pound of Bacto-Tryptose Agar will make 11 liters of medium.

[1] Standard Methods for the Examination of Dairy Products, 9th Edition:149:1948.
[2] Diagnostic Procedures and Reagents, 3rd Edition:246:1950.
[3] Tech. Bull., 49 Mich. Exp. Sta., 1920.
[4] J. Infectious Diseases, 40:353:1937.
[5] Huddleson: Brucellosis in Man and Animals, 14:1939.
[6] J. Am. Med. Assoc., 109:1971:1937.
[7] Am. J. Clin. Path., 5:313:1935.
[8] J. Bact., 37:153:1939.
[9] Proc. Soc. Expl. Biol. Med., 64:114:1947.
[10] Am. J. Clin. Path., 19:697:1949.
[11] Tech. Bull. 100, Mich. Exp. Sta., 1929.
[12] Am. J. Pub. Health, 21:491:1931.
[13] Am. J. Clin. Path., 21:894:1951.
[14] J. Infectious Diseases, 3:633:1906.
[15] Monograph No. 9 Rockefeller Inst. Med. Research, 1919.
[16] J. Path. Bact., 49:83:1939.
[17] Am. J. Clin. Path., 9:1939, Tech., Suppl. 3:20:1939.
[18] Am. J. Vet. Res., 11:252:1950.
[19] J. Immunol., 65:163:1950.
[20] Public Health Reports, 66:44:1951.
[21] J. Bact., 52:453:1946.
[22] J. Bact., 55:471:1948.
[23] J. Bact., 59:443:1950.
[24] Am. Vet. Med. Assoc., 118:242:1951.
[25] J. Bact., 57:1:1949.
[26] Personal Communication, 1949.

BACTO

TRYPTOSE BLOOD AGAR BASE (B232)
DEHYDRATED

Bacto-Tryptose	10 g.
Bacto-Beef Extract	3 g.
Sodium Chloride	5 g.
Bacto-Agar	15 g.

Bacto-Tryptose Blood Agar Base is a nutritious, infusion-free peptone medium designed especially for use as a base in the preparation of Blood Agar. Blood Agar prepared with this base supports excellent growth of many fastidious organisms and also gives typical clear-cut hemolytic reactions. Bacto-Tryptose Blood Agar Base, without added blood, may be recommended as a Nutrient Agar for general routine culture purposes.

Investigations of the nutritive properties of Bacto-Tryptose demonstrated that culture media prepared with this peptone were superior to the meat infusion peptone media previously used for the cultivation of *Brucella,* streptococci, pneumococci, meningococci and other fastidious pathogenic bacteria. The use of Bacto-Tryptose in place of infusion in Blood Agar Base yields a medium of uniform composition and provides a substrate which maintains the blood cells in an excellent state of preservation, thus insuring typical hemolytic reactions. Casman[1,2] reported that a medium consisting of 2 per cent Bacto-Tryptose, 0.3 per cent Bacto-Beef Extract, 0.5 per cent sodium chloride, 1.5 per cent Bacto-Agar and 0.03 per cent dextrose equalled fresh beef infusion base with respect to growth of organisms. The small amount of carbohydrate, however, interfered with hemolytic reactions unless the medium was incubated in an atmosphere of carbon dioxide.

To rehydrate the medium, suspend 33 grams of Bacto-Tryptose Blood Agar Base in 1000 ml. cold distilled water and heat to boiling to dissolve the medium completely. Distribute in tubes or flasks and sterilize in the autoclave for 15 minutes at 15 pounds pressure (121°C.). The final reaction of the sterilized medium, before adding blood, will be pH 7.2.

If Blood Agar is to be prepared immediately, the sterile agar base is cooled at once to 45–50°C. and while still liquid, 5 per cent sterile defibrinated blood is added aseptically. Mix thoroughly, avoiding incorporation of air bubbles, and dispense into sterile petri dishes or sterile tubes as desired. Between 12 and 15 ml. of Blood Agar per 100 mm. petri dish is satisfactory. Blood Agar should be incubated to insure sterility before use.

One pound of Bacto-Tryptose Blood Agar Base will make 13.8 liters of finished basal medium or 14 5 liters of Blood Agar.

[1] J. Bact., 43:33:1942.   [2] Am. J. Clin. Path., 17:281:1947.

BACTO
PROTEOSE NO. 3 AGAR (B65)
DEHYDRATED

Proteose Peptone No. 3, Difco	20 g.
Bacto-Dextrose	0.5 g.
Sodium Chloride	5 g.
Disodium Phosphate	5 g.
Bacto-Agar	15 g.

Bacto-Proteose No. 3 Agar, enriched with Bacto-Hemoglobin and Bacto-Supplement A or Bacto-Supplement B, is recommended for the cultural isolation of *Neisseria gonorrhoeae* from chronic and acute cases of gonorrhoea in the male and female and in other gonococcal infections. The medium permits excellent growth of the gonococcus without overgrowth by contaminating organisms. In a survey,[1] under carefully controlled conditions, twelve media recommended for the isolation of the gonococcus were compared. Bacto-Proteose No. 3 Agar enriched with Bacto-Hemoglobin and Bacto-Supplement A compared very favorably with other decidedly more complex media. A discussion of a 24 hour medium for the cultural diagnosis of gonorrhoea is given under Bacto-G C Medium Base on page 122. In the survey[1] this 24 hour incubation medium gave but slightly better results than Bacto-Proteose No. 3 Agar.

The diagnosis and control of gonorrhoea have been greatly facilitated by improved laboratory methods for detecting, isolating and studying *N. gonorrhoeae*. Foremost among these developments is the cultural method for detecting the presence of the gonococcus in exudates and body fluids. The greater efficiency of this procedure over the microscopic technique has established its indispensability in the routine diagnosis of gonococcal infections. The plating procedure is not only more sensitive in indicating the presence of the gonococcus, but also permits isolation of the organism for further study. Improved media developed for identification of the isolated organisms simplify the procedure making it practical for use in all laboratories. Furthermore, cultural methods have been designed to check the response of the gonococcus to chemotherapeutic agents, thereby enabling the clinician to select more effectively the materials used in treating gonococcal infections.

Interest in the cultural procedure for the diagnosis of gonococcal infections was stimulated by Ruys and Jens,[2] McLeod and co-workers,[3] Thompson,[4] Leahy and Carpenter,[5] Carpenter, Leahy and Wilson[6] and Carpenter,[7] who clearly demonstrated the superiority of this method over the microscopic technique. The procedure introduced by McLeod and associates with slight modifications offered itself most advantageously to practical usage for the detection and isolation of N. gonorrhoeae.

Lack of a simple, readily available and easily prepared culture medium retarded immediate and widespread acceptance of this new technique. In cooperation with Dr. Carpenter, and availing ourselves of suggestions received from Drs. McLeod and Herrold, we devoted considerable effort to the development of a culture medium suitable for isolation of the gonococcus from urethral and cervical exudates. The development of this medium was premised upon the stipulations that it must possess a high degree of efficiency, readily lend itself to practical use, be of relatively simple composition and that it be duplicable with ease.

During our experimental work several media were developed which supported luxuriant growth of the gonococcus in pure culture, but which were unsatisfactory with mixed cultures, since other organisms outgrew the gonococcus. In diagnostic work the medium must support the growth of the gonococcus not only when in pure culture, but also permit its development from the mixed flora encountered in chronic gonococcal infections.

A Chocolate Agar, prepared with Bacto-Proteose No. 3 Agar and Bacto-Hemoglobin, was developed and proved to be satisfactory for the isolation of the organism from all types of gonococcal infections. Nearly 3.5 times as many positives were secured with the cultural method as were obtained by the usual smear technique. In a number of instances the gonococcus was isolated from treated female cases which had shown five to seven consecutive negative smears.

Since its introduction in 1938 Bacto-Proteose No. 3 Agar, enriched with Bacto-Hemoglobin, has become the most generally accepted medium employed in the laboratory diagnosis of gonorrhoeal infections by the culture method. Carpenter[8] reported that this Difco dehydrated medium was as good as or superior to the Douglas Digest Agar described by McLeod. Pelouze[9] suggested the use of Bacto-Proteose No. 3 Agar and Bacto-Hemoglobin for the cultural detection of the gonococcus. Sulkin and Gottlieb[10] used Bacto-Proteose No. 3 Agar and Bacto-Hemoglobin with success, and emphasized the simplicity of the medium and the ease with which it could be prepared. Sewell, Clarke and Nelson[11] reported their findings on 4500 cultures plated upon Bacto-Proteose No. 3 Agar and Bacto-Hemoglobin and claimed excellent results. Sewell, Salchow, and Nelson[12] obtained excellent results with urine sediment and urethral secretions plated upon Bacto-Proteose No. 3 Agar enriched with Bacto-Hemoglobin. Carpenter[13] suggested the use of the Bacto-Proteose No. 3 Agar and Bacto-Hemoglobin for isolation of the gonococcus.

In an extended effort to increase the growth rate of the gonococcus by enriching the Chocolate Agar with plant and animal fluids and thereby shortening the incubation period, some gonococcal strains were encountered that grew well on such enriched Chocolate Agar and only sparsely or not at all on the unenriched medium. Concurrently with this finding Lankford[14] reported similar results and suggested enriching the Chocolate Agar with fresh liver extract. Lankford, Scott, Cox and Cooke[15] extended their studies on the nutritional requirements of the gonococcus and obtained 12 per cent more positive isolations on the Chocolate Agar enriched with liver extract or yeast extract, than upon the unenriched medium. Following this work, Lankford and Snell[16] identified the required growth factor as glutamine. Lankford[17] called our attention to the fact that a second growth factor, cocarboxylase, was required by a small percentage of gonococcal strains and that cystine helped under certain conditions. With this information, an extensive study to provide a satisfactory enrichment for supplementing the Chocolate Agar was undertaken, and resulted in the development of Bacto-Supplement A and Bacto-Supplement B, as discussed on page 276.

Nelson,[18] using the Bacto-Proteose No. 3 Agar and Bacto-Hemoglobin enriched with Bacto-Supplement A, increased his positive isolations 5 per cent over the unenriched medium. In addition to increasing the number of positive isolations, the efficiency of the medium was improved by reduction of extraneous growth and an increase in size and number of gonococcal colonies. Rosenblatt, Meyer, and Robbins[19] found the Chocolate Agar enriched with Bacto-Supplement A superior to the unenriched medium. Morton and Leberman[20] recommended the use of Bacto-Supplement A in the Chocolate Agar as it restricted growth of extraneous forms, gave rise to larger gonococcal colonies and increased the positive isolations over that obtained on the unenriched medium. A practical method for the isolation of the gonococcus using Chocolate Agar prepared from Bacto-Proteose No. 3 Agar, Bacto-Hemoglobin and Bacto-Supplement A, is given in detail by Morton[21].

A recommended procedure for the cultural detection of the gonococcus is described in detail below.

Collection of Specimen and Inoculation

Methods for preparing the patient, obtaining adequate specimens and culturing exudates suspected of harboring *N. gonorrhoeae* are described in detail by Carpenter[7,22] and Morton.[21] Specimens are usually collected on sterile cotton swabs. These may be used to inoculate the Chocolate Agar directly or preferably placed in 1–2 ml. of sterile broth. A broth consisting of 2 per cent Proteose Peptone No. 3, 0.5 per cent sodium chloride and 1 per cent soluble starch and adjusted to pH 7.2 is recommended as a suspending fluid. Specimens should be inoculated onto Chocolate Agar as soon as possible after collection and in no case should plating be delayed longer than 8 hours. Specimens not immediately inoculated onto plates should be kept in the ice box.

The exudate is suspended in the broth by rotating the swab and pressing against the inside of the tube to remove as much material as possible, after which the swab is discarded. About 0.05–0.1 ml. (1–2 drops) of the suspension is then transferred onto sterile plates and smeared over the surface of the medium with a bent glass rod.

Incubation

The plates after inoculation should be incubated in an inverted position at 35–37°C. for 36–48 hours.

Best results are obtained in an atmosphere containing carbon dioxide. Cans with a tight fitting cover or Novy jars are satisfactory containers for the plates during incubation. Carbon dioxide can be supplied in one of the following procedures outlined by Christensen and Schoenlein.[23]

1. Place a lighted, smokeless candle near the top of the container, with the plates and put the cover on the container.

2. Replace about 10 per cent of the air in the container with carbon dioxide.

3. Place sodium bicarbonate in a beaker in the container with the inverted plates. Cover the sodium bicarbonate with cotton to reduce foaming. Add dilute

sulfuric acid to the beaker and place cover on the can at once. One gram sodium bicarbonate with 3 ml. of sulfuric acid diluted to 100 ml. with water will give about a 10 per cent carbon dioxide atmosphere to a container of about 2.5 liters capacity.

Laboratory workers wishing more detailed information on optimum carbon dioxide tensions should consult Ferguson[24] and Morton.[25]

Observation

Remove plates from the containers after the incubation period, keeping them in the inverted position until the time of examination to prevent flooding of the plate with water of condensation.

The following procedure as given by Carpenter[7,22] is recommended: Make a direct examination of the plates for colonies of the gonococcus. Typically such colonies are convex, transparent, from 1 to 3 mm. in diameter, with undulate margins. By their transparency and character of their margins they can usually be differentiated from young colonies of streptococci and diphtheroids which they simulate. Films are prepared from the selected colonies, stained and examined. Cultural confirmation of typical Gram-negative diplococci is made by subculturing typical colonies on enriched Chocolate Agar for purification and inoculation into the appropriate carbohydrate media.

When no typical gonococcus colonies can be detected by direct inspection, the culture is subjected to the oxidase test which is of especial value in detecting colonies of N. gonorrhoeae in mixed cultures. The test is based upon the production of an enzyme, oxidase, by organisms belonging to the genus Neisseria. From 1 to 2 ml. of a one per cent solution of para-aminodimethylaniline monohydrochloride (dimethyl-p-phenylenediamine hydrochloride) or the oxalate salt, are dropped on each primary plate culture and the plate tilted to spread the reagent over the entire surface. The plate is observed for a period of 6–10 minutes for evidence of color change of the colonies. The series of color reactions, i.e., pink, maroon, and black, identifies the colonies of Neisseria. Films are made from the "oxidase-positive" colonies, stained and examined microscopically. If subcultures are to be made for further identification, the colonies should be picked as soon as they become pink, because the dye component is toxic for the organisms.

Confirmation

In the routine diagnosis of gonococcal infections and in the release of patients under treatment, the oxidase test followed by a confirming Gram stain, in the hands of an experienced operator, is generally sufficient for the identification of the gonococcus. The identity of the organism may be further confirmed by studying the reactions of purified cultures on carbohydrate media. The following table shows the characteristic reactions of N. gonorrhoeae and other Neisseria which are occasionally encountered.

Microorganism	Dextrose	Maltose	Saccharose	Lactose
Neisseria catarrhalis	—	—	—	—
Neisseria gonorrhoeae	+	—	—	—
Neisseria meningitidis	+	+	—	—
Neisseria sicca	+	+	+	—

In the study of carbohydrate fermentation we recommend the use of Bacto-Phenol Red Carbohydrate Broths, or of Bacto-Phenol Red Broth Base containing 0.5 per cent of the desired carbohydrate, and to which has been added 0.15

per cent Bacto-Agar. The carbohydrate media should be freshly prepared or reheated and cooled without agitation before inoculation. The inoculum should be fairly heavy and should be placed on the surface layer of the medium not to exceed a depth of 0.5 cm. Bacto-Phenol Red Broth Base with 0.5 per cent added carbohydrate and 0.15 per cent agar is suggested as a satisfactory medium for fermentation determinations as given in Diagnostic Procedures and Reagents[22].

Some laboratories prefer a more solid fermentation medium containing enrichment substances. A satisfactory medium of such character can be prepared by adding 0.8 per cent Bacto-Agar to Bacto-Phenol Red Broth Base, sterilizing it in the autoclave for 15 minutes at 15 pounds pressure (121°C.), cooling below 60°C., and adding 0.5 per cent of the carbohydrate previously sterilized in 10 or 20 per cent solution, and 5 per cent sterile fresh rabbit serum. Sera from other animals have not been found satisfactory. A similar medium for determination of fermentation by *N. gonorrhoeae* has been described by Faber, Gonzales and Pelczar.[26]

Other Primary Isolation Media

Some laboratories prefer to use a clear medium rather than a Chocolate Agar for culturing *N. gonorrhoeae*. This may be accomplished by omitting the Bacto-Hemoglobin and enriching the Proteose No. 3 Agar with other substances capable of supporting growth of the gonococcus. Peizer and Steffen[27] reported the use of a horse plasma hemoglobin dextrose nile blue A enrichment which, when added to Proteose No. 3 Agar, gave a clear medium and yielded excellent results in the culturing of the gonococcus. Steinberg and Mollov[28] enriched Proteose No. 3 Agar with starch and blood and produced a satisfactory, clear medium.

Mueller and Hinton[29] described a casein hydrolysate infusion medium which they reported to give good results in the primary culturing of the gonococcus. This medium is available in the dehydrated form as Bacto-Mueller Hinton Medium as discussed on page 93.

Sulfonamide Resistance of N. Gonorrhoeae

Goodale, Gould, Schwab and Winter[30] developed a culture technique for testing the resistance of *N. gonorrhoeae* to sulfonamides. The method consisted of inoculating plates of Mueller Hinton Medium containing 0.10, 0.25 and 0.50 mg. per cent of sulfathiazole, respectively. Susceptible strains fail to grow in the presence of the sulfonamides, while resistant strains do grow.

Nelson,[31] using the Bacto-Mueller Hinton Medium as Goodale, et al.[30] had described for checking sulfonamide resistant gonococci, obtained very close correlation with the clinical picture on thousands of cases. Nelson also employed the Proteose No. 3 Hemoglobin Agar in the same manner for sulfonamide resistance tests with equally good results. Frisch, Edwards, and Edwards[32] found that the Proteose No. 3 Hemoglobin Agar worked well as a basal medium for testing the sulfonamide resistance of *N. gonorrhoeae*.

Mass Culture and Stock Strains

Mass cultivation of newly isolated strains for vaccine production is readily accomplished on Bacto-Dextrose Starch Agar as discussed on page 124. This medium supports luxuriant growth of the organism, and colonies of the gonococcus frequently exceed 3–5 mm. in diameter. Bacto-Dextrose Starch Agar cannot be recommended for cultural detection of the gonococcus due to overgrowth by extraneous organisms. Bacto-Dextrose Starch Agar, prepared in half strength, is an ideal medium for maintaining stock cultures of the gonococcus. In tubes of this medium the gonococci generally are viable after 6–8 weeks incubation at 37°C.

Preparation of Media

Prepare a double strength Proteose No. 3 Agar by suspending 9.0 grams in 100 ml. of cold distilled water, and steaming or boiling to dissolve the medium completely. At the same time prepare a double strength hemoglobin solution by placing 2 grams Bacto-Hemoglobin in a dry flask and adding 100 ml. cold distilled water, while the flask is being agitated vigorously. The Bacto-Hemoglobin suspension is shaken intermittently for 10–15 minutes to break up all aggregates and effect complete solution. Both double strength solutions of Proteose No. 3 Agar and Bacto-Hemoglobin are sterilized in the autoclave for 15 minutes at 15 pounds pressure (121°C.).

The sterile solutions are allowed to cool to 50–60°C. Add 1 per cent of Bacto-Supplement A or Bacto-Supplement B, based on the final volume of medium, to the double strength Proteose No. 3 Agar (2 ml. per 100 ml. double strength sterile agar base). Mix well and add an equal volume of double strength sterile Bacto-Hemoglobin solution at 50–60°C. Mix well and distribute into sterile petri dishes. Caution: Do not add Bacto-Supplement A or Bacto-Supplement B to the hemoglobin solution before mixing with the agar base. Best results will be obtained if the medium is prepared in advance so that the surface of the medium is dry before inoculation.

When the single strength medium, without enrichment, is desired, the medium is rehydrated by suspending 45 grams of Bacto-Proteose No. 3 Agar in 1000 ml. of cold distilled water and heating to boiling to dissolve the medium completely. Distribute in tubes or flasks and sterilize in the autoclave for 15 minutes at 15 pounds pressure (121°C.). The final reaction of the medium without enrichment will be pH 7.3.

One pound of Bacto-Proteose No. 3 Agar will make 10 liters of medium.

ACKNOWLEDGMENT

We are indebted to the personnel of the Division of Social Hygiene of the Detroit Department of Health for their cooperation in supplying the clinical material for these studies.

[1] Am. J. Syphilis Gonorrh. Venereal Diseases, 33:164:1949.
[2] Muench. Wochschr., 80:846:1933.
[3] J. Path. Bact., 39:221:1934.
[4] J. Infectious Diseases, 61:129:1937.
[5] Am. J. Syphilis, 20:347:1936.
[6] Am. J. Syphilis, 22:55:1938.
[7] Seventh Annual Yearbook (1936–37), p. 133, Suppl., Am. J. Pub. Health, 27:No. 3:1937.
[8] Bull. Genitoinfectious Diseases, Mass. State Health Dept., 2:1:1938.
[9] Felouze: Gonorrhea in the Male and Female, 3rd Edition;55:1939.
[10] Am. J. Syphilis Gonorrh. Venereal Diseases, 25:22:1941.
[11] Am. J. Public Health, 31:457:1941.
[12] J. Venereal Disease Inform., 24:218:1943.
[13] J. Venereal Disease Inform., 24:133:1943.
[14] J. Bact., 44:139:1942.
[15] J. Bact., 45:321:1943.
[16] J. Bact., 45:410:1943.

[17] Personal Communication 1943.
[18] Personal Communication 1944.
[19] Am. J. Syphilis Gonorrh. Venereal Diseases, 28:634:1944.
[20] U.S. Naval Med. Bull., 43:409:1944.
[21] Encyclopedia of Medicine, Surgery and Specialties, 3rd Edition. Now in press.
[22] Diagnostic Procedures and Reagents, 3rd Edition:107:1950.
[23] J. Bact., 40:162:1940.
[24] Am. J. Syphilis Gonorrh. Venereal Diseases, 29:19:1945.
[25] J. Bact., 50:589:1945.
[26] Am J Clin. Path., 18:16:1940.
[27] J. Venereal Disease Inform., 23:224:1942.
[28] J. Lab. Clin. Med., 27:656:1940.
[29] Proc. Soc. Exp. Biol. Med., 48:330:1941.
[30] J. Am. Med. Assoc., 123:547:1943.
[31] Personal Communication 1945.
[32] Am. J. Syphilis Gonorrh. Venereal Diseases, 28:397:1944.

BACTO
G C MEDIUM BASE   (B289)
DEHYDRATED

Proteose Peptone No. 3, Difco ...... 15 g.
Corn Starch .... 1 g.
Dipotassium Phosphate .... 4 g.
Monopotassium Phosphate .... 1 g.
Sodium Chloride .... 5 g.
Bacto-Agar .... 10 g.

Bacto-G C Medium Base, enriched with Bacto-Hemoglobin and Bacto-Supplement A or Bacto-Supplement B, is recommended as a 24 hour culture medium for the cultural diagnosis of gonorrhoea from acute and chronic cases in the male and female. This medium has the advantage of requiring a shorter incubation period than the medium prepared with Bacto-Proteose No. 3 Agar.

In a survey[1] under carefully controlled conditions twelve media recommended for the isolation of the gonococcus were compared. Bacto-G C Medium Base enriched with Bacto-Hemoglobin and Bacto-Supplement A or Bacto-Supplement B was as effective in the number of gonococci cultures isolated as was any of the media. In Diagnostic Procedures and Reagents[2] a medium prepared with Bacto-G C Medium Base enriched with Bacto-Hemoglobin and Bacto-Supplement B possessed several advantages over the other media described for the isolation of the gonococcus. It was pointed out that this medium is always immediately available and can be prepared in either large or small quantities, insuring a supply of fresh moist medium essential for dependable results. This medium needs only an incubation period of 24 hours instead of 48 hours usually required by other media.

Johnston[3] described a medium for culturally detecting *Neisseria gonorrhoeae* in exudates within 24 hours. The medium employed was a Chocolate Agar prepared from Bacto-Proteose No. 3 Agar and Bacto-Hemoglobin to which was added 30 per cent ascitic fluid and 1:50,000 tyrothricin. Inoculated plates of this medium incubated in a partial carbon dioxide atmosphere in closed containers at 37°C. for 24 hours yielded more positives than did the same medium incubated for 48 hours.

Attempts to elucidate the cause for the accelerated early growth response on Johnston's modified medium over that of the regular enriched Chocolate Agar indicated that the variation in growth rates on the two media was due principally to the difference in solidity of the media. As a result of this observation a new medium, Bacto-G C Medium Base, was designed for use as a 24 hour medium in the laboratory diagnosis of gonococcal infections.

In the examination of over 500 clinical specimens Christensen and Schoenlein[4] found the Bacto-G C Medium Base enriched with Bacto-Hemoglobin and Bacto-Supplement A or Bacto-Supplement B to give equally as good or better results after 24 hour incubation as did the Chocolate Agar prepared from Bacto-Proteose No. 3 Agar, Bacto-Hemoglobin and Bacto-Supplement A or Bacto-Supplement B incubated for similar or longer periods. Johnston[5] compared Bacto-G C Medium Base enriched with Bacto-Hemoglobin and Bacto-Supplement A or Bacto-Supplement B with the medium containing ascitic fluid and tyrothricin which she described and found their effectiveness to be comparable. Johnston preferred the use of Supplement A as an enrichment since the crystal violet helped in suppressing extraneous contaminating organisms. McRoy and Salachow[6] of the Detroit Venereal Disease Clinics also reported excellent results with Bacto-G C Medium Base enriched with Bacto-Hemoglobin and Bacto-Supplement A and incubating for only 24 hours. Carpenter[1,7] in his report on a study evaluating the media employed for the cultural diagnosis of gonorrhoea declared that the G C Medium Base enriched with Bacto-Hemoglobin and Bacto-Supplement B yielded results in 24 hours comparable with those obtained on the best plating media requiring a similar or longer incubation period.

Wax[8] used Bacto-G C Medium Base enriched with Bacto-Hemoglobin and Bacto-Supplement B, with tyrothricin as a selective agent in the isolation of *Neisseria* other than *N. gonorrhoeae* from the genito-urinary tract.

For a complete discussion of the development of the cultural diagnosis of gonorrhoea, including detailed recommendations for the collection of specimen, inoculation of plates and observation and confirmation of results, reference should be made to the discussion given under Bacto-Proteose No. 3 Agar, page 116–123.

Since Bacto-G C Medium Base contains only 1 per cent Bacto-Agar, care must be exercised not to penetrate through the surface during inoculation. Following inoculation, plates should be incubated at 35–37°C. for 24 hours. Best results are obtained in an atmosphere of carbon dioxide obtained by one of the procedures outlined under Bacto-Proteose No. 3 Agar, page 118.

The enriched Chocolate Agar, using Bacto-G C Medium Base and Bacto-Hemoglobin, is prepared in the following manner:

Prepare a double strength G C Medium Base by suspending 7.2 grams in 100 ml. cold distilled water and steaming or boiling to dissolve the medium completely. At the same time prepare a double strength hemoglobin solution by placing 2 grams Bacto-Hemoglobin in a dry flask and adding 100 ml. cold distilled water, while the flask is being agitated vigorously. The Bacto-Hemoglobin suspension is shaken intermittently for 10–15 minutes to break up all aggregates and effect complete solution. Both double strength solutions of G C Medium Base and Bacto-Hemoglobin are sterilized in the autoclave for 15 minutes at 15 pounds pressure (121°C.).

The sterile solutions are allowed to cool to 50–60°C. Add 1 per cent of Bacto-Supplement A or Bacto-Supplement B, based on the final volume of medium, to the double strength G C Medium Base (2 ml. per 100 ml. double strength sterile agar base). Mix well and add an equal volume of double strength sterile Bacto-Hemoglobin solution at 50–60°C. Mix well and distribute into sterile petri dishes. Caution: Do not add Bacto-Supplement A or Bacto-Supplement B to the hemoglobin solution before mixing with the agar base.

Best results will be obtained if the medium is prepared in advance so that the surface of the medium is dry before inoculation.

When the single strength medium, without enrichment, is desired, the medium is rehydrated by suspending 36 grams Bacto-G C Medium Base in 1000 ml. cold distilled water and heating to boiling to dissolve the medium completely. Distribute in tubes or flasks and sterilize in the autoclave for 15 minutes at 15 pounds pressure (121°C.). The final reaction of the medium without enrichment will be pH 7.2.

One pound of Bacto-G C Medium Base will make 12.6 liters of medium.

[1] Am. J. Syphilis Gonorrh. Venereal Diseases, 33:164:1949.
[2] Diagnostic Procedures and Reagents, 3rd Edition:30–107:1950.
[3] J. Venereal Disease Inform., 26:239:1945.
[4] Paper read at the annual meeting of the Canadian Pub. Health Assoc., 1947.
[5] Personal Communication 1947.
[6] Personal Communication 1947.
[7] Paper read at the annual meeting of the Am. Pub. Health Assoc., 1947.
[8] J. Venereal Disease Inform., 31:208:1950.

DEXTROSE STARCH AGAR   (B66)
DEHYDRATED

Proteose Peptone No. 3, Difco	15 g.
Bacto-Dextrose	2 g.
Soluble Starch, Difco	10 g.
Sodium Chloride	5 g.
Disodium Phosphate	3 g.
Bacto-Gelatin	20 g.
Bacto-Agar	10 g.

Bacto-Dextrose Starch Agar is recommended as a complete solid medium for the propagation of pure cultures of *Neisseria gonorrhoeae*. This highly nutritious medium without any additions will also support excellent growth of a large number of pathogenic organisms such as the meningococcus, streptococcus and pneumococcus. This medium is far superior to the ordinary infusion media for the cultivation of these discriminating bacteria. Bacto-Dextrose Starch Agar, in half concentration, is recommended as a Stock Culture Agar for the maintenance of cultures of gonococcus, meningococcus and others not capable of splitting starch.

In the development of a simple medium for the cultural detection of the gonococcus, it was considered that luxuriant growth of all strains of *N. gonorrhoeae* was a requisite. Bacto-Dextrose Starch Agar, a nutritious medium without enrichment, fulfilled this requirement satisfactorily, giving luxuriant growth of freshly isolated fastidious strains of the gonococcus. It was soon shown, however, on this highly nutritious medium that in mixed cultures, as were encountered especially in chronic cases of gonorrhoea, extraneous forms developed too rapidly and overgrew the gonococcus. For this reason, an enriched Chocolate Agar prepared with Bacto-Proteose No. 3 Agar as discussed on page 116 or Bacto-G C Medium Base, page 122, is recommended for the isolation of the gonococcus.

For the cultivation of the gonococcus, it is imperative to have the incubation atmosphere saturated with moisture. Satisfactory conditions can be obtained if the plates of Dextrose Starch Agar are incubated in a closed container, which contains cotton, a towel or a sponge saturated with water. A can with a suitable cover, Novy jar, desiccator or any other convenient sized container capable of retaining the moisture is entirely satisfactory. About 200 ml. of water added in this manner is ample for a container of one or two gallons capacity. Plates incubated under these conditions will give a luxuriant growth of many gonococci when identically inoculated plates incubated in the ordinary manner in the incubator show no growth. If the culture requires carbon dioxide for growth this may be supplied as indicated under Bacto-Proteose No. 3 Agar, page 118. Carbon dioxide is recommended for isolation, but is not generally necessary, in the presence of abundant moisture, for growth of isolated strains.

Swancara[1] described a method of obtaining partial carbon dioxide tension in individual tubes by placing a cotton plug just over the medium following inoculation. The percussion tip from a match is removed and the match broken and placed on this plug. The tube is then sealed with a rubber stopper or screw cap. The match head is then ignited by applying heat to the outside of the tube.

Nutritional factors so conducive to the growth of the gonococcus proved equally satisfactory for many other pathogenic bacteria, making Bacto-Dextrose Starch Agar, without added enrichment, a most excellent medium for the propagation of streptococci, pneumococci, meningococci and others. For mass growth of these organisms Bacto-Dextrose Starch Agar is recommended as being superior to many highly enriched media with complicated formulae and methods of preparation.

Bacto-Dextrose Starch Agar prepared in half strength is an excellent medium for maintaining stock cultures of the gonococcus. In tubes of this medium the gonococcus generally remains viable for 6–8 weeks at 37°C. This medium cannot be recommended to carry stock cultures of organisms capable of attacking starch; some streptococci, for example, produce sufficient acid from the starch in the medium to make it unsatisfactory for this purpose. Bacto-Stock Culture Agar or Bacto-Cooked Meat Medium as discussed on page 98 and 85, is recommended for the maintenance of starch hydrolyzing organisms.

To rehydrate the medium suspend 65 grams of Bacto-Dextrose Starch Agar in 1000 ml. of cold distilled water, and heat to boiling to dissolve the medium completely. Distribute in tubes or flasks and sterilize in the autoclave for 15 minutes at 15 pounds pressure (121°C.). For carrying stock cultures the medium is prepared in the same manner, except that only 32.5 grams of Bacto-Dextrose Starch Agar are used in 1000 ml. of cold distilled water. The medium normally contains a flocculent precipitate which in no way detracts from the value of the medium. Final reaction of the medium will be pH 7.3.

Since best results are obtained with a solid medium having a moist surface, Dextrose Starch Agar should be used the same day it is prepared, or if not used at once, the medium should be melted and allowed to re-solidify just prior to inoculation. It is recommended that sterile rubber stoppers be substituted for the cotton plugs as soon as the slants have cooled. Screw-cap tubes also yield satisfactory results. Cultures of gonococci on plates should be incubated in an atmosphere saturated with moisture as indicated above.

One pound of Bacto-Dextrose Starch Agar will make 7 liters of medium or 14 liters of half-strength medium.

[1] Am. J. Med. Tech., 14:214:1948.

BACTO
DEXTROSE AGAR (B67)
DEHYDRATED

Bacto-Beef Extract	3 g.
Bacto-Tryptose	10 g.
Bacto-Dextrose	10 g.
Sodium Chloride	5 g.
Bacto-Agar	15 g.

Bacto-Dextrose Agar is recommended as a solid medium for cultivation of a large variety of organisms and is especially adapted to the preparation of a Dextrose Blood Agar. In deep tubes, or with removal of oxygen, it will support good growth of anaerobes.

Dextrose (d-glucose) is a readily available source of energy, utilized by a large number of microorganisms. This fact makes Dextrose Agar excellently suited for the production of early and abundant growth, shortening lag periods of old cultures and the initiation of growth of bacteria capable of utilizing dextrose. Bacto-Dextrose Agar contains 1.0 per cent dextrose with a combination of other ingredients that make an excellent Dextrose Agar capable of supporting growth of all the more common bacteria and, in addition, such organisms as streptococci, pneumococci and meningococci. Norton[1] recommended an agar medium containing 0.5 to 1.0 per cent dextrose and about 5 per cent defibrinated blood as being valuable for the isolation of organisms from pus, as well as being an excellent medium for cultivating the meningococcus, gonococcus, *Hemophilus influenzae* and *H. pertussis*.

To rehydrate the medium, suspend 43 grams of Bacto-Dextrose Agar in 1000 ml. cold distilled water and heat to boiling to dissolve the medium completely. Distribute in tubes or flasks and sterilize in the autoclave for 15 minutes at 15 pounds pressure (121°C.). Final reaction of the medium will be pH 7.3.

Since best results are obtained with solid media having a moist surface, Dextrose Agar should be used the same day as it is prepared. If not used at once, melt the medium and allow to re-solidify just prior to inoculation.

One pound of Bacto-Dextrose Agar will make 10.5 liters of medium.

[1] J. Lab. Clin. Med., 17:585:1932.

BACTO
BREWER ANAEROBIC AGAR   (B279)
DEHYDRATED

Bacto-Yeast Extract	5 g.
Bacto-Tryptone	5 g.
Proteose Peptone No. 3, Difco	10 g.
Bacto-Dextrose	10 g.
Sodium Chloride	5 g.
Bacto-Agar	20 g.
Sodium Thioglycollate, Difco	2 g.
Sodium Formaldehyde Sulfoxylate	1 g.
Resazurin, Certified	0.002 g.

Bacto-Brewer Anaerobic Agar is prepared for use with the Brewer anaerobic cover as described by Brewer.[1] This special petri dish cover was designed to permit surface growth of anaerobes and micro-aerophiles on agar with a low oxidation-reduction potential without the use of anaerobic jars or other special apparatus. Brewer Anaerobic Agar is recommended to those laboratories wishing to use this procedure for anaerobic culture.

To rehydrate the medium, suspend 58 grams of Bacto-Brewer Anaerobic Agar in 1000 ml. cold distilled water and heat to boiling to dissolve the medium completely. Distribute in flasks and sterilize in the autoclave for 15 minutes at 15 pounds pressure (121°C.). Dispense the medium in petri dishes using 50-75 ml. of medium in 95 x 15-20 mm. petri dish bottoms. For best results use porous tops on the dishes containing the medium during solidification in order to obtain a dry surface. Inoculate the surface of the medium by smearing or streaking. Cover the inoculated dish with a sterile Brewer anaerobic petri dish cover. It is essential that the sealing ring inside the cover makes perfect contact with the medium. This seal must not be broken before the end of the incubation period. Poured plates may be made by placing the inoculum in the dish and mixing with the medium before solidification. The final reaction of the medium will be pH 7.2.

One pound of Bacto-Brewer Anaerobic Agar will make 8.5 liters of medium.

[1] Science, 95:587:1942.

BACTO
BREWER ANAEROBIC AGAR (B433)
without Dextrose or Eh Indicator
DEHYDRATED

Bacto-Brewer Anaerobic Agar without dextrose or Eh Indicator has the same composition as Bacto-Brewer Anaerobic Agar except dextrose and resazurin have been omited. This carbohydrate-free modification may be used for the isolation and growth of anaerobes and may be used as a base for Blood Agar. Upon the addition of carbohydrates the medium may be employed for fermentation studies. The addition of 1 per cent of the test carbohydrate is recommended for these studies.

To rehydrate the medium, suspend 48 grams Bacto-Brewer Anaerobic Agar without Dextrose or Eh Indicator in 1000 ml. cold distilled water. Heat to boiling to dissolve the medium completely. Distribute in tubes or flasks and sterilize in the autoclave for 15 minutes at 15 pounds pressure (121°C.). Final reaction of the medium will be pH 7.2.

One pound of Bacto-Brewer Anaerobic Agar without dextrose or Eh Indicator will make 9.4 liters of medium.

BACTO
NUTRIENT AGAR 1.5% (B69)
DEHYDRATED

Bacto-Beef Extract	3 g.
Bacto-Peptone	5 g.
Sodium Chloride	8 g.
Bacto-Agar	15 g.

Bacto-Nutrient Agar 1.5% is recommended as a slightly alkaline Nutrient Agar, for use in the cultivation of bacteria not requiring a highly nutritious medium. This medium contains 0.8 per cent sodium chloride, making it well suited for the addition of blood, ascitic fluid or other enriching fluids. With added food material, Bacto-Nutrient Agar 1.5% is satisfactory for the cultivation of pathogenic bacteria.

Bacto-Blood Agar Base, Bacto-Tryptose Blood Agar Base or Bacto-Heart Infusion Agar, as discussed on pages 88, 115 or 87, is recommended as being superior to Bacto-Nutrient Agar 1.5% for use in making Blood Agar. For general culture purposes, with or without enrichment, Bacto-Tryptose Agar, Bacto-Proteose No. 3 Agar, Bacto-Dextrose Proteose No. 3 Agar and Bacto-Dextrose Starch Agar, as discussed on pages 111, 116, 147 and 124, respectively, are recommended as being more satisfactory than Bacto-Nutrient Agar 1.5%.

To rehydrate the medium, suspend 31 grams of Bacto-Nutrient Agar 1.5% in 1000 ml. cold distilled water and heat to boiling to dissolve the medium completely. Distribute in tubes or flasks and sterilize in the autoclave for 15 minutes at 15 pounds pressure (121°C.). The final reaction of the medium will be pH 7.3. If enrichment is desired, the freshly sterilized medium is cooled to 45-50°C. and sterile blood, ascitic fluid or other sterile serous enrichment is added.

Since best results are obtained on a solid medium having a moist surface, Nutrient Agar 1.5% should be used the same day as prepared, or, if not used at once, the medium should be melted and allowed to re-solidify just prior to inoculation.

One pound of Bacto-Nutrient Agar 1.5% will make 14.6 liters of medium.

BACTO
LOEFFLER BLOOD SERUM (B70)
DEHYDRATED

Beef Blood Serum .... 3 parts
Dextrose Broth .... 1 part

Bacto-Loeffler Blood Serum is employed in the cultural diagnosis of diphtheria. The medium is of particular value in the determination of pigment production by bacteria, and of the ability of anaerobes and other microorganisms to attack protein, and for other special uses. Bacto-Loeffler Blood Serum has been prepared in dehydrated form for the convenience of those laboratories where adequate supplies of fresh blood serum are not available.

Bacto-Loeffler Blood Serum is a modification of the horse serum, dextrose broth medium described by Loeffler in 1887[1] for the cultivation of *Coryne-bacterium diphtheriae*. In our modern laboratories Loeffler Blood Serum still retains its important position for the diagnosis of diphtheria. On Loeffler Blood Serum *C. diphtheriae* grows luxuriantly and rapidly, developing morphologically typical organisms, in 12–16 hours, aiding greatly in the diagnosis of diphtheria.

Cleveland and Sanders,[2] and Spector[3] have used Bacto-Loeffler Blood Serum in media for the cultivation of *Endamoeba histolytica*. Thompson[4] hydrolyzed Bacto-Loeffler Blood Serum with sodium hydroxide and added this to a citrate agar for the isolation of *C. diphtheriae*, on which diphtheria bacilli are stimulated and other throat organisms are inhibited.

To rehydrate the medium, dissolve 80 grams of Bacto-Loeffler Blood Serum in 1000 ml. of warm (42–45°C.) distilled water.

During the dehydration process certain components of the medium become insoluble. The removal of this insoluble material by filtration on a Buchner funnel with the use of filter aid or by centrifugation at high speed for 15–20 minutes will result in better appearing final slants. *The use of tubes that can be sealed with a tight fitting closure such as a screw cap will produce slants free from bubbles.* It is recommended that the medium be distributed in tubes and coagulated and sterilized in the autoclave as follows:

1. Place not more than three rows of tubes in a slanting position, in wire baskets, in the autoclave.

2. Close all the ports and the door *before* turning on the steam to maintain a mixture of air and steam for coagulation of the medium. If the exhaust of the autoclave is equipped with an automatic thermo-element type trap, it is necessary to have this line equipped with a valve which can be closed, thereby making it possible to maintain a mixture of air and steam in the autoclave during coagulation.

3. Run the pressure as quickly as possible to 15 pounds and hold for 10 minutes to coagulate the medium.

4. At the end of coagulation, open the lowest port (or valve in thermo-element type trap line if such is used) and replace the entrapped air with steam, maintaining constant pressure while replacing the air-steam mixture with live steam, as any appreciable change in pressure will cause the slants to be filled with bubbles and render the medium useless.

5. Maintain steam pressure for 15 minutes at 15 pounds (121°C.).

6. After sterilization is completed, the source of steam is cut off. All ports and the safety valve should be tightly closed as soon as the steam is shut off, allowing the autoclave to cool slowly. Do not open any ports until the steam pressure is nil. Final reaction of the medium will be pH 7.2.

The autoclave sterilization methods of Hinkleman[5] or Dupray[6] may be used with satisfaction. Heise[7] has also described a method for the autoclave sterilization of Loeffler Medium in fruit jars.

Levin[8] gives in detail the method of inspissation and sterilization of serum media using a single chambered autoclave, pressure cooker field autoclave and a double chambered dressing type autoclave.

Foster and Cohn,[9] and Spray and Johnson[10] have described methods which they use in obtaining bubble-free slants of serum media.

One pound of Bacto-Loeffler Blood Serum will make 5.6 liters of medium.

[1] Centr. Bakt., 2:105:1887.
[2] Arch. Protistenkunde, 70:223:1930.
[3] J. Preventive Med., 6:117:1932.
[4] J. Infectious Diseases, 45:163:1929.
[5] J. Bact., 8:315:1923.
[6] J. Bact., 9:179:1924.
[7] J. Lab. Clin. Med., 15:1025:1929.
[8] J. Bact., 46:223:1943.
[9] J. Bact., 50:561:1945.
[10] J. Bact., 52:141:1946.

ADDITIONAL MEDIA

The media listed below have been rather extensively employed in the past for general or special purposes. Other media have been developed which are considered superior and serve the purpose more adequately than the older media. For the present we will continue to carry these media in stock for those laboratories where they have been in routine use or where it is desired to continue their use for comparative purposes.

PRESENT RECOMMENDATIONS

Bacto-Dextrose Infusion Broth	Bacto-Dextrose Broth, page 101, or add 0.5 per cent Bacto-Dextrose to Bacto-Heart Infusion Broth, page 80
Bacto-Cabbage Infusion Broth	Bacto-Brain Heart Infusion, page 77 Bacto-Tryptose Broth, page 102 Bacto-Tryptose Phosphate Broth, page 100
Bacto-Dextrose Heart Agar	Bacto-Dextrose Agar, page 125, Bacto-Dextrose Proteose No. 3 Agar, page 147; or add 1.0 per cent Bacto-Dextrose to Bacto-Heart Infusion Agar, page 87
Bacto-Liver Infusion Agar	Bacto-Tryptose Agar, page 111 Bacto-Endamoeba Medium, page 97
Bacto-Legumin Trypagar	Bacto-Proteose No. 3 Agar, page 116 Bacto-G C Medium Base, page 122 Bacto-Tryptose Agar, page 111 Bacto-Dextrose Starch Agar, page 124
Bacto-Testicular Agar . . . . Bacto-North Gelatin Agar	Bacto-Proteose No. 3 Agar, page 116 Bacto-G C Medium Base, page 122 Bacto-Dextrose Starch Agar, page 124
Bacto-Cabbage Infusion Agar	Bacto-Tryptose Agar, page 111 Bacto-Proteose No. 3 Agar, page 116 Bacto-G C Medium Base, page 122 Bacto-Dextrose Starch Agar, page 124
Bacto-Nutrient Phosphate Agar	Bacto-Tryptose Agar, page 111 Bacto-Proteose No. 3 Agar, page 116 Bacto-G C Medium Base, page 122 Bacto-Dextrose Starch Agar, page 124 Bacto-Blood Agar Base, page 88
Bacto-Starch Agar	Bacto-Dextrose Starch Agar, page 124 Bacto-Proteose No. 3 Agar, page 116 Bacto-G C Medium Base, page 122
Bacto-Brain Liver Heart (Semisolid) . .	Bacto-Cooked Meat Medium, page 85 Bacto-Dextrose Starch Agar, page 124

DIFFERENTIAL MEDIA

MANY MEDIA have been designed for the separation or differentiation of closely related organisms or groups of organisms. The differentiation by means of cultural characteristics is of decided value and importance especially where morphology and other biological characteristics are almost identical. The following dehydrated culture media represent a group of differential media, some of which are not selective and depend on cultural characteristics for differentiation, while others are selective and in addition show colonial differences between organisms. The isolation of members of the enteric group by means of differential media has been a routine procedure for many years. More recently differential media have been described for the isolation of other groups of organisms such as diphtheria, staphylococci and streptococci. Differential media for these isolation purposes are discussed in this section.

Suggested Schema for the Examination of Stools or Other Material for Bacterial Incitants of Enteric Disease

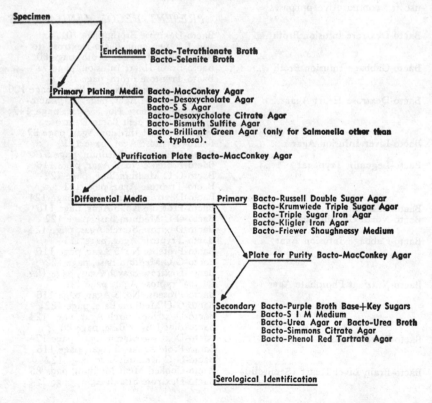

Specimen

Enrichment   Bacto-Tetrathionate Broth
              Bacto-Selenite Broth

Primary Plating Media   Bacto-MacConkey Agar
                         Bacto-Desoxycholate Agar
                         Bacto-S S Agar
                         Bacto-Desoxycholate Citrate Agar
                         Bacto-Bismuth Sulfite Agar
                         Bacto-Brilliant Green Agar (only for Salmonella other than
                             S. typhosa).

Purification Plate   Bacto-MacConkey Agar

Differential Media

Primary   Bacto-Russell Double Sugar Agar
           Bacto-Krumwiede Triple Sugar Agar
           Bacto-Triple Sugar Iron Agar
           Bacto-Kligler Iron Agar
           Bacto-Friewer Shaughnessy Medium

Plate for Purity   Bacto-MacConkey Agar

Secondary   Bacto-Purple Broth Base+Key Sugars
             Bacto-S I M Medium
             Bacto-Urea Agar or Bacto-Urea Broth
             Bacto-Simmons Citrate Agar
             Bacto-Phenol Red Tartrate Agar

Serological Identification

Primary Plating Media

THE MEDIA listed in this section are used generally in petri dishes for initial isolation. In most cases the composition of the medium is such that it is selective for a particular group of organisms.

BACTO
MacCONKEY AGAR (B75)
DEHYDRATED

Bacto-Peptone	17 g.
Proteose Peptone, Difco	3 g.
Bacto-Lactose	10 g.
Bacto-Bile Salts No. 3	1.5 g.
Sodium Chloride	5 g.
Bacto-Agar	13.5 g.
Bacto-Neutral Red	0.03 g.
Bacto-Crystal Violet	0.001 g.

Bacto-MacConkey Agar is a differential plating medium recommended for use in the detection and isolation of all types of dysentery, typhoid and paratyphoid bacteria from stool specimens, urine and other materials harboring these organisms. MacConkey Agar is suggested for direct plating of water samples for coliform counts in Appendix I of "Standard Methods for the Examination of Water and Sewage."[1] "Standard Methods for the Examination of Dairy Products"[2] prefers dehydrated Bacto-MacConkey Agar for the isolation of pathogenic bacteria from cheese. MacConkey Agar is also specified in "Diagnostic Procedures and Reagents"[3] of the American Public Health Association.

Over a period of years, particularly in Great Britain, the Neutral Red Bile Salt Agar of MacConkey[4] has been quite generally used for differentiating strains of *Salmonella typhosa* from members of the coliform group. Bacto-MacConkey Agar, as modified by the addition of 0.5 per cent sodium chloride, decreasing the agar content to 1.35 per cent, and by altering the concentrations of bile salts and neutral red, has the added advantage of supporting excellent growth of all *Shigella* and *Salmonella* strains. It also gives a more clear-cut differential between these enteric pathogens and the coliform group, making it easier to read than the original medium. Block and Ferguson[5] investigating an outbreak of Shiga dysentery found MacConkey Agar satisfactory in the isolation of this fastidious strain.

The fact that this medium promotes development of these organisms, and at the same time differentiates them from lactose fermenting Gram-negative bacilli, makes it an excellent substrate for the cultural detection of dysentery, typhoid and other *Salmonella* organisms in stools and other infected material. Gram-positive bacteria are inhibited.

About 20 ml. of medium should be poured into previously sterilized petri dishes to form a relatively thick layer. It is important that the surface of the medium be quite dry when inoculated; this may be accomplished by allowing the medium to solidify and to stand for about two hours with the covers of the plates partially removed.

The medium is inoculated by streaking or smearing with the material under investigation. Serial inoculation of several plates is recommended to insure suitable distribution of well isolated colonies. After inoculation, the plates should be incubated at 35–37°C. for 16–18 hours and should be observed at the end of this period because prolonged incubation may lead to confusion of results.

The differential action of Bacto-MacConkey Agar is clear and distinct. Isolated colonies of coliform bacteria are brick red in color and may be surrounded by a zone of precipitated bile. This reaction is due to the action of the acids, produced by fermentation of lactose, upon the bile salts and the subsequent absorption of neutral red. Typhoid, paratyphoid and dysentery bacilli do not ferment lactose and do not greatly alter the appearance of the medium. These colonies, in reality giving an alkaline reaction, are uncolored and transparent. When growing in proximity to coliform colonies, they have the appearance of clearing the areas of precipitated bile. On plates which are not overcrowded the differentiation is exceptionally distinct. A plate crowded with coli will appear red and opaque, yet, if not too crowded, typhoid or other lactose non-fermenting organisms may easily be detected by transmitted light. On such plates they will appear as small transparent areas against the red background. A plate showing discrete colonies is to be desired for isolation purposes.

For the cultural detection of typhoid organisms in infected material, it is recommended that Bacto-MacConkey Agar be used in conjunction with the more selective media, Bacto-S S Agar and Bacto-Bismuth Sulfite Agar as discussed on pages 134 and 139.

A procedure designed to show the largest number of pathogens from a specimen would be:

A. Streak or smear a large inoculum on one plate of S S Agar and one plate of Bismuth Sulfite Agar.

B. Streak or smear a light inoculum on one plate of MacConkey Agar.

C. Prepare Bismuth Sulfite Agar poured plates with a 5 ml. and a one drop inoculum.

D. Enrich for 12–18 hours in Tetrathionate Broth or Selenite Broth, followed by streaking on one plate of Bismuth Sulfite Agar or Brilliant Green Agar and one plate of S S Agar.

Saccharose in 1 per cent concentration may be added to isolation media, such as Bacto-MacConkey Agar to permit the detection of certain members of the coliform group which ferment saccharose more readily than lactose. This principle was described by Holt-Harris and Teague[6] and has been employed by many other bacteriologists. In some laboratories pathogenic significance is assigned to these organisms, and under such conditions, saccharose should not be added to the medium.

To rehydrate the medium, suspend 50 grams of Bacto-MacConkey Agar in 1000 ml. of cold distilled water and heat to boiling to dissolve the medium completely. Distribute in tubes or flasks and sterilize by autoclaving for 15 minutes at 15 pounds pressure (121°C.). MacConkey Agar inoculated the same day as rehydrated may be used without autoclave sterilization. Under these conditions the medium need be heated only to boiling to dissolve it completely before pouring into petri plates. The final reaction of the medium will be pH 7.1.

One pound of Bacto-MacConkey Agar will make 9 liters of medium.

[1] Standard Methods for the Examination of Water and Sewage, 9th Edition:228:1946.
[2] Standard Methods for the Examination of Dairy Products, 9th Edition:166:1948.
[3] Diagnostic Procedures and Reagents, 3rd Edition:24, 195:1950.
[4] J. Hyg., 5:333:1905.
[5] Am. J. Pub. Health, 130:42:1940.
[6] J. Infectious Diseases, 18:596:1916.

BACTO
DESOXYCHOLATE AGAR
DEHYDRATED

A complete discussion of Bacto-Desoxycholate Agar as used for the isolation of members of the *Shigella* and *Salmonella* groups is given on page 63.

BACTO
E.M.B. AGAR (B76)
DEHYDRATED

Bacto-Peptone	10 g.
Bacto-Lactose	5 g.
Saccharose, Difco	5 g.
Dipotassium Phosphate	2 g.
Bacto-Agar	13.5 g.
Bacto-Eosin Y	0.4 g.
Bacto-Methylene Blue	0.065 g.

Bacto-E.M.B. Agar, a differential plating medium, is recommended for the detection and isolation of the Gram-negative intestinal pathogenic bacteria.

The original Eosin Methylene Blue Agar was devised by Holt-Harris and Teague.[1] These workers employed a combination of eosin and methylene blue as an indicator which gave a sharp and distinct differential between colonies of lactose fermenting organisms and those which did not ferment lactose. These authors included saccharose in their medium since certain members of the coliform group ferment this carbohydrate more readily than lactose. Colonies of the coli-aerogenes group were either black or possessed dark centers with transparent colorless peripheries, while those of typhoid and other organisms which did not ferment lactose or saccharose remained uncolored. The Eosin Methylene Blue Agar of Holt-Harris and Teague possessed definite advantages over the Fuchsin Sulfite Agar of Endo, in that it was more sensitive, more accurate, more stable and gave an earlier differentiation.

Two years after Holt-Harris and Teague had introduced their new medium, Levine[2] described an Eosin Methylene Blue Agar for the purpose of differentiating the fecal and non-fecal types of the colon-aerogenes group. Levine's medium, as discussed on page 35, also differentiated the typhoid and other lactose non-fermenters from the coliform organisms.

Bacto-E.M.B. Agar is a combination of the Levine and the Holt-Harris and Teague formulae. It contains Bacto-Peptone and phosphate as recommended by Levine, and retains the two carbohydrates lactose and saccharose, as suggested by Holt-Harris and Teague. The ratio of the two indicator dyes has been worked out to give the best differentiation and minimum toxicity. This medium has all the advantages of the original media referred to above.

It is recommended that for the detection of the more fastidious *Shigella* and *Salmonella* organisms, Bacto-MacConkey Agar, the selective Bacto-S S Agar and Bacto-Bismuth Sulfite Agar, as discussed on pages 131, 134 and 139, be run in conjunction with Bacto-E.M.B. Agar.

To rehydrate the medium, suspend 36 grams of Bacto-E.M.B. Agar in 1000 ml. of cold distilled water and heat to boiling to dissolve the medium completely. Distribute in tubes or flasks and sterilize in the autoclave for 15 minutes at 15 pounds pressure (121°C.). Bacto-E.M.B. Agar inoculated the same day as rehydrated may be used without autoclave sterilization. Under these conditions the medium need be heated only to boiling to dissolve it completely before pouring into petri plates.

Sterilization reduces the methylene blue, leaving the medium orange color. The normal purple color of the medium may be restored by gentle shaking. If the reduced medium is not shaken to oxidize the methylene blue, a dark zone beginning at the top and extending downward through the medium will gradually make its appearance. The sterilized medium normally contains a flocculant precipitate which should not be removed. By cooling to 50°C. and gently agitating the medium before pouring it into plates, this flocculation will be finely dispersed, giving a medium without any objectionable precipitate.

One pound of Bacto-E.M.B. Agar will make 12.6 liters of medium.

¹ J. Infectious Diseases, 18:596:1916.   ² J. Infectious Diseases, 23:43:1918.

BACTO
LEVINE E.M.B. AGAR
DEHYDRATED

Levine E.M.B. Agar has been used for the isolation of enteric pathogens. A complete discussion of Bacto-Levine E.M.B. Agar is given on page 35.

BACTO
ENDO AGAR
DEHYDRATED

Endo Agar has been used rather extensively in the past for the isolation of enteric pathogens. A complete discussion of Bacto-Endo Agar is given on page 34.

BACTO
S S AGAR   (B74)
DEHYDRATED

Bacto-Beef Extract	5 g.
Proteose Peptone, Difco	5 g.
Bacto-Lactose	10 g.
Bacto-Bile Salts No. 3	8.5 g.
Sodium Citrate	8.5 g.
Sodium Thiosulfate	8.5 g.
Ferric Citrate	1 g.
Bacto-Agar	13.5 g.
Bacto-Brilliant Green	0.00033 g.
Bacto-Neutral Red	0.025 g.

Bacto-S S Agar is a highly selective medium recommended for the isolation of *Shigella* and *Salmonella* from stools and other materials suspected of containing these organisms. Bacto-S S Agar was devised to provide excellent differentiation of lactose fermenters from lactose non-fermenters, and to give maximum inhibition of coliform organisms without restriction of the growth of pathogenic Gramnegative bacilli occurring in specimens. Inasmuch as Bacto-S S Agar is a selective medium, we recommend that a non-selective medium such as Bacto-MacConkey Agar be used in conjunction with it. To insure the highest percentage of positive isolations of all intestinal pathogens, we further recommend the use of Bacto-

Bismuth Sulfite Agar and enrichment in Bacto-Tetrathionate Broth Base or Bacto-Selenite Broth.

The search for the inciting agents in bacillary intestinal disorders is of vital importance in the public health laboratory. The value of the detection of typhoid bacilli in active cases of typhoid fever as well as from carriers has long been recognized, and a number of media are being successfully used for these purposes. Media suitable for the isolation of *Salmonella typhosa* have not always proved entirely satisfactory for the detection of *Shigella* and other *Salmonella* organisms due either to the overgrowth of coliform organisms, or the inability of the medium itself to support the growth of some particularly fastidious strains.

Bacto-S S Agar gives excellent growth from small inocula of the different types of *Shigella* and *Salmonella* organisms as they occur in fresh fecal specimens. Strains of Flexner, Newcastle, Schmitz, Shiga, Sonne and alkalescens, as well as the *Salmonella*, grow unrestricted. All strains of *S. typhosa* that have been encountered show excellent growth on S S Agar. Coliform organisms are quite generally inhibited even when heavy inocula are employed.

Shigella, *Salmonella* and other organisms not fermenting lactose form opaque, transparent or translucent uncolored colonies, which generally are smooth. The few lactose fermenting organisms which may develop on the medium are readily differentiated due to the formation of a red color in the colony. At times, isolated coliform colonies may not show a definite red color, being pink or nearly colorless with a pink center. Occasionally an aerogenes type will develop a characteristic large, white or cream colored opaque and mucoid colony. Some *Proteus* and *Salmonella* types may, under certain conditions, produce black centered colonies.

Hormaeche and Surraco,[1] Hardy and co-workers[2] and Rose and Kolodny,[3] have reported S S Agar as superior to other media that have been recommended for isolation of *Shigella* and *Salmonella* organisms. Mayfield and Goeber[4] compared media for isolation of *Shigella* organisms and found Bacto-S S Agar to yield the greatest number of positive isolations. Pots[5] and Caudill[6] have reported on the satisfactory use of S S Agar in isolation of *Shigella* organisms. In their studies of the acute diarrheal diseases, Mosher, Wheeler, Chant and Hardy[7] first enriched their specimens in Selenite Broth and then plated on Bismuth Sulfite Agar, S S Agar, MacConkey Agar and Desoxycholate Agar, while Watt and Cummings[8] plated directly upon S S Agar. Hormaeche and his co-workers[9] used S S Agar in conjunction with others for isolation of *Shigella* as the causative agent of infantile summer diarrhea. Vacarro et al.[10] employed S S Agar in conjunction with other plating media in the isolation of *Salmonella* and *Shigella* from healthy carriers, and Neter[11] used it similarly in his study of the Proteus and Paracolobactrum (paracolon bacilli) in feces of healthy infants. McClure and Crossley,[12] using S S Agar and other media, isolated *S. newport* in an epidemic of food poisoning, and Cordy and Davis[13] isolated *S. morbificans* from horses and mules in an outbreak of salmonellosis. Watt, DeCapito and Morgan[14] isolated *S. texas* on S S Agar after enrichment in Tetrathionate Broth. For the isolation and typing of *Salmonella* and *Shigella*, Borman, Wheeler and Mickle[15] and Nelson et al.[16] indicate the desirability of plating specimens on S S Agar and other substrates before and after enrichment. Neter and Clark[17] have reported on the effectiveness of culture media in isolation of enteric organisms, the usefulness of S S Agar, especially with other media, being clearly demonstrated by their results.

Bacto-S S Agar is specified for use in "Standard Methods for the Examination of Dairy Products"[18] for the isolation of pathogenic bacteria from cheese and in "Diagnostic Procedures and Reagents"[19] for the examination of specimens for evidence of infection with *Salmonella* and *Shigella*.

A survey of the methods used in the collection and preservation of stool specimens for the isolation and identification of *Salmonella*, *Shigella* and intestinal protozoa by Felsenfeld[20] showed that generally specimens were promptly plated. Glycerol-saline was the most frequently used preservative. S S Agar was the most popular plating medium. It was used especially frequently for direct plating. There was a decrease in the use of Endo Agar. Desoxycholate Agars were found to be more frequently used than the Endo Agar. There were more laboratories using the poured plate of Bismuth Sulfite Agar, MacConkey Agar and Brilliant Green Agar in 1949 than in 1944. The use of streaked plates of Bismuth Sulfite Agar showed a decrease during this period if occasional users were not considered. All but three laboratories were using dehydrated Bismuth Sulfite Agar. He stated that these changes point toward evaluation of experience and economy in public health laboratories.

Neter and Brody[21] added saccharose and also saccharose and salicin to Bacto-S S Agar in studies on the bacteriological diagnosis and epidemiological aspects of Salmonellosis. The modified media were especially valuable in the follow-up of proven *Salmonella* cases and in epidemiological studies, but were not suggested in routine work since pathogenic paracolons would be discarded by the modified media. These media would also discard Proteus.

Schaub[22,23] in her study of the differentiation of paracolon bacilli reported Bacto-S S Agar to give more satisfactory results than the other selective media tried, in that on S S Agar growth of the paracolon bacilli, regarded as aberrant coliforms, is inhibited, as is that of the typical coliform bacillus. Certain other paracolon bacilli grew well. Correlating growth on Bacto-S S Agar with biochemical characteristics, the paracolon bacilli were divided into four large groups:

Group I—aberrant coliform bacilli, consisting of paracolon *Escherichia*, paracolon *Aerobacter* and paracolon intermediates; growth inhibited on S S Agar.

Group II—hydrogen-sulfide-producing paracolon bacilli, growth not inhibited on S S Agar. This group may be divided culturally into three subgroups, II-A, II-B and II-C.

Group III—anaerogenic paracolon bacilli; growth not inhibited on S S Agar.

Group IV—malonate-positive paracolon bacilli; growth not inhibited on S S Agar.

Schaub also used S S Agar as slants in tubes and found that this was a satisfactory method of demonstrating hydrogen sulfide production. The medium at the base of the slant became markedly blackened when the surface of the slant was streaked with a hydrogen sulfide producing organism.

Newman,[24] in a study of the detection of food poisoning attributable to dairy products, used direct streaking on S S Agar as well as enrichment in Tetrathionate Broth followed by streaking on S S Agar and Bismuth Sulfite Agar for the isolation of *Salmonellae*. In a study of methods to be used as a standard for the bacterial examination of pullorum reactors Jungherr, Hall and Pomeroy,[25] in a committee report showed that in a comparative study of media and enrichments from October, 1946 to February, 1950, Bismuth Sulfite Agar and S S Agar permitted the highest number of specific isolations of *S. pullorum* and *S. gallinarum*. These favored selective media suppressed the growth of coliform organisms. Following enrichment of the specimens in Selenite Broth streaking on Bismuth Sulfite Agar gave the largest number of positive isolations, followed by S S Agar and then MacConkey Agar. Selenite Broth yielded a higher number of successful isolations on follow-up media than did Tetrathionate Broth. The highest percentage of organisms were isolated from the ovary, followed by gall bladder, peritoneum, oviduct, intestines and pericardial sac in the order listed.

The outstanding selectivity of Bacto-S S Agar permits the use of heavy inocula, which should be evenly distributed over the entire surface of the medium. The plates are incubated at 35–37°C. for a full 24 hours, at which time at least three or four of each type of suspected colonies are picked from each plate for identification.

Bacto-S S Agar inhibits the formation of colonies of contaminating types but does not destroy them. In the identification procedures it is necessary to have a pure culture, and, for this reason, only the center of the colony should be picked for transfer. If the suspected colonies are not well isolated, they should be purified by subculturing on some non-selective medium such as Bacto-MacConkey Agar. Suspected colonies are transferred to appropriate differential tube media, such as Bacto-Kligler Iron Agar, Bacto-Triple Sugar Iron Agar or Bacto-Krumwiede Triple Sugar Agar, for ascertaining the group to which they belong. The use of Bacto-Triple Sugar Iron Agar is particularly recommended as a single medium for separation of the *Salmonella* and *Shigella* groups. *Salmonella* may be further differentiated by their inability to produce indole from Bacto-Tryptone, as the experience of recent investigators indicates that indole is not formed by pathogenic *Salmonella*. The hydrolysis of urea as demonstrated on Urea Broth or Urea Agar, as discussed on pages 170 and 171, may be used to identify *Proteus* or *Paracolobactrum* (paracolon) organisms. Agglutination tests for further identification of isolated strains may be run on organisms from any of these differential tube media.

Bacto-S S Agar is particularly adapted for the isolation of *Shigella* and *Salmonella* but as this is a selective medium, a non-inhibitive medium such as Bacto-MacConkey Agar, which permits the growth of even the most fastidious Gram negative intestinal pathogens, should be run in conjunction with it. If typhoid is suspected, it is recommended that a poured plate of Bismuth Sulfite Agar be run on each specimen. Enrichment of the specimen in Tetrathionate Broth or Selenite Broth followed by streaking on Bismuth Sulfite Agar or S S Agar is also recommended. This latter procedure is especially desirable in the isolation of *Salmonella*.

A procedure designed to show the largest number of pathogens from a specimen would be:

A. Streak or smear a large inoculum on one plate of S S Agar and one plate of Bismuth Sulfite Agar.

B. Streak or smear a light inoculum on one plate of MacConkey Agar.

C. Prepare Bismuth Sulfite Agar poured plates with a 5 ml. and a one drop inoculum.

D. Enrich for 12–18 hours in Tetrathionate Broth or Selenite Broth followed by streaking on one plate of Bismuth Sulfite Agar or Brilliant Green Agar and one plate of S S Agar.

Saccharose in 1 per cent concentration may be added to isolation media, such as Bacto-S S Agar to permit the detection of certain members of the coliform group which ferment saccharose more readily than lactose. This principle was described by Holt-Harris and Teague[26] and has been employed by many other bacteriologists. In some laboratories pathogenic significance is assigned to these organisms, and under such conditions, saccharose should not be added to the medium.

To rehydrate the medium, suspend 60 grams of Bacto-S S Agar in 1000 ml. of cold distilled water and heat to boiling to dissolve the medium completely. *Do not sterilize in the autoclave.* About 20 ml. of the medium should be poured into standard petri dishes of 90–100 mm. in diameter. It is important that the surfaces of the medium be quite dry when inoculated and this may be accomplished by allowing the medium to solidify and to stand for about 2 hours with the covers

of the plates partially removed. The final reaction of the medium will be pH 7.0.
One pound of Bacto-S S Agar will make 7.4 liters of the final medium.

[1] Apartado De Los Archivos Uruguayos De
     Medicina, 18:485:1941.
[2] Public Health Reports, 57:521, 524:1942.
[3] J. Lab. Clin. Med., 27:1081:1942.
[4] Am. J. Pub. Health, 31:363:1941.
[5] The Lancet, Vol. I, (XXIII):677:1942.
[6] J. Am. Med. Assoc., 119:1402:1942.
[7] Public Health Reports, 56:2415:1944.
[8] Public Health Reports, 60:1355:1945.
[9] Am. J. Diseases Children, 66:539:1943.
[10] Rev. Chileana Hyg. Med. Prev., 4:353:1942.
[11] J. Pediatrics, 26:39:1945.
[12] Can. J. Pub. Health, 36:401:1945.
[13] J. Am. Vet. Med. Assoc., 58:20:1946.
[14] Public Health Reports, 62:806:1947.
[15] Am. J. Pub. Health, 33:127:1943.

[16] Am. J. Pub. Health, 36:51:1946.
[17] Am. J. Digestive Diseases, 7:229:1944.
[18] Standard Methods for the Examination of
      Dairy Products, 9th Edition:166:1948.
[19] Diagnostic Procedures and Reagents, 3rd Edi-
      tion:23:1950.
[20] Pub. Health Reports, 65:1075:1950.
[21] Paper read at Microbiological Congress, 1950.
[22] J. Bact., 54:1:1947.
[23] Bull. Johns Hopkins Hospital, 83:367:1948.
[24] J. Milk and Food Tech., 13:226:1950.
[25] Proc. 22nd Ann. Meet. Northeastern Conf.
      Lab. Workers in Pullorum Disease Control,
      Burlington, Vermont, June 20–21, 1950.
[26] J. Infectious Diseases, 18:596:1916.

BACTO

DESOXYCHOLATE CITRATE AGAR   (B274)

DEHYDRATED

Pork, Infusion from	330 g.
Proteose Peptone No. 3, Difco	10 g.
Bacto-Lactose	10 g.
Sodium Citrate	20 g.
Ferric Ammonium Citrate	2 g.
Sodium Desoxycholate	5 g.
Bacto-Agar	13.5 g.
Bacto-Neutral Red	0.02 g.

Bacto-Desoxycholate Citrate Agar, a modification of the original Leifson[1]
formula, is a selective medium for use in the isolation of enteric pathogens. It is
recommended for use in all cases wherein a selective Desoxycholate Citrate Agar
is specified or desired. The use of Desoxycholate Citrate Agar is recommended
as a plating procedure for examination of specimens for evidence of infection
with *Salmonella* and *Shigella* as given in "Diagnostic Procedures and Reagents"[2]
of the American Public Health Association.

On Desoxycholate Citrate Agar the growth of coliform bacteria is inhibited
or greatly suppressed. Gram-positive bacteria are generally inhibited. *Salmonella*
and *Shigella* organisms grow quite unrestricted. The selectivity of this medium
permits the use of fairly heavy inocula without danger of overgrowth of the
Shigella and *Salmonella* by extraneous organisms. Occasionally, however, coliform strains are encountered that persist on Desoxycholate Citrate Agar. Such
strains, if present in large numbers, produce acid from the lactose, precipitate the
bile salt, and give an opaque red medium which makes it difficult to detect the
pathogens. Distribution of the inoculum over the surface of the medium to give
a sparsely populated section helps to insure against complete masking of the
pathogens by such coliform organisms. Inoculated plates are incubated at 37°C.
for 24 hours.

Organisms which grow on Desoxycholate Citrate Agar but which do not
ferment lactose produce colorless raised colonies. *Salmonella typhosa* produces
translucent colonies with a bluish cast. Other *Salmonella* colonies are large,
opaque and may possess a brownish center. *Shigella* produce opaque ground-
glass appearing colonies with even margins. Coliform organisms which persist
on Desoxycholate Citrate Agar form raised, even, red colonies that are often
surrounded by a red halo of precipitated bile salt.

For the routine examination of stool and urine specimens it is recommended that Bacto-MacConkey Agar, a non-selective medium, and Bacto-Bismuth Sulfite Agar or Bacto-S S Agar be run in conjunction with Bacto-Desoxycholate Citrate Agar.

Saccharose in 1 per cent concentration may be added to isolation media, such as Bacto-Desoxycholate Citrate Agar to permit the detection of certain members of the coliform group which ferment saccharose more readily than lactose. This principle was described by Holt-Harris and Teague[3] and has been employed by many other bacteriologists. In some laboratories, pathogenic significance is assigned to these organisms, and under such conditions, saccharose should not be added to the medium.

To rehydrate the medium, suspend 70 grams of Bacto-Desoxycholate Citrate Agar in 1000 ml. of cold distilled water and heat to boiling to dissolve the medium completely. *Do not sterilize the medium in the autoclave.* Pour the medium into petri dishes and allow the surface to dry for two hours with the covers partially removed before inoculation. The final reaction of the medium will be pH 7.5.

One pound of Bacto-Desoxycholate Citrate Agar will make 6.5 liters of medium.

[1] J. Path. Bact., 40:581:1935.   Edition:212:1950.
[2] Diagnostic Procedures and Reagents, 3rd   [3] J. Infectious Diseases, 18:596:1916.

BACTO

BISMUTH SULFITE AGAR (B73)

DEHYDRATED

Bacto-Beef Extract	5 g.
Bacto-Peptone	10 g.
Bacto-Dextrose	5 g.
Disodium Phosphate	4 g.
Ferrous Sulfate	0.3 g.
Bismuth Sulfite Indicator	8 g.
Bacto-Agar	20 g.
Bacto-Brilliant Green	0.025 g.

Bacto-Bismuth Sulfite Agar, a modification of the Wilson and Blair formula, is a highly selective medium designed especially for the isolation of *Salmonella typhosa* from feces, urine, sewage and other materials harboring this organism. It is of special value in detecting typhoid carriers and in checking cases before release. It is also satisfactory for the isolation of other members of the *Salmonella* group, particularly after preliminary enrichment in Tetrathionate Broth. The use of Bismuth Sulfite Agar is specified in "Standard Methods for the Examination of Dairy Products"[1] for the isolation of pathogenic bacteria from cheese, and in "Diagnostic Procedures and Reagents"[2] of the American Public Health Association for the examination of specimens for evidence of infection with *Salmonella* and *Shigella*.

The early history of the development of Bismuth Sulfite Agar may be found in the reports of Wilson, [3,4] and Wilson and Blair[5,6,7] who clearly demonstrated the superiority of this type of medium over other media in the isolation of typhoid. The unusually interesting claims of the proponents, and the many enthusiastic reports of its successful use by other investigators, stimulated us in an endeavor to prepare this medium in the dehydrated form. The result of this investigation was Bacto-Bismuth Sulfite Agar.

Bacto-Bismuth Sulfite Agar closely approaches the ideal medium for the isolation of *S. typhosa* from feces, urine, sewage and other infectious materials. Upon this medium the typhoid organism grows luxuriantly, forming characteristic black colonies, while the Gram-positive bacteria and members of the coliform group are inhibited. This unique inhibitory action of Bacto-Bismuth Sulfite Agar toward Gram-postive and coliform organisms permits the use of a much larger inoculum than has been possible with other media employed for similar purposes in the past. The use of larger inocula greatly increases the possibility of recovering the organisms, especially when they are present in relatively small numbers, such as may be encountered in the early course of the disease or in the checking of carriers and releases.

Cope and Kasper[8] increased their positive findings of typhoid from 1.2 to 16.8 per cent among food handlers and from 8.4 to 17.5 per cent among contacts by the use of Bacto-Bismuth Sulfite Agar. Employing this medium in the routine laboratory examination of fecal and urine specimens these same authors[9] obtained 40 per cent more positive isolations of S. typhosa than were obtained on Endo Medium. Gunther and Tuft,[10] employing various media in a comparative way for the isolation of typhoid from stool and urine specimens, found Bacto-Bismuth Sulfite Agar most efficient. Upon this medium they obtained 38.4 per cent more positives than on Endo, 33 per cent more positives than on Eosin Methylene Blue Agar, and 80 per cent more positives on Bismuth Sulfite Agar than on the desoxycholate media. These workers found Bacto-Bismuth Sulfite Agar to be superior to Wilson's original medium, being easier to prepare, relatively more stable and more sensitive. Green and Beard,[11] using Bacto-Bismuth Sulfite Agar in their studies on the "Survival of E. typhi in Sewage Treatment Plant Processes," claimed that this medium so successfully inhibited sewage organisms that their interference was negligible. Beard[12] stated that such a highly selective medium as Bismuth Sulfite Agar made possible the study of the survival of typhoid in nature.

Since these earlier references to the use of Bismuth Sulfite Agar, this medium has been generally accepted as routine for the detection of incitants of enteric disease. The value of the medium is demonstrated by the many references to the use of Bismuth Sulfite Agar in scientific publications, laboratory manuals and texts.

As surface and subsurface colonies on Bismuth Sulfite Agar are strikingly characteristic, it is possible to use the medium both as a smear plate and as a poured plate in the isolation of S. typhosa. Smear plates are prepared by pouring 15–20 ml. quantities of the medium into sterile petri dishes (90 mm.) and allowing the medium to solidify with the cover removed to obtain a dry surface. In preparing poured plates the inoculum is placed in the sterile petri dish and the dissolved medium at 45°C. is added and mixed in the usual manner.

The following technique is recommended for the isolation of typhoid organisms from fecal specimens.

Method of Inoculation

Streak or Smear Plate

Streak or smear the surface of a plate with a heavy inoculum of the fecal material in such a way that on some portion of the plate the inoculum will be light, permitting the development of discrete colonies.

Poured Plate

(a) Transfer about 2 or more grams of the fecal material to a test tube, add 12–15 ml water, and mix well, being careful to break up all the larger particles of the material. Specimens preserved in glycerol must be diluted with water to reduce the glycerol content since S. typhosa in poured plates is inhibited in the presence of 2 per cent glycerol.

(b) Insert a loosely packed cotton plug, about 1 inch long, into the tube, and slowly force it down through the fecal mixture by means of a glass rod or pipette, so that all the gross particles are carried to the bottom of the tube on the cotton plug, and an opaque fluid rises through the cotton. A second cotton filtration may be necessary, since it is essential that the supernatant fluid be free from gross particles. Such solid particles in the medium may support growth of the extraneous organisms, giving pseudo-blackening which may be mistaken for typhoid colonies.

Some workers may prefer to allow the gross solid particles of fecal suspension to settle by gravity instead of removing them by filtration with cotton. In such cases it is not advisable to allow the suspension to stand longer than 30 minutes in order to obtain a supernatant fluid free from gross particles. Other methods of preparing fecal suspensions that will give a liquid free from gross solid suspended material without removing typhoid may also be employed.

(c) Transfer about 5 ml. of the prepared fecal suspension to one petri dish and 1 drop to a second dish. Add 20 ml. of Bismuth Sulfite Agar, cooled to 45°C., to each dish, and mix thoroughly. It is necessary to use at least 20 ml. of the medium to each 5 ml. of inoculum, for dilution of the medium beyond this point will allow the development of extraneous fecal forms.

(d) Incubate at 37°C. and observe after 24 hours for typical colonies as described below. Frequently typical colonies develop within 24 hours incubation; however, in all cases the plates should be incubated for at least 48 hours to allow the development of all typhoid strains, before considering the specimen negative. Specimens containing only a small number of typhoid should show isolated colonies from the 5 ml. inoculum, while those specimens containing increasingly large numbers of typhoid organisms should show isolated colonies from the 1 drop inoculum in the poured plate or on the smear plate.

In the examination of samples of urine, blood, sewage or other material, either the poured plate or smear method with Bismuth Sulfite Agar may be used. It is suggested that in examining blood specimens, the specimen first be inoculated into a tube of broth and after preliminary incubation of 8–12 hours, smeared onto the Bismuth Sulfite Agar plate.

Description of Colonies

Streak or Smear Plate

The typical discrete surface typhoid colony is black and is surrounded by a black or brownish-black zone which may be several times the size of the colony. By reflected light, preferably daylight, this zone exhibits a distinctly characteristic metallic sheen. Plates heavily seeded with typhoid may not show this reaction except possibly near the margin of the mass inoculation. In these congested areas, typhoid frequently appears as small light green colonies. This fact emphasizes the importance of inoculating plates in such a manner as to have some sparsely populated areas with discrete typhoid colonies.

Poured Plate

Well isolated subsurface typhoid colonies are circular, jet black and well defined. The size of the black colony may vary from 1 to 4 mm. in diameter depending upon the particular strain, length of incubation and position of the colony in the agar. Only those colonies growing very close to the surface or on the surface will show a decided black metallic sheen. Plates containing typhoid too numerous to permit the development of individual colonies give a black plate or a plate dotted with black areas. Plates with about three hundred to a thousand typhoid colonies will exhibit this appearance. When typhoid develops in a plate in still larger numbers, typical blackening does not occur and the appearance is that of a negative plate.

Ordinarily typhoid will develop well isolated colonies showing typical round jet black colonies with or without sheen, from either the 5 ml. or 1 drop inoculation of cotton-filtered fecal suspension using the poured plate method. However, the typhoid organisms developing from the specimens containing large numbers of typhoid may be so numerous that the blackening cannot occur typically and the plate may appear dotted black or greenish gray. From such heavily seeded specimens the direct smear on Bismuth Sulfite Agar from feces should demonstrate typhoid, while the poured plate should give positive results from specimens containing lesser numbers of typhoid.

Description of Colonies Other Than Typhoid

S. schottmuelleri (*Paratyphoid B*) and *S. enteritidis* grow luxuriantly upon Bacto-Bismuth Sulfite Agar forming black surface and subsurface colonies slightly more moist, but otherwise similar to those produced by *S. typhosa*.

S. paratyphi (*Paratyphoid A*), *S. typhimurium*, *S. choleraesuis* and *Proteus morganii* develop upon Bacto-Bismuth Sulfite Agar, yielding flat or only slightly raised green colonies.

Generally, the members of the dysentery group other than Flexner and Sonne are inhibited. The Flexner and Sonne strains that do develop upon this medium produce brownish raised colonies with depressed centers and exhibit a crater-like appearance.

Coli is usually completely inhibited. Occasionally a strain will be encountered that will develop small black, brown or greenish glistening surface colonies. This color is confined entirely to the colony itself and shows no metallic sheen. Likewise a few strains of aerogenes may develop on this medium forming raised, mucoid colonies. These may exhibit a silvery sheen, appreciably lighter in color than that produced by typhoid. Subsurface colonies of the coliform group, when they develop, are green or brown in color, generally lenticular in shape, and not at all to be confused with the typical round black typhoid subsurface colony. There are some members of the coliform group capable of producing hydrogen sulfide that may develop on the medium, giving colonies similar in appearance to typhoid. These may readily be differentiated in that they produce gas from lactose in differential media—Bacto-Russell Double Sugar Agar, Bacto-Kligler Iron Agar or Bacto-Triple Sugar Iron Agar, for example. The hydrolysis of urea as demonstrated on Bacto-Urea Broth or Bacto-Urea Agar, as discussed on pages 170 and 171, may be used to identify proteus or paracolon organisms.

The isolation and purification of *S. typhosa* for agglutination or fermentation studies may be readily accomplished by picking characteristic black colonies from smeared or poured plates of Bismuth Sulfite Agar, and subculturing them upon Bacto-MacConkey Agar. The purified colonies thus obtained may then be picked to differential tube media such as Bacto-Russell Double Sugar Agar, Bacto-Kligler Iron Agar, Bacto-Triple Sugar Iron Agar or other satisfactory differential media for partial identification. Agglutination tests may be made from the fresh growth on the differential tube media or from the growth on Nutrient Agar slants inoculated from the differential media. The growth on the differential tube media may also be used for inoculating carbohydrate media for fermentation studies. It is a common practice among many bacteriologists to pick colonies typical of *S. typhosa* directly from Bismuth Sulfite Agar onto the differential tube media. This may be permissible if the colonies are discrete and well isolated, but it must be remembered that although coliform bacteria are inhibited they are not destroyed by the medium.

It is recommended that Bacto-MacConkey Agar, as discussed on page 131, a non-selective medium, and Bacto-S S Agar, a selective medium, page 134, supporting luxuriant growth of all *Shigella* and *Salmonella* strains, be used in conjunction with Bacto-Bismuth Sulfite Agar for the routine examination of stool and urine specimens. Bacto-Tetrathionate Broth Base, page 157, a fluid enrichment medium for *Salmonella*, is also recommended for use in conjunction with Bacto-Bismuth Sulfite Agar. Results in our laboratory show that the number of positive isolations obtained from Tetrathionate Broth enrichment is decidedly greater when the enriched specimen is plated on Bismuth Sulfite Agar than on MacConkey Agar or S S Agar. The value of Bismuth Sulfite Agar as a plating medium subsequent to enrichment was also demonstrated by Hajna and Perry.[13]

A procedure designed to show the largest number of pathogens from a specimen would be:

A. Streak or smear a large inoculum on one plate of S S Agar and one plate of Bismuth Sulfite Agar.

B. Streak or smear a light inoculum on one plate of MacConkey Agar.

C. Prepare Bismuth Sulfite Agar poured plates with a 5 ml. and a one drop inoculum.

D. Enrich for 12–18 hours in Tetrathionate Broth, follow by streaking on one plate of Bismuth Sulfite Agar and one plate of S S Agar.

A survey of the methods used in the collection and preservation of stool specimens for the isolation and identification of *Salmonella*, *Shigella* and intestinal protozoa by Felsenfeld[14] showed that generally specimens were promptly plated. Glycerol-saline was the most frequently used preservative. S S Agar was the most popular plating medium. There was a decrease in the use of Endo Agar. Desoxycholate Agars were found to be more frequently used than Endo Agar. There were more laboratories using the poured plate of Bismuth Sulfite Agar, MacConkey Agar and Brilliant Green Agar in 1949 than in 1944. The use of streaked plates of Bismuth Sulfite Agar showed a decrease during this period if occasional users were not considered. All but three laboratories were using dehydrated Bismuth Sulfite Agar. He stated that these changes point toward evaluation of experience and economizing in public health laboratories. Newman,[15] in a study of the detection of food poisoning attributable to dairy products, used direct streaking on Bismuth Sulfite Agar as well as enrichment in Tetrathionate Broth followed by streaking on Bismuth Sulfite Agar and S S Agar for the isolation of *Salmonellae*. In a study of methods to be used as a standard for the bacterial examination of pullorum reactors Junghen, Hall and Pomeroy[16] in a committee report showed that in a comparative study of media and enrichments from October, 1946 to February, 1950, Bismuth Sulfite Agar and S S Agar permitted the highest number of specific isolations of *S. pullorum* and *S. gallinarium*. These favored selective media suppressed the growth of coliform organisms. Streaking on Bismuth Sulfite Agar, following enrichment of the specimens in Selenite Broth gave the largest number of positive isolations, followed by S S Agar and then MacConkey Agar. Selenite Broth yielded a higher number of successful isolations on follow-up media than did Tetrathionate Broth. The highest percentage of organisms were isolated from the ovary, followed by gall bladder, peritoneum, oviduct, intestines and pericardial sac in the order listed.

To rehydrate the medium, suspend 52 grams of Bacto-Bismuth Sulfite Agar in 1000 ml. of cold distilled water and heat to boiling to dissolve the medium completely. *The medium should not be sterilized in the autoclave or by fractional sterilization, since heating for a longer period than is necessary to dissolve the medium destroys the selectivity of the medium.* A uniformly correct medium may be obtained at all times merely by dissolving the powder in water. Upon a medium prepared in this way, reactions typical of those described by Wilson and Blair are routinely obtained. The characteristic precipitate present in the medium should be evenly dispersed by twirling the flask just prior to pouring plates. Best results are obtained when the medium is dissolved and used immediately. If it is necessary to prepare the medium several days before using, it should be poured into plates and stored in a cold moist atmosphere to prevent drying. The melted medium should not be allowed to solidify in flasks and be remelted. The final reaction of the medium will be pH 7.7.

One pound of Bacto-Bismuth Sulfite Agar will make 8.7 liters of medium.

1 Standard Methods for the Examination of Dairy Products, 9th Edition:165:1948.
2 Diagnostic Procedures and Reagents, 3rd Edition:212:1950.
3 J. Hyg., 21:392:1923.
4 Brit. Med. J., 1:1061:1928.
5 J. Path. Bact., 29:310:1926.
6 J. Hyg., 26:374:1927.
7 J. Hyg., 31:139:1931.
8 J. Bact., 34:565:1937.
9 Am. J. Pub. Health, 28:1065:1938.
10 J. Lab. Clin. Med., 24:461:1939.
11 Am. J. Pub. Health, 28:762:1938.
12 J. Am. Water Works Assoc., 30:124:1938.
13 J. Lab. Clin. Med., 23:1185:1938.
14 Public Health Reports, 65:1075:1950.
15 J. Milk and Food Tech., 13:226:1950.
16 Proc. 22. Ann. Mtg. N. E. Conf. Lab. Workers Pullorum Disease Control Burlington, Vt., 1950.

BACTO

BRILLIANT GREEN AGAR   (B285)

DEHYDRATED

Bacto-Yeast Extract	3 g.
Proteose Peptone No. 3, Difco	10 g.
Sodium Chloride	5 g.
Bacto-Lactose	10 g.
Saccharose, Difco	10 g.
Bacto-Phenol Red	0.08 g.
Bacto-Brilliant Green	0.0125 g.
Bacto-Agar	20 g.

Bacto-Brilliant Green Agar is a highly selective medium recommended for the isolation of *Salmonella,* other than typhosa, directly from stools or other materials suspected of containing these organisms, or after preliminary enrichment in Tetrathionate Broth.

The use of a Brilliant Green Agar as a primary plating medium for the isolation of *Salmonella* was first described by Kristensen, Lester, and Jurgens[1] who reported it useful for the differentiation of "paratyphoid B" from other intestinal Gram-negative bacilli. Later, Kauffmann[2] modified their formula and used the Brilliant Green Agar in conjunction with a Tetrathionate Broth for the isolation of *Salmonella* from stools. Galton and Quan[3] increased their positive *Salmonella* findings by 164 per cent by the use of Tetrathionate Broth and plating on Brilliant Green Agar. Broh-Kahn[4] and Edwards[5] similarly employed the Kauffmann modification of Brilliant Green Agar with superior results.

Bacto-Brilliant Green Agar is a slight modification of the medium as described by Kauffmann. The outstanding selectivity of this medium permits the use of moderately heavy inocula, which should be evenly distributed over the surface. Inoculation with heavy suspensions of stools or other materials suspected of containing *Salmonella* usually results in an almost pure culture of these organisms. Growth of other bacteria is almost completely inhibited. Following incubation at 37°C. for 18–24 hours the plates are examined for typical *Salmonella* colonies. These appear as slightly pink-white opaque colonies surrounded by a brilliant red medium. The few lactose or sucrose fermenting organisms which may develop on the medium are readily differentiated due to the formation of a yellow-green colony surrounded by an intense yellow-green zone. Bacto-Brilliant Green Agar is highly recommended for the isolation of *Salmonella*. However, it is not suitable for the isolation of *S. typhosa* or *Shigella* organisms. Some strains of *S. typhosa* will develop on this medium forming colonies identical to other *Salmonella*. Some strains of Proteus may also grow forming red colonies. In the routine examination of stools, rectal swabs or other materials for the Gram-negative intestinal pathogens, other primary plating media such as Bacto-S S Agar, Bacto-Bismuth Sulfite Agar and Bacto-MacConkey Agar, as well as fluid enrichments such as Bacto-Tetrathionate Broth and Bacto-Selenite Broth, should be used with Bacto-Brilliant Green Agar.

To rehydrate the medium, suspend 58 grams of Bacto-Brilliant Green Agar in 1000 ml. cold distilled water and heat to boiling to dissolve the medium completely. Distribute in tubes or flasks and sterilize in the autoclave for 15 minutes at 15 pounds pressure (121°C.). A longer period of sterilization will tend to decrease the selectivity of the medium.

The final reaction of the medium will be pH 6.9.

One pound of Bacto-Brilliant Green Agar will make 7.8 liters of medium.

¹ Brit. J. Exp. Path., 6:291:1925.
² Zeit. Hyg., 117:26:1935.
⁴ Am. J. Pub. Health, 34:1071:1944.
⁴ Military Surgeon, 99:770:1946.
⁵ Personal Communication, 1947.

BACTO
LITMUS LACTOSE AGAR (B81)
DEHYDRATED

Bacto-Beef Extract	3 g.
Bacto-Peptone	5 g.
Bacto-Lactose	10 g.
Bacto-Agar	10 g.
Bacto-Litmus	1 g.

Bacto-Litmus Lactose Agar has been used in water bacteriology and in other examinations for the detection of members of the coliform group. This medium may also be used for the determination of the fermentation of lactose with the production of acid and gas.

Litmus Lactose Agar, originally described by Wurtz in 1892, is one of the oldest of the differential plate media. It has been employed in the past and is still being used, to a slight extent, in water bacteriology and other examinations for the detection of members of the coliform group. Upon this medium, colonies of the lactose fermenting bacteria are surrounded by a red zone which distinguishes them from colonies of other organisms that either do not change the surrounding medium or make it more intensely blue due to production of ammonia.

Bacto-Litmus Lactose Agar is prepared according to the generally accepted formula for this medium; when made up for use it contains 1 per cent of lactose and 0.1 per cent of Bacto-Litmus.

Bacto-Violet Red Bile Agar as discussed on page 61 is recommended for use in making coliform counts of water, milk, dairy and other food products. Bacto-Brilliant Green Bile Agar as discussed on page 52 is also a satisfactory medium for counts of the coliform bacteria in water.

To rehydrate the medium, suspend 29 grams of Bacto-Litmus Lactose Agar in 1000 ml. of cold distilled water and heat to boiling to dissolve the medium completely. Distribute in tubes or flasks and sterilize in the autoclave for 15 minutes at 15 pounds pressure (121°C.). The final reaction of the medium will be pH 7.0.

One pound of Bacto-Litmus Lactose Agar will make 15.6 liters of medium.

BACTO
PURPLE LACTOSE AGAR　(B82)
DEHYDRATED

Bacto-Beef Extract	3 g.
Bacto-Peptone	5 g.
Bacto-Lactose	10 g.
Bacto-Agar	10 g.
Bacto-Brom Cresol Purple	0.025 g.

Bacto-Purple Lactose Agar like Litmus Lactose Agar has been used in water bacteriology and in other examinations for the detection of members of the coliform group. This medium may also be used for the determination of the fermentation of lactose with the production of acid and gas.

The disadvantages resulting from the use of litmus in culture media are well known. Litmus has been replaced quite generally by the more stable and sensitive sulfonephthalein indicators which are more sensitive to slight changes in hydrogen ion concentration.

Bacto-Purple Lactose Agar duplicates the formula of Bacto-Litmus Lactose Agar except that brom cresol purple has been substituted for the litmus in order to provide a more satisfactory differential between colonies of the lactose fermenting bacteria and those which do not attack lactose. The color change of this indicator is from blue-purple (alkaline) to yellow (acid). The medium is used for the same purposes and in the same manner as Litmus Lactose Agar. Inoculated plates should be observed frequently after the first 18–24 hours incubation to avoid confusing results due to diffusion of the acid through the medium.

Bacto-Violet Red Bile Agar as discussed on page 61 is recommended for use in making coliform counts of water, milk, dairy and other food products. Bacto-Brilliant Green Bile Agar as discussed on page 52 is a most satisfactory medium for counts of the coliform bacteria in water.

To rehydrate the medium, suspend 29 grams of Bacto-Purple Lactose Agar in 1000 ml. of cold distilled water and heat to boiling to dissolve the medium completely. Distribute in tubes or flasks and sterilize in the autoclave for 15 minutes at 15 pounds pressure (121°C.). The final reaction of the medium will be pH 6.8.

One pound of Bacto-Purple Lactose Agar will make 15.6 liters of medium.

BACTO
CONRADI DRIGALSKI AGAR　(B83)
DEHYDRATED

Bacto-Peptone	10 g.
Bacto-Isoelectric Casein	10 g.
Bacto-Lactose	10 g.
Sodium Chloride	5 g.
Bacto-Agar	15 g.
Bacto-Brom Cresol Purple	0.03 g.
Bacto-Crystal Violet	0.004 g.

Bacto-Conradi Drigalski Agar has been rather extensively employed in the past for the isolation of typhoid and other intestinal pathogens from fecal specimens. Media described subsequent to Conradi Drigalski Agar have proved more satisfactory, and are now recommended for this purpose. For the present we will continue to carry Bacto-Conradi Drigalski Agar for those laboratories where it has been in routine use, but for the isolation of members of the *Salmonella* and *Shigella* groups we recommend the following media:

Bacto-MacConkey Agar, as discussed on page 131.
Bacto-S S Agar, as discussed on page 134.
Bacto-Bismuth Sulfite Agar, as described on page 139.
Bacto-Tetrathionate Broth, as discussed on page 157.
Bacto-Selenite Broth as discussed on page 158.

The differential restraining action exerted by certain dyes on the growth of bacteria is a well-known property, and is utilized frequently in culture media. Crystal violet, for example, when present in a dilution of 1:250,000 in agar media, inhibits quite generally the development of Gram-positive organisms, but has no appreciable effect on the growth of Gram-negative bacteria. This property is employed in the medium of Conradi and Drigalski[1] for the isolation of the Gram-negative intestinal bacteria from contaminated material such as water, feces, etc.

Bacto-Conradi Drigalski Agar is a dehydrated culture medium, prepared to duplicate the original formula. Crystal violet is retained because of its selective action, but the litmus which was originally used as the indicator has been replaced with Bacto-Brom Cresol Purple. This indicator is much more satisfactory than litmus. Colonies fermenting the lactose in the medium are surrounded by a yellow zone. Bacto-Isoelectric Casein, prepared in our own laboratories, has been substituted for the Nutrose specified in the original formula.

To rehydrate the medium, suspend 50 grams of Bacto-Conradi Drigalski Agar in 1000 ml. of cold distilled water and heat to boiling to dissolve the medium completely. Distribute in tubes or flasks and sterilize by autoclaving for 15 minutes at 15 pounds pressure (121°C.). The final reaction of the medium will be pH 6.8.

One pound of Bacto-Conradi Drigalski Agar will make 9 liters of medium.

[1] Zeit. Hyg., 39:283:1902.

BACTO
DEXTROSE PROTEOSE NO. 3 AGAR (B68)
DEHYDRATED

Proteose Peptone No. 3, Difco	20 g.
Bacto-Dextrose	2 g.
Sodium Chloride	5 g.
Bacto-Agar	13 g.

Bacto-Dextrose Proteose No. 3 Agar, used with Bacto-Tellurite Blood Solution is suggested as a selective medium for the detection and isolation of *Corynebacterium diphtheriae*. The medium is of particular value in the release of patients and in the detection of diphtheria carriers. This medium inhibits the streptococci and staphylococci, but permits *C. diphtheriae* to grow. Without added tellurite and blood this medium is recommended as a general laboratory medium containing 0.2 per cent dextrose.

In 1912 Conradi and Troch[1] described a selective serum medium, containing tellurite, used for the isolation of *C. diphtheriae*. On their medium *C. diphtheriae* colonies were coal black due to the reduction of the tellurite. Since then many methods for the use of potassium tellurite in media have been described for the isolation and identification of *C. diphtheriae*. Clauberg[2] in 1929 described a serum medium containing glycerol and potassium tellurite for growth of *C. diphtheriae* from nose and throat smears. Anderson, Happold, McLeod, and Thompson[3] described a heated-blood agar tellurite medium, having the advantage of giving a differentiation of gravis, mitis and intermediate strains. Horgan and Marshall[4] described a Blood Tellurite Agar which gave a high proportion of positive results, and also permitted differentiation between gravis and mitis types. Wilson[5] described a blood agar tellurite arsenate selective medium for *C. diphtheriae* and used a preserved laked blood. McGuigan and Frobisher[6] and Frobisher[7] have used a Cystine Tellurite Blood Agar for isolation of *C. diphtheriae*. Hall[8] described a medium prepared from Bacto-Cabbage Infusion Agar, 10 per cent defibrinated blood, and potassium tellurite for the isolation and identification of *C. diphtheriae*. Many other investigators have described similar media using tellurite to inhibit Gram-positive organisms and permit the development of *C. diphtheriae*. The advantage of these media lies in the fact that *C. diphtheriae*, if present in relatively small numbers, would not be overgrown by streptococci, staphylococci or other contaminating forms.

Bacto-Dextrose Proteose No. 3 Agar, enriched with Bacto-Tellurite Blood Solution, produces a selective medium for *C. diphtheriae*. Staphylococci and streptococci are generally inhibited, while the diphtheria bacilli develop black or grayish black colonies in 18–24 hours. Occasionally a strain of staphylococcus is encountered which grows on this medium, producing black colonies. These, however, may be readily recognized as cocci by microscopic examination. Confirmation of typical colonies is made by microscopic examination of the cells and by testing their fermentation reactions. The morphology of *C. diphtheriae* grown upon tellurite medium varies somewhat from that obtained upon Loeffler Medium. On the selective medium the organisms are generally club shaped, many are barred and only a few show the bipolar staining characteristic of *C. diphtheriae* on Loeffler Medium. Confirmation may be made by transferring the black suspected colony to Loeffler Medium on which typical morphology can be demonstrated as soon as there has been sufficient growth.

Wilson[5] used a preserved laked blood in the preparation of his medium. Neil[9] likewise used this preserved laked blood very satisfactorily in his Tellurite Chocolate Agar. Bacto-Tellurite Blood Solution, as discussed on page 277 contains potassium tellurite in blood so that upon the addition of 5 ml. to 100 ml. of sterile Dextrose Proteose No. 3 Agar a selective medium for *C. diphtheriae*, will be obtained. The use of 4 ml. of Bacto-Tellurite Blood Solution per 100 ml. of agar will give a less selective medium, while 6 ml. will produce a more inhibitive medium. For ordinary purposes 5 ml. of the Tellurite Blood Solution will give satisfactory selectivity without marked inhibition of the diphtheria bacillus.

Chocolate tellurite media prepared from Bacto-Dextrose Proteose No. 3 Agar and Bacto-Tellurite Blood Solution are recommended for a variety of purposes including the diagnosis of diphtheria, typing of strains and determination of virulence and are especially useful in release of cases and detection of carriers. It is recommended that some non-selective medium, Loeffler's for example, be run in conjunction with the selective tellurite medium for detection of *C. diphtheriae* in acute cases.

To rehydrate the medium, suspend 40 grams of Bacto-Dextrose Proteose No. 3 Agar in 1000 ml. of cold distilled water and heat to boiling to dissolve the medium completely. Distribute in flasks and sterilize in the autoclave for 15 minutes at 15 pounds pressure (121°C.). Add 5 ml. of Bacto-Tellurite Blood Solution to each 100 ml. of sterile melted agar at 70–80°C., under aseptic conditions. Heat at 75–80°C. until it has the appearance of a "chocolate agar" and then cool to 50°C. Distribute into sterile tubes or plates as desired. For best results inoculate the medium the same day as prepared.

For a plain Dextrose Agar, use without the addition of Bacto-Tellurite Blood Solution. Final reaction of the medium without enrichment will be pH 7.4.

One pound of Bacto-Dextrose Proteose No. 3 Agar will make 11.3 liters of medium.

[1] Muench. Wochschr., 59:1652:1912.
[2] Zentr. Bakt., 114:539:1929.
[3] J. Path. Bact., 34:667:1931.
[4] J. Hyg., 32:544:1932.
[5] J. Path. Bact., 38:114:1934.

[6] J. Infectious Diseases, 59:22:1936.
[7] J. Infectious Diseases, 60:99:1937.
[8] Am. J. Pub. Health., 29:664:1939.
[9] J. Hyg., 37:552:1937.

BACTO

MUELLER TELLURITE BASE (B264)

DEHYDRATED

Bacto-Casamino Acids, Technical ..	20 g.
Casein	5 g.
l-Tryptophane	0.05 g.
Potassium Dihydrogen Phosphate ..	0.3 g.
Magnesium Sulfate	0.1 g.
Bacto-Agar	20 g.

Bacto-Mueller Tellurite Base enriched with Bacto-Mueller Tellurite Serum is recommended for the isolation, differentiation and identification of *Corynebacterium diphtheriae*. The basal medium and sterile enrichment are prepared according to the formula given by Mueller and Miller.[1]

Many selective media containing tellurite have been described for the initial cultivation of members of the *Corynebacterium* group. The medium as described by Mueller and Miller is transparent, requires no heating following the addition of the sterile tellurite enrichment, and may be prepared from standardized materials to give a uniform desired growth response. The availability of the components of the medium in the form of the dehydrated base and sterilized enrichment is pointed out by the authors making the preparation of the final medium containing all the nutriments required by the *Corynebacterium* group and of the correct selectivity an easy task. A discussion of Bacto-Mueller Tellurite Serum, the enrichment used in preparing the transparent medium, is described on page 278.

The presence or absence of organisms consistent with the morphological characteristics of *C. diphtheriae* in a suspected diphtheria case materially assists the physician in making an accurate diagnosis. This medium was developed after 4 years of practical use of tellurite plate media in the detection of diphtheria carriers. It has given excellent results in other laboratories in detecting diphtheria organisms. It permits a differentiation of the mitis, gravis and intermedius types. As described by Mueller and Miller easily visible confluent growth of either mitis or gravis types of *C. diphtheriae* is obtained from a fresh case after 15–18 hours incubation. Plates showing no growth should be incubated for an additional 21 hours. In 48 hours mitis colonies are 1.0–1.5 mm. in diameter, black and convex with a glistening surface. Gravis types in contrast show flat irregular colonies with a dull surface, slate gray in color and 2–3 mm. in diameter. Gravis types seldom show typical "daisy head" colonies. The size of the colony and degree of darkening increases with length of incubation. Intermedius colonies are pin point in size in 24 hours and approximately 0.2–0.3 mm. in diameter after 48 hours incubation. The colonies show little darkening but appear brownish gray with a white background in a good light. Hoffman's bacillus and other diphtheroids grow on the medium, often resembling mitis types. Cocci, non-diphtheroid bacilli and yeast are generally inhibited. Cocci, when they do produce colonies, resemble mitis types. Colonies or growth suggestive of diphtheria bacilli should be examined microscopically to determine the presence of organism having Corynebacterial characteristics. Mueller and Miller state that the morphology of the various types of *C. diphtheriae* on the tellurite medium is entirely uniform. They further suggest that the diphtheria organisms developing on this medium must be tested for virulence or toxin production.

About 20 ml. of the final medium are poured into plates. The surface of the medium must be dry prior to inoculation; this is accomplished by allowing the medium to cool and solidify with covers removed. The surface of the plate is then streaked with the swab. A more selective medium for the initial cultivation of *Corynebacteria* is described on page 147, prepared with Bacto-Dextrose Proteose No. 3 Agar, enriched with Bacto-Tellurite Blood Solution.

To rehydrate the medium, suspend 45 grams Bacto-Mueller Tellurite Base in 1000 ml. of cold distilled water. Heat to boiling to dissolve the medium completely. Sterilize in the autoclave for 10 minutes at 10 pounds pressure (116°C). Cool to 50°C. and add 25 ml. Bacto-Mueller Tellurite Serum. Mix thoroughly avoiding formation of air bubbles and distribute by pouring 20 ml. quantities in sterile 95 mm. plates. Final reaction of the medium will be pH 7.6.

One pound of Bacto-Mueller Tellurite Base will make 10.2 liters final medium.

¹ J. Bact., 51:743:1946.

BACTO
MANNITOL SALT AGAR   (B30)
DEHYDRATED

Bacto-Beef Extract	1 g.
Proteose Peptone No. 3, Difco	10 g.
Sodium Chloride	75 g.
d-Mannitol, Difco	10 g.
Bacto-Agar	15 g.
Bacto-Phenol Red	0.025 g.

Bacto-Mannitol Salt Agar is a selective medium for the isolation of pathogenic staphylococci. It is prepared according to the formula suggested by Chapman.¹ Growth of most bacteria other than staphylococci is inhibited on this medium.

Koch² reported that on solid media staphylococci were not inhibited by a concentration of 7.5 per cent sodium chloride. Chapman¹ confirmed this observation and noted that the addition of 7.5 per cent sodium chloride to Bacto-Phenol Red Mannitol Agar gave a medium on which staphylococci that coagulated rabbit plasma grew luxuriantly, producing colonies with yellow zones. Nonpathogenic staphylococci on the contrary produced small colonies surrounded by red or purple zones. Other bacteria were generally inhibited, making possible the use of a heavy inoculation without danger of overgrowth. Chapman recommended incubation for 36 hours at 37°C. In a study of the resistance of chronic staphylococcal bovine mastitis to massive penicillin therapy McCulloch³ stated that the staphylococci responsible for the mastitis grew well and formed acid in Phenol Red Mannitol Agar to which 7.0 per cent sodium chloride had been added. Velilla, Faber and Pelczar⁴ used Bacto-Mannitol Salt Agar for the isolation of coagulase producing staphylococci from milk in bovine mastitis. They recommended the use of both Bacto-Mannitol Salt Agar and Bacto-Staphylococcus Medium No. 110, to insure maximum recovery of these organisms.

To rehydrate the medium suspend 111 grams Bacto-Mannitol Salt Agar in 1000 ml. cold distilled water, and heat to boiling to dissolve the medium completely. Distribute in tubes or flasks and sterilize in the autoclave for 15 minutes at 15 pounds pressure (121°C.). The final reaction of the medium will be pH 7.4.

One pound of Bacto-Mannitol Salt Agar will make 4.0 liters of medium.

¹ J. Bact., 50:201:1945.   ³ Am. J. Vet. Res., 8:173:1947.
² Zentr. Bakt., I Abt. Orig., 149:122:1942.   ⁴ Am. J. Vet. Res., 8:275:1947.

BACTO
STAPHYLOCOCCUS MEDIUM NO. 110   (B297)
DEHYDRATED

Bacto-Yeast Extract	2.5 g.
Bacto-Tryptone	10 g.
Bacto-Gelatin	30 g.
Bacto-Lactose	2 g.
d-Mannitol, Difco	10 g.
Sodium Chloride	75 g.
Dipotassium Phosphate	5 g.
Bacto-Agar	15 g.

Bacto-Staphylococcus Medium No. 110 is a selective medium for the isolation of staphylococci. In addition, pigment and coagulase production, Stone's method for liquefaction of gelatin and fermentation of mannitol may be determined directly on this medium without the necessity of making transplants for these conformity tests. These characteristics, and the selective properties of the medium due to its high sodium chloride content, make it of particular value for the isolation of staphylococci, especially those suspected of being pathogenic or involved in cases of food poisoning. The medium has the additional advantage that, with few exceptions, pathogenic strains produce typical orange pigmented colonies whereas nonpathogenic types produce white colonies, a relationship that is not obtained on any other medium. The coagulase test should be made using a subculture of the suspected colony in Brain Heart Infusion or a Brain Heart Infusion suspension of the organism grown on Heart Infusion Agar slants.

Koch¹ reported that staphylococci were not inhibited by a concentration of 7.5 per cent sodium chloride in solid media. Chapman² noted that most bacteria, other than staphylococci, were inhibited on such media and that pathogenic staphylococci grew more luxuriantly than did nonpathogenic strains. He suggested that 7.5 per cent sodium chloride be added to Bacto-Phenol Red Mannitol Agar as a selective isolation medium for staphylococci. In a study of the resistance of chronic staphylococcal bovine mastitis to massive penicillin therapy McCulloch³ stated that the staphylococci responsible for the mastitis grew well and formed acid on Bacto-Phenol Red Mannitol Agar to which 7.0 per cent sodium chloride had been added. Stone⁴ described a culture medium on which food poisoning staphylococci gave a gelatinase test, or were "Stone reaction" positive. Chapman, Lieb and Curcio⁵ pointed out the nonspecificity of this single test and reported that in addition to being "Stone reaction" positive, typical food poisoning staphylococci must produce pigment, coagulate plasma, hemolyze rabbit blood and ferment mannitol.

Continued study of the isolation of staphylococci by Chapman⁶ led to the development of a medium designated as Staphylococcus Medium No. 110. In addition to being selective for staphylococci due to the high sodium chloride content, this medium is well suited for pigment formation, may be used for the determination of the fermentation of mannitol, for the Stone type gelatinase test and gives a growth satisfactory for the coagulase test. According to Chapman⁷

and Chapman and Domingo[8] staphylococci incriminated in food poisoning produce an orange pigment, coagulate plasma, ferment mannitol and give a
positive "Stone reaction" or gelatinase test on Staphylococcus Medium No. 110
when tested at the time of isolation. Velilla, Faber and Pelczar[9] suggested the use
of both Mannitol Salt Agar and Staphylococcus Medium No. 110 to insure maximum recovery of coagulase producing staphylococci from suspected bovine
mastitis.

Evans[10] in his studies of coagulase positive staphylococci reported that
pigmentation was much stronger on Staphylococcus Medium No. 110 than on
Infusion Agar and some showed pigment on Chapman's medium but were white
on the Infusion Agar. Newman,[11] in a study of the detection of food poisoning
attributable to dairy products, used Staphylococcus Medium No. 100 and Chapman Stone Medium for the isolation of staphylococci. The coagulase test was run
to assist in the detection of pathogenic staphylococci. The cultures for the performance of coagulase test were grown in Brain Heart Infusion.

Following streaking or smearing of the specimens on plates of Bacto-Staphylococcus Medium No. 110 the medium is incubated at 30°C.[12] for exactly 48 hours
or for exactly 43 hours at 37°C. The colonies are first observed for signs of the
production of any orange or yellow pigment. Such colonies are picked from the
surface of the medium and emulsified in 0.1–0.2 ml. of Brain Heart Infusion or
Bacto-Tryptose Phosphate Broth for the coagulase test. A drop of brom
cresol purple indicator is added to several of the areas from which typical pigmented colonies were removed. Any change in color of the indicator compared
with that of the uninoculated medium is indicative of fermentation of mannitol.
The plate is then flooded with 5 ml. saturated solution of ammonium sulfate kept
in the incubator and let stand 10 minutes. Any clear zone around areas from
which colonies have been picked, or around colonies, are gelatinase positive.

Chapman[18] recently reported that a 20 per cent solution of sulfosalicylic
acid (Chapman-Stone Developer) is superior to saturated ammonium sulfate
solution for the test. The plate is flooded with the solution, and at the end of
10 minutes, a clear zone around the colonies denotes a positive "Stone reaction."
The lytic zones stand out as clear areas in an opaque white background. Chapman[14] has also described a method of applying confirmation tests directly to
colonies on the medium. Chapman tubes (10 mm. length and diameter) are
sterilized and pressed slightly into the surface of the medium. In the cup thus
formed is added a drop of 0.04 per cent brom thymol blue. Replace cover on
plate and let stand 10 minutes before reading result. The formation of a yellow
color indicated a positive reaction, while a green color denotes a negative reaction. In a similar manner the "Stone reaction" may be determined by using a
19 mm. tube, placing it around the colony to be tested. Add 1 ml. of Chapman
Stone Developer (20 per cent sulfosalicylic acid) or saturated Ammonium Sulfate solution. Examine after standing 10 minutes. A clear zone around the colony
denotes a positive "Stone reaction."

To determine the coagulative power, use a 16–24 hour culture of the suspected
organism in Brain Heart Infusion or a Brain Heart Infusion suspension of a
16–24 hour culture on a slant of Heart Infusion Agar. Two drops of the culture
or suspension of the organism is added to 0.5 ml. of Bacto-Coagulase Plasma Solution. Incubate at 37°C. Most coagulase positive staphylococci will clot Bacto-
Coagulase Plasma Solution within one hour. However, readings should be made
after two and three hours of incubation before discarding as negative. A positive
culture will show a definite clot often in 20–30 minutes. Chapman clearly states
that with few exceptions those colonies that produce pigment, coagulate plasma,
ferment mannitol and give a gelatinase reaction are food poisoning staphylococci.
According to Chapman[18] this type of staphylococcus may be isolated from only

about 6 per cent of the population. A complete discussion of Bacto-Coagulase Plasma is given on page 330.

To rehydrate the medium, suspend 149 grams of Bacto-Staphylococcus Medium No. 110 in 1000 ml. cold distilled water and heat to boiling to dissolve the medium completely. Distribute in tubes or flasks and sterilize in the autoclave for 15 minutes at 15 pounds pressure (121°C.). When cool enough to handle, but hotter than the usual pouring temperatures, disperse the precipitate by gentle agitation, avoiding air bubbles and pour into plates. If plates are not used when poured, keep in refrigerator in sealed cans. For field work the medium may be boiled for 5 minutes without further sterilization and poured into the plates, preferably while still hot. The final reaction of the medium will be pH 7.0.

One pound of Bacto-Staphylococcus Medium No. 110 will make 3 liters of medium.

[1] Zentr. Bakt. I Abt. Orig., 149:122:1942.
[2] J. Bact., 50:201:1945.
[3] Am. J. Vet. Res., 8:173:1947.
[4] Proc. Soc. Exp. Biol. Med., 33:185:1935.
[5] Food Research, 2:349:1937.
[6] J. Bact., 51:409:1946.
[7] Trans. N. Y. Academy Sciences, 9:52:1946.
[8] J. Bact., 51:405:1946.
[9] Am. J. Vet. Res., 8:275:1947.
[10] J. Bact., 55:793:1948.
[11] J. Milk and Food Tech., 13:226:1950.
[12] J. Bact., 53:367:1947.
[13] Personal Communication.
[14] J. Bact., 63:147:1952.

BACTO

CHAPMAN STONE MEDIUM (B313)

DEHYDRATED

Bacto-Yeast Extract	2.5 g.
Bacto-Tryptone	10 g.
Bacto-Gelatin	30 g.
d-Mannitol, Difco	10 g.
Sodium Chloride	55 g.
Ammonium Sulfate	75 g.
Dipotassium Phosphate	5 g.
Bacto-Agar	15 g.

Bacto Chapman Stone Medium is a selective medium for the isolation of staphylococci, prepared according to the formula described by Chapman.[1] This medium is similar to Bacto-Staphylococcus Medium No. 110 except that ammonium sulfate is included in the medium and the amount of sodium chloride reduced to 5.5 per cent. Flooding the plate with ammonium sulfate solution is therefore unnecessary for the determination of Stone's method for the liquefaction of gelatin.

Sodium chloride is used as the selective agent in this medium. A complete discussion of the use of high concentrations of this salt and details for the isolation of staphylococci are given on page 151 under Bacto Staphylococcus Medium No. 110. In the examination of specimens, they are streaked on the surface of the medium and incubated 48 hours at 30°C. Any yellow or orange colonies, surrounded by a clear zone, which also ferment mannitol and are coagulase positive, are likely to be those of food poisoning or pathogenic staphylococci. White or nonpigmented colonies, even though there may be a decided clear zone, are not significant.

Colonies showing any pigment production are picked from the surface of the medium and emulsified in 0.1–0.2 ml. of Brain Heart Infusion or Tryptose Phosphate Broth for the performance of the coagulase test. A drop of brom cresol purple indicator is added to several areas from which typical pigmented colonies were removed. Any change in color of the indicator compared with that of the uninoculated medium is indicative of the fermentation of mannitol. To determine coagulase production, violently shake the colonies emulsified in Brain Heart Infusion for 15 minutes. Add 0.2 ml. of Bacto-Coagulase Plasma Solution. Incubate at 37°C. for one hour. Most coagulase positive staphylococci will form a clot within one hour; however, readings should be made after 2 and 3 hours incubation before being considered as negative. A complete discussion of Bacto-Coagulase Plasma is given on page 330.

Newman,[2] in a study of the detection of food poisoning attributable to dairy products, used Chapman Stone Medium and Staphylococcus Medium No. 110 for the isolation of staphylococci. The coagulase test was run to assist in the detection of pathogenic staphylococci. The cultures for the performance of the coagulase test were grown in Brain Heart Infusion.

To rehydrate the medium, suspend 20.2 grams of Bacto-Chapman Stone Medium in 100 ml. cold distilled water and heat to boiling to dissolve the medium completely. Distribute in tubes or flasks and sterilize in the autoclave for 10 minutes at 15 pounds pressure (121°C.). For field work, or if the medium is to be inoculated the same day as prepared, sterilization in the autoclave may be omitted, heating the medium to effect complete solution is sufficient. Pour into plates while the medium is hot, avoiding formation of bubbles. The medium after solidification should be opaque and white. Final reaction of the medium will be pH 7.0.

One pound of Bacto-Chapman Stone Medium will make 2.2 liters of medium.

[1] Food Research, 13:100:1948.
[2] J. Milk and Food Tech., 13:226:1950.

BACTO
MITIS SALIVARIUS AGAR　　(B298)
DEHYDRATED

Bacto-Tryptose	10 g.
Proteose Peptone No. 3, Difco	5 g.
Proteose Peptone, Difco	5 g.
Bacto-Dextrose	1 g.
Saccharose, Difco	50 g.
Dipotassium Phosphate	4 g.
Trypan Blue	0.075 g.
Bacto-Crystal Violet	0.0008 g.
Bacto-Agar	15 g.

Bacto-Mitis Salivarius Agar is prepared according to the formula described by Chapman[1,2] for the isolation of *Streptococcus mitis, S. salivarius* and enterococci. Some bacteriologists refer to these organisms as *"Streptococcus viridans"* and "nonhemolytic streptococci," respectively, because of their alpha and gamma hemolysis on Blood Agar prepared from Bacto-Heart Infusion Agar or Bacto-Tryptose Blood Agar Base. The final medium, containing Bacto-Chapman Tellurite Solution, is highly selective for these organisms, making possible their isolation from grossly contaminated specimens such as feces or exudates from different body cavities.

Different methods have been employed for the isolation of streptococci and enterococci from mixed cultures. Snyder and Lichstein[3] and Lichstein and Snyder[4] used sodium azide as inhibiting agents for Gram-negative bacteria including proteus. Chapman[5] described a Tellurite Medium and an Azide Medium for isolation of *S. salivarius* and *S. mitis*.

Chapman,[1,2] continuing his studies, reported a complete and detailed method for the isolation and testing for the pathogenicity of fecal streptococci. Decimal dilutions of the specimen are prepared and 0.01 ml. amounts spread by a glass spreader, over the surface of the Mitis Salivarius Agar containing tellurite. Plates are incubated for exactly 24 hours at 37°C. *S. mitis* produces small or minute blue colonies. Some *S. mitis* colonies may be more easily distinguished with a longer incubation. *S. salivarius* produces blue, smooth or rough "gum drop" colonies 1–5 mm. in diameter, depending on the number of colonies on the plate. Enterococci form colonies dark blue or black in color, shiny, slightly raised, 1–2 mm. in diameter. These organisms, few of which are pathogenic, may be readily differentiated from *S. mitis* and *S. salivarius*, particularly when viewed by reflected light. Beta hemolytic streptococci resemble *S. mitis*. Other types of streptococci have not been studied on this medium. Chapman[6] reported that *Erysipelothrix rhusiopathiae* produce colorless circular convex colonies. He also reported that when coliform organisms do grow they produce brown colonies; however, generally they are not only inhibited but are actually killed. Spreaders are rarely observed. Molds grow after 2 days incubation. Using this medium Chapman was able to demonstrate pathogenic streptococci in about 95 per cent of fecal specimens from chronic invalids. Pathogenicity of these streptococci was determined culturally according to the method described by Chapman[1,5] using hexylresorcinol.

Bacto-Mitis Salivarius Agar, to which Bacto-Chapman Tellurite Solution has been added, duplicates the medium as described by Chapman.[1,5] Comparative tests have shown this medium to be satisfactory for the isolation of streptococci and enterococci from grossly contaminated specimens such as body secretions and excretions.

To rehydrate the medium, suspend 90 grams of Bacto-Mitis Salivarius Agar in 1000 ml. cold distilled water and heat to boiling to dissolve the medium completely. Sterilize in the autoclave for 15 minutes at 15 pounds pressure (121°C.). Cool to 50–55°C. and just prior to pouring the plates add exactly 1.0 ml. of Bacto-Chapman Tellurite Solution (discussed in detail on page 277). Prepare plates with 25 ml. medium per 95 mm. diameter plate. *Do not heat the medium after the addition of the Tellurite Solution.* Final reaction of the medium will be pH 7.0.

One pound of Bacto-Mitis Salivarius Agar will make 5 liters of medium.

[1] Am. J. Digestive Diseases, 13:105:1946.
[2] Trans. N. Y. Acad. Sciences, 10:45:1947.
[3] J. Infectious Diseases, 67:113:1940.
[4] J. Bact., 42:653:1941.
[5] J. Bact., 48:113:1944.
[6] Personal Communication.

BACTO
AZIDE BLOOD AGAR BASE (B409)
DEHYDRATED

Bacto-Tryptose	10 g.
Bacto-Beef Extract	3 g.
Sodium Chloride	5 g.
Sodium Azide	0.2 g.
Bacto-Agar	15 g.

Bacto-Azide Blood Agar Base is a selective medium for the isolation of streptococci from stools, sewage and other specimens. It is also suggested as a selective medium for the isolation of staphylococci. The medium may be employed with the addition of blood permitting the production of typical hemolytic reactions by the streptococci, or may be used without added blood.

The addition of sodium azide to culture media as a selective agent has been suggested by a number of investigators. Edwards[1] in 1933 used a liquid medium containing crystal violet and sodium azide as a selective broth in the isolation of mastitis streptococci. Hartman[2] reported the value of sodium azide as a selective agent for the isolation of streptococci causing mastitis. Bryan, Devereux, Hirschey and Corbett[3] reported that sodium azide in a concentration of 1:5,000 was a better selective preservative for milk cultures and gave more accurate results for the microscopic and Hotis tests for *Streptococcus mastitis* than 1:50,000 brilliant green. Snyder and Lichstein[4] and Lichstein and Snyder[5] reported that sodium azide in 0.01 per cent concentration in blood agar prevented the swarming of proteus, and permitted the isolation of streptococci from known mixtures of bacteria. The common Gram-negative bacteria were inhibited on this medium. Packer[6] modified Edwards' medium and prepared an Infusion Blood Agar containing 1:15,000 sodium azide and 1:500,000 crystal violet for the study of bovine mastitis and recommended it as a selective medium for the cultural examination of pathogenic streptococci from human sources.

Mallmann, Botwright and Churchill[7] in studying the selective bacteriostatic effect of slow oxidizing agents reported that sodium azide exerted a bacteriostatic effect on Gram-negative bacteria and permitted the growth of Gram-positive organisms. Packer[8] used 1:15,000 sodium azide and 1:500,000 crystal violet in a Blood Agar prepared with 1.5 per cent Bacto-Tryptose for the selective isolation of *Erysipelothrix rhusiopathiae*. "Standard Methods for the Examination of Dairy Products"[9] specifies the use of sodium azide in agar media prepared with Bacto-Tryptose for the isolation of pathogenic bacteria from cheese.

Sodium azide has also been used in liquid media for the detection of fecal streptococci in stools, sewage, swimming pools and drinking water supplies. See Bacto-S F Medium, page 46, Bacto-B A G G Broth, page 47, and Bacto-Azide Dextrose Broth, page 48 for the discussion of these media.

To rehydrate the medium, suspend 33 grams of Bacto-Azide Blood Agar Base in 1000 ml. of cold distilled water and heat to boiling to dissolve the medium completely. Distribute in tubes or flasks and sterilize in the autoclave for 15 minutes at 15 pounds pressure (121°C.). In the preparation of Azide Blood Agar, cool the sterile melted medium to 45–50°C. and add 5 per cent sterile defibrinated blood, under aseptic conditions. Distribute in tubes or flasks.

One pound of Bacto-Azide Blood Agar Base will make 13.7 liters of medium.

[1] J. Comp. Path. Therap., 46:211:1933.
[2] Milchw. Forsch., 18:116:1936.
[3] North Am. Vet., 20:424:1939.
[4] J. Infectious Diseases, 67:113:1940.
[5] J. Bact., 42:653:1941.
[6] J. Bact., 42:138:1941.
[7] J. Infectious Diseases, 69:215:1941.
[8] J. Bact., 46:343:1943.
[9] Standard Methods for the Examination of Dairy Products, 9th Edition:165:1948.

Differential Liquid Enrichments

THE USE of selective enrichment media is a recommended procedure for aiding in the isolation of *Salmonella*. Preliminary inoculation of the suspected sample into liquid enrichments, followed by incubation for 18 hours before inoculation on suitable plating media, materially increases the percentage of isolations of *Salmonella*.

BACTO
TETRATHIONATE BROTH BASE (B104)
DEHYDRATED

Proteose Peptone, Difco	5 g.
Bacto-Bile Salts	1 g.
Calcium Carbonate	10 g.
Sodium Thiosulfate	30 g.

Bacto-Tetrathionate Broth Base is a selective liquid enrichment medium employed in the isolation of *Salmonella typhosa* and other members of the *Salmonella* (paratyphoid) group from feces, urine, water, sewage and infected materials such as eggs and other foodstuffs. Its use is particularly indicated in the early stages of enteric disorders, in determining the release of patients, and in detecting carriers of typhoid and paratyphoid organisms. The use of Tetrathionate Broth is specified in "Standard Methods for the Examination of Dairy Products"[1] for the isolation of bacteria from cheese. "Diagnostic Procedures and Reagents"[2] modify the formula by the addition of Brilliant Green to the enrichment as used in the examination of specimens for *Salmonella* and *Shigella*.

The credit for discovering the usefulness of a Tetrathionate Broth for enriching typhoid and the paratyphoid group is ascribed to Mueller[3] who demonstrated clearly that it inhibited or killed the coliform organisms and permitted typhoid and the paratyphoids to grow almost unrestrictedly. Mueller obtained pure cultures of typhoid by incubating mixtures containing few typhoid organisms and infinite numbers of coli in his Tetrathionate Enrichment.

Kauffmann,[4,5] using a modified Mueller's broth claimed to have increased his positive isolations of *S. typhosa* over 30 per cent and of other members of the *Salmonella* group from 100 to 700 per cent over that possible by direct streaking onto plate media. Schaeffer,[6] using Tetrathionate Broth also demonstrated the greater efficiency of Tetrathionate Enrichment by detecting four times as many typhoid and paratyphoid positive fecal specimens as could be found by direct plating. Further demonstrations of the usefulness of Tetrathionate Enrichment were made by Jones,[7] Ruys[8] and by Szper,[9] who effected a technique for its use in examining large volumes of water and sewage material. Newman[10] in a study of the detection of food poisoning attributable to dairy products, used Tetrathionate Broth followed by streaking to Bismuth Sulfite Agar and S S Agar for the isolation of *Salmonella*.

The prepared broth is inoculated by adding 1–3 grams of stool, sewage, urine or other infected material to 10 ml. of the medium and mixing with a swab, glass rod or pipette to suspend the particulate matter. Many workers find it advantageous to pass a loosely packed cotton plug down through the inoculated broth to carry the coarser particles of fecal material to the bottom of the tube. The inoculated medium is then incubated for 12–24 hours, and streaked out upon Bacto-MacConkey Agar and Bacto-Bismuth Sulfite Agar. The inoculated plates are incubated at 37°C. Examine the MacConkey Agar plates after 18–24 hours and the Bismuth Sulfite Agar plates at 24–48 hours for typical typhoid or paratyphoid colonies. Confirm typical colonies on Bacto-Triple Sugar Iron Agar or by other suitable means. In cases of suspected *Salmonella* infections other than typhoid, some bacteriologists prefer to use Bacto-Brilliant Green Agar as a plating medium after enrichment because of its selective reaction for these organisms.

To rehydrate the medium, suspend 4.6 grams of Bacto-Tetrathionate Broth Base in 100 ml. of distilled water, and heat to boiling. Cool below 45°C. Add 2.0 ml. of iodine solution.* Shake to mix, and tube in 10 ml. quantities, in sterile

*The iodine solution is prepared by dissolving 6 g. iodine crystals and 5 g. potassium iodide in 20 ml. of water.

tubes, exercising care to obtain an even distribution of the insoluble material. Do not heat after the iodine has been added. The complete medium containing iodine should be used the day it is prepared, the base medium without the iodine can be stored indefinitely after sterilization.

One pound of Bacto-Tetrathionate Broth Base will make 9.8 liters of base medium.

[1] Standard Methods for the Examination of Dairy Products, 9th Edition:165:1948.
[2] Diagnostic Procedures and Reagents, 3rd Edition:212:1950.
[3] Compt. rend. soc. biol., 89:434:1923.
[4] Zentr. Bakt., I Abt., Orig., 113:148:1930–31.
[5] Zeit. Hyg., 117:26:1935–36.
[6] Zentr. Bakt., I Abt., Orig., 133:458:1935.
[7] J. Path. Bact., 42:455:1936.
[8] Brit. Med. J., 1:606:1940.
[9] Comp. rend. soc. biol., 118:1675:1935.
[10] J. Milk and Food Tech., 13:226:1950.

BACTO
SELENITE BROTH   (B275)
DEHYDRATED

Bacto-Tryptone	5 g.
Bacto-Lactose	4 g.
Disodium Phosphate	10 g.
Sodium Selenite	4 g.

Bacto-Selenite Broth is recommended as an enrichment medium in the isolation of *Salmonella typhosa* and other members of the *Salmonella* group from feces, urine and infected tissues. The formula of this medium is essentially the same as that of Selenite F Broth described by Leifson.[1] Selenite Broth, for the enrichment of enteric pathogens, is described in "Diagnostic Procedures and Reagents."[2]

Handel and Theodorascu according to Guth[3] observed that *Escherichia coli* was much more susceptible to the toxicity of sodium selenite than was *S. typhosa*. Guth[8] confirmed the observations of these authors and employed sodium selenite as a selective agent in an agar medium and in an enrichment broth for the isolation of *S. typhosa* from feces. Leifson[1] extended Guth's observations and developed a Selenite Agar and a Selenite Broth for use in the isolation of typhoid and paratyphoid bacilli from feces and urine and found the broth enrichment to offer the greater promise.

Leifson showed that the Selenite Broth was not sufficiently toxic to inhibit fecal coli and enterococci completely. However, the colon bacilli were reduced in numbers during the first 8–12 hours and thereafter increased rapidly. The typhoid bacilli on the other hand multiplied fairly rapidly from the start. Proteus and pyocyaneus were not inhibited. Dysentery and alcaligenes were inhibited. In the Selenite Broth the growth behavior of coli and typhoid in the presence of feces or urine was similar to that of pure cultures.

Leifson observed that the selenite medium functioned most efficiently under reduced oxygen tension. To provide optimal conditions, the broth was distributed in tubes to give a depth of 2 inches or more. Using the enrichment under optimal conditions Leifson was able to isolate many more typhoid and paratyphoid organisms than by direct plating without primary enrichment.

In a survey of methods used for the collection and preservation of stool specimens for the isolation and identification of *Salmonella, Shigella* and intestinal protozoa, Felsenfeld[4] reported an increasing number of laboratories using the Selenite Broth as an enrichment. In a study of methods to be used as a standard for the bacterial examination of pullorum reactors, Jungherr, Hall and Pomeroy[5] in a committee report showed that in a comparative study of media and enrichments, from October, 1946 to February, 1950, Bismuth Sulfite Agar and S S Agar permitted the highest number of specific isolations of *S. pullorum* and *S. gallinarum*. These favored selective media suppressed the growth of coliform organisms. Following enrichment of the specimens in Selenite Broth streaking on Bismuth Sulfite Agar gave the largest number of positive isolations, followed by S S Agar and then MacConkey Agar. Selenite Broth yielded a higher number of successful isolations on follow-up media than did Tetrathionate Broth. The highest percentage of organisms were isolated from the ovary, followed by gall bladder, peritoneum, oviduct, intestines and pericardial sac in the order listed.

For the examination of fecal specimens Selenite Broth is inoculated by adding 1–2 ml. of fecal suspension to tubes of 10–15 ml. of medium. After thorough mixing, the tubes are incubated at 37°C. for 18–24 hours. For the examination of infected tissues 1–2 grams of material are mascerated in 10–15 ml. Selenite Broth by means of a sterile pipette or stirring rod before incubation. For examination of urine the Selenite Broth should be prepared in double strength and tubed in 5–7.5 ml. amounts. This broth is inoculated with an equal volume of urine sample and is incubated as described above. After incubation a loopful of the enriched culture is streaked on one plate of Bismuth Sulfite Agar and a similar amount is streaked on one plate of S S Agar. These plates are incubated at 37°C. and are examined after 18–24 hours. The Bismuth Sulfite Agar plate should be incubated for 48 hours before being discarded as negative.

To rehydrate the medium, suspend 23 grams Bacto-Selenite Broth in 1000 ml. of distilled water and heat to boiling. Distribute in sterile culture tubes to give a depth of medium of at least 2 inches. Avoid excessive heating. *Do not sterilize in the autoclave.* The final reaction of the medium will be pH 7.0.

One pound of Bacto-Selenite Broth will make 19 liters of medium.

[1] Am. J. Hyg., 24:423:1936.
[3] Diagnostic Procedures and Reagents, 3rd Edition:25:1950.
[6] Centr. Bakt. I Abt. Orig., 77:487:1916.
[4] Public Health Reports, 63:1075:1950.
[5] Proc. 22nd Ann. Mtg. N. E. Conf. Lab. Workers Pullorum Disease Control, Burlington, Vt., 1950.

Differential Tube Media

DIFFERENTIAL tube media afford the bacteriologist a simple and effective cultural means of identifying pure cultures of bacteria. Both solid media and liquid media have been devised for this purpose. Many of the solid differential tube media contain one or more fermentable carbohydrates and a suitable indicator for the detection of acid or alkali production; some contain substances rich in sulfur and an indicator to detect hydrogen sulfide formation; still others contain a combination of both. The solid tube media containing fermentable carbohydrates permit the study of both aerobic and anaerobic dissimilation processes by the bacteria under study. Screw capped tubes are not satisfactory for solid differential media as pointed out by Marcus and Greaves[1] unless the caps be placed on the tubes loosely, or replaced by cotton plugs. The changes produced in the media by an organism or group are characteristic, thus differentiating it from other strains or groups. Differential semisolid media are used to demonstrate motility and certain biochemical characteristics of microorganisms. Liquid differential tube media, in general, are employed in studying the fermentation reactions of pure cultures of bacteria, or their ability to utilize certain nutriments.

[1] J. Lab. Clin. Med., 36:134:1950.

TYPICAL REACTIONS OF VARIOUS ORGANISMS ON DIFFERENTIAL TUBE MEDIA

ORGANISM†	BACTO-PURPLE BROTH BASE containing									BACTO S I M MEDIUM			Bacto Urea Broth	Bacto Urea Agar		Bacto Simmons Citrate Agar
	Xylose	Dextrose	Maltose	Saccharose	Lactose	Rhamnose	Mannitol	Dulcitol	Salicin	Indol	Motility	H₂S		Butt	Slant	
Shigella dysenteriae (Shiga)	NC	Y	NC	NC	NC	NC	NC	NC	NC	−	−	−	−	−	−	−
Shigella ambigua (Schmitz)	NC	Y	NC	NO	NC	Y	NC	NC	NC	+	−	−	−	−	−	−
Shigella sonnei	NC or Y	Y	Y	Y	Y slow	Y	Y	NC	NC	−	−	−	−	−	−	−
Shigella paradysenteriae—Boyd and Flexner	NC	Y	NC or Y	NC	NC	NC	Y	NC	NC	±	−	−	−	−	−	−
Shigella paradysenteriae—Newcastle	NC	YG	NC or YG	NC	NC	NC	YG	YG	NC	−	−	−	−	−	−	−
Shigella alkalescens	Y	Y	Y	NC or Y	NC	Y	Y	Y	NC	+	−	−	−	−	−	−
Shigella madampensis	Y	Y	Y	Y	Y	Y	Y	NC	NC	+	−	−	−	−	−	−
Shigella ceylonensis (dispar)	Y	Y	Y	Y	Y	Y	Y	Y	NC	+	−	−	−	−	−	−
Salmonella typhosa (Eberthella typhosa)	Y	Y	Y	NC	NC	NC	Y	NC	NC	−	+	+	−	−	−	−
Salmonella paratyphi	NC	YG	YG	NC	NC	YG	YG	YG	NC	−	+	+	−	−	−	−
Salmonella schottmuelleri	YG	YG	YG	NC	NC	YG	YG	YG	NC	−	+	+	−	−	−	+
Salmonella typhimurium		YG	YG	NC	NC		YG	YG	NC	−	+	+	−	−	−	+
Salmonella cholbraesuis	YG	YG	YG	NC	NC	YG	YG	YG	NC	−	+	−	−	−	−	+
Salmonella enteritidis	YG	YG	YG	NC	NC	YG	YG	YG	NC	−	+	+	−	−	−	+
Salmonella pullorum	YG	YG	NC	NC	NC		YG	NC	NC	−	−	+	−	−	−	−
Salmonella gallinarum	Y	Y	Y	NC	NC	NC or Y	Y	Y	NC	−	−	±	−	−	−	−
Aerobacter aerogenes	YG	YG	YG	NC or YG	YG	YG	YG	NC or YG	YG	±	−	−	−	−	−	+
Aerobacter cloacae	YG	YG	YG	YG	YG	NC	YG	NC	YG	−	+	−	−	−	−	+
Escherichia coli	YG	YG	YG	NC or YG	YG	YG	YG	NC or YG	NC or YG	+	+	−	−	−	−	−
Escherichia freundii	YG	YG	YG	NC or YG	YG	YG	YG	NC or YG	NC or YG	±	±	+	−	−	−	+
Escherichia intermedium	YG	YG	YG	NC or YG	YG	YG	YG	NC or YG	NC or YG	±	±	+	−	−	−	+
Proteus vulgaris	YG	YG	YG	YG	NC	YG	NC	NC	NC or YG	+	+	+	R	R	R	±
Proteus mirabilis		YG	NC	YG	NC		NC		NC	−	+	+	R	R	R	+
Proteus morganii	NC or Y	YG	NC	NC	NC	NC	NC	NC	NC	+	+	−	R	R	R	−
Proteus rettgeri		Y or YG	NC	NC or Y	NC		Y or YG	NC	NC or YG	+	±	−	R	R	R	+
Klebsiella pneumoniae		NC or YG	NC or YG	NC or YG	NC or YG		NC or YG	NC or YG	NC or YG	±	−	−	−	−	−	±
Pseudomonas aeruginosa	NC	NC or Y	NC	NC	NC	NC	NC	NC	NC	−	+	−	−	−	−	±
Alcaligenes faecalis	NC	NC	NC	NC	NC	NC	NC	NC	NC	−	+	−	−	−	−	±
Paracolobactrum aerogenoides	Reactions are the same as those of Aerobacter aerogenes except that the fermentation of lactose is consistently delayed.															
Paracolobactrum intermedium	Reactions are the same as those of Escherichia freundii or E. intermedium except that the fermentation of lactose is consistently delayed															
Paracolobactrum coliforme	Reactions are the same as those of Escherichia coli except that the fermentation of lactose is consistently delayed.															

NC— No change or alkaline reaction,
Y— Yellow—acid formation.
YG= Acid and gas formation,
R= Red—urea hydrolyzed.
+= Positive for a given reaction,
—= Negative.
±= Variable.

†Names of organisms according to Bergey's "Manual of Determinative Bacteriology", Sixth Edition, 1948.

TYPICAL REACTIONS OF VARIOUS ORGANISMS ON DIFFERENTIAL TUBE MEDIA

ORGANISM†	Bacto Russell Double Sugar Agar		Bacto-Kligler Iron Agar			Bacto Krumwiede Triple Sugar Agar		Bacto Triple Sugar Iron Agar			Bacto Friewer Shaughnessy Medium		
	Butt	Slant	Butt	Slant	H₂S	Butt	Slant	Butt	Slant	H₂S	Fermentation	Motility	H₂S
Shigella dysenteriae (Shiga)	Y	NC	Y	NC	–	Y	NC	Y	NC	–	NC	–	–
Shigella ambigua (Schmitz)	Y	NC	Y	NC	–	Y	NC	Y	NC	–	NC	–	–
Shigella sonnei	Y	NC	Y	NC	–	Y	NC	Y	NC	–	NC	–	–
Shigella paradysenteriae—Boyd and Flexner	Y	NC	Y or YG	NC	–	Y	NC	Y	NC	–	NC	–	–
Shigella paracysenteriae—Newcastle	Y or YG	NC	Y or YG	NC	–	Y or YG	NC	Y or YG	NC	–	NC	–	–
Shigella alkalascens	Y	NC	Y	NC	–	Y	NC or Y	Y	NC or Y	–	NC	–	–
Shigella madampensis	Y	Y	Y	Y	–	Y	Y	Y	Y	–	Y	–	–
Shigella ceylonensis (disper)	Y	Y	Y	Y	–	Y	Y	Y	Y	–	Y	–	–
Salmonella typhosa (Eberthella typhosa)	Y	NC	Y	NC	+	Y	NC	Y	NC	+	NC	+	+
Salmonella paratyphi	YG	NC	YG	NC	–	YG	NC	YG	NC	–	NC	+	+
Salmonella schottmuelleri	YG	NC	YG	NC	+	YG	NC	YG	NC	+	NC	+	+
Salmonella typhimurium	YG	NC	YG	NC	+	YG	NC	YG	NC	+	NC	+	+
Salmonella choleraesuis	YG	NC	YG	NC	–	YG	NC	YG	NC	–	NC	+	–
Salmonella enteritidis	YG	NC	YG	NC	+	YG	NC	YG	NC	+	NC	+	+
Salmonella pullorum	YG	NC	YG	NC	+	YG	NC	YG	NC	+	NC	–	+
Salmonella gallinarum	Y	NC	Y	NC	±	Y	NC	Y	NC	±	NC	–	±
Aerobacter aerogenes	YG	Y	YG	Y	–	YG	Y	YG	Y	–	YG	–	–
Aerobacter cloacae	YG	Y	YG	Y	–	YG	Y	YG	Y	–	YG	+	–
Escherichia coli	YG	Y	YG	Y	–	YG	Y	YG	Y	–	YG	±	–
Escherichia freundii	YG	Y	YG	Y	+	YG	Y	YG	Y	+	YG	±	+
Escherichia intermedium	YG	Y	YG	Y	–	YG	Y	YG	Y	–	YG	±	–
Proteus vulgaris	YG	NC	YG	NC	+	YG	Y	YG	Y	+	NC	+	+
Proteus mirabilis	YG	NC	YG	NC	+	YG	Y	YG	NC or Y	+	NC	+	+
Proteus morganii	Y or YG	NC	Y or YG	NC	–	Y or YG	NC or Y	YG	NC or Y	+	NC	+	–
Proteus rettgeri	Y or YG	NC	Y or YG	NC	–	Y or YG	NC	Y or YG	NC	–	NC	±	–
Klebsiella pneumoniae	Y or YG	RG	Y or YG	NC	–	Y or YG	NC	Y or YG	NC	–	NC	–	–
Pseudomonas aeruginosa	NC	NC	NC	NC	–	NC	NC	NC	NC	–	NC	+	–
Alcaligenes faecalis	NC	NC	NC	NC	–	NC	NC	NC	NC	–	NC	+	–
Paracolobactrum aerogenoides	Reactions are the same as those of Aerobacter aerogenes except that the fermentation of lactose is consistently delayed.												
Paracolobactrum intermedium	Reactions are the same as those of Escherichia freundii or E. intermedium except that the fermentation of lactose is consistently delayed.												
Paracolobactrum coliforme	Reactions are the same as those of Escherichia coli except that the fermentation of lactose is consistently delayed.												

NC= No change or alkaline reaction.   YG= Acid and gas formation.   += Positive for a given reaction.   ±= Variable.
Y= Yellow—acid formation.   —= Negative.

†Names of organisms according to Bergey's "Manual of Determinative Bacteriology", Sixth Edition, 1948.

RUSSELL DOUBLE SUGAR AGAR (B84)
DEHYDRATED

Bacto-Beef Extract	1 g.
Proteose Peptone No. 3, Difco ..	12 g.
Bacto-Lactose	10 g.
Bacto-Dextrose	1 g.
Sodium Chloride	5 g.
Bacto-Agar	15 g.
Bacto-Phenol Red	0.025 g.

Bacto-Russell Double Sugar Agar is widely employed in the primary identification of Gram-negative enteric pathogenic organisms, particularly the colon-typhoid-salmonella-dysentery group. It distinguishes the dextrose-acid, dextrose-gas, lactose-acid and lactose-gas forming organisms. Russell Double Sugar Agar may be used to aid in the identification of pure cultures of colonies picked from primary plating media such as MacConkey Agar, S S Agar, Bismuth Sulfite Agar and others.

Bacto-Russell Double Sugar Agar conforms to the original formula of Russell[1] except that phenol red replaces litmus, and Proteose Peptone No. 3 is utilized in place of Bacto-Peptone. The phenol red indicator gives exceptionally clear-cut brilliant reactions on both sides of the neutral point. Alkaline reactions turn the indicator red, and acid reactions change it to yellow. Investigations have also demonstrated that faster and clearer reactions are secured in the medium prepared with Proteose Peptone No. 3.

Russell Double Sugar Agar is used in tubes which are slanted so as to provide a deep butt. Inoculation is made from isolated colonies or pure cultures by smearing over the surface of the slant and stabbing the butt. After suitable incubation, the production of acid under aerobic and under anaerobic conditions, on the slant and in the butt, respectively, can be detected by changes in color of the indicator. Gaseous fermentation is indicated by splitting of the agar or formation of bubbles in the butt.

Organisms capable of fermenting dextrose but not lactose, *Salmonella typhosa* for example, will show an initial acid slant in short incubation periods. As the dextrose is utilized, the reaction under aerobic conditions reverts and becomes alkaline. Under anaerobic conditions, in the butt of the tube, these same organisms are not capable of causing a reversion of the reaction, and remain acid.

After 24–48 hours incubation a properly inoculated tube showing a red or cerise slope and a yellow butt with or without gas formation indicates fermentation of the dextrose. Some strains of typhoid may require as long as 30–40 hours to produce a characteristic alkaline slant. A tube showing a yellow slant and butt with or without gas indicates fermentation of the lactose. A tube showing no change indicates that neither dextrose nor lactose has been fermented. See the table on page 161 for the reactions of various bacteria on Bacto-Russell Double Sugar Agar and other differential tube media.

To rehydrate the medium, suspend 44 grams of Bacto-Russell Double Sugar Agar in 1000 ml. of cold distilled water and heat to boiling to dissolve the medium completely. The solution is distributed in tubes which are stoppered with cotton plugs or loosely fitting caps. Sterilize in the autoclave for 15 minutes at 15 pounds pressure (121°C.). The tubes should be slanted so as to give a deep butt when solid. The final reaction of the medium will be pH 7.4.

One pound of Bacto-Russell Double Sugar Agar will make 10.3 liters of medium.

[1] J. Med. Research, 25:217:1911.

BACTO
SACCHAROSE MANNITOL AGAR (B87)
DEHYDRATED

Bacto-Beef Extract	1 g.
Proteose Peptone No. 3, Difco	12 g.
Saccharose, Difco	10 g.
d-Mannitol, Difco	1 g.
Bacto-Agar	15 g.
Bacto-Phenol Red	0.03 g.

Bacto-Saccharose Mannitol Agar is a tube medium employed in the differentiation of pure cultures of Gram-negative intestinal bacteria. This medium permits the determination of the formation of acid and gas from saccharose and mannitol. It is employed to aid in the identification of pure cultures of colonies picked from primary plating media such as MacConkey Agar, S S Agar, Bismuth Sulfite Agar and others.

Russell[1] made a noteworthy contribution toward the identification of the Gram-negative intestinal bacterial rods by the introduction of his Dextrose Lactose Agar. Kendall and Ryan[2] introduced a new agar medium containing saccharose and mannitol, two important sugars in the differentiation and identification of members of the intestinal group. Their Saccharose Mannitol Agar is used in the same manner as Russell's and, when employed in conjunction with it, permits observations of the fermentation reactions of the bacteria on four sugars by using only two media.

Bacto-Saccharose Mannitol Agar duplicates the original formula of Kendall and Ryan except that phenol red has replaced Andrade indicator. The phenol red indicator responds rapidly to slight changes in reaction due to growth of inoculated organisms. The tubes are inoculated with pure cultures by smearing the surface of the slant and stabbing into the butt. On this medium cultural reactions are clear-cut and readings may be made after 18–24 hours incubation at 37°C. A red slant and yellow butt, with or without gas formation, indicates fermentation of the mannitol. A yellow slant and butt, with or without gas, indicates that either saccharose alone or both sugars have been fermented. A tube remaining unchanged, or becoming cerise, indicates that neither sugar has been attacked. For a table showing typical cultural reactions on this and other differential tube media, see page 161.

To rehydrate the medium, suspend 39 grams of Bacto-Saccharose Mannitol Agar in 1000 ml. of cold distilled water and heat to boiling to dissolve the medium completely. The solution is distributed in tubes which are stoppered with cotton plugs or loosely fitting caps. Sterilize in the autoclave for 15 minutes at 15 pounds pressure (121°C.). Allow the tubes to solidify in a slanting position to provide a generous butt. The final reaction of the medium will be pH 7.5.

One pound of Bacto-Saccharose Mannitol Agar will make 11.6 liters of medium.

[1] J. Med. Research, 25:217:1911. [2] J. Infectious Diseases, 24:400:1919.

BACTO
KRUMWIEDE TRIPLE SUGAR AGAR (B85)
DEHYDRATED

Bacto-Beef Extract	1 g.
Proteose Peptone No. 3, Difco ..	12 g.
Bacto-Lactose	10 g.
Saccharose, Difco	10 g.
Bacto-Dextrose	1 g.
Sodium Chloride	5 g.
Bacto-Agar	15 g.
Bacto-Phenol Red	0.025 g.

Bacto-Krumwiede Triple Sugar Agar is a differential medium employed in the primary identification of Gram-negative enteric pathogens. This medium permits the determination of the formation of acid and gas from dextrose, lactose and saccharose. It is employed to aid in the identity of pure cultures of colonies picked from primary plating media such as MacConkey Agar, S S Agar, Bismuth Sulfite Agar and others.

Bacto-Krumwiede Triple Sugar Agar is prepared in accordance with the formula of Krumwiede and Kohn,[1] except in the choice of indicators. In place of the Andrade indicator originally recommended, the more stable and sensitive sulfonephthalein indicator, phenol red, is used. In addition to lactose and dextrose, as contained in Russell's Double Sugar Agar, this medium contains saccharose. This saccharose-containing medium has the advantage over Russell's medium in giving an earlier and more accurate differentiation between the so-called slow lactose fermenting strains of the coliform group and the *Salmonella* group. The explanation for this increased rapidity of differential is that the slow lactose fermenters attack the saccharose with greater avidity than they do lactose under aerobic conditions. *Salmonella* are not influenced by the saccharose. Therefore, with the Triple Sugar Agar many of the organisms giving a doubtful or atypical *Salmonella* reaction on Russell's medium can promptly be excluded, as a rule, as only slow fermenters of lactose.

Like Russell's medium this Triple Sugar Agar is a differential tube medium and inoculations are made from pure cultures by smearing the surface of the slant and stabbing the butt. A properly inoculated tube showing, after incubation, a red or cerise slope and a yellow butt, with or without gas formation, indicates fermentation of the dextrose. Some strains of intestinal pathogens require 30–40 hours to produce an alkaline slope. A tube showing a yellow slant and butt, with or without gas, indicates fermentation of the saccharose, or lactose, or both. A tube showing no change indicates that none of the sugars has been fermented. See the table on page 161 for the reactions of various intestinal bacteria on differential media.

To rehydrate the medium, suspend 54 grams of Bacto-Krumwiede Triple Sugar Agar in 1000 ml. of cold distilled water and heat to boiling to dissolve the medium completely. The solution is distributed in tubes which are stoppered with cotton plugs or loosely fitting caps. Sterilize in the autoclave for 15 minutes at 15 pounds pressure (121°C.). Allow the tubes to solidify in a slanting position so as to provide a deep butt. The final reaction of the medium will be pH 7.4.

One pound of Bacto-Krumwiede Triple Sugar Agar will make 8.4 liters of medium.

[1] J. Med. Research, 37:225:1917.

KLIGLER IRON AGAR (B86)
DEHYDRATED

Bacto-Beef Extract	3 g.
Bacto-Yeast Extract	3 g.
Bacto-Peptone	15 g.
Proteose Peptone, Difco	5 g.
Bacto-Lactose	10 g.
Bacto-Dextrose	1 g.
Ferrous Sulfate	0.2 g.
Sodium Chloride	5 g.
Sodium Thiosulfate	0.3 g.
Bacto-Agar	12 g.
Bacto-Phenol Red	0.024 g.

Bacto-Kligler Iron Agar is a most useful differential tube medium in the study of the Gram-negative intestinal microorganisms. It combines the principles of Russell Double Sugar Agar and Lead Acetate Agar into one medium which permits a differentiation of the Gram-negative rods both on the basis of their ability to ferment dextrose or lactose, and on their ability to produce hydrogen sulfide. It differentiates the lactose-splitting organisms from the lactose nonfermenters, distinguishes *Salmonella typhosa* from the other *Salmonella* and the *Shigella* groups and differentiates *S. paratyphi* (paratyphoid A) from *S. schottmuelleri* and *S. enteritidis*. Kligler Iron Agar is recommended to identify further pure cultures of colonies picked from primary plating media such as MacConkey Agar, S S Agar, Bismuth Sulfite Agar and others.

Kligler's[1] original medium was a soft Nutrient Agar containing dextrose, Andrade indicator and lead acetate. While experimenting with this medium and other combinations, Kligler discovered that Russell's medium containing Andrade indicator and lead acetate gave a good differentiation, and later[2] recommended it as being satisfactory for differentiation of the typhoid, paratyphoid and dysentery groups. Bailey and Lacey[3] made a study of such a medium in an attempt to simplify it and to select a more suitable indicator. They found that phenol red was particularly adaptable and recommended that it be used as the indicator of hydrogen ion concentration. A similar medium, including saccharose and incorporating Bacto-Tryptone as a nutrient, with ferrous sulfate and thiosulfate as the indicator of hydrogen sulfide production, was developed by Sulkin and Willett.[4] They found such a medium to be unique in its ability to give rapid clear-cut reactions. A complete discussion of this medium is given under Bacto-Triple Sugar Iron Agar, page 166.

Bacto-Kligler Iron Agar is prepared with phenol red as an indicator of the production of acid, and ferrous sulfate as an indicator of hydrogen sulfide production. This combination of ingredients gives sensitive, distinct clear-cut reactions.

For typical cultural reactions in 18 hours, it is recommended that tubes of Kligler Iron Agar be inoculated heavily with growth from a solid culture medium by smearing over the surface of a slant and stabbing in the butt. If inoculated from a suspension of organisms, or from broth culture, typical reactions of hydrogen sulfide production, and reversion, may not be obtained until 36–40 hours at 37°C. To obtain true differential cultural reactions of this medium it is necessary to have a pure culture. In inoculating directly from isolation media such as MacConkey Agar, S S Agar or Bismuth Sulfite Agar plates, select well isolated colonies and pick only the very center of the colony. If there is any question as to the ability to obtain a pure culture from a certain colony, it is recommended that the suspicious colony be purified by streaking on MacConkey Agar before inoculating into Kligler Iron Agar. This procedure is always recommended to insure culture purity when picking from poured plates of Bismuth Sulfite Agar. It is often possible to detect contaminated cultures on Kligler Iron Agar slants, and when this is the case it is necessary to isolate the organism in pure culture before its typical cultural reaction can be determined.

Organisms capable of fermenting dextrose but not lactose, *S. typhosa* for example, will show an initial acid slant in short incubation periods. As the dextrose is utilized, the reaction under aerobic conditions reverts and becomes alkaline. Under anaerobic conditions, in the butt of the tube, these same organisms are not capable of causing a reversion of the reaction, and remain acid.

The fermentation reactions in Kligler Iron Agar are similar to those in Russell Double Sugar Agar, i.e., a red slant and yellow butt with or without gas indicates fermentation of the small quantity of dextrose, a yellow slant and butt with or without gas formation indicates fermentation of the lactose, while a tube showing no change indicates that neither dextrose nor lactose has been attacked. In addition to these fermentation reactions, Kligler Iron Agar indicates whether or not hydrogen sulfide is produced. This is shown by a blackening of the medium. Freshly prepared media will give the best reactions. For characteristic reactions of some of the enteric organisms on this medium see the table on page 161.

To rehydrate the medium, suspend 55 grams of Bacto-Kligler Iron Agar in 1000 ml. of cold distilled water and heat to boiling to dissolve the medium completely. The solution is distributed in tubes which are stoppered with cotton plugs or loosely fitting caps. Sterilize by autoclaving for 15 minutes at 15 pounds pressure (121°C.). The reaction of the medium after sterilization will be pH 7.4. Allow the tubes to solidify in a slanting position in a manner which will give a generous butt. Best reactions are obtained on freshly prepared media.

One pound of Bacto-Kligler Iron Agar will make 8.2 liters of medium.

[1] Am. J. Pub. Health, 7:1042:1917.   [3] J. Bact., 13:183:1927.
[2] J. Exp. Med., 28:319:1918.   [4] J. Lab. Clin. Med., 25:649:1940.

BACTO
TRIPLE SUGAR IRON AGAR   (B265)
DEHYDRATED

Bacto-Beef Extract	3 g.
Bacto-Yeast Extract	3 g.
Bacto-Peptone	15 g.
Proteose Peptone, Difco	5 g.
Bacto-Lactose	10 g.
Saccharose, Difco	10 g.
Bacto-Dextrose	1 g.
Ferrous Sulfate	0.2 g.
Sodium Chloride	5 g.
Sodium Thiosulfate	0.3 g.
Bacto-Agar	12 g.
Bacto-Phenol Red	0.024 g.

Bacto-Triple Sugar Iron Agar is recommended as a medium for use in the identification of Gram-negative enteric pathogens in the routine examination of stools. It is of especial value when used in conjunction with MacConkey Agar, S S Agar, Bismuth Sulfite Agar, Brilliant Green Agar, E.M.B. Agar and Endo Agar. This medium indicates the ability of an organism to ferment lactose, saccharose and dextrose with formation of acid and gas, and also its ability to produce hydrogen sulfide. These characteristics are employed in most schema for identifying members of the *Salmonella-Shigella* groups.

In 1911 Russell[1] described the use of two sugars in an agar medium to differentiate Gram-negative organisms of intestinal origin. The ability of members of this group to produce hydrogen sulfide was recognized as a valuable characteristic and to detect its presence lead or iron salts have been added to the Russell Medium by many investigators. Kligler[2,3] reported that by adding lead acetate to Russell Double Sugar Agar, a medium capable of differentiating typhoid, paratyphoid and dysentery could be obtained. A modification of this medium, Bacto-Kligler Iron Agar, using phenol red as an indicator of acidity, and iron salts to detect hydrogen sulfide production, has been used extensively for many years in the differentiation of enteric organisms. Krumwiede and Kohn[4] modified Russell Double Sugar Agar by the addition of saccharose to the medium. This permitted an earlier detection of those coliform organisms which ferment lactose slowly, since many of these organisms attack saccharose more readily than lactose. The added saccharose also permits the exclusion of certain coliform and proteus organisms which have the ability to attack saccharose, but not lactose, in a 24–48 hour incubation period.

In 1940 Sulkin and Willett[5] described a triple sugar ferrous sulfate medium for use in the identification of enteric organisms. This medium consisted of a Beef Extract Tryptone Agar Base to which was added 1 per cent lactose, 1 per cent saccharose, 0.1 per cent dextrose, 0.02 per cent ferrous sulfate, 0.015 per cent sodium thiosulfate and brom thymol blue as an indicator of change in reaction. In our laboratory, independently and concurrently with the work of Sulkin and Willett, we prepared a similar medium by adding 1 per cent saccharose to Bacto-Kligler Iron Agar. This latter medium contained phenol red as an indicator. Bacto-Triple Sugar Iron Agar, so prepared, was distributed at that time to a number of laboratories for comparative trials. Hajna[6] described a similar medium for the identification of bacteria of the intestinal group. The importance of saccharose, as already pointed out, is to eliminate certain saccharose fermenting bacteria of the paracolon group which ferment lactose slowly as well as certain proteus organisms capable of fermenting saccharose. Those laboratories especially interested in recovery of paracolon bacilli or members of the proteus and paracolon groups which ferment saccharose should use Bacto-Kligler Iron Agar, or bear in mind when using Bacto-Triple Sugar Iron Agar that these organisms produce an acid and gas butt with an acid slant.

The pathogenic significance of these saccharose fermenting organisms, members of the paracolon and proteus groups, is not clearly defined, as has been shown by many investigators. Parr[7] showed the close relationship of the Morgan bacillus, paracolons, anaerogenic *Escherichia coli* and slow lactose fermenting coliform bacilli to the *Shigella* and *Salmonella* groups. Several outbreaks of gastroenteritis have been attributed to these normal or aberrant types. Stuart, Wheeler, Rustigian and Zimmerman[8] reported that paracolons are often associated with, and can cause, mild or acute gastroenteritis of short duration. Neter[9] pointed out that the Triple Sugar Iron Agar does not eliminate all saccharose fermenting strains of proteus and paracolons, and further that the pathogenic significance of some of these organisms as incitants of diarrheal diseases is not clearly known. He pointed out that these facts should be taken into consideration when using the Triple Sugar Iron Agar as a diagnostic medium.

Ewing and Bruner[10] used Triple Sugar Iron Agar as a differential tube medium in isolation of *Salmonella* and *Shigella* for serological classification. Typical suspicious colonies were picked from the primary media and were inoculated into Triple Sugar Iron Agar. After overnight incubation at 37°C. the cultures showing an alkaline slant and acid or acid and gas in the butt were transferred to the Urea Medium of Christensen.[11] (A complete discussion of this medium, Bacto-Urea Agar Base, is given on page 171). After incubation for 2–4 hours at

37°C. a preliminary examination was made and all tubes showing an alkaline reaction were discarded. The remaining tubes were reincubated and their reactions were generally complete in 24 hours. All cultures showing an alkaline reaction were *Proteus* or members of the paracolon-aerobacter group. The *Salmonella* and *Shigella* cultures failed to produce increased alkalinity in the Urea Medium. Hydrogen sulfide positive cultures, as determined on the previously inoculated Triple Sugar Iron Agar, were investigated with *Salmonella* polyvalent antiserums, while hydrogen sulfide negative cultures were investigated with *Shigella* polyvalent or *Salmonella* polyvalent antiserums. In a survey of methods used for the collection and preservation of stool specimens for the isolation and identification of *Salmonella, Shigella* and intestinal protozoa Felsenfeld[12] reported that the use of Triple Sugar Iron Agar was increasing while the use of double sugar agar was decreasing. The use of a single differential medium indicates a trend towards standardization of laboratory techniques.

Bacto-Triple Sugar Iron Agar is essentially the formula originally described by Sulkin and Willett.[5] The Bacto-Tryptone has been replaced by a combination of Bacto-Peptone and Proteose Peptone, Bacto-Yeast Extract has been added, the agar concentration increased to 1.5 per cent and phenol red used as an indicator instead of brom thymol blue. On this medium, cultural reactions are clear-cut, and readings may be made at 18–24 hours incubation. For typical cultural reactions in 18 hours, it is recommended that the medium be inoculated heavily with growth from a solid culture medium. If inoculated from a suspension of organisms, or from broth culture, typical reactions of hydrogen sulfide production, and reversion, may not be obtained until 36–40 hours at 37°C. To obtain true differential cultural reactions on this medium it is necessary to have a pure culture. In inoculating directly from isolation media such as MacConkey Agar, S S Agar or Bismuth Sulfite Agar plates, select well isolated colonies and pick only the very center of the colony. If there is any question as to the ability to obtain a pure culture from a certain colony, it is recommended that the suspicious colony be purified by streaking on MacConkey Agar before inoculating into Triple Sugar Iron Agar. This procedure is always recommended to insure culture purity when picking from poured plates of Bismuth Sulfite Agar. It is often possible to detect contaminated cultures on Triple Sugar Iron Agar slants, and when this is the case it is necessary to isolate the organism in pure culture before its typical cultural reactions can be determined.

The cultural reactions on Bacto-Triple Sugar Iron Agar are similar to those obtained on Kligler Iron Agar, but to it is added the information of the ability of an organism to ferment saccharose. A table of typical reactions on this and other differential media is given on page 161. Results obtained on Triple Sugar Iron Agar, as on Kligler Iron Agar, constitute presumptive evidence only, and must be confirmed biochemically and serologically.

To rehydrate the medium, suspend 65 grams of Bacto-Triple Sugar Iron Agar in 1000 ml. cold distilled water and heat to boiling to dissolve the medium completely. The solution is distributed in tubes which are stoppered with cotton plugs or loosely fitting caps. Tube and sterilize in the autoclave for 15 minutes at 15 pounds pressure (121°C.). Slant in such a manner as to allow a generous butt. The final reaction of the medium will be pH 7.4.

One pound of Bacto-Triple Sugar Iron Agar will make 6.6 liters of medium.

1 J. Med. Research, 25:217:1911.
2 Am. J. Pub. Health, 7:1042:1917.
3 J. Exp. Med., 28:319:1918.
4 J. Med. Research, 37:225:1917.
5 J. Lab. Clin. Med., 25:649:1940.
6 J. Bact., 49:516:1945.
7 Bact. Rev., 3:1:1939.
8 J. Bact., 45:101:1943.
9 J. Bact., 50:609:1945.
10 Am. J. Clin. Path., 17:1:1947.
11 J. Bact., 52:461:1946.
12 Public Health Reports, 65:1075:1950.

BACTO
LEAD ACETATE AGAR (B88)
DEHYDRATED

Bacto-Peptone	15 g.
Proteose Peptone, Difco	5 g.
Bacto-Dextrose	1 g.
Lead Acetate	0.2 g.
Sodium Thiosulfate	0.08 g.
Bacto-Agar	15 g.

Bacto-Lead Acetate Agar, like Russell's medium, is used primarily as a tube medium for the differentiation of the various Gram-negative intestinal bacteria.

Certain bacteria possess the ability of liberating hydrogen sulfide from proteins or their split products. This property has been widely used in culture media for differentiating and identifying members of the Gram-negative intestinal group of bacteria, as well as for the identification of other microorganisms. Orlowski[1] noted that *Salmonella typhosa* could be distinguished from the coliform organisms by culturing them in a medium containing lead acetate, an indicator of hydrogen sulfide production. Jordan and Victorson[2] showed further that *S. paratyphi* (paratyphoid A) and *S. schottmuelleri* (paratyphoid B) could be distinguished on the basis of hydrogen sulfide production by growing them in a lead acetate medium. *S. paratyphi* produced no browning, whereas *S. schottmuelleri* gave a definite browning of the medium within 18–24 hours after inoculation.

Bacto-Lead Acetate Agar was developed after a careful study of the literature on the subject, and after considerable research to obtain a medium which would give an accurate differentiation. The modification finally developed was suggested by R. S. Spray. Unlike many other formulae, this medium shows no inhibition due to the toxicity of lead. The non-toxicity of Bacto-Lead Acetate Agar for certain bacteria is confirmed in "Pure Culture Study of Bacteria."[3] See the table on page 161 showing reactions of some of the intestinal bacteria on this and other differential media.

Bacto-Lead Acetate Agar is sensitive in its cultural reactions, and can be used for plating when it is desired to demonstrate the relative number of strong hydrogen sulfide producing colonies. Its usual method of use is in tubes. Pure cultures of Gram-negative microorganisms isolated from MacConkey Agar, Bismuth Sulfite Agar, Eosin Methylene Blue Agar or other plating media should be streaked upon the surface of the slant and stabbed into the butt of the Lead Acetate Agar. With this procedure, surface browning can be observed, as well as browning along the line of puncture. Since the medium contains dextrose it will also indicate gas production from this carbohydrate by the presence of bubbles in the butt of the tube. For the determination of hydrogen sulfide production in a medium free from dextrose, see Bacto-Peptone Iron Agar, as discussed on page 181.

Morrison and Tanner[4] used Bacto-Lead Acetate Agar in their study of hydrogen sulfide production by the thermophilic bacteria from water. They found the medium well adapted to the determination of this characteristic. Spray[5] employed it with success in his studies on semisolid media for the cultivation and identification of the sporulating anaerobes.

To rehydrate the medium, suspend 36 grams of Bacto-Lead Acetate Agar in 1000 ml. of cold distilled water and heat to boiling to dissolve the medium completely. The solution is dispensed into tubes and sterilized in the autoclave for 15 minutes at 15 pounds pressure (121°C.). The tubes are slanted to allow for a generous butt. The final reaction of the medium will be pH 6.6.

One pound of Bacto-Lead Acetate Agar will make 12.6 liters of medium.

[1] Dissert. St. Petersburg, 1897.
[2] J. Infectious Diseases, 21:554:1917.
[3] Pure Culture Study of Bacteria, 1:No. 8:1933.
[4] J. Bact., 7:343:1922.
[5] J. Bact., 32:135:1936.

BACTO

UREA BROTH   (B272)

DEHYDRATED

Bacto-Yeast Extract	0.1 g.
Monopotassium Phosphate	9.1 g.
Disodium Phosphate	9.5 g.
Urea, Difco	20 g.
Bacto-Phenol Red	0.01 g.

Bacto-Urea Broth is recommended for the identification of the genus *Proteus*. It is prepared according to the formula of Stuart, Van Stratum and Rustigian[1] and provides all the essential growth factors for *Proteus*.

The decomposition of urea by members of the *Proteus* group has been especially helpful to differentiate these organisms from other Gram negative intestinal bacteria and to eliminate them from further study in various schema for the identification of the Gram negative intestinal pathogens. Using their strongly buffered medium, and under proper conditions, Stuart, Van Stratum and Rustigian, reported that *Proteus* could be differentiated from all other members of the enteric group by its ability to produce sufficient ammonia to give a reaction more alkaline than pH 8.1 after 12–48 hours incubation at 37°C. These investigators pointed out that a large number of organisms other than *Proteus* were capable of urease production and would give a positive test in weakly buffered media. They also noted that by decreasing the amount of buffer in their standard medium to one tenth or one hundredth that of the original concentration, the time of incubation for identification of *Proteus* could be decreased from 12–48 hours to 2–4 hours. Rustigian and Stuart[2] used urea decomposition as a limiting characteristic for the identification of *Proteus* strains from other members of the family *Enterobacteriaceae*. Ferguson and Hook[3] also reported that urease production, as indicated by the Rustigian and Stuart method, was an excellent means of differentiating between members of the *Proteus* and *Salmonella* groups.

According to the procedure recommended by Stuart, Van Stratum and Rustigian[1], the filter sterilized medium is distributed under aseptic conditions in approximately 3 ml. amounts in tubes 14 mm. inside diameter and 125 mm. long. Inoculation is made with a straight needle from 18–24 hour agar slant cultures, and the tubes are incubated at 37°C. When possible, reactions are recorded after 8, 12, 24 and 48 hours incubation. A positive urease reaction (hydrolysis of urea) is indicated by a change in color from yellow (pH 6.8) to a red to a cerise color (pH 8.1 or more alkaline).

To rehydrate the medium, dissolve 38.7 grams Bacto-Urea Broth, Dehydrated, in 1000 ml. of distilled water, filter sterilize and distribute under aseptic conditions in 3 ml. amounts into sterile plugged 14 x 125 mm. tubes. Final reaction of the medium will be pH 6.8.

One pound of Bacto-Urea Broth, Dehydrated, will make 11.7 liters of medium.

[1] J. Bact., 49:437:1945.
[3] Proc. Soc. Exp. Biol. Med., 53:241:1943.
[2] J. Lab. Clin. Med., 28:1715:1943.

BACTO
UREA BROTH CONCENTRATE (B280)
(Filter Sterilized Solution)

Bacto-Urea Broth is also supplied in a filter sterilized concentrated solution as Bacto-Urea Broth Concentrate. The dehydrated medium is recommended for those laboratories using large amounts of medium and equipped with filter sterilizing apparatus. For laboratories requiring only small amounts of medium Bacto-Urea Broth Concentrate is recommended.

Bacto-Urea Broth Concentrate is a filter sterilized concentrated solution of Bacto-Urea Broth, 10 ml. being sufficient for the preparation of 100 ml. final medium. It is especially recommended for use by those laboratories desiring to save time, or requiring smaller quantities of medium.

To prepare the medium from Bacto-Urea Broth Concentrate, add the contents of one 10 ml. tube of Bacto-Urea Broth Concentrate to 90 ml. of sterile cold distilled water, under aseptic conditions. The distilled water should be sterilized in the autoclave for 15 minutes at 15 pounds pressure (121°C.). The water must be cooled to below 55°C. before adding Bacto-Urea Broth Concentrate. This complete medium is distributed under aseptic conditions in 3 ml. amounts into sterile plugged 14 x 125 mm. tubes.

One 10 ml. tube of Bacto-Urea Broth Concentrate will make 100 ml. of medium.

BACTO
UREA AGAR BASE (B283)
DEHYDRATED

Bacto-Peptone	1 g.
Bacto-Dextrose	1 g.
Sodium Chloride	5 g.
Monopotassium Phosphate	2 g.
Urea, Difco	20 g.
Bacto-Phenol Red	0.012 g.

Bacto-Urea Agar Base is recommended for use in the preparation of a differential medium for the detection of *Proteus* and most members of paracolon aerobacter and paracolon intermediate groups. It aids in the elimination of these cultures from further study in schema for the identification of intestinal pathogens.

Christensen[1] considered the well buffered liquid Urea Medium described by Rustigian and Stuart,[2] as discussed under Bacto-Urea Broth above, as being suited only for the identification of *Proteus*. However, other Gram negative intestinal bacteria which are capable of splitting urea cannot do so in this medium because of the small amount of nutritive material and increased amount of buffer present. In order to overcome these limitations, Christensen[1] devised the Urea Agar Medium in which he included peptone and dextrose and reduced the buffer content. His medium supported a more vigorous growth of many of the Gram-negative enteric bacilli and readily permitted observation of urease production by *Proteus* and members of the paracolon aerobacter and paracolon intermediate groups.

Ewing[3] used Urea Agar as a differential medium in the examination of many cultures from stool specimens and confirmed the findings of Christensen. Ewing and Bruner[4] utilized the urease reaction as a screening medium in the selection of *Salmonella* and *Shigella* cultures for serologic classification. Typical colonies suspected of being pathogens were picked from primary plating media into Triple Sugar Iron Agar. All tubes showing acid and gas in the slant and butt were discarded. Transfers were made from tubes showing an alkaline slant and acid or acid and gas butt onto Urea Agar. A preliminary reading was made at the end of 2–4 hours at 37°C. and all tubes showing alkaline reactions were discarded. The tubes were reincubated and reactions were generally complete in 24 hours. All cultures producing an alkaline reaction were *Proteus* or members of the paracolon aerobacter group. *Salmonella* and *Shigella* cultures failed to produce any increase in alkalinity in the medium. Hydrogen sulfide positive cultures, as determined on the previously inoculated Triple Sugar Iron Agar, were investigated with *Salmonella* polyvalent antisera, while hydrogen sulfide negative cultures were investigated with *Shigella* polyvalent or *Salmonella* polyvalent antisera. Urea Agar is used to determine the decomposition of urea by organisms in the examination of specimens for *Salmonella* and *Shigella* according to the method given in "Diagnostic Procedures and Reagents"[5] of the American Public Health Association.

Bacto-Urea Agar Base, when prepared for use, gives reactions similar to those described by Christensen[1] and Ewing and Bruner.[4] *Proteus* attacks the urea rapidly and after 2–4 hours incubation the color change, due to ammonia production, has penetrated deep into the medium. After 24 hours incubation the entire butt of the tube is alkaline in reaction. Urease positive paracolons, in contrast, hydrolyze urea much more slowly, showing only slight penetration of the alkaline reaction into the butt of the medium in 6 hours and requiring 3 to 5 days to change the reaction of the entire butt. According to Christensen[1] most paracolon aerobacter and paracolon intermediate cultures are urease positive and paracolon *Escherichia* cultures are urease negative. *Salmonella* and *Shigella* species fail to produce any trace of alkalinity on this medium. Urea Agar may also be used to show urease production by other organisms. Some Gram positive cocci and diphtheroids, as well as certain pigment producing members of the pyocyaneous group and others give a positive reaction on this medium.

To prepare the medium, dissolve 29 grams of Bacto-Urea Agar Base, Dehydrated, in 100 ml. of distilled water. Filter sterilize this concentrated base. Dissolve 15 grams Bacto-Agar in 900 ml. distilled water by boiling and sterilize in the autoclave for 15 minutes at 15 pounds pressure (121°C.). Cool to 50–55°C. and add 100 ml. filter sterilized concentrated Bacto-Urea Agar Base, under aseptic conditions. Mix thoroughly and distribute in sterile tubes. Slant the tubes so as to have a butt of about 1 inch in depth and a slant of about 1.5 inches in length. After solidification the slants are heavily inoculated by spreading growth from an agar culture over the entire surface. Do not inoculate into the butt. Final reaction of the medium will be pH 6.8.

Bacto-Urea Agar Base cannot be sterilized by heat because of the presence of urea. The complete Urea Agar Medium must be slanted before the medium solidifies to avoid the necessity of remelting the agar and causing hydrolysis of the urea in the medium.

One pound of Bacto-Urea Agar Base, Dehydrated, will make 15.6 liters of medium.

[1] J. Bact., 52:461:1946.
[3] Proc. Soc. Exp. Biol. Med., 47:108:1941.
[0] J. Bact., 51:433:1946.
[4] Am. J. Clin. Path., 17:1:1947.
[5] Diagnostic Procedures and Reagents, 3rd Edition:227:1950.

BACTO
UREA AGAR BASE CONCENTRATE (B284)
(Filter Sterilized Solution)

Bacto-Urea Agar Base is also supplied in a filter sterilized concentrated solution as Bacto-Urea Agar Base Concentrate. The dehydrated medium is recommended for those laboratories using large amounts of medium and equipped with filter sterilizing apparatus. For laboratories requiring only small amounts of medium Bacto-Urea Agar Base Concentrate is recommended.

Bacto-Urea Agar Base Concentrate is a filter sterilized concentrated solution of Bacto-Urea Agar Base, 10 ml. being sufficient for the preparation of 100 ml. final medium. It is especially recommended for use by those laboratories desiring to save time, or requiring smaller quantities of medium.

To prepare the medium from Bacto-Urea Agar Base Concentrate, dissolve 1.5 grams of Bacto-Agar in 90 ml. distilled water by boiling. Sterilize in the autoclave for 15 minutes at 15 pounds pressure (121°C.). Cool to 50-55°C. and add the contents of one tube of Bacto-Urea Agar Base Concentrate (10 ml.), under aseptic conditions. Mix thoroughly and tube as indicated above.

One tube of Bacto-Urea Agar Base Concentrate will make 100 ml. of complete medium.

BACTO
S I M MEDIUM (B271)
DEHYDRATED

Bacto-Beef Extract	3 g.
Bacto-Peptone	30 g.
Peptonized Iron, Difco	0.2 g.
Sodium Thiosulfate	0.025 g.
Bacto-Agar	3 g.

Bacto-S I M Medium was devised for use as a routine medium in the cultural identification of members of the *Salmonella* and *Shigella* groups, showing hydrogen sulfide production, indole production and motility in the same tube. These characteristics, along with other biochemical reactions, are of prime importance in the cultural identification of members of the Gram-negative enteric group.

Orlowski[1] noted that *Salmonella typhosa* could be distinguished from the coliform organisms by culturing them in a medium containing lead acetate, an indicator of hydrogen sulfide production. Jordan and Victorson[2] showed further that *S. paratyphi* (paratyphoid A) and *S. schottmuelleri* (paratyphoid B) could be distinguished on the basis of hydrogen sulfide production by growing them in a Lead Acetate Medium.

Semisolid media, as described by Hiss,[3] Hesse,[4] Jackson and Melia,[5] Tittsler and Sandholzer[6] and others, have been employed quite extensively in the determination of motility by bacteria. Sulkin and Willett,[7] in Bacto-Triple Sugar Iron Agar, used 1 per cent agar to demonstrate motility or lack of motility in addition to hydrogen sulfide production and carbohydrate fermentation by members of the *Salmonella* and *Shigella* groups. They called attention to the "brush-like" growth or motility of the typhoid organisms. Friewer and Shaughnessy[8] used the fermentation of lactose, hydrogen sulfide production and motility in a Lead Acetate Semisolid Agar as a screening medium in the isolation of enteric pathogens from stool culture. Sosa[9] described a peptone medium with a low agar concentration to determine motility, and stated that indole determination could be made using the Ehrlich reagent in this medium.

In the development of Bacto-S I M Medium it was determined that 0.0025 per cent sodium thiosulfate added to the semisolid 3 per cent Bacto-Peptone medium produced results comparable to those secured when hydrogen sulfide was determined in a 1 per cent Bacto-Peptone solution, using lead acetate paper strips as an indicator of hydrogen sulfide. Smaller quantities of sodium thiosulfate did not give a satisfactory response in the semisolid medium, while larger quantities obscured motility and also permitted some false reactions. Any blackening along the line of inoculation is considered as a positive hydrogen sulfide reaction. Hydrogen sulfide producing organisms generally give a positive reaction in 18–24 hours.

Motile cultures in Bacto-S I M Medium show diffuse growth or turbidity away from the line of inoculation. Hydrogen sulfide reactions are intensified by motile cultures. Cultures vary in the amount of motility as pointed out by Friewer and Shaughnessy.[8] Strains of *Proteus* and *Salmonella* often show diffuse growth throughout the entire medium, while *S. typhosa* is not as actively motile. In Bacto-S I M Medium motility of typical members of the enteric group is demonstrated in 18–24 hours, or less, incubation at 37°C. Green and co-workers[10] used Bacto-S I M Medium in 1–2 ml. amounts in 75 x 10 mm. tubes and reported the detection of motility by a large series of cultures following incubation at 37°C. for 90 to 120 minutes.

Bacto-Tryptone has been used universally in the test for indole production. It has been demonstrated that Bacto-S I M Medium gives parallel indole production in comparison with a 1 per cent Bacto-Tryptone solution after 18–24 hours incubation at 37°C. The oxalic acid paper test for indole production may be used with this medium. This test has the advantage of making it possible to observe motility, hydrogen sulfide production and indole formation after any desired incubation period. Oxalic acid paper for testing is prepared by soaking filter paper in a saturated oxalic acid solution, drying and then cutting the paper into strips. For the performance of the test, after the medium has been inoculated, suspend a strip of the paper in the mouth of the tube so that the strip projects one-half inch below the cotton plug holding it in place. The paper must not become wet as this may contaminate the medium. Indole production is shown by the formation of a pink color on the paper during incubation.

If desired, other tests for indole may be employed; the Kovacs or Ehrlich test gives good results. When using these tests hydrogen sulfide and motility readings should be made before testing for indole. The recommended procedure for the Kovacs' test is to overlay the medium with 2 ml. of chloroform without agitation, followed by the direct addition of 2 ml. of Kovacs' reagent. A pink to deep red color is formed in the chloroform layer if indole is present. In a negative test no color is formed in the chloroform layer. Kovacs' reagent consists of 75 ml. amyl alcohol, 25 ml. concentrated hydrochloric acid and 5 grams *p*-dimethylaminobenzaldehyde. The indole test may also be performed in accordance with the "Manual of Methods of Pure Culture Study of Bacteria,"[11] of the Society of American Bacteriologists. To perform this test, add about 2 ml. of ethyl ether to each tube. Shake gently, but do not break the agar. Let stand several minutes and then add about 1 ml. Ehrlich reagent by dropping it down the side of the tube so that it spreads out as a layer between the ether and the medium. The formation of a purplish red color at the interface of the two liquids within 5 minutes indicates indole production. In negative reactions, after the Ehrlich reagent has been in contact with the medium for a period longer than 5 minutes, a slight pink color may be observed on the surface of the medium. This should not be mistaken for a positive reaction, since in a positive test the color must appear within 5 minutes at the *interface* of the ether and the Ehrlich reagent. Ehrlich reagent consists of 1 gram of *p*-dimethylaminobenzaldehyde, 95 ml. ethyl alcohol (95 per cent) and 20 ml. of concentrated hydrochloric acid.

Bacto-S I M Medium is especially recommended as an aid in the routine confirmation of members of the *Salmonella* and *Shigella* groups following presumptive evidence as obtained on the differential tube media (Russell Double Sugar Agar, Krumwiede Triple Sugar Agar and Triple Sugar Iron Agar). As with other differential media, it is necessary to use pure cultures for inoculation. Generally, an incubation period of 18–24 hours or less is sufficient to give reactions by typical organisms in this group. Occasionally an atypical culture may be encountered which will fail to produce hydrogen sulfide, indole or motility in 18–24 hours incubation. Typical cultural reactions of the pathogenic Gram negative enteric bacteria are:

	S. typhosa	*Salmonella*	*Shigella*
Motility	+	+	−
Hydrogen sulfide	+	±	−
Indole	−	−	±

To rehydrate the medium, suspend 36 grams Bacto-S I M Medium in 1000 ml. cold distilled water and heat to boiling to dissolve the medium completely. Distribute the medium in tubes to a depth of about 3 inches and sterilize in the autoclave for 15 minutes at 15 pounds pressure (121°C.). The tubes of medium are solidified in a vertical position. Inoculate with a single stab using a straight needle through the center and to a depth of about two-thirds of the medium. Incubate for 18–24 hours at 37°C. and observe for motility, hydrogen sulfide and indole, as indicated above. Final reaction of the medium will be pH 7.3.

One pound of Bacto-S I M Medium will make 12.6 liters of medium.

[1] Dissert. St. Petersburg, 1897.
[2] J. Infectious Diseases, 21:554:1917.
[3] J. Exp. Med., 2:677:1897.
[4] Zeit. Hyg. Infektionskrank., 58:441:1908.
[5] J. Infectious Diseases, 6:194:1909.
[6] J. Bact., 31:575:1936.
[7] J. Lab. Clin. Med., 25:649:1940.
[8] Tech. Bull. Reg. Med. Tech., 5:1:1944.
[9] Rev. Inst. Bact., "Dr. Carlos G. Malbran", 11:286:1943.
[10] J. Bact., 62:347:1951.
[11] Manual of Methods of Pure Culture Study of Bacteria, Leaflet V, page 6, 7th Edition, 1939.

BACTO

TERGITOL-7 AGAR (B455)

DEHYDRATED

Proteose Peptone No. 3, Difco	5 g.
Bacto-Yeast Extract	3 g.
Bacto-Lactose	10 g.
Bacto-Agar	15 g.
Tergitol 7	0.1 ml.
Bacto Brom Thymol Blue	0.025 g.

Bacto-Tergitol 7 Agar is a selective medium for *Escherichia coli* and members of the coliform group, prepared according to the formula given by Chapman.[1] Chapman [2,3] reported that the addition of triphenyltetrazolium chloride (TTC) to this medium permitted the confirmation of *E. coli* after 10 hours incubation, and also that this medium gave excellent results in the cultivation of *Monilia* and other fungi.

Chapman[1] reported that the addition of Tergitol 7 to an agar medium consisting of Proteose Peptone No. 3, Bacto-Yeast Extract, Lactose and Brom Thymol Blue permitted unrestricted development of all coliform organisms and inhibited the development of Gram-negative spore formers as well as Gram-positive microorganisms. *Escherichia* produce yellow colonies surrounded by yellow zones; *Aerobacter* produce large mucoid colonies, usually surrounded by yellow zones; paracoli and other lactose non-fermenting organisms produce colonies usually surrounded by blue zones, on this medium. Proteus and other organisms have little tendency to form spreading colonies. Counts of coliform organisms on Tergitol 7 Agar were found to be 30 per cent higher than on other selective media for members of this group. Tergitol 7 Agar is inoculated by smearing the surface with the specimen using a bent glass rod. As much as 0.1 ml. of inoculum may be used per plate if the surface of the medium is dry. Pour plates do not give satisfactory results.

The addition of 40 mg. of TTC to a liter of sterile Tergitol 7 Agar permitting the confirmation of *E. coli* after 10 hours incubation was described by Chapman.[2] *E. coli* does not reduce the dye while other coliform organisms rarely fail to do so. Surface colonies of *E. Coli* on this medium are greenish yellow surrounded by a yellow halo while other coliform surface colonies are dark red. Readings can be made following incubation at 37°C. for 10 hours. Chapman[3] also reported that Tergitol 7 Agar with added TTC (40 mg. per liter) gave a selective medium for the isolation of *Monilia* and other fungi. *Monilia* growing on this medium produce white circular convex entire colonies about 1 mm. in diameter in 24–48 hours. The colonies may appear pale blue because of the color of the medium. Yeasts produce red colonies. Since the medium permits the development of coliform organisms this fact must be taken into consideration in the isolation of *Monilia* from specimens. Chapman[4] also used Tergitol 7 in a modified Sabouraud Maltose Agar, for the isolation and differentiation of *Monilia* and other fungi. This medium is described in detail on page 239, under Bacto-Sabouraud Maltose Agar.

To rehydrate the medium, suspend 33 grams of Bacto-Tergitol 7 Agar in 1000 ml. of cold distilled water. Heat to boiling to dissolve the medium completely. Distribute in tubes or flasks and sterilize in the autoclave for 15 minutes at 15 lbs. pressure (121°C.). Final reaction of the medium will be pH 6.9.

[1] J. Bact., 53:504:1947.
[3] Am. J. Pub. Health, 41:1381:1951.
[5] In press.
[4] Trans. New York Acad. Sci. Series II, 14:254:1952.

BACTO

MOTILITY SULFIDE MEDIUM (B450)

DEHYDRATED

Bacto-Beef Extract	3	g.
Proteose Peptone No. 3, Difco	10	g.
l-Cystine, Difco	0.2	g.
Ferrous Ammonium Citrate	0.2	g.
Sodium Citrate	2	g.
Sodium Chloride	5	g.
Bacto-Gelatin	80	g.
Bacto-Agar	4	g.

Bacto-Motility Sulfide Medium is a semisolid medium suitable for determining motility and the production of hydrogen sulfide from *l*-cystine. It is prepared according to the formula given by Hajna,[1] and used in the rapid method of differentiation and identification of bacteria of the intestinal group as described by him.[2] As pointed out by Hajna,[1] this medium is the semisolid agar-gelatin medium of Edwards and Bruner[3] modified to permit observation of motility and simultaneous hydrogen sulfide production from *l*-cystine. Hydrogen sulfide reactions on this medium may differ from the reactions usually obtained by a group of organisms since it contains free 1-cystine which may give a positive reaction by organisms considered negative by classical methods.

Bacto-Motility Sulfide Medium is used in the proposed rapid method of differentiating and identifying bacteria of the intestinal group described by Hajna,[2] to detect the capacity of an organism to produce hydrogen sulfide from 1-cystine, and to determine motility. Motility is evidenced by presence of diffuse growth away from the line of inoculation, non-motile organisms growing only along the line of inoculation. Hydrogen sulfide producing organisms show a blackening of the medium, blackening being confined to the inoculated portion of the medium with non-motile organisms, but diffusing throughout the medium with motile organisms. In this procedure the medium is dispensed in 4 ml. amounts in 13 x 100 mm. tubes, sterilized and cooled in a verticle position. The suspected colony on the primary plating medium is picked with a straight needle and inoculated in succession, without securing additional inoculum, into Bacto-Motility Sulfide Medium, to a depth of about a quarter of the column, and then into Triple Sugar Iron Agar and H Broth. The Motility Sulfide Medium is incubated at 30°C. overnight.

The ability of the organism to hydrolyze urea is determined following observation of motility and hydrogen sulfide production. The Motility Sulfide Medium culture is overlaid with 1 ml. of Bacto-Urea Broth, and incubated at 37°C., for not more than 6 hours. A positive urease reaction is indicated by a reddish purple color forming in the Urea Broth.

To rehydrate the medium, suspend 104 grams Bacto-Motility Sulfide Medium in 1000 ml. cold distilled water. When the medium is thoroughly wetted, carefully heat to boiling to dissolve the medium completely. The medium requires nearly constant agitation during the heating process. Dispense in 4 ml. amounts in 13 x 100 mm. tubes and sterilize in the autoclave for 15 minutes at 10 pounds pressure (117°C.). Final reaction of the medium will be pH 7.3.

One pound of Bacto-Motility Sulfide Medium will make 4.3 liters of medium.

[1] Pub. Health Lab., 8:36:1950.
[2] Pub. Health Lab., 9:23:1951.
[3] Univ. Ky. Cir., 54:1942.

BACTO
H BROTH (B451)
DEHYDRATED

Bacto-Peptone	5 g.
Bacto-Tryptone	5 g.
Bacto-Beef Extract	3 g.
Bacto-Dextrose	1 g.
Sodium Chloride	5 g.
Dipotassium Phosphate	2.5 g.

Bacto-H Broth is recommended for the preparation of the "H" agglutination antigen as used in the differentiation and identification of members of the *Salmonella* group. It is prepared according to the formula described by Hajna and Damon.[1] This medium is used in the rapid method of differentiating and identifying bacteria of the intestinal group as described by Hajna.[2] The production of the "O" type antigen and the elaboration of indole is also shown on this medium. Hajna[3] reported that the combination of Bacto-Peptone and Bacto-Tryptone in this medium has proven excellent in every way.

Serological analysis of the "H" and "O" antigens has been used as a practical means in schema for identification of organisms. Hajna[2] has used "H" and "O" agglutination together with other characteristics and serological reactions for the identification of *Salmonella*. In this method, typical colonies are picked from the primary plating medium, S S Agar, or Bismuth Sulfite Agar plates, and inoculated into tubes of semisolid agar, Triple Sugar Iron Agar and finally into H Broth, without securing further inoculum. The inoculated tubes are then incubated at 30°C. overnight. Cultures showing reactions on the semi-solid agar and Triple Sugar Iron Agar suggestive of *Salmonella typhosa* or other "*Salmonella* like organisms" are examined for "H" antigen. Place 0.02 ml. of a 1–5 dilution of Edwards mixed polyvalent *Salmonella* "H" Serum in the bottom of an agglutination tube. Then remove 1 ml. of the H Broth culture and add 1 ml. of 0.6 per cent formalinized saline, mix thoroughly and place in a water bath at 50°C. for 1 hour, but not to exceed two hours. A flocculant agglutination in the tube is an indication of the presence of *Salmonella* "H" antigen. The individual "H" antigens are detected by specific H antisera, using the tube agglutination technique. The presence of "O" antigens is determined by an initial slide agglutination test using the H Broth and polyvalent "O" antiserum followed by specific "O" antiserum. The balance of the H Broth is used for the indole test by adding 0.5 ml. of Kovacs' reagent to the tube. A dark red color in the surface layer indicates a positive test; a yellow color indicates a negative test.

To rehydrate the medium, dissolve 21.5 grams Bacto-H Broth in 1000 mL cold distilled water. Distribute in 4 ml. amounts in 13 x 100 mm. tubes. Sterilize in the autoclave for 15 minutes at 10 pounds pressure (117°C.). The final reaction of the medium will be pH 7.2.

One pound of Bacto-H Broth will make 21.1 liters of medium.

[1] Pub. Health Rep., 65:116:1950.
[2] Pub. Health Lab., 9:23:1951.
[3] Personal Communication, 1951.

FRIEWER SHAUGHNESSY MEDIUM

BACTO
FRIEWER SHAUGHNESSY BASE NO. 1   (B310)
DEHYDRATED

Bacto-Beef Extract	3 g.
Bacto-Peptone	30 g.
Bacto-Agar	3 g.
Bacto-Brom Thymol Blue	0.01 g.

BACTO
FRIEWER SHAUGHNESSY BASE NO. 2   (B311)
DEHYDRATED

Bacto-Lactose	10 g.
Lead Acetate	0.05 g.

Bacto-Friewer Shaughnessy Medium prepared according to the formula of Friewer and Shaughnessy[1] is recommended for use as a primary screening medium in the laboratory diagnosis of enteric infections. The medium is prepared in two parts, Bacto-Friewer Shaughnessy Base No. 1 and Bacto-Friewer Shaughnessy Base No. 2. A solution of each base is prepared separately and mixed before sterilization to secure the complete medium.

A Lead Semisolid Agar was developed by Friewer and Shaughnessy[1] as a screening medium, in the preliminary classification of the *Salmonella-Shigella* group. The determination of motility, considered by some workers to be most helpful as an early step in the classification of the group, is achieved by the use of a semisolid agar. This Lead Semisolid Agar also contained lactose and brom thymol blue in addition to lead acetate. It was possible, therefore, with this single medium to determine motility, the production of acid or acid and gas from lactose and the production of hydrogen sulfide. These characteristics, i.e., motility, lactose fermentation and hydrogen sulfide production, are essential criteria in practically all methods of classification of members of the enteric group.

Using this medium under practical conditions, colonies may be picked from any primary plating medium such as Bacto-S S Agar, Bacto-Bismuth Sulfite Agar or Bacto-MacConkey Agar, or inoculation may be made from a broth or agar subculture from these media to the Friewer Shaughnessy Medium.

If there is any question as to the purity of the suspected colony, it should be inoculated into a broth or peptone tube and streaked on a plating medium such as Bacto-MacConkey Agar or Bacto-E.M.B. Agar, to establish its purity, before proceeding with the screening test. A stab inoculation, using a straight wire, and extending down the center of the medium to approximately one-half its depth, is most satisfactory.

After 12–24 hours incubation at 37°C. the tubes are read for the following information:

1. Motility. A motile culture is characterized by a diffusion of the growth from the line of inoculation. Some cultures, such as certain members of the *Proteus* and *Salmonella* groups, are actively motile, producing complete diffusion throughout the medium. Other cultures, as for example most strains of *Salmonella typhosa,* are less actively motile, and growth extends out from the line of inoculation without giving the appearance of diffuse turbidity. This difference in the degree of motility is an aid in the choice of subsequent tests, for the cultures with moderate diffusion from the line of inoculation plus a hydrogen sulfide reaction can be selected for special tests for *S. typhosa.*

Shigella organisms are non-motile and grow only along the line of inoculation. Strictly aerobic rods and cocci grow only on the surface of the medium and are readily differentiated from the non-motile facultative anaerobes such as members of the *Shigella* group.

2. Hydrogen Sulfide. The production of a brown or black color is an indication that hydrogen sulfide has been produced. Motility accentuates the diffusion of the hydrogen sulfide, whereas in a non-motile culture the brown or black coloration is confined to the line of inoculation.

3. Lactose Fermentation. When lactose is fermented, the medium in the growth area develops a yellow color. Formation of gas is evidenced by gas bubbles in the medium or at the surface. The intensity of the lead sulfide reaction is not great enough to mask the color change.

The following key, suggested by Friewer and Shaughnessy,[2] may be used as a guide for the identification of the pathogenic Gram-negative bacilli. Serological reactions are used for final confirmation.

I   Fermentation of Lactose.
    A. Acid and Gas—DISCARD.
    B. Acid fermentation, motile culture—DISCARD.
    C. Acid fermentation, non-motile culture (see non-motile cultures, III, below).

II   Surface Growth Reactors. (No growth along line of stab, growth only at surface).

Inoculate a Dextrose Broth tube.

Acid fermentation—Suspect *Shigella* and proceed as in III B.

No reaction in dextrose—DISCARD.

(Alkaligines and pseudomonas groups. An occasional pseudo-monas strain produces a slight reaction in dextrose).

III Non-motile types.

A. Gram-stain all non-motile types.

Gram-positive types—DISCARD.

B. Gram-negative types—Proceed with tests for the *Shigella* group. (An occasional Sonne strain produces fermentation of lactose rather rapidly. For this reason all non-motile, Gram-negative types are put through suitable tests for this species).

IV Motile cultures.

A. Moderate motility, hydrogen sulfide production.

Proceed with tests for *S. typhosa*.

B. Active motility with or without hydrogen sulfide production. Inoculate Bacto-Peptone or Bacto-Tryptone tube for indole test, and fermentation tubes of Mannitol and Saccharose Broths.

    1. Mannitol fermenter, no fermentation of saccharose, indole negative.

        a. Mannitol fermented (with acid and gas), no hydrogen sulfide production—*S. paratyphi* and a few other *Salmonella* types.

        b. Hydrogen sulfide production.

           (I) Mannitol fermented with acid and gas—Proceed with tests for *Salmonella*.

           (II) Mannitol fermented with acid only—Proceed with tests for *S. typhosa*.

        c. Indole positive and/or saccharose fermenting types (coli-aerogenes, proteus groups)—DISCARD.

    2. Mannitol non-fermenting types (Morgan's bacillus and other proteus groups)—DISCARD.

To prepare 200 ml. of the medium, suspend 7.2 grams of Bacto-Friewer Shaughnessy Base No. 1 in 100 ml. of cold distilled water and heat to boiling to dissolve the medium completely. To a second flask containing 100 ml. distilled water, add 2.1 grams Bacto-Friewer Shaughnessy Base No. 2, and warm to 45°C. When Base No. 2 is in complete solution add to the hot solution of Base No. 1. *Caution:* To avoid a precipitate in the medium, it is necessary to have Base No. 1 in complete solution and hot when the warm solution of Base No. 2 is added. Distribute in tubes to a depth of about 3 inches. Sterilize in the autoclave for 15 minutes at 15 pounds pressure (121°C.). Allow the sterile tubes to solidify in an upright position. Final reaction of the medium will be pH 7.5.

One pound of Bacto-Friewer Shaughnessy Base No. 1 will make 12.5 liters of medium.

One pound of Bacto-Friewer Shaughnessy Base No. 2 will make 43.2 liters of medium.

[1] Am. J. Clin. Path., Tech. Sect., 8:1:1944.
[2] Personal Communication, 1947.

BACTO
PEPTONE IRON AGAR (B89)
DEHYDRATED

Bacto-Peptone	15 g.
Proteose Peptone, Difco	5 g.
Ferric Ammonium Citrate	0.5 g.
Dipotassium Phosphate	1 g.
Sodium Thiosulfate	0.08 g.
Bacto-Agar	15 g.

Bacto-Peptone Iron Agar is a medium designed for use as an indicator of hydrogen sulfide production by microorganisms.

Levine and co-workers,[1,2] in their studies on the reactions in the colon group of bacteria, described a medium containing Proteose Peptone, Difco and ferric citrate as being particularly satisfactory for the detection of hydrogen sulfide. They further showed that such a medium served to differentiate the strains which were Voges-Proskauer negative, methyl red positive and citrate positive from other members of the colon-aerogenes group.

Levine reported that the ferric citrate was a much more sensitive indicator of hydrogen sulfide production than was lead acetate. Their medium gave definite clear-cut reactions within 12 hours.

Bacto-Peptone Iron Agar is a modification of Levine's original formula, in which Bacto-Peptone has been included with Proteose Peptone and the more soluble ferric ammonium citrate is used in place of ferric citrate. The medium in tubes is inoculated by the stab method. Blackening of the medium indicates the production of hydrogen sulfide. The reaction is intense and takes place quite rapidly. Bacto-Peptone Iron Agar is not toxic and may be used in plates as well as in tubes. Plates are convenient when it is desired to estimate the number of hydrogen sulfide producers.

Tittsler and Sandholzer[3] compared Bacto-Peptone Iron Agar with Lead Acetate Agar for the detection of hydrogen sulfide and found that the Bacto-Peptone Iron Agar had the advantage of giving earlier reactions and more clear-cut results.

Bacto-S I M Medium as discussed on page 173 may be recommended as a more sensitive medium for the detection of hydrogen sulfide. This is a semisolid medium and, in addition to indicating early clear-cut hydrogen sulfide producton, is also recommended for motility determinations and indole production.

To rehydrate the medium, suspend 36 grams of Bacto-Peptone Iron Agar in 1000 ml. of cold distilled water and heat to boiling to dissolve the medium completely. Distribute in tubes and sterilize in the autoclave for 15 minutes at 15 pounds pressure (121°C.). The final reaction of the medium will be pH 6.7.

One pound of Bacto-Peptone Iron Agar will make 12.6 liters of medium.

[1] Proc. Soc. Exp. Biol. Med., 29:1022:1932.
[2] Am. J. Pub. Health, 24:505:1934.
[3] Am. J. Pub. Health, 27:1240:1937.

BACTO

SIMMONS CITRATE AGAR　(B91)

DEHYDRATED

Magnesium Sulfate	0.2 g.
Monoammonium Phosphate	1 g.
Dipotassium Phosphate	1 g.
Sodium Citrate	2 g.
Sodium Chloride	5 g.
Bacto-Agar	15 g.
Bacto-Brom Thymol Blue	0.08 g.

Bacto-Simmons Citrate Agar is a medium capable of differentiating between fecal coli and members of the aerogenes group on the basis of citrate utilization. It may also be used to differentiate certain members of the *Salmonella* group. Bacto-Simmons Citrate Agar is prepared according to the formula of Simmons.[1]

The differential between fecal coli and aerogenes as described by Koser[2] is based upon the inability of fecal coli to develop in a medium containing inorganic ammonium salts as the only source of nitrogen with citrate as the sole source of carbon, whereas strains of aerogenes grow quite unrestrictedly. Likewise, *Salmonella typhosa, S. paratyphi* and *Shigella* can be differentiated from *S. schottmuelleri, S. enteritidis* and *S. typhimurium,* the latter group being able to utilize citrate in such a medium while the former cannot.

This principle was first employed in a liquid medium by Koser. The liquid medium had the disadvantage of appearing turbid when large inocula were used even when no growth ensued. This observation led Simmons[1] to devise a solid medium which obviates the disadvantage of turbidity as a criterion of growth.

Simmons' Medium is essentially Koser's Medium to which brom thymol blue and 1.5 per cent agar have been added. It is a valuable aid in differentiating certain members of the *Salmonella* group from *S. paratyphi, S. typhosa* and *Shigella.* The medium is usually prepared as agar slopes, inoculated by stab and streak, and incubated at 37°C. Some workers, however, prefer to use the medium in petri dishes. On such a solid medium, growth is indicated very clearly by colony formation and is usually accompanied by a color change of the indicator due to acid or alkali production. Strains of aerogenes grow luxuriantly upon Simmons Citrate Agar, producing alkali and changing the medium from its initial green to deep blue in 24–48 hours. Fecal coli either do not grow at all upon this medium or grow so sparsely that no change in reaction is apparent. *S. schottmuelleri, S. enteritidis* and *S. typhimurium,* which develop on the medium, produce alkali as indicated by a deep prussian blue color.

Simmons also recommended its use for isolating and identifying certain fungi and fungi imperfecti.

To rehydrate the medium, suspend 24.2 grams of Bacto-Simmons Citrate Agar in 1000 ml. of cold distilled water and heat to boiling to dissolve the medium completely. Distribute in tubes or flasks and sterilize by autoclaving for 15 minutes at 15 pounds pressure (121° C.). Allow the tubed medium to cool in a slanting position. The final reaction of the medium will be pH 6.8.

One pound of Bacto-Simmons Citrate Agar will make 18.7 liters of medium.

[1] J. Infectious Diseases, 39:209:1926.　　　[2] J. Bact., 8:493:1923.

BACTO
MALONATE BROTH (B395)
DEHYDRATED

Ammonium Sulfate	2 g.
Dipotassium Phosphate	0.6 g.
Monopotassium Phosphate	0.4 g.
Sodium Chloride	2 g.
Sodium Malonate	3 g.
Bacto-Brom Thymol Blue	0.025 g.

Bacto-Malonate Broth is liquid medium prepared with materials of known chemical composition, with ammonium sulfate and sodium malonate as the only source of nitrogen and carbon. It is prepared according to the formula described by Leifson[1] and used for the differentiation of members of the *Aerobacter-Escherichia* group.

The ability of members of the *Aerobacter* group to utilize malonate as a source of carbon in a medium of known chemical composition, and the inability of members of the *Escherichia* group to grow in this medium was pointed out by Leifson. A pH indicator, brom thymol blue, was incorporated in the medium. *Aerobacter*, utilize malonate as a source of energy, produce an alkaline reaction, and change the color of the medium to blue. *Escherichia*, not capable of utilizing malonate, fail to grow, leaving the medium unchanged.

To rehydrate the medium, dissolve 8 grams Bacto-Malonate Broth in 1000 ml. distilled water. Sterilize in the autoclave for 15 minutes at 15 pounds pressure (121°C.). Avoid introduction of carbon and nitrogen from other sources. Final reaction of the medium will be pH 6.7.

One pound of Bacto-Malonate Broth will make 56.7 liters of medium.

[1] J. Bact., 26:329:1933.

BACTO
PHENOL RED TARTRATE AGAR (B90)
DEHYDRATED

Bacto-Peptone	10 g.
Sodium Potassium Tartrate	10 g.
Sodium Chloride	5 g.
Bacto-Agar	15 g.
Bacto-Phenol Red	0.024 g.

Bacto-Phenol Red Tartrate Agar is a solid tube medium valuable in the differentiation and identification of members of the *Salmonella* (paratyphoid) group. Brown, Duncan and Henry[1] observed that the members of the paratyphoid group varied in their ability to attack sodium tartrate, and incorporated this principle in a medium for subdividing the group. Jordan and Harmon[2] claimed that the medium of Brown, Duncan and Henry failed to give sharp differentiation, and devised a medium which possessed the advantage of being more definite in its differentiation. On this medium an acid reaction is produced by *Salmonella typhimurium, S. enteritidis, S. choleraesuis, S. abortivoequina, S. typhosa, Escherichi coli* and *Proteus vulgaris* strains, while the *S. schottmuelleri* and *S. paratyphi* strains produce an alkaline reaction.

Bacto-Phenol Red Tartrate Agar duplicates the medium of Jordan and Harmon. It is used unslanted, and is inoculated by stabbing. Observations are made at 24 and 48 hour intervals. An acid reaction is indicated by the development of a distinct yellow color in the lower portion of the tube, the surface zone remaining red.

To rehydrate the medium, suspend 40 grams of Bacto-Phenol Red Tartrate Agar in 1000 ml. of cold distilled water and heat to boiling to dissolve the medium completely. The solution is distributed in tubes which are stoppered with cotton plugs or loosely fitting caps. Sterilize in the autoclave for 15 minutes at 15 pounds pressure (121°C.). Allow the tubes to cool in an unslanted position. The medium will have a final reaction of pH 7.6.

One pound of Bacto-Phenol Red Tartrate Agar will make 11.3 liters of medium.

[1] J. Hyg., 23:1:1924.   [2] J. Infectious Diseases, 42:238:1928.

BACTO
MOTILITY TEST MEDIUM   (B105)
DEHYDRATED

Bacto-Tryptose	10 g.
Sodium Chloride	5 g.
Bacto-Agar	5 g.

Bacto-Motility Test Medium, a modification of the formula of Tittsler and Sandholzer,[1] as suggested by Darby,[2] is a semisolid medium employed in the testing of bacteria for motility. The sterile medium is inoculated by stabbing through the center of the medium and is incubated at the proper temperature for the organism under consideration and examined at the end of 8, 24 and 48 hours. Motility is manifested macroscopically by a diffuse zone of growth spreading from the line of inoculation. Certain species of motile bacteria will show diffuse growth throughout the entire medium, while others may show diffusion from one or two points only, appearing as nodular outgrowths along the stab. Tittsler and Sandholzer reported that tubes incubated for one day gave identical results with the hanging drop method and that incubation for two days permitted them to demonstrate motility in an additional 4 per cent of the cultures tested.

Bacto-S I M Medium as discussed on page 173 is also recommended for determination of motility. In addition to motility, hydrogen sulfide production and the production of indole may be determined on Bacto-S I M Medium.

To rehydrate the medium, suspend 20 grams of Bacto-Motility Test Medium in 1000 ml. of cold distilled water and heat to boiling to dissolve the medium completely. Distribute in tubes and sterilize by autoclaving for 15 minutes at 15 pounds pressure (121°C.). Allow the medium to cool with the tubes in an upright position. The medium will have a final reaction of pH 7.2.

One pound of Bacto-Motility Test Medium will make 22.7 liters of medium.

[1] J. Bact., 31:575:1936.   [2] Personal Communication.

BACTO
NITRATE BROTH   (B268)
DEHYDRATED

Bacto-Beef Extract	3 g.
Bacto-Peptone	5 g.
Potassium Nitrate	1 g.

Bacto-Nitrate Broth is recommended for testing the ability of bacteria to reduce nitrate to nitrite, a characteristic which often has differential value. The medium is prepared according to the formula published in "Pure Culture Study of Bacteria"[1] of the Society of American Bacteriologists.

For determining the ability of an organism to reduce nitrate to nitrite, tubes of medium, prepared from Bacto-Nitrate Broth, are inoculated with a pure culture of the strain under examination. The tubes are then incubated at 37°C. for 12 to 24 hours. The medium is tested for the presence of nitrites by adding a few drops each of sulfanilic acid and a-naphthylamine reagent solutions. The sulfanilic acid reagent is prepared by dissolving 8 grams of sulfanilic acid in 1000 ml. 5N acetic acid. The a-napththylamine reagent consists of 5 grams of a-naphthylamine dissolved in 1000 ml. 5N acetic acid. A distinct pink or red color indicates the presence of nitrite reduced from original nitrate. If an organism grows rapidly and reduces nitrate actively, it is suggested that the test for nitrite be performed at an early incubation period since the reduction may be carried beyond the nitrite stage. The test must always be controlled by comparison with an uninoculated tube of medium.

To rehydrate the medium, dissolve 9 grams of Bacto-Nitrate Broth in 1000 ml. distilled water. Distribute in tubes and sterilize in the autoclave for 15 minutes at 15 pounds pressure (121°C.). The final reaction of the medium will be pH 7.0.

One pound of Bacto-Nitrate Broth will make 50 liters of medium.

[1] Pure Culture Study of Bacteria, 12:Leaflet II:8:1944.

BACTO
NITRATE AGAR (B106)
DEHYDRATED

Bacto-Beef Extract	3 g.
Bacto-Peptone	5 g.
Potassium Nitrate	1 g.
Bacto-Agar	12 g.

Bacto-Nitrate Agar is a dehydrated medium for use in testing nitrate reduction by bacteria. It is prepared according to the formula of the "Manual of Methods" of the Society of American Bacteriologists.

Nitrate reduction by microorganisms is a valuable criterion in the differentiation and identification of various types of bacteria. Certain bacteria reduce the nitrates to nitrites only, while others are capable of further reduction to free nitrogen or even ammonia. Furthermore, many aerobic bacteria can grow under anaerobic conditions in the presence of nitrates from which they derive their oxygen.

Tubes of sterile slanted medium are inoculated by streaking over the surface of the slant, and stabbing into the butt. Incubate at 37°C. Examine the cultures on various days for gas production which will be indicated by splitting of the agar. Test for nitrates with sulfanilic acid and a-naphthylamine reagent solutions. The sulfanilic acid reagent is prepared by dissolving 8 grams of sulfanilic acid in 1000 ml. 5N acetic acid. The a-naphthylamine reagent consists of 5 grams of a-naphthylamine dissolved in 1000 ml. 5N acetic acid. A few drops of each reagent are put into the tube to be tested. A distinct pink or red color indicates the presence of nitrite reduced from original nitrate. The test should always be controlled by comparing with an uninoculated tube of the medium which has been kept under the same conditions as the inoculated tubes. The evolution of gas in a nitrate medium containing no sugar or fermentable substance is a definite indication of reduction to free nitrogen.

To rehydrate the medium, suspend 21 grams of Bacto-Nitrate Agar in 1000 ml. of cold distilled water and heat to boiling to dissolve the medium completely. Distribute in tubes and sterilize in the autoclave for 15 minutes at 15 pounds pressure (121°C.). The final reaction of the medium will be pH 6.8.

One pound of Bacto-Nitrate Agar will make 21 liters of medium.

BACTO

PHENOL RED BROTH BASE   (B92)

DEHYDRATED

Bacto-Beef Extract	1 g.
Proteose Peptone No. 3, Difco ..	10 g.
Sodium Chloride	5 g.
Bacto-Phenol Red	0.018 g.

Bacto-Phenol Red Broth Base, and the complete carbohydrate* media described below, are used in fermentation studies for the cultural identification of pure cultures of microorganisms. The fermentative properties of bacteria are valuable criteria in their identification, and may be determined by culturing the organisms in a suitable medium containing the appropriate fermentable substance. A satisfactory basic medium for determining the fermentation reactions of microorganisms must be capable of supporting growth of the organisms under study, and free from fermentable carbohydrates which could give erroneous interpretations. It must be stable, uniform in composition, give distinct reactions and yield accurate results.

Bacto-Phenol Red Broth Base is an excellent substrate for streptococci, pneumococci, meningococci and gonococci, as well as for other less fastidious types. The cultural value of the medium can be greatly improved for some of the more delicate strains by the addition of a small amount (0.1–0.2 per cent) of Bacto-Agar. A medium containing this small quantity of agar may be used to best advantage by heating it to the boiling point to drive out the dissolved air and cooling it below 40°C., without excessive agitation, just previous to inoculation. Such a procedure also makes the medium sufficiently oxygen-free for propagation of the obligate anaerobes as well as microaerophiles. Bacto-Phenol Red Broth Base with 0.5 per cent selected carbohydrate and 0.15 per cent agar is suggested as a satisfactory medium for the fermentation determinations as given in Diagnostic Procedures and Reagents.[1] Some bacteriologists, determining the fermentation reactions of gonococci, may prefer to use 0.8 per cent Bacto-Agar and add 5 per cent sterile fresh rabbit serum to the sterile Phenol Red Broth containing the selected carbohydrate, as discussed under Bacto-Proteose No. 3 Agar, page 116.

For the determination of fermentative properties of members of the enteric group of bacteria, Bacto-Purple Broth Media are recommended, as discussed on page 190. These media have the same nutrients, but have a slightly more acid reaction, and brom cresol purple is employed as an indicator.

With the exception of the carbohydrate, which has been omitted, Bacto-Phenol Red Broth Base is a complete basic medium prepared with phenol red as an indicator of changes in reaction. This product makes it possible to prepare as much or as little medium as is required, adding to different portions any fermentable substance in any concentration desired. The concentration of carbohydrate generally employed for testing the fermentation reactions of bacteria is 0.5 or 1.0 per cent. Some investigators prefer to use 1.0 per cent rather than 0.5 per cent to insure against reversion of the reaction due to depletion of the carbo-

*The term carbohydrate, as used here, includes carbohydrates, polyhydric alcohols, glucosides and other fermentable carbon compounds.

hydrate by some microorganisms. An entire series of carbohydrate broths may thus be made up readily, conveniently, and economically.

To rehydrate the medium, dissolve 16 grams of Bacto-Phenol Red Broth Base in 1000 ml. of distilled water. To this solution the test carbohydrate is added in proper quantity, and, when solution is complete, the medium is distributed in fermentation tubes. Sterilize by autoclaving for not more than 15 minutes at 15 pounds pressure (121°C.). The minimum amount of heat required for complete sterilization is to be desired. By packing the tubes loosely in the autoclave to allow free circulation of steam, the time required may be appreciably shortened, provided the temperature in the autoclave is actually 121°C. The final reaction of the medium, without added carbohydrate, will be pH 7.4.

The addition of some carbohydrates may result in an acid reaction. In this case it is suggested that 0.1N sodium hydroxide be added drop by drop to restore the original color, taking care not to obtain too deep red or cerise color.

One pound of Bacto-Phenol Red Broth Base will make 28.3 liters of medium.

An extensive number of carbohydrates, polyhydric alcohols and glucosides, Difco, are available (see page 291) for use with Bacto-Phenol Red Broth Base. There is also available a selected list of filter-sterilized ampuled solutions of some of these carbohydrates, each ampul containing 10 ml. of a 10 per cent solution, or 1 gram of carbohydrate (see page 292).

[1] Diagnostic Procedures and Reagents 3rd Edition:107:1950.

BACTO

PHENOL RED CARBOHYDRATE BROTHS

DEHYDRATED

Complete fermentation media, prepared with Bacto-Phenol Red Broth Base and 0.5 per cent of the more frequently used carbohydrates, are available. The dehydrated media included in this group are:

BACTO-PHENOL RED DEXTROSE BROTH (B93)
BACTO-PHENOL RED LACTOSE BROTH (B94)
BACTO-PHENOL RED MANNITOL BROTH (B97)
BACTO-PHENOL RED SACCHAROSE BROTH (B95)
BACTO-PHENOL RED MALTOSE BROTH (B96)

To rehydrate the media, dissolve 21 grams of the Bacto-Phenol Red Carbohydrate Broth in 1000 ml. distilled water. The complete media are sterilized as described above, using the minimum amount of heat necessary for sterilization, for not more than 15 minutes at 15 pounds pressure (121°C.). The final reaction of these media will be pH 7.4.

One pound of each complete Bacto-Phenol Red Carbohydrate Broth will make 21.6 liters of medium.

BACTO

PHENOL RED AGAR BASE (B98)

DEHYDRATED

Bacto-Beef Extract	1 g.
Proteose Peptone No. 3, Difco	10 g.
Sodium Chloride	5 g.
Bacto-Agar	15 g.
Bacto-Phenol Red	0.025 g.

Bacto-Phenol Red Agar Base and the complete carbohydrate* media described below, are used in fermentation studies for the cultural identification of pure cultures of microorganisms. While liquid media are generally employed in studying the fermentation reactions of microorganisms, many bacteriologists prefer a solid medium for this purpose. The solid media employed usually contain one per cent of the selected carbohydrate and an indicator of reaction. They are dispensed in tubes, slanted, and inoculated by smearing over the surface of the slant and stabbing into the butt.

The advantages claimed for a solid fermentation medium are that it permits observation of the fermentation reactions under both aerobic and anaerobic conditions, that gas formation is indicated by splitting of the agar or accumulation of gas bubbles in the base, and that deep tubes can provide sufficiently anaerobic conditions for the development of the obligately anaerobic bacilli.

Bacto-Phenol Red Agar Base is particularly well adapted to the study of fermentation reactions of microorganisms. This medium supports excellent growth of many fastidious bacteria. The basal medium is free from fermentable carbohydrates which could give erroneous interpretation. With the exception of the carbohydrate, which has been omitted, it is a complete medium prepared with phenol red as an indicator of changes in reaction. Bacto-Phenol Red Agar Base permits the user to prepare as much or as little medium as he requires, adding to different portions any fermentable substance desired (usually one per cent of the test carbohydrate being added). An entire series of carbohydrate agars may thus be made up readily, conveniently and economically.

Tubes of the sterile medium are inoculated by smearing over the surface of the slant and stabbing into the butt. Obligately anaerobic bacteria may be inoculated into the melted medium previously cooled to 45°C. and subsequently allowing it to solidify. After incubation, fermentation will be denoted by a change in the color of the medium from red to canary yellow. Gas formation is indicated by the collection of gas bubbles in the base, or by splitting of the agar.

To rehydrate the medium, suspend 31 grams of Bacto-Phenol Red Agar Base in 1000 ml. cold distilled water and heat to boiling to dissolve the medium completely. To this solution the selected carbohydrate is added. When the solution is complete the medium is distributed in tubes which are stoppered with cotton plugs or loosely fitting caps and sterilized in the autoclave for not more than 15 minutes at 15 pounds pressure (121°C.). The minimum amount of heat required for sterilization is to be desired. By packing tubes loosely in the autoclave to allow free circulation of the steam, the time required for sterilization may be appreciably shortened, provided the temperature in the autoclave is actually 121°C. Some workers may prefer to add the carbohydrate in the form of a sterile solution to the melted sterile base, and then dispense the complete medium into sterile tubes. This latter procedure is particularly recommended where only slow operating autoclaves are available. In either case the sterile tubed medium containing the carbohydrate is allowed to cool in a slanting position so as to provide a slope and generous butt. The final reaction of the medium, without added carbohydrate, will be pH 7.4.

The addition of some carbohydrates may result in an acid reaction. In this case, it is suggested that 0.1N sodium hydroxide be added drop by drop to restore the original color, taking care not to obtain too deep red or cerise color.

One pound of Bacto-Phenol Red Agar Base will make 14.6 liters of medium.

An extensive number of carbohydrates, polyhydric alcohols and glucosides, Difco, is available (see page 291) for use in conjunction with Bacto-Phenol Red Agar Base. There is also available a selected list of filter-sterilized ampuled solu-

---

*The term carbohydrate, as used here, includes carbohydrates, polyhydric alcohols, glucosides and other fermentable substances.

tions of some of these carbohydrates, each ampul containing 10 ml. of a 10 per cent solution, or 1 gram of the carbohydrate (see page 292).

(see page 292)

BACTO
PHENOL RED CARBOHYDRATE AGARS
DEHYDRATED

Complete fermentation media, prepared with Bacto-Phenol Red Agar Base and 1 per cent of the more frequently used carbohydrates, are also available. The dehydrated media included in this group are:

BACTO-PHENOL RED DEXTROSE AGAR (B99)
BACTO-PHENOL RED LACTOSE AGAR (B100)
BACTO-PHENOL RED MANNITOL AGAR (B103)
BACTO-PHENOL RED SACCHAROSE AGAR (B101)
BACTO-PHENOL RED MALTOSE AGAR (B102)

To rehydrate the media, suspend 41 grams of the Bacto-Phenol Red Carbohydrate Agar in 1000 ml. cold distilled water and heat to boiling to dissolve the media completely. The complete media are sterilized, as described above, using the minimum amount of heat necessary, for not more than 15 minutes at 15 pounds pressure (121°C.). The final reaction of these media will be pH 7.4.

One pound of each complete Bacto-Phenol Red Carbohydrate Agar will make 12.6 liters of medium.

BACTO
PURPLE BROTH BASE (B227)
DEHYDRATED

Bacto-Beef Extract	1 g.
Proteose Peptone No. 3, Difco	10 g.
Sodium Chloride	5 g.
Bacto-Brom Cresol Purple	0.015 g.

Bacto-Purple Broth Base is recommended for the preparation of carbohydrate broths used in fermentation studies for the cultural identification of pure cultures of microorganisms, particularly members of the enteric group. We have prepared Bacto-Purple Broth Base, containing the indicator brom cresol purple, and adjusted to a final reaction of pH 6.8, for the convenience of bacteriologists desiring carbohydrate differential broths of slightly acid reaction and containing a sensitive sulfonephthalein indicator capable of demonstrating minute change in reaction. It is free from fermentable carbohydrates which could give erroneous results.

The concentration of carbohydrate generally employed for testing the fermentation reactions of bacteria is 0.5 or 1.0 per cent. Some investigators prefer to use 1.0 per cent rather than 0.5 per cent to insure against reversion of the reaction due to depletion of the carbohydrate by some microorganisms. Tubes of Purple Lactose Broth and Purple Saccharose Broth should be tightly stoppered during the incubation period for fermentation studies of the enteric group, to avoid reversion of reaction.

To rehydrate the medium, dissolve 16 grams of Bacto-Purple Broth Base in 1000 ml. of distilled water. To this solution the selected carbohydrate is added in the desired quantity and when solution is complete the medium is distributed in fermentation tubes. Sterilize by autoclaving for not more than 15 minutes at 15 pounds pressure (121°C.). The minimum amount of heat required for sterilization is to be desired, so as to avoid hydrolysis of the carbohydrate. By packing the tubes loosely in the autoclave to allow free circulation of steam, the time required may be appreciably shortened, provided the temperature in the autoclave is actually 121°C. The final reaction of the medium without added carbohydrate, will be pH 6.8.

The addition of some carbohydrates may result in an acid reaction. In this case it is suggested that 0.1N sodium hydroxide be added drop by drop to restore original color.

One pound of Bacto-Purple Broth Base will make 28.3 liters of medium.

BACTO
PURPLE AGAR BASE   (B228)
DEHYDRATED

Bacto-Beef Extract	1 g.
Proteose Peptone No. 3, Difco ...	10 g.
Sodium Chloride	5 g.
Bacto-Agar	15 g.
Bacto-Brom Cresol Purple	0.02 g.

Bacto-Purple Agar Base is recommended for the preparation of carbohydrate agars used in fermentation studies for the cultural identification of pure cultures of microorganisms, particularly members of the enteric group. Although broth media are generally employed in studying the fermentation reactions of microorganisms, many bacteriologists prefer a solid medium for this purpose. Bacto-Purple Agar Base is available for those bacteriologists preferring a fermentation medium of slightly acid reaction (pH 6.8). This medium supports luxuriant growth of organisms and with the indicator brom cresol purple gives clear-cut reactions from slight changes in the pH of the medium. This medium is free from fermentable carbohydrates which could give erroneous results.

To rehydrate the medium, suspend 31 grams of Bacto-Purple Agar Base in 1000 ml. of cold distilled water and heat to boiling to dissolve the medium completely. To this solution add 5–10 grams of the test carbohydrate, and, when dissolved, dispense into culture tubes and sterilize in the autoclave for not more than 15 minutes at 15 pounds pressure (121°C.). The final reaction of the medium without added carbohydrate will be pH 6.8.

The addition of some carbohydrates may result in an acid reaction. In this case, it is suggested that 0.1N sodium hydroxide be added drop by drop to restore the original color.

One pound of Bacto-Purple Agar Base will make 14.6 liters of medium.

BACTO
SNYDER TEST AGAR   (B247)
DEHYDRATED

Bacto-Tryptone	20 g.
Bacto-Dextrose	20 g.
Sodium Chloride	5 g.
Bacto-Agar	20 g.
Bacto-Brom Cresol Green	0.02 g.

Bacto-Snyder test Agar is prepared for the colorimetric diagnosis of caries activity as described by Snyder.[1,2] The method is based on acid production in a carbohydrate medium by acidogenic microorganisms from the buccal cavity, and is evidenced by a change in color of the indicator, brom cresol green, from a blue-green to a yellow color. The test gives excellent correlation with the *Lactobacillus* plate count and with the clinical picture, and provides a simple reliable method for ordinary clinical use in the diagnosis of caries activity.

The following method of procedure and interpretation of results are suggested by Snyder.

Procedure

The saliva specimens are obtained by having the patient chew a small piece of paraffin for three minutes, during which time the saliva is collected in sterile test tubes or bottles. The time for collecting specimens is preferably before breakfast and before the teeth are brushed, otherwise just before lunch or dinner. The specimens of saliva are then shaken vigorously and 0.2 ml. of the saliva added by means of a sterile pipette to tubes of melted Snyder test Agar. The medium is melted by placing the tubes in a boiling water bath for 10 minutes and then cooling at 45°C. The medium and inoculum are mixed and then allowed to solidify by standing at room temperature for one-half hour. The inoculated solidified tubes are incubated at 37°C. for 72 hours. If a thermostatically controlled incubator is not available, a thermos bottle may be substituted, as described by Appleton[3] and Grossman.[4] Briefly stated, the method is to take a quart sized thermos bottle of reliable make, and place a mercury thermometer through the center of the cork, sealing it in securely. The thermos bottle is then filled half full of warm water previously adjusted to 43°C. (110°F.) as determined by the thermometer. The bottle is then closed with the stopper and shaken to warm the inner walls of the container. When the temperature of the water in the thermos bottle reaches 38°C. (100°F.) the culture tubes may be placed inside, care being taken to avoid wetting the cotton plugs, or screw caps.

Observations

Examine the tubes daily for three days and record changes in color compared with an uninoculated control tube. Observation of the color changes is facilitated by means of reflected light, with the tubes held against a white background. The color will change from the bluish-green of the control to yellow.

Positive: Change in color so that green is no longer dominant is recorded as $++$ to $++++$.

Negative: No change in color or only slight deviation, but green still dominant is recorded 0 to $+$.

Interpretation

Caries Activity	Hours Incubation		
	24	48	72
Marked	Positive	....	....
Moderate	Negative	Positive	....
Slight	Negative	Negative	Positive
Negative	Negative	Negative	Negative

The interpretation of laboratory data as given above with clinical activity depends upon experience and understanding of several factors:

1. The data indicate only what is happening at the time the specimen was collected.
2. At least two specimens collected within 2–4 days must be obtained to establish a base-line or reference point.

3. Only when two or more specimens have been cultured can any reliability or prediction be obtained.

4. The clinician must study enough cases by use of periodic laboratory data to establish in his own mind the value or significance for the purpose intended.

Snyder[5] tabulated the correlation between the Snyder colorimetric test and *Lactobacillus* counts on specimens of saliva collected routinely:

COLORIMETRIC CHANGE (HOURS)

No. Lactobacilli per ml. Saliva	No. Spec.	24		48		72	
		Pos.	% Pos.	Pos.	% Pos.	Pos.	% Pos.
0	348	2	0.6	22	6.3	85	24.5
0–100	59	0	0.0	7	11.9	32	54.3
100–1000	157	5	3.2	47	30.0	111	70.0
1000–10,000	105	6	5.7	69	65.7	99	94.3
10,000–20,000	138	18	13.0	105	71.2	131	95.0
20,000–50,000	264	59	22.2	229	86.8	260	98.7
50,000–100,000	245	72	29.4	221	90.3	243	99.3
100,000–	497	231	46.6	476	95.5	494	99.3

To rehydrate the medium, suspend 65 grams Bacto-Snyder test Agar in 1000 ml. cold distilled water and heat to boiling to dissolve the medium completely. Distribute in tubes and sterilize in the autoclave for 15 minutes at 15 pounds pressure (121°C.). Final reaction of the medium will be pH 4.8.

One pound of Bacto-Snyder Test Agar will make 7 liters of medium.

3 J. Dental Res., 19:349:1940.   4 Grossman: Root Canal Therapy, 2nd Edition:
4 J. Am. Dental Assoc., 28:44:1941.   273:1946.
5 Dental Items Int., 49:589:1927.   5 Personal Communication, 1948.

BACTO
LITMUS MILK   (B107)
DEHYDRATED

Bacto-Skim Milk .... 100 g.
Bacto-Litmus .... 0.75 g.

Bacto-Litmus Milk is recommended for propagating and carrying stock cultures of the lactic acid bacteria associated with dairy products, and also for determining the action of bacteria, upon milk.

Milk has been used for the propagation and study of microorganisms since the beginning of bacteriology. In addition to its being an excellent substrate for propagating the lactic acid bacteria commonly associated with dairy products, milk may be employed as a differential medium for bacteria on the basis of lactose fermentation, caseolysis, and casein coagulating properties.

The usefulness of milk in the study of bacteria is increased by the addition of suitable indicators. Among the many indicators employed litmus has perhaps enjoyed the widest usage. Litmus has the advantage of being readily reduced by certain bacteria. This reduction of the litmus is useful as a differential aid.

To rehydrate the medium, dissolve 100 grams of Bacto-Litmus Milk in 1000 ml. of distilled water. Distribute in tubes or flasks as desired and sterilize by autoclaving for 15 minutes at 15 pounds pressure (121°C.). During the sterilization period the litmus is reduced to the colorless leuco base, taking on color as the medium cools and absorbs oxygen. Overheating during sterilization results in the carmelization of the milk sugar. This is to be avoided since this resulting discoloration may give an atypical appearance of the sterile medium and may be reflected in the appearance of growing cultures. The final reaction of the medium will be pH 6.8.

One pound of Bacto-Litmus Milk will make 4.3 liters of medium.

BACTO

ULRICH MILK (B251)

DEHYDRATED

Bacto-Skim Milk .... 100 g.
Bacto-Methylene Blue .... 0.005 g.
Bacto-Chlor Phenol Red .... 0.015 g.

Bacto-Ulrich Milk is recommended for propagating and carrying stock cultures of the lactic acid bacteria associated with dairy products, and for determining the action of bacteria in general on milk. Ulrich,[1] in 1944, described an indicator system for use to replace litmus in Litmus Milk. His system consists of a mixture of chlor phenol red (dichlorophenolsulfonphthalein) and methylene blue. Chlor phenol red is a hydrogen ion indicator, yellow at pH 4.8 and more acid reactions, and pink to red at pH 6.5 and more alkaline reactions. Methylene blue in the concentration employed is used to indicate changes in the oxidation-reduction potential (Eh) in the medium, being blue when oxidized and colorless when reduced, by growth of organisms and when heated to boiling, or when first removed from the autoclave following sterilization. The combination of the two indicators in milk gives information similar to Litmus Milk, plus indication of alkalinity and acidity in the lower (reduced) portion of the tube.

In his descriptions of the color changes occurring in his medium due to the growth of various types of lactic bacteria Ulrich used the Ridgeway[2] color classification. The table showing the Ridgeway color description, the Munsell[3] color system, and the Inter-Society Color Council and National Bureau of Standards terminology, which uses familiar terms, is given below to show typical color changes of some of the more common biological reactions in Ulrich Milk. Slight variations in color, due to the variable alteration of the milk during sterilization, and to changes in pH or Eh of the growing cultures, may occur.

	Ulrich Description (Ridgeway)	Munsell Color Description	*ISCC—NBS Terminology
Uninoculated Medium	Pale Glaucous Green	5.0 B6/1 to 5.0 B7/1	Medium Bluish-Gray
Slight acid	Yellowish Glaucous	10.0 GY8/4 to 10.0 GY8/2	Pale Yellow-Green
Acid with Reduction	Ivory Yellow	10.0 YR9/2 to 10.0 YR9/4	Pale Yellow-Orange
Alkaline	Pale Russian Blue	5.0 P7/6 to 5.0 RP7/4 to 5.0 RP7/6	Pale Bluish-Purple passing through various graduations of Light Red-Purple and Pale Purplish-Pink into Pale-Pink to Strong Red-Purple (Transparent)
Alkaline with Reduction	Pale Pinkish Cinnamon	to 5.0 RP8/2 to 5.0 RP8/4	
Alkaline with Peptonization	Clear, Transparent Red	to 10.0 P3/10 to 10.0 P3/8	

*We are greatly indebted to Dr. H. J. Conn, Biological Stain Commission, Geneva, New York, and to Prof. F. L. Dimmick, Hobart College, Geneva, New York, for this color terminology.

Ulrich Milk, when first taken from the autoclave after sterilization, is nearly white in color but quickly develops a bluish-gray top layer with a pink under portion. As the methylene blue oxidizes the blue color extends progressively downward until the entire medium is uniformly bluish-gray. In contrast, Litmus Milk takes on a pink coloration.

When inoculated with lactic acid producing organisms Ulrich Milk first changes to a pale pink in the subsurface areas, the upper layer remaining blue. The depth of the top layer will depend on the rate of reduction of the methylene blue by the growing organism against air oxidation. As more acid is produced the blue top layer changes to a pale yellow-green and the pink portion fades to white and then becomes a pale yellow-orange. If the medium does not become coagulated, or if acid is produced slowly, 60 per cent of the tube may be yellowish-green in color. If the medium is coagulated the greenish zone is limited to a narrow band or collar at the top because of the decreased oxidation. In Litmus Milk, as acid is produced, the pink color develops, and as the litmus is reduced, especially in the lower portion of the tube, the medium becomes white.

Proteolytic organisms, or those producing alkali, do not generally coagulate milk. In Ulrich Milk they change the lower portion of the tube from blue to white and then to pink. If peptonization occurs the medium becomes transparent and reddish-purple in color.

To rehydrate the medium, dissolve 100 grams of Bacto-Ulrich Milk in 1000 ml. distilled water. Distribute into tubes or flasks as desired and sterilize for 15 minutes at 15 pounds pressure (121°C.). Overheating during sterilization results in the carmelization of the milk sugar. This is to be avoided since this resulting discoloration may give an atypical appearance to the sterile medium which may be further reflected in the appearance of growing cultures. The final reaction of the medium will be pH 6.5.

One pound of Bacto-Ulrich Milk will make 4.5 liters of medium.

[1] Science, 99:352:1944.   [3] Munsell Color Company, Inc., Baltimore,
[2] Color Standards and Color Nomenclature, 1912.   Maryland.

ADDITIONAL MEDIA

THE MEDIA listed below have been rather extensively employed in the past. Recently other media have been developd which are considered superior and serve the purpose more adequately than the older media. For the present we will continue to carry these media in stock for those laboratories where they have been in routine use, or where it is desired to continue them for comparative purposes.

PRESENT RECOMMENDATIONS

Bacto-B.T.B. Lactose Agar ..... Bacto-Mannitol Salt Agar, page 150
Bacto-Crystal Violet Agar ..... Bacto-Staphylococcus Medium No. 110, page 151
Bacto-Stone Gelatin Agar ......Bacto-Chapman Stone Medium, page 153
Bacto-Purple Milk ....Bacto-Litmus Milk, page 192

STERILITY TEST MEDIA

THE MEDIA listed in this section are recommended for sterility testing. Included are the media specified by the National Institute of Health in its circular "Culture Media for the Sterility Test" 2nd. Rev. February 5, 1946. Media for sterility testing according to the "Compilation of Regulations for Tests and Methods of Assay and Certification of Antibiotic Drugs," Federal Security Agency, Food and Drug Administration and U. S. Pharmacopeia and the National Formulary are also described in this section.

BACTO
FLUID THIOGLYCOLLATE MEDIUM (B256)
DEHYDRATED

Bacto-Yeast Extract	5 g.
Bacto-Casitone	15 g.
Bacto-Dextrose	5 g.
Sodium Chloride	2.5 g.
l-Cystine, Difco	0.75 g.
Thioglycollic Acid	0.3 ml.
Bacto-Agar	0.75 g.
Resazurin, Certified	0.001 g.

Bacto-Fluid Thioglycollate Medium conforms to the formula specified by the National Institute of Health[1] for the sterility testing of biologicals and for the sterility testing of antibiotics according to the method of the "Compilation of Regulations for Tests and Methods of Assay and Certification of Antibiotic Drugs," Federal Security Agency, Food and Drug Administration. The medium is prepared according to the formula given for Thioglycollate Medium in the U.S. Pharmacopeia[3] and the National Formulary.[4] It may be recommended as a liquid medium for the cultivation of anaerobes. The suitability of Bacto-Fluid Thioglycollate Medium for the sterility testing of surgical catgut sutures has been reported by Clock.[5]

The advantages of a small amount of agar in liquid media used for the cultivation of anaerobes has been pointed out by a number of investigators. Hitchens[6] demonstrated that broth containing 0.1 per cent agar was particularly well suited for the growth of both aerobes and anaerobes. In such a medium anaerobes grew well without any seal or other special precautions. Falk, Bucca and Simmons[7] pointed out the advantages of the use of small quantities of agar (0.06–0.25 per cent) in the detection of contaminants in the sterility testing of biologicals.

In 1898 Trenkmann[8] first reported the aerobic growth of anaerobes in the presence of alkaline sulfide. Quastel and Stephenson[9] reported that the presence of a small amount of compound containing an -SH group permitted "aerobic" growth of *Clostridium sporogenes* in a Tryptic Digest Broth. The -SH group could be supplied by cysteine, thioglycollic acid or glutathione.

The value of combining a small amount of agar and a reducing substance was demonstrated by Brewer.[10] He showed that in a liquid medium containing 0.05 per cent agar, anaerobes grew equally well in the presence or absence of sodium thioglycollate. He noted the value of media containing thioglycollic acid and agar particularly in the initiation of growth of anaerobes from catgut sutures. Marshall, Gunnison and Luxen[11] reported that the Thioglycollate Medium of Brewer was satisfactory for the cultivation of anaerobes, and permitted the growth of organisms in the presence of mercurial preservative. Nungester, Hood and Warren[12] and Portwood[13] confirmed the neutralization of the bacteriostatic effect of mercurial compounds by sodium thioglycollate. Malin and Finn[14] reported that it has been observed that the commonly used medium containing thioglycollate is inhibitory to some organisms in the presence of carbohydrate.

The National Institute of Health in 1941[15] specified the use of two Thioglycollate Media in sterility testing. The Brewer formula was prepared from infusion of meat and 1 per cent peptone. The Linden formula contained 2 per cent peptone and 0.2 per cent yeast extract. Each medium, in addition to 0.1 per cent sodium thioglycollate, contained potassium phosphate, sodium chloride, dextrose, agar and 1:500,000 methylene blue as an Eh indicator. In a study of media used for sterility testing Christensen[16,17] reported that methylene blue as used in the media was toxic for a number of organisms, and suggested the use of resazurin as an Eh indicator. Sodium chloride and potassium phosphate were toxic for some organisms encountered in sterility tests. Sodium thioglycollate, if used in concentrations not greater than 0.05 per cent, was only slightly toxic and in this concentration adequately neutralized the toxicity of mercurial preservatives used in biologicals. A reaction of pH 7.0 was suggested as being optimum for the sterility test medium. Many suggestions on the media for sterility testing leading to the present revised formula, as given by the National Institute of Health,[1] were carefully investigated and summarized by Pittman.[18]

Bacto-Fluid Thioglycollate Medium is prepared according to the latest revision as given by the "Compilation of Regulations for Tests and Methods of Assay and Certification of Antibiotic Drugs," Federal Security Agency, Food and Drug Administration, and conforms also to the specifications of the Federal Register of the Food and Drug Administration,[2] the U. S. Pharmacopeia[3] and the National Formulary.[4] This medium is carefully tested for its growth-promoting abilities, oxidation-reduction qualities and its suitability to arrest mercurial stasis. The medium supports the growth of aerobic as well as anaerobic organisms in a cotton plugged tube without a special seal or other manipulation. Tubes 20 x 150 mm. containing 15 ml. of medium give the best ratio of surface exposed to depth of medium for all types of organisms. Following autoclave sterilization the medium should be cooled promptly to 25°C. and kept at 20–30°C., preferably in the dark, until ready for inoculation. If 30 per cent of the upper layer has a pink color (oxidized resazurin) the medium should be heated in a boiling water or steam bath to drive off absorbed oxygen. Do not reheat the medium more than once, as continued reheating gives rise to toxicity.

In testing the sterility of solutions containing one of the customary mercury salts in 1:10,000 dilution as a preservative, 15 ml. of Bacto-Fluid Thioglycollate Medium will inactivate the mercurial preservative contained in 3 ml. of the solution. When testing preparations containing other preservatives, the amount of Fluid Thioglycollate Medium used must be sufficient to dilute the inoculum beyond the bacteriostatic limits of the preservative. Using 1 ml. of inoculum of biologicals or other preparations containing various preservatives, the minimum quantities of culture media to use are given in the accompanying table.

Following inoculation the contents of the container must be thoroughly mixed and mixed again when the first or 48 hour sterility test reading is made.

To rehydrate the medium, suspend 29.5 grams of Bacto-Fluid Thioglycollate Medium in 1000 ml. cold distilled water, and heat to boiling to dissolve the medium completely. Distribute in tubes or flasks and sterilize in the autoclave

Minimum Amount of Culture Media per 1 ml. of Inoculum

Preservative	Concentration of Preservative	Biological Product	Minimum Volume of Culture Medium
Phenol	0.5 per cent	Serums and vaccine	40 ml.
Cresol, U.S.P.	0.35 per cent	Serum	60 ml.
Merthiolate	1:10,000	Toxoids	
	1:35,000	Human Plasma	10 ml.
Phenylmercuric Acetate	1:50,000	Human Plasma	
	1:100,000	Normal saline	10 ml.
Phenylmercuric Borate	1:50,000	Human Plasma	
	1:100,000	Normal saline	10 ml.
Phenylmercuric Nitrate	1:50,000	Human Plasma	
	1:100,000	Normal saline	10 ml.
Merthiolate and Phenol	1:10,000 and 0.2 per cent	Serum	20 ml.
Chlorobutanol	0.5 per cent	....	40 ml.
Formalin	0.4 per cent	....	40 ml.

for 18–20 minutes at 15–17 pounds pressure (121–123°C.). Cool quickly to 25°C. The final reaction of the medium will be pH 7.1.

One pound of Bacto-Fluid Thioglycollate Medium will make 15.4 liters of medium.

National Institute of Health Circular: Culture Media for the Sterility Test, 2nd Revision, Feb. 5, 1946.

[2] Compilation of Regulations for Tests and Methods of Assay and Certification of Antibiotic Drugs, Federal Security Agency, Food and Drug Administration.

[3] Pharmacopeia of the United States, XIV Revision: 758: 1950.

[4] National Formulary, 9th Edition: 768: 1950.

[5] J. Lab. Clin. Med., 32:1153:1947.

[6] J. Infectious Diseases, 29:390:1951.

[7] J. Bact., 37:121:1939.

[8] Centr. Bakt. I., Abt., 23:1038:1898.

[9] Biochem. J., 20:1125:1926.

[10] J. Am. Med. Assoc., 115:598:1940.

[11] Proc. Soc. Exp. Biol. Med. 43:672:1940.

[12] Proc. Soc. Exp. Biol. Med. 52:287:1943.

[13] J. Bact., 48:255:1944.

[14] J. Bact., 62:349:1951.

[15] National Institute of Health. Fluid Thioglycollate Medium for the Sterility Test, Dec. 30, 1941.

[16] J. Bact., 48:256:1944.

[17] Paper Read at New York Meeting of Am. Pub. Health Assoc., 1944.

[18] J. Bact., 51:19:1946.

BACTO
BREWER THIOGLYCOLLATE MEDIUM (B236)
DEHYDRATED

BACTO
LINDEN THIOGLYCOLLATE MEDIUM (B237)
DEHYDRATED

These media formerly specified by the National Institute of Health have been used in the past for testing of sterility or other purposes. For those laboratories desiring to continue to use these media Bacto-Brewer Thioglycollate Medium and Bacto-Linden Thioglycollate Medium are carried in stock.

BACTO

N.I.H. THIOGLYCOLLATE BROTH   (B257)
DEHYDRATED

Bacto-Yeast Extract	5 g.
Bacto-Casitone	15 g.
Bacto-Dextrose	1 g.
Sodium Chloride	2.5 g.
l-Cystine, Difco	0.05 g.
Thioglycollic Acid	0.3 ml.

Bacto-N.I.H. Thioglycollate Broth is prepared according to the formula for Broth Medium for sterility tests as specified by the National Institute of Health.[1] This medium may be substituted for Bacto-Fluid Thioglycollate Medium in the sterility testing of certain biological products that are turbid or otherwise cannot be cultured satisfactorily in Fluid Thioglycollate Medium because of its viscosity. Bacto-N.I.H. Thioglycollate Broth conforms to the specifications for the alternate fluid medium for sterility tests as given in the U. S. Pharmacopeia[2] and the National formulary.[3]

In testing solutions for sterility, Bacto-N.I.H. Thioglycollate Broth should be used in Smith fermentation tubes and be heated in boiling water or on a steam bath just prior to use to drive off dissolved oxygen. When testing the sterility of solutions containing preservatives, the preservative must be inactivated, or sufficient medium used to dilute the inoculum beyond the bacteriostatic limits of the preservative. Bacto-N.I.H. Thioglycollate Broth contains thioglycollate to neutralize the bacteriostatic effect of mercurial preservatives. The table on page 197 under Bacto-Fluid Thioglycollate Medium indicates minimum quantities of medium to use in testing the sterility of solutions containing other preservatives.

To rehydrate the medium, suspend 24 grams Bacto-N.I.H. Thioglycollate Broth in 1000 ml. cold distilled water and heat to boiling to dissolve the medium completely. Distribute in Smith fermentation tubes and sterilize in the autoclave for 18–20 minutes at 15–17 pounds pressure (121–123°C.). The final reaction of the medium will be pH 7.1.

One pound of Bacto-N.I.H. Thioglycollate Broth will make 18.9 liters of medium.

[1] National Institute of Health Circular: Culture Media for the Sterility Test, 2nd Revision, Feb. 5, 1946.

[2] Pharmacopeia of the United States, XIV Revision: 759:1950.
[3] National Formulary, 9th Edition:769:1950.

BACTO

N.I.H. AGAR MEDIUM   (B258)
DEHYDRATED

Bacto-Yeast Extract	5 g.
Bacto-Casitone	15 g.
Bacto-Dextrose	1 g.
Sodium Chloride	2.5 g.
l-Cystine, Difco	0.05 g.
Bacto-Agar	15 g.

Bacto-N.I.H. Agar Medium is prepared according to the formula for the Agar Medium as specified by the National Institute of Health Circular for Culture Media for Sterility Test.[1] It is recommended for use when a solid agar medium is needed for the maintenance of cultures isolated in connection with the sterility testing of biological products. It may also be used as a solid medium for sterility testing.

Bacto-N.I.H. Agar Medium contains no thioglycollate. If the medium is to be used to test the sterility of a biological product containing a mercurial preservative, 0.05 per cent sodium thioglycollate or 0.03 per cent thioglycollic acid should be added.

To rehydrate the medium, suspend 38.5 grams of Bacto-N.I.H. Agar Medium in 1000 ml. cold distilled water and heat to boiling to dissolve the medium completely. Distribute in tubes or flasks and sterilize in the autoclave for 18–20 minutes at 15–17 pounds pressure (121–123°C.). The final reaction of the medium will be pH 7.1.

One pound of Bacto-N.I.H. Agar Medium will make 11.7 liters of medium.

[1] National Institute of Health Circular: Culture Media for the Sterility Test, 2nd Revision, Feb. 5, 1946.

BACTO
THIOGLYCOLLATE MEDIUM (B363)
without Dextrose
DEHYDRATED

Bacto-Yeast Extract	5 g.
Bacto-Casitone	15 g.
Sodium Chloride	2.5 g.
l-Cystine, Difco	0.25 g.
Thioglycollic Acid	0.3 ml.
Bacto-Agar	0.75 g.
Bacto-Methylene Blue	0.002 g.

Bacto-Thioglycollate Medium without Dextrose is a sugar-free basal medium containing thioglycollic acid and 0.075 per cent Bacto-Agar and to which carbohydrate can be added for studying the fermentation reactions of anaerobic microorganisms. The medium contains thioglycollic acid and Bacto-Agar which gives and maintains a low Eh, permitting the growth of the strictest anaerobes without special seal, making the medium ideally suited for fermentation studies of anaerobes. Similar media prepared without Eh indicator and without Dextrose or Eh Indicator are described below.

The value of small amounts of agar in liquid media used for the cultivation of anaerobes and microaerophiles as well as aerobes has been pointed out by Hitchens[1] and others. The use of alkaline sulfides and of sulfhydryl compounds such as thioglycollate, cysteine and glutathione for the reduction of the Eh potential of culture media for the propagation of anaerobes was first described by Trenkmann[2] and Quastel and Stephenson.[3] Later Brewer[4] combined the use of thioglycollate with agar in liquid media for anaerobic culture.

The presence of the thioglycollate in the medium will also inactivate any mercurial that might be carried over with the inoculum, as was demonstrated by Marshall, Gunnison and Luxen.[5] Methylene blue serves as an indicator of Eh. Most organisms, including anaerobes, will show earlier and more vigorous growth in the presence of a carbohydrate.

The sterile medium should not be stored in the refrigerator, especially if the medium is to be used for the cultivation of anaerobes. The amount of oxidation in the medium is shown by the depth of the color zone of the Eh indicator. Tubes showing about one-third or more oxidized methylene blue are not satisfactory for anaerobe cultivation and should be heated to the boiling point in steam or hot water to drive off dissolved gases and rapidly cooled prior to inoculation. The medium should be heated but once in this manner.

To rehydrate the medium, suspend 24 grams Bacto-Thioglycollate Medium without Dextrose in 1000 ml. cold distilled water and heat to boiling to dissolve the medium completely. Add selected carbohydrate, distribute in tubes and sterilize in the autoclave for 15 minutes at 15 pounds pressure (121°C.). Final reaction of the medium will be pH 7.2.

One pound of Bacto-Thioglycollate Medium without Dextrose will make 19 liters of medium.

[1] J. Infectious Diseases, 29:390:1921.
[2] Centr. Bakt., I Abt., 23:1038:1898.
[3] Biochem. J., 20:1125:1926.

[4] J. Am. Med. Assoc., 115:598:1940.
[5] Proc. Soc. Exp. Biol. Med., 43:672:1940.

BACTO

THIOGLYCOLLATE MEDIUM   (B430)
without Indicator
DEHYDRATED

Bacto-Thioglycollate Medium without Indicator has the same composition as Bacto-Thioglycollate Medium without Dextrose, described above except that it contains 0.5 per cent Bacto-Dextrose and no methylene blue as an indicator of Eh.

To rehydrate the medium, suspend 29 grams Bacto-Thioglycollate Medium without Indicator in 1000 ml. cold distilled water and heat to boiling to dissolve the medium completely. Distribute in tubes or flasks and sterilize in the autoclave for 15 minutes at 15 pounds pressure (121°C.). Final reaction of the medium will be pH 7.2.

One pound of Bacto-Thioglycollate Medium without Indicator will make 15.6 liters of medium.

BACTO

THIOGLYCOLLATE MEDIUM   (B432)
without Dextrose or Indicator
DEHYDRATED

Bacto-Thioglycollate Medium without Dextrose or Indicator has the same composition as Bacto-Thioglycollate Medium without Dextrose as described on page 199 except that it does not contain methylene blue as an indicator of Eh.

To rehydrate the medium, suspend 24 grams Bacto-Thioglycollate Medium without Dextrose or Indicator in 1000 ml. cold distilled water and heat to boiling to dissolve the medium completely. Add selected carbohydrate, distribute in tubes and sterilize in the autoclave for 15 minutes at 15 pounds pressure (121°C.). Final reaction of the medium will be pH 7.2.

One pound of Bacto-Thioglycollate Medium without Dextrose or Indicator will make 19 liters of medium.

BACTO

SABOURAUD LIQUID MEDIUM   (B382)
DEHYDRATED

Neopeptone, Difco .... 10 g.
Bacto-Dextrose .... 20 g.

Bacto-Sabouraud Liquid Medium is recommended as a liquid medium for the cultivation of yeast. molds and aciduric and acidophilic bacteria. This medium is particularly well suited for sterility test procedures for the detection of fungi. It is prepared according to the formula specified in the U. S. Pharmacopeia[1] and National Formulary[2] as used in sterility test procedures. The acid reaction of the final medium, pH 5.7, is inhibitive to a large number of bacteria, but particularly well suited for the cultivation of fungi and acidophilic microorganisms. Neopeptone is used in the preparation of this medium since this peptone is particularly well suited for the cultivation of fungi.

To rehydrate the medium dissolve 30 grams Bacto-Sabouraud Liquid Medium in 1000 ml. of distilled water. Distribute in tubes or flasks and sterilize in the autoclave for 15 minutes at 15 pounds pressure (121°C.). Final reaction of the medium will be pH 5.7.

One pound of Bacto-Sabouraud Liquid Medium will make 15.1 liters of medium.

[1] Pharmacopeia of the United States, XIV Revision:760:1950.   [2] National Formulary, 9th Edition:769:1950.

BACTO

A C MEDIUM (B316)
DEHYDRATED

Bacto-Beef Extract	3 g.
Bacto-Yeast Extract	3 g.
Bacto-Malt Extract	3 g.
Proteose Peptone No. 3, Difco	20 g.
Bacto-Dextrose	5 g.
Bacto-Agar	1 g.
Ascorbic Acid	0.2 g.

Bacto-A C Medium is recommended for use in controlling sterility of products in the process of manufacture and for testing sterility of solutions and other materials not containing mercurial preservatives. For the sterility testing of biologicals and solutions containing mercurials as a preservative, Bacto-Fluid Thioglycollate Medium, page 195, should be employed.

Bacto-A C Medium is an infusion-free medium possessing unique growth-promoting properties for both aerobic and anaerobic microorganisms, making possible an early and voluminous growth. It is recommended as a general culture medium for the propagation of anaerobes, micro-aerophiles and aerobes. Bacto-A C Medium does not exhibit the toxicity shown by media containing sodium thioglycollate for some organisms as reported by Christensen,[1] and Malin and Finn.[2]

Reed and Orr[3] obtained excellent growth of all species of *Clostridium* on Bacto A C Medium. Schneiter, Dunn and Caminita[4] in their studies on the bacterial content of air samples reported Proteose Extract Agar, the same composition as A C Medium with 0.85 per cent sodium chloride and 1.7 to 2.4 per cent Bacto-Agar added to be satisfactory for the growth of staphylococci and sporulates, and superior to all other media tested for the growth of streptococci. Bailey et al.[5] employed A C Medium in assaying for potency of streptomycin products using *Clostridium perfringens* as a test organism and reported excellent, rapid results. Schneiter and Kolb[6] used Bacto-A C Medium for the growth of *Bacillus anthracis* and related mesophilic aerobic bacilli in their studies of the heat resistance of these organisms from hair and bristles. They reported that the medium permitted the distinctive cottonball appearance of the anthrax colonies. Kolb and Schneiter[7] used Bacto-A C Medium to test the viability of *B. anthracis* following exposure to methyl bromide to test the efficiency of this compound as a germicidal and sporicidal agent.

For best growth of anaerobes and most aerobes, A C Medium should be distributed in tubes or flasks to give a depth of at least 70 mm. of medium. For obligately aerobic bacteria shallower layers permitting aeration of the substrate are desirable.

To rehydrate the medium, suspend 35 grams of Bacto-A C Medium in 1000 ml. of cold distilled water and heat to boiling to dissolve the medium completely. Distribute in tubes or bottles to give the desired depth of medium and sterilize in the autoclave for 15 minutes at 15 pounds pressure (121°C.). If the medium is not used the same day it is prepared and sterilized, it is advisable to place it in flowing steam or in a boiling water bath to drive off dissolved gases and then cool before inoculating. The final reaction of the medium will be pH 7.3.

One pound of Bacto-A C Medium will make 13 liters of medium.

[1] Paper read at New York Meeting Am. Pub. Health Assoc., 1944.
[2] J. Bact., 62:349:1951.
[3] J. Bact., 45:309:1943.
[4] Pub. Health Reports, 60:789:1945.
[5] Personal Communication, 1947.
[6] Pub. Health Reports, Sup. No. 207, June, 1948.
[7] J. Bact., 59:401:1950.

BACTO

A C BROTH (B317)

DEHYDRATED

Bacto-Beef Extract	3 g.
Bacto-Yeast Extract	3 g.
Bacto-Malt Extract	3 g.
Proteose Peptone No. 3, Difco	20 g.
Bacto-Dextrose	5 g.
Ascorbic Acid	0.2 g.

Bacto-A C Broth is particularly suitable for use as a sterility test broth in the detection of obligately aerobic contaminants in biologicals and other products. Sterility tests on materials containing mercurial preservative should be made in Bacto-Fluid Thioglycollate Medium, as discussed on page 195.

Bacto-A C Broth is recommended as a general culture medium for the propagation of pathogenic and saprophytic microorganisms. It has the same formula as Bacto-A C Medium, as discussed on page 201, except that the small amount of agar has been omitted. This medium with the addition of 0.85 per cent sodium chloride and 1.8 to 2.5 per cent Bacto-Agar was reported by Schneiter, Dunn and Caminita[1] to be a superior medium for bacteriological examination of air, especially for recovery of streptococci.

To rehydrate the medium, dissolve 34 grams of Bacto-A C Broth in 1000 ml. of distilled water. Distribute in tubes or other suitable containers and sterilize in the autoclave for 15 minutes at 15 pounds pressure (121°C.). The final reaction of the medium will be pH 7.2.

One pound of Bacto-A C Broth will make 13 liters of medium.

[1] Pub. Health Reports, 60:789:1945.

BACTO

MALT EXTRACT BROTH

DEHYDRATED

Bacto-Malt Extract Broth is recommended as a sterility test medium for the detection of yeasts and molds. This acid medium supports early and luxuriant growth of these organisms from small inocula. A complete discussion of Bacto-Malt Extract Broth is given on page 242.

BACTO-PENASE

Bacto-Penase and Bacto-Penase Concentrate are potent penicillinase preparations recommended for the inactivation of penicillin in the sterility testing of penicillin or penicillin products. A complete discussion of these products are given on pages 283 and 284.

MEDIA FOR MICROBIOLOGICAL ASSAYS

MEDIA FOR THE ASSAY OF ANTIBIOTICS

The Difco dehydrated media described in this section are prepared especially for the assay of the potency of antibiotics. The use of dehydrated media corresponding to the specified formula is permitted for the assay of antibiotics according to the method prescribed by the "Compilation of Regulations for Tests and Methods of Assay and Certification of Antibiotic Drugs," Federal Security Agency, Food and Drug Administration and the United States Pharmacopeia. Included in this section are media conforming to their specifications.

BACTO

PENASSAY BROTH (B243)

DEHYDRATED

Bacto-Beef Extract	1.5 g.
Bacto-Yeast Extract	1.5 g.
Bacto-Peptone	5 g.
Bacto-Dextrose	1 g.
Sodium Chloride	3.5 g.
Dipotassium Phosphate	3.68 g.
Monopotassium Phosphate	1.32 g.

Bacto-Penassay Broth duplicates the formula of the medium recommended by Schmidt and Moyer[1] for use in the serial dilution method for assaying penicillin. It also corresponds to the formula of the broth prescribed in "Tests and Methods of Assay for Antibiotic Drugs,"[2] Federal Security Agency, Food and Drug Administration, for the preparation of the inoculum in the cylinder assay of penicillin, or in the tube dilution method of penicillin assay; in the turbidimetric assay of streptomycin; for the preparation of the suspension of *Sarcina lutea* (PCI 1001) in the cylinder assay of aureomycin and chloramphenicol; in the turbidimetric assay of bacitracin. Waksman and Lechevalier[3] used Bacto-Penassay Broth for the turbidimetric assay of neomycin with *Escherichia coli* ≠9637 as the test organism.

Schmidt and Moyer[1] used the serial dilution method for assaying ethereal solutions and untreated culture liquor of penicillin as a check on the results obtained by the cylinder plate method. Serial dilution methods may also be used in assaying for penicillin in body fluids of individuals under treatment.

Essentially the serial dilution methods are based upon determinations of the lowest concentration of antibiotic capable of inhibiting growth of the test organism in the Penassay Broth. The approximate amount of antibiotic present in an unknown is determined by comparing its activity in parallel with that of a standard preparation of known potency. A quantity of the sample to be tested is added to the first of a series of tubes containing broth previously inoculated with the test organism. Further dilutions are made from this tube. Comparable dilutions of the standard are also made. All tubes are thoroughly shaken and incubated at 30°C. for 18 or 40 hours. More definite readings may be made in 40 hours than in 18. The highest dilution in which no growth appears is the end point of the series, and the dilution of the unknown which gives such an end point contains the same amount of antibiotic as that in the end point tube of the standard series.

It is sometimes difficult to obtain a sharp end point in the serial dilution methods of penicillin or streptomycin assay. Also, the amount of antibiotic required is usually much larger in these methods than in the turbidimetric procedure. Foster[4] described a turbidimetric method for penicillin assay and claimed that it was the most accurate method available. McMahan[5] offered a 3–4 hour turbidimetric procedure based on the same procedure used in the microbiological assay of vitamins and considered it more precise than the cup plate method. Lee, Foley, Epstein and Wallace[6] modified the method of Foster and Woodruff[7] and obtained results in 90 minutes instead of four hours.

The turbidimetric method is based on the proportional inhibition of the growth of the test organism in the liquid medium as a function of the antibiotic concentration. The growth measurements are made turbidimetrically and compared with a standard curve obtained by running various concentrations of a standard antibiotic in parallel with the unknown.

To rehydrate the medium, dissolve 17.5 grams of Bacto-Penassay Broth in 1000 ml. distilled water. When used in the serial dilution method, distribute in 200 ml. quantities in 500 ml. Erlenmeyer flasks. For carrying tests organisms, as described by the Food and Drug Administration,[2] distribute in 10 ml. quantities in tubes. For the turbidimetric procedure, distribute as required by the specific procedure used. The medium is sterilized for 15 minutes at 15 pounds pressure (121°C.). The final reaction of the medium will be pH 7.0.

One pound of Bacto-Penassay Broth will make 25.8 liters of medium.

[1] J. Bact., 47:199:1944.
[2] The Compilation of Tests and Methods of Assay for Antibiotic Drugs, Federal Security Agency, Food and Drug Administration.
[3] Science, 109:305:1949.
[4] J. Biol. Chem., 144:285:1942.
[5] J. Biol. Chem., 153:249:1944.
[6] J. Biol. Chem., 152:485:1944.
[7] J. Bact., 46:187:1943.

BACTO

PENASSAY BASE AGAR (B270)

DEHYDRATED

Bacto-Beef Extract	1.5 g.
Bacto-Yeast Extract	3 g.
Bacto-Peptone	6 g.
Bacto-Agar	15 g.

Bacto-Penassay Base Agar is prepared according to the formula specified in "The Compilation of Tests and Methods of Assay for Antibiotic Drugs,"[1] Federal Security Agency, Food and Drug Administration, for antibiotic assay. It is recommended as a base layer in the cylinder assay of penicillin; for the cylinder assay of aureomycin; for the plate assay of bacitracin and for maintaining cultures of *Micrococcus pyogenes* var. *aureus* (PCI 1203) in the turbidimetric assay of bacitracin.

The discovery of penicillin[2] and of streptomycin[3] and the widespread use of these and other antibiotics in the treatment of many bacterial infections necessitated the development of methods for their detection and assay. A number of methods for the microbiological assay of antibiotic drugs have been described. These include serial dilution methods with liquid or solid media, turbidimetric methods and the Oxford cup or cylinder plate method.

The cylinder plate method for the assay of penicillin was first described by Abraham et al.[4] and later modified by Foster and Woodruff[5] and by Schmidt and Moyer.[6] This method depends upon the diffusion of the antibiotic material from steel or porcelain cups placed upon agar plates which have been seeded with the test organism. Inhibition of growth of the organism occurs in the proximity of the cup, and the diameter of the inhibited zone varies with the concentration of the antibiotic in the material being tested. This method is commonly employed for assaying commercial penicillin preparations and is also adapted for the detection of penicillin in body fluids of patients under penicillin treatment.

The cylinder plate method has given uniform results which may be duplicated. Continued study of this method of penicillin assay showed that a modification of the Schmidt and Moyer formula[6] resulted in more accurate readings; also, that if dextrose is present in the seed layer but omitted from the base layer the zones of inhibition are more clear-cut and defined. These modifications were adopted by the Food and Drug Administration[1] as standard for penicillin assay using *Micrococcus pyogenes* var. *aureus* as the test organism.

Plates are prepared the same day samples are to be tested, using the cylinder method of assay for antibiotics by adding 21 ml. of sterile Bacto-Penassay Base Agar to sterile petri dishes (100 x 20 mm.). After the base layer has solidified it is overlaid with 4 ml. of Bacto-Penassay Seed Agar previously inoculated with a carefully standardized dilution of the test organism.

To rehydrate the medium, suspend 25.5 grams Bacto-Penassay Base Agar in 1000 ml. of cold distilled water and heat to boiling to dissolve the medium completely. Distribute in 500 ml. quantities in one-liter Erlenmeyer flasks and sterilize in the autoclave for 15 minutes at 15 pounds pressure (121°C.). The final reaction of the medium will be pH 6.6.

One pound of Bacto-Penassay Base Agar will make 17.7 liters of medium.

[1] The Compilation of Tests and Methods of Assay for Antibiotic Drugs, Federal Security Agency, Food and Drug Administration.
[3] Brit. J. Exp. Path., 10:226:1929.
[2] Proc. Soc. Exp. Biol. Med., 55:66:1944.
[4] Lancet, 2:177:1941.
[5] J. Bact., 46:187:1943.
[6] J. Bact., 47:199:1944.

BACTO
PENASSAY SEED AGAR (B263)
DEHYDRATED

Bacto-Beef Extract	1.5 g.
Bacto-Yeast Extract	3 g.
Bacto-Casitone	4 g.
Bacto-Peptone	6 g.
Bacto-Dextrose	1 g.
Bacto-Agar	15 g.

Bacto-Penassay Seed Agar conforms to the medium specified by "The Compilation of Tests and Methods of Assay for Antibiotic Drugs,"[1] Federal Security Agency, Food and Drug Administration, for antibiotic assay. It is recommended as a seed layer and for carrying stock cultures of *Micrococcus pyogenes* var. *aureus* (PCI 209P) in penicillin cylinder assay; for maintaining test organism, *Bacillus subtilis* (ATCC ✻6633) in streptomycin assay; for seed layer in aureomycin cylinder assay and for maintaining cultures of *M. pyogenes* var. *aureus* (PCI 209P) for the turbidimetric assay of aureomycin; for seed and base layer and for maintaining cultures of *Sarcina lutea* (PCI 1001) in chloramphenicol cylinder assay; for seed layer in bacitracin plate assay.

In the assay of antibiotics by the cylinder method it has been found that for penicillin, aureomycin and bacitracin, better results are obtained with a small amount of dextrose in the seed layer and no dextrose in the medium used for the base layer. For the assay of these antibiotics the use of Bacto-Penassay Seed Agar has resulted in more clear-cut zones of inhibition. A layer of Bacto-Penassay Base Agar is allowed to solidify in plates, and is overlaid with about 4 ml. of Penassay Seed Agar (100 x 20 mm. plate) containing a carefully standardized inoculum of the test organism. The plate is tilted to obtain an even distribution of the inoculum on the surface. Following solidification of the seed layer, the plate is ready to receive the cylinders and antibiotic solutions under assay.

Formerly, the base agar was used for both the base and seed layers; however, it was found that the zones of inhibition were not as sharply defined as was desired. The use of Bacto-Penassay Seed Agar as the seed layer has resulted in a more clear-cut zone of inhibition.

Plates are prepared the day samples are to be tested by adding 21 ml. of Penassay Base Agar to sterile petri dishes (100 x 20 mm.). After the base layer has solidified it is overlaid with 4 ml. of Bacto-Penassay Seed Agar, inoculated with the test organism.

To rehydrate the medium, suspend 30.5 grams of Bacto-Penassay Seed Agar in 1000 ml. of cold distilled water and heat to boiling to dissolve the medium completely. Distribute in 100 ml. quantities in 300 ml. Erlenmeyer flasks. Sterilize in the autoclave for 15 minutes at 15 pounds pressure (121°C.). The final reaction of the medium will be pH 6.6.

One pound of Bacto-Penassay Seed Agar will make 14.8 liters of medium.

[1] The Compilation of Tests and Methods of Assay for Antibiotic Drugs, Federal Security Agency, Food and Drug Administration.

BACTO

YEAST BEEF AGAR (B244)

DEHYDRATED

Bacto-Beef Extract	1.5 g.
Bacto-Yeast Extract	3 g.
Bacto-Peptone	6 g.
Bacto-Dextrose	1 g.
Bacto-Agar	15 g.

Bacto-Yeast Beef Agar is a slight modification of the medium recommended by Schmidt and Moyer[1] for use in the cylinder plate procedure for assaying penicillin as described by Abraham, et al.[2]

As a result of their extensive use of the cylinder plate method, Schmidt and Moyer made a number of observations and refinements which improved the technique of penicillin assay by this method. They claimed that the cylinder plate method was a more practical procedure than the serial dilution method, that it is more adaptable for assay of a large number of specimens, that samples need not be sterile, as is necessary in the serial dilution method, and that more potent penicillin preparations can be assayed with fewer dilutions than in the serial dilution technique.

More recently the Food and Drug Administration[3] recommended modifications of this medium for use in the cylinder plate method. Bacto-Penassay Base Agar and Bacto-Penassay Seed Agar used in this procedure are discussed on pages 204 and 205.

Plates are prepared the day previous to the actual testing of penicillin samples by adding 22 ml. of Yeast Beef Agar to petri dishes (100 x 20 mm.) which then stand at room temperature for 24 hours before being overlaid with 3 ml. of Yeast Beef Agar previously inoculated with the test organism, *Micrococcus pyogenes* var. *aureus* (P209).

To rehydrate the medium, suspend 26.5 grams of Bacto-Yeast Beef Agar in 1000 ml. cold distilled water and heat to boiling to dissolve the medium completely. Distribute in 500 ml. quantities in one liter Erlenmeyer flasks. Sterilize in the autoclave for 15 minutes at 15 pounds pressure (121°C.). The final reaction of the medium will be pH 6.6.

One pound of Bacto-Yeast Beef Agar will make 17.5 liters of medium.

[1] J. Bact., 47:199:1944.
[2] Lancet, 2:177:1941.
[3] The Compilation of Tests and Methods of

Assay for Antibiotic Drugs, Federal Security Agency, Food and Drug Administration.

BACTO

MYCIN ASSAY BROTH (B295)

DEHYDRATED

Bacto-Beef Extract	5 g.
Bacto-Peptone	10 g.
Sodium Chloride	2.5 g.

Bacto-Mycin Assay Broth duplicates the formula of the medium recommended by Price, Nielsen and Welch[1] for their serial dilution method of assay of streptomycin in body fluids.

The authors found that the turbidimetric method in use for assaying streptomycin in aqueous or buffered solution gave erroneous results when used for testing body fluids because of the stimulating properties of these fluids for the test organism. Also, that the equipment and material required for the agar cylinder plate method may not be readily available to the small laboratory. For these reasons a study was made to determine which organism would lend itself to use in a simple serial dilution procedure for determining streptomycin in body fluids. They found that *Bacillus circulans* was the most sensitive to streptomycin and gave reproducible results.

Essentially, the test consists in preparing various dilutions of the fluid under test in sterile Bacto-Mycin Assay Broth. A streptomycin of known potency is used as a standard and is serially diluted in a similar manner. The tubes are inoculated with the test organism and incubated at 37°C. over night. The concentration of streptomycin in the unknown is determined by comparing the end point in the unknown with that in the standard.

To rehydrate the medium, dissolve 17.5 grams of Bacto-Mycin Assay Broth in 1000 ml. cold distilled water. Distribute in tubes and sterilize in the autoclave for 15 minutes at 15 pounds pressure (121°C.). The final reaction of the medium will be pH 7.9.

One pound of Bacto-Mycin Assay Broth will make 25.9 liters of medium.

[2] Science, 103:56:1946.

BACTO
STREPTOMYCIN ASSAY AGAR   (B277)
DEHYDRATED

Bacto-Beef Extract	1.5 g.
Bacto-Yeast Extract	3 g.
Bacto-Peptone	6 g.
Bacto-Agar	15 g.

Bacto-Streptomycin Assay Agar was originally developed with the cooperation of Dr. Phillip S. Skell, University of Illinois, for the assay of streptothrycin.
Later, this medium was found to give excellent results for the streptomycin
assay, using the cylinder plate technique with *Bacillus subtilis* (ATCC #6633)
as the test organism. The use of this medium assures well-defined zones of inhibition of growth of the test organism.

Plates are prepared the same day samples are to be tested by adding 21 ml.
of Bacto-Streptomycin Assay Agar to petri dishes (100 x 20 mm.). After this base
layer has solidified, it is overlaid with 4 ml. of Streptomycin Assay Agar previously inoculated with spores of the test organism.

To rehydrate the medium, suspend 25.5 grams Bacto-Streptomycin Assay Agar
in 1000 ml. cold distilled water and heat to boiling to dissolve the medium completely. Distribute in 500 ml. quantities in one-liter Erlenmeyer flasks. Sterilize in
the autoclave for 15 minutes at 15 pounds pressure (121°C.). The final reaction
of the medium will be pH 8.0.

One pound of Bacto-Streptomycin Assay Agar will make 17.7 liters of medium.

BACTO
MYCIN ASSAY AGAR   (B281)
DEHYDRATED

Bacto-Beef Extract	3 g.
Bacto-Peptone	5 g.
Bacto-Agar	15 g.

Bacto-Mycin Assay Agar duplicates the formula of the medium specified by
the Food and Drug Administration[1] for assay of streptomycin by the cylinder
plate method. The use of this medium assures well defined zones of inhibition of
the test organism.

The general principles used for the assay of penicillin have proved practical
for the assay of streptomycin. However, different antibiotics require different test
organisms and a slight change in the composition of the medium employed. The
Food and Drug Administration has specified that the medium used in the assay
of streptomycin should have an alkaline reaction and that the test organism be
Bacillus subtilis (ATCC #6633).

Plates are prepared the same day samples are to be tested by adding 21 ml. of
Mycin Assay Agar to petri dishes (100 x 20 mm.). After this base layer has solidified it is overlaid with 4 ml. of Mycin Assay Agar previously inoculated with
spores of the test organism.

To rehydrate the medium, suspend 23 grams of Bacto-Mycin Assay Agar in
1000 ml. cold distilled water and heat to boiling to dissolve the medium completely. Distribute in 500 ml. quantities in one-liter Erlenmeyer flasks. Sterilize in

the autoclave for 15 minutes at 15 pounds pressure (121°C.). The final reaction of the medium is pH 7.9.

One pound of Bacto-Mycin Assay Agar will make 19.6 liters of medium.

[1] The Compilation of Tests and Methods of Assay for Antibiotic Drugs, Federal Security Agency, Food and Drug Administration.

BACTO

TYROTHRICIN ASSAY BROTH (B415)
DEHYDRATED

Bacto-Tryptone	10 g.
Bacto-Dextrose	5 g.
Disodium Phosphate	1.6 g.

Bacto-Tyrothricin Assay Broth is prepared according to the U. S. Pharmacopeia formula[1] for the inoculum broth used in the assay of tyrothricin. The test organism, streptococcus sp., Lancefield group D, strain No. H69D$_5$ (ATCC #9854) is carried in stock on Blood Agar prepared with Bacto-Tyrothricin Assay Agar. Inoculation is made from the slant into Bacto-Tyrothricin Assay Broth and tubes are incubated at 37°C. for 18–20 hours. The cultures are examined microscopically at this time to check their purity. Bacto-Tyrothricin Assay Broth is also recommended as a buffered Dextrose Broth for the cultivation of a large variety of saprophytic and pathogenic microorganisms.

In the assay of tyrothricin by the U. S. Pharmacopeia method, 80 ml. of the sterile Tyrothricin Assay Broth is enriched with 20 ml. of a filter sterilized 5 per cent solution of bovine serum albumin at pH 6.8–7.2 to give the assay medium. To 100 ml. of this mixture is added 1 ml. of an 18–20 hour culture of the test organism. The Tyrothricin Reference Standard, and the sample under assay properly diluted, are mixed with propylene glycol diluting solution in 5 ml. amounts to give 10 tubes with 0.0, 0.1, 0.15, etc., to 0.5 microgram tyrothricin. To each tube containing 5 ml. of the mixture of tyrothricin and propylene glycol is added 5 ml. of the 1:100 dilution of the test organism in the assay medium. Tubes are prepared in triplicate. The tubes are thoroughly shaken and incubated at 37°C., for 16–20 hours. The amount of growth is determined by any suitable photometric method. The average value of the readings of each set of triplicate tubes is used to obtain a single value for each tube. Prepare a standard curve for the U. S. P. Tyrothricin Reference Standard by plotting the average density measurements against the concentration of tyrothricin in micrograms per ml. Similarly, prepare a curve from the average values obtained from the tyrothricin being assayed. From the average density of the control tubes, determine the photometric reading equivalent to one-half the density of the controls and interpolate this point on both of the above curves. Intercepts drawn from these points to the base line will indicate the quantity of tyrothricin.

To rehydrate the medium, dissolve 16.6 grams Bacto-Tyrothricin Assay Broth in 1000 ml. of distilled water. Distribute in tubes and sterilize in the autoclave for 15 minutes at 15 pounds pressure (121°C.). Avoid excessive heat during the sterilization period and cool the medium rapidly. Final reaction of the medium will be pH 7.0. To prepare the complete liquid medium for the assay of tyrothricin add 20 ml. of a 5 per cent filter sterilized solution of bovine serum albumin, adjusted to pH 6.8–7.2 with normal sodium hydroxide solution to each 80 ml. of sterile Bacto-Tyrothricin Assay Broth cooled to 45°C., or less.

One pound of Bacto-Tyrothricin Assay Broth will make 27.4 liters medium.

[1] Pharmacopeia of the United States, XIV Revision:650:1950.

BACTO
TYROTHRICIN ASSAY AGAR (B414)
DEHYDRATED

Bacto-Tryptone .... 5 g.
Bacto-Beef Extract .... 3 g.
Bacto-Agar .... 15 g.

Bacto-Tyrothricin Assay Agar is recommended for carrying stock cultures of streptococcus sp., Lancefield group D, strain No. H69D₅ (ATCC ⚹9854) employed in the assay of tyrothricin according to the procedure given by U. S. Pharmacopeia.[1] This medium is also suggested as a solid medium for the cultivation of a large variety of microorganisms.

In the assay of tyrothricin the test organism is carried in stock on a Blood Agar prepared by adding 2 per cent sterile defibrinated human, horse or rabbit blood to sterile melted and cooled Tyrothricin Assay Agar. The complete medium is allowed to solidify in a slanted position. If Blood Agar is to be prepared for purposes other than carrying cultures of streptococcus sp., Lancefield group D, strain No. H69D₅ for tyrothricin assay, it is suggested that 0.5 per cent sodium chloride be added to the medium to make it isotonic, in order to prevent hemolysis of the blood cells.

To rehydrate the medium, suspend 23 grams of Bacto-Tyrothricin Assay Agar in 1000 ml. of cold distilled water. Heat to boiling to dissolve the medium completely. Distribute in tubes or flasks and sterilize in the autoclave for 15 minutes at 15 pounds pressure (121°C.). To prepare Blood Agar, cool the sterile melted agar to 45–50°C. and add the desired sterile defibrinated blood under aseptic conditions. Final reaction of the medium will be pH 6.8.

One pound of Bacto-Tyrothricin Assay Agar will make 19.7 liters of medium.

[1] Pharmacopeia of the United States, XIV Revision:650:1950.

BACTO
POLYMYXIN BASE AGAR (B462)
DEHYDRATED

Bacto-Casitone .... 17 g.
Bacto-Soytone .... 3 g.
Bacto-Dextrose .... 2.5 g.
Sodium Chloride .... 5 g.
Dipotassium Phosphate .... 2.5 g.
Bacto-Agar .... 20 g.

Bacto-Polymyxin Base Agar is prepared according to the formula specified by "The Compilation of Tests and Methods of Assay for Antibiotic Drugs,"[1] Federal Security Agency, Food and Drug Administration for base layer in the cylinder assay of polymyxin B. This medium is also used for carrying stock cultures of the test organism, *Brucella bronchiseptica* (ATCC ⚹4617), and preparing the inoculum in the polymyxin B. assay.

To rehydrate the medium, suspend 50 grams Bacto-Polymyxin Base Agar in 1000 ml. distilled water and heat to boiling to dissolve the medium completely. Distribute in tubes or flasks and sterilize in the autoclave for 15 minutes at 15 pounds pressure (121°C.). Final reaction of the medium will be pH 7.3.

One pound of Bacto-Polymyxin Base Agar will make 9.1 liters of medium.

[1] The Compilation of Tests and Methods of Assay for Antibiotic Drugs, Federal Security Agency, Food and Drugs Administration.

BACTO
POLYMYXIN SEED AGAR (B463)
DEHYDRATED

Bacto-Casitone	17 g.
Bacto-Soytone	3 g.
Bacto-Dextrose	2.5 g.
Sodium Chloride	5 g.
Dipotassium Phosphate	2.5 g.
Bacto-Agar	12 g.
Tween 80	10 g.

Bacto-Polymyxin Seed Agar is prepared according to the formula specified by "The Compilation of Tests and Methods of Assay for Antibiotic Drugs,"[1] Federal Security Agency, Food and Drug Administration for the seed layer in the cylinder assay of Polymyxin B. This medium has the same composition as Bacto-Polymyxin Base Agar, as described above, except the agar content has been reduced to 1.2 per cent and contains 1.0 per cent Tween 80. In the assay of Polymyxin B, *Brucella bronchiseptica* ATCC 4617 is the test organism using this method.

To rehydrate the medium, suspend 52 grams Bacto-Polymyxin Seed Agar in 1000 ml. distilled water and heat to boiling to dissolve the medium completely. Distribute in tubes or flasks and sterilize in the autoclave for 15 minutes at 15 pounds pressure (121°C.). Final reaction of the medium will be pH 7.3.

One pound of Bacto-Polymyxin Seed Agar will make 8.7 liters of medium.

[1] The Compilation of Tests and Methods of Assay for Antibiotic Drugs, Federal Security Agency, Food and Drug Administration.

BACTO
FLUID THIOGLYCOLLATE MEDIUM
DEHYDRATED

Fluid Thioglycollate Medium is specified in the Compilation of Tests and Methods of Assay for Antibiotic Drugs, Federal Security Agency, Food and Drug Administration in the sterility testing of antibiotics. A complete discussion of this medium is given on page 195.

BACTO-PENASE

Bacto-Penase and Bacto-Penase Concentrate are potent penicillinase preparations recommended for the inactivation of penicillin in the sterility testing of penicillin or penicillin products. A complete discussion of these products is given on page 283 and 284.

MEDIA FOR THE ASSAY
OF VITAMINS AND AMINO ACIDS

THE DIFCO dehydrated media described in this section are prepared especially for use in the microbiological assay of vitamins and amino acids. Two types of media are employed for this purpose, one for carrying the culture in stock or preparing the inoculum, the other for assay. The latter type of media contain all the factors necessary for growth of the test organism except one essential ingredient.

Each medium for assay purposes is free from the essential growth requirement factor for which the medium is recommended. When this factor is added, in specified increasing concentrations, the growth response of the particular test organism is measured either acidimetrically or turbidimetrically. In the performance of the various tests the basal medium is prepared and is generally tubed in 5 ml. amounts. To one series of tubes are added graded quantities of the known essential ingredient. To the second similar series are added varying amounts of the material under investigation. Included in each series of tubes is one containing only distilled water and the basal medium. This tube acts as a blank control. The tubes of each series are then made up to 10 ml. with distilled water.

Great care to avoid contamination of media or glassware must be taken in microbiological assay procedures. Extremely small amounts of foreign material may be sufficient to give erroneous results. Scrupulously clean glassware free from detergents and other chemicals must be used. For example, in the assay of Vitamin B_{12}, as small a quantity as 0.01 millimicrogram will give rise to a definite growth response. The importance of clean glassware in the assay of this vitamin was stressed by the U. S. Pharmacopeia Vitamin B_{12} Study Panel, since they stated that glassware for this purpose required special handling, and as many as twelve rinses appeared to be necessary for satisfactory results.

For the successful execution of these procedures all conditions of the assay must be adhered to meticulously. In the description of each medium points of prime importance for successful assays have been stressed.

BACTO
MICRO ASSAY CULTURE AGAR (B319)
DEHYDRATED

Bacto-Yeast Extract	20 g.
Proteose Peptone No. 3, Difco	5 g.
Bacto-Dextrose	10 g.
Monopotassium Phosphate	2 g.
Sorbitan Monooleate Complex	0.1 g.
Bacto-Agar	10 g.

Bacto-Micro Assay Culture Agar is recommended for carrying stock cultures of *Lactobacilli* and other test organisms used for microbiological assay. This medium is also recommended for the general cultivation of *Lactobacilli* and many other microorganisms.

In the microbiological assay of vitamins and other essential nutriments, the organism employed is an essential part of the test. In addition to selecting the proper strain, the previous environment, the age of the culture and size of the inoculum are of prime importance in the satisfactory performance of the test. Micro Assay Culture Agar has proved to be an excellent medium in which to carry stock cultures of *Lactobacilli* and other test organisms used for microbiological assay work, while Micro Inoculum Broth is recommended for the preparation of the inoculum.

Stock cultures of the test organism are prepared by stab inoculation. It is desirable to prepare stock cultures at least in triplicate at monthly intervals. One of the transfers is saved for the preparation of stock cultures, and the others used to prepare inoculum in Micro Inoculum Broth, for assay, as needed. Stock cultures following incubation at 35–37°C. for 24–48 hours should be kept in the refrigerator at 2–6°C.

To rehydrate the medium, suspend 47 grams of Bacto-Micro Assay Culture Agar in 1000 ml. of cold distilled water and heat to boiling to dissolve the medium completely. The medium is then distributed in 10 ml. quantities in tubes of 16–20 mm. diameter. Sterilize in the autoclave for 15 minutes at 15 pounds pressure (121°C.). The tubes are then allowed to cool in an upright position. Final reaction of the medium will be pH 6.7.

One hundred grams of Bacto-Micro Assay Culture Agar will make 2.1 liters of medium.

BACTO

MICRO INOCULUM BROTH (B320)
DEHYDRATED

Bacto-Yeast Extract	20 g.
Proteose Peptone No. 3, Difco	5 g.
Bacto-Dextrose	10 g.
Monopotassium Phosphate	2 g.
Sorbitan Monooleate Complex	0.1 g.

Bacto-Micro Inoculum Broth is recommended for the cultivation of *Lactobacilli* used in microbiological assays. It is of particular value in the preparation of the inoculum for these tests.

Bacto-Micro Inoculum Broth may be employed in preparing the inoculum of *Lactobacilli* used in microbiological assay. This medium eliminates the necessity of using various basal media for this purpose. Subcultures of *Lactobacilli* are made from Bacto-Micro Assay Culture Agar into 10 ml. tubes of Bacto-Micro Inoculum Broth and incubated for 24 hours at 37°C. The culture is then centrifuged, washed with sterile isotonic sodium chloride solution, and diluted before use as inoculum. It is essential that the directions given in the discussion of each assay medium be followed in minute detail, since the age, preparation and size of the inoculum are most important factors in obtaining a satisfactory assay. Although other media and methods may be used successfully for carrying the cultures and preparing the inocula, we feel that uniformly good results will be obtained if the methods described under each medium are followed.

To rehydrate the medium, dissolve 37 grams of Bacto-Micro Inoculum Broth in 1000 ml. distilled water. Distribute in 10 ml. quantities in tubes of 16–20 mm. diameter. Sterilize in the autoclave for 15 minutes at 15 pounds pressure (121°C.). Final reaction of the medium will be pH 6.7.

One hundred grams of Bacto-Micro Inoculum Broth will make 2.7 liters of medium.

BACTO
NEUROSPORA CULTURE AGAR (B321)
DEHYDRATED

Bacto-Yeast Extract	5	g.
Proteose Peptone No. 3, Difco	5	g.
Bacto-Maltose	40	g.
Bacto-Agar	15	g.

Bacto-Neurospora Culture Agar was developed for the cultivation of *Neurospora* to be used in microbiological assays as for example for the assays of pyridoxine and choline. It is recommended that the spores from a 48 hour culture of *Neurospora* be used as an inoculum in such assays. This medium is also recommended as a nearly neutral medium with 4 per cent maltose, for the cultivation of a large variety of fungi. A selective medium for fungi may be prepared by the addition of penicillin and streptomycin as discussed under Bacto-Sabouraud Dextrose Agar page 238.

To rehydrate the medium, suspend 65 grams of Bacto-Neurospora Culture Agar in 1000 ml. cold distilled water and heat to boiling to dissolve the medium completely. Distribute in tubes and sterilize in the autoclave for 15 minutes at 15 pounds pressure (121°C.). Final reaction of the medium will be pH 6.7.

One hundred grams of Bacto-Neurospora Culture Agar will make 1.5 liters of medium.

BACTO
RIBOFLAVIN ASSAY MEDIUM (B325)
DEHYDRATED

Photolyzed Peptone	22	g.
Yeast Supplement	2	g.
Bacto-Dextrose	20	g.
Sodium Acetate	1.8	g.
l-Cystine, Difco	0.2	g.
Dipotassium Phosphate	1	g.
Monopotassium Phosphate	1	g.
Magnesium Sulfate	0.4	g.
Sodium Chloride	0.02	g.
Ferrous Sulfate	0.02	g.
Manganese Sulfate	0.02	g.

Bacto-Riboflavin Assay Medium is a complete dehydrated medium for the microbiological assay of riboflavin. It is free from riboflavin but contains all other factors necessary for the growth of *Lactobacillus casei e* 7469 ATCC. The addition of riboflavin, in certain increasing concentrations, gives a growth response by *L. casei e* 7469 which may be measured acidimetrically or turbidimetrically. This medium is a slight modification of the medium described by Snell and Strong[1]. It is prepared according to the specifications given in the U. S. Pharmacopeia,[2] National Formulary[3] and the Official Method of Analyses of the Association of Official Agricultural Chemists[4] except that it contains 2 per cent anhydrous dextrose in the basal medium instead of 6 per cent. Additional dextrose may be added if desired, however, in our experience this causes carmelization during the preparation of the medium with adverse effects on the assay procedure. The lower concentration of dextrose has given parallel results.

Best results, using Bacto-Riboflavin Assay Medium, have been obtained through the use of the following procedure:

Stock cultures of *L. casei e* 7469 are prepared by stab inoculation into 10 ml. of Bacto-Micro Assay Culture Agar. After 24–48 hours incubation at 35–37°C., the stock cultures are kept in the refrigerator. Transplants are made at monthly intervals, in triplicate. Inoculum for assay is prepared by subculturing from a stock culture of *L. casei e* 7469 into 10 ml. of Bacto-Micro Inoculum Broth. Following incubation for 24 hours at 35–37° C., the culture is centrifuged, under aseptic conditions, and the supernatant liquid decanted. The cells are resuspended in 10 ml. sterile isotonic sodium chloride. The cell suspension is then diluted 1–20 with sterile isotonic sodium chloride. One drop of this latter suspension is then used to inoculate each of the assay tubes.

Bacto-Riboflavin Assay Medium may be used for both turbidimetric and acidimetric determinations. Turbidimetric readings should be made after 18–24 hours incubation at 35–37°C., whereas acidimetric determinations are best made after 72 hours incubation at 35–37°C. We have found the most effective assay range, using Bacto-Riboflavin Assay Medium, to be between 0.025 microgram and 0.15 microgram riboflavin.

It is essential that a standard curve be constructed each time an assay is run, since conditions of autoclaving, temperature of incubation, etc., which influence the standard curve readings, cannot be duplicated exactly from time to time. The standard curve is obtained by using riboflavin at levels of 0.0, 0.025, 0.05, 0.075, 0.1, 0.15, 0.2 and 0.3 microgram riboflavin per assay tube (10 ml.).

The concentrations of riboflavin required for the preparation of the standard curve may be prepared by dissolving 0.1 gram of riboflavin in 1000 ml. of distilled water by heating, giving a stock solution of 100 micrograms per ml. Dilute the stock solution by adding 1 ml. to 999 ml. distilled water. Use 0.0, 0.25, 0.5, 0.75, 1.0, 1.5, 2.0 and 3 ml. of the diluted stock solution per tube. The stock solution of riboflavin used for preparing the standard curve is stable for 2 months when stored at 2–6°C. under toluene.

To rehydrate the basal medium, suspend 48 grams of Bacto-Riboflavin Assay Medium in 1000 ml. of distilled water and heat to boiling for 2–3 minutes. The flask should be well shaken to distribute evenly the slight precipitate which forms. Five (5) ml. of the medium are added to each tube in the preparation of the tubes for the standard curve and to each tube containing material under assay. For the assay, each tube must contain 5 ml. of rehydrated medium, increasing amounts of the standard or the unknown and sufficient distilled water to give a total volume of 10 ml. per tube. The tubes are then autoclaved for 10 minutes at 15 pounds pressure (121°C.). Oversterilization of the medium will give unsatisfactory results.

One hundred grams of Bacto-Riboflavin Assay Medium will make 4 liters of final medium.

[1] Ind. Eng. Chem. Anal. Ed., 11:346:1939.   [2] National Formulary, 9th Edition:763:1950.
[3] Pharmacopeia of the United States Revision   [4] A.O.A.C., 7th Edition: 779:1950.
XIV:753:1950.

BACTO
NIACIN ASSAY MEDIUM (B322)
DEHYDRATED

Bacto-Vitamin Free		Pyridoxine Hydrochloride	..	0.0004 g.
Casamino Acids	12 g.	Riboflavin		0.0004 g.
Bacto-Dextrose	40 g.	p-Aminobenzoic Acid, Difco		0.0001 g.
Sodium Acetate	20 g.	Biotin		0.0000008 g.
l-Cystine, Difco	0.4 g.	Dipotassium Phosphate		1 g.
dl-Tryptophane	0.2 g.	Monopotassium Phosphate		1 g.
Adenine Sulfate	0.02 g.	Magnesium Sulfate		0.4 g.
Guanine Hydrochloride	0.02 g.	Sodium Chloride		0.02 g.
Uracil	0.02 g.	Ferrous Sulfate		0.02 g.
Thiamine Hydrochloride	0.0002 g.	Manganese Sulfate		0.02 g.
Calcium Pantothenate	0.0002 g.			

Bacto-Niacin Assay Medium is a complete dehydrated medium for the assay of nicotinic acid or nicotinamide (niacin). It is free from nicotinic acid and its analogs, but contains all the other factors necessary for the growth of *Lactobacillus arabinosus* 17-5 ATCC 8014. The addition of nicotinic acid or its analogs in specified increasing concentrations gives a growth response by *L. arabinosus* 17-5 which may be measured acidimetrically or turbidimetrically. Bacto-Niacin Assay Medium is prepared according to the formula described by Snell and Wright[1] and modified by Krehl, Strong, and Elvehjem[2] and Barton-Wright.[3] The formula duplicates that listed in the U. S. Pharmacopeia,[4] and National Formulary[5] and the Official Method of Analyses of the Association of Official Agricultural Chemists.[4]

Best results, using Bacto-Niacin Assay Medium, are obtained through the use of the following procedure:

Stock cultures of *L. arabinosus* 17-5 are prepared by stab inoculation of Bacto-Micro Assay Culture Agar. Following incubation at 35–37°C. for 24–48 hours, the tubes are kept in the refrigerator. Transplants are made at monthly intervals. Inoculum for assay is prepared by subculturing from a stock culture of *L. arabinosus* 17-5 into a tube containing 10 ml. of Bacto-Micro Inoculum Broth. After 24 hours incubation at 35–37°C., the cells are centrifuged, under aseptic conditions, and the supernatant liquid decanted. The cells are resuspended in 10 ml. sterile isotonic sodium chloride. The cell suspension is then diluted 1–100 with sterile isotonic sodium chloride. The suspension should be just faintly cloudy. One drop of this suspension is then used to inoculate each of the assay tubes.

It is essential that a standard curve be set up for each separate assay since conditions of autoclaving, temperature of incubation, etc., which influence the standard curve readings, cannot be duplicated exactly from time to time. The standard curve is obtained by using niacin at levels of 0.0, 0.05, 0.1, 0.2, 0.3, 0.4, and 0.5 micrograms niacin per assay tube (10.0 ml.). Bacto-Niacin Assay Medium may be used for both turbidimetric and acidimetric analyses. Turbidimetric readings should be made after 16–18 hours incubation at 35–37°C. Acidimetric determinations are best made following 72 hours incubation at 35–37°C. We have found the most effective assay range, using Bacto-Niacin Assay Medium, to be between 0.05 micrograms and 0.3 micrograms niacin.

The concentrations of niacin required for the preparation of the standard curve may be prepared by dissolving 0.1 gram of niacin in 1000 ml. of distilled water, giving a stock solution of 100 micrograms per ml. Dilute the stock solution by adding 1 ml. to 999 ml. distilled water. Use 0.0, 0.5, 1.0, 2, 3, 4 and 5 ml. per tube. The stock solution of niacin used for preparing the standard curve is stable for 2 months when stored at 2–6°C. under toluene.

To rehydrate the basal medium, suspend 75 grams of Bacto-Niacin Assay Medium in 1000 ml. distilled water and heat to boiling for 2–3 minutes. The slight precipitate which forms should be evenly distributed by shaking. Five (5) ml. of the medium are added to each tube in the preparation of the tubes for the standard curve and to each tube containing material under assay. For the assay, each tube must contain 5 ml. of rehydrated medium, increasing amounts of the standard or the unknown and sufficient distilled water to give a total volume of 10 ml. per tube. The tubes are then autoclaved for 10 minutes at 15 pounds pressure (121°C.). Oversterilization of the medium will give unsatisfactory results.

One hundred grams of Bacto-Niacin Assay Medium will make 2.6 liters of final medium.

[1] J. Biol. Chem., 139:675:1941.
[2] Ind. Eng. Chem. Anal. Ed., 15:471:1943.
[3] Biochem. J., 38:314:1944.
[4] Pharmacopeia of the United States, XIV

Revision:737:1950.
[5] National Formulary, 9th Edition: 746:1950.
[6] A.O.A.C., 7th Edition:782: 1950.

BACTO

THIAMINE ASSAY MEDIUM (B326)

DEHYDRATED

Photolyzed Peptone	22 g.	Niacin	0.0002 g.
Bacto-Vitamin Free		Pyridoxine Hydrochloride	0.0002 g.
Casamino Acids	5 g.	p-Aminobenzoic Acid, Difco	0.0002 g.
Bacto-Dextrose	40 g.	Folic Acid	0.0000005 g.
Sodium Acetate	15 g.	Biotin	0.0000008 g.
l-Cystine, Difco	0.2 g.	Dipotassium Phosphate	1 g.
Adenine Sulfate	0.02 g.	Monopotassium Phosphate	1 g.
Guanine Hydrochloride	0.02 g.	Magnesium Sulfate	0.4 g.
Uracil	0.02 g.	Sodium Chloride	0.02 g.
Riboflavin	0.0002 g.	Ferrous Sulfate	0.02 g.
Calcium Pantothenate	0.0002 g.	Manganese Sulfate	0.02 g.

Bacto-Thiamine Assay Medium is a complete dehydrated medium for the assay of thiamine. It is free from thiamine but contains all the other factors necessary for the growth of *Lactobacillus fermentum* 36 ATCC 9833. The addition of thiamine, in certain increasing concentrations, gives a growth response which may be measured turbidimetrically. Bacto-Thiamine Assay Medium is prepared according to the formula given by Sarett and Cheldelin.[1]

The following procedure is recommended for the use of Bacto-Thiamine Assay Medium:

Stock cultures of the test organism, *L. fermentum* 36, are prepared by stab inoculation of Bacto-Micro Assay Culture Agar. After 24–48 hours incubation at 35–37°C., the tubes are kept in the refrigerator. Transplants are made at monthly intervals, in triplicate.

Inoculum for assay is prepared by subculturing from a stock culture to 10 ml. of Bacto-Micro Inoculum Broth. After 16–18 hours incubation at 35–37°C., the cells are centrifuged, under aseptic conditions, and the supernatant liquid is decanted. The cells are resuspended in 10 ml. sterile isotonic sodium chloride. One-half (0.5) ml. of this cell suspension are then added to 100 ml. of sterile saline. One drop of this suspension is then used to inoculate the assay tubes.

The tubes for the standard curve, which should be set up each time an assay is run, contain 0.0, 0.005, 0.01, 0.015, 0.02, 0.03, 0.04 and 0.05 microgram of thiamine hydrochloride per tube (10 ml.). It is essential that a standard curve be run with each assay since conditions of heating, temperature of incubation, etc., which influence the standard curve readings cannot be duplicated exactly from time to time. Using Bacto-Thiamine Assay Medium we have found the most effective assay range to be between 0.005 and 0.03 microgram thiamine.

The concentrations of thiamine required for the preparation of the standard curve may be prepared by dissolving 0.1 gram of thiamine in 1000 ml. of distilled water, giving a stock solution of 100 micrograms per ml. Dilute the stock solution by adding 1 ml. to 99 ml. of distilled water. This solution is further diluted by adding 1 ml. to 99 ml. distilled water to give the final solution. Use 0.0, 0.5, 1.0, 1.5, 2.0, 3, 4 and 5 ml. of this final solution per tube. The stock solution of thiamine used for preparing the standard curve is stable for 2 months when stored at 2–6°C. under toluene.

After 20–24 hours incubation at 35–37°C., *L. fermentum* 36 is capable of utilizing the pyrimidine and thiazole moieties of the thiamine molecule. It is essential, therefore, that the growth response be measured turbidimetrically prior to this time. The tubes should be incubated at 35–37°C. for *not longer* than 16–18 hours, and then placed in the refrigerator for 15–30 minutes in order to stop growth. The growth can then be measured by any suitable nephelometric method.

To rehydrate the basal medium, suspend 85 grams of Bacto-Thiamine Assay Medium in 1000 ml. distilled water and heat to boiling for 2–3 minutes. The slight precipitate which forms should be evenly distributed by shaking. Five (5) ml. of the medium are added to each tube in the preparation of the tubes for the standard curve and to each tube containing material under assay. For the assay, each tube must contain 5 ml. of rehydrated medium, increasing amounts of the standard or the unknown and sufficient distilled water to give a total volume of 10 ml. per tube. The tubes should not be autoclaved because of possible destruction of thiamine, but are steamed at 100°C. for 15 minutes. Overheating of the medium will give unsatisfactory results.

One hundred grams of Bacto-Thiamine Assay Medium will make 2.2 liters of final medium.

1 J. Biol. Chem., 155:153:1944.

PANTOTHENATE ASSAY MEDIUM (B323)
DEHYDRATED

Bacto-Vitamin Free		Niacin	0.002 g.
Casamino Acids	12 g.	Pyridoxine Hydrochloride	0.004 g.
Bacto-Dextrose	40 g.	p-Aminobenzoic Acid, Difco	0.0002 g.
Sodium Acetate	20 g.	Biotin	0.0000008 g.
l-Cystine, Difco	0.2 g.	Dipotassium Phosphate	1 g.
dl-Tryptophane	0.2 g.	Monopotassium Phosphate	1 g.
Adenine Sulfate	0.02 g.	Magnesium Sulfate	0.4 g.
Guanine Hydrochloride	0.02 g.	Sodium Chloride	0.02 g.
Uracil	0.02 g.	Ferrous Sulfate	0.02 g.
Thiamine Hydrochloride	0.002 g.	Manganese Sulfate	0.02 g.
Riboflavin	0.002 g.		

Bacto-Pantothenate Assay Medium is a complete dehydrated medium for the assay of pantothenic acid. It is free from pantothenic acid or pantothenate but contains all the other factors necessary for the growth of *Lactobacillus arabinosus* 17-5 ATCC 8014. The addition of pantothenate, in specified increasing concentration, gives a linear growth response by *L. arabinosus* 17-5 which may be measured acidimetrically or turbidimetrically. Bacto-Pantothenate Assay Medium is a slight modification of the medium described by Skeggs and Wright.[1]

The following procedure is recommended for the use of Bacto-Pantothenate Assay Medium:

Stock cultures of the test organism, *L. arabinosus* 17-5, are prepared by stab inoculation of Bacto-Micro Assay Culture Agar. Following incubation at 35–37°C. for 24–48 hours, the tubes are kept in the refrigerator. Transplants are made at monthly intervals. Inoculum for assay is prepared by subculturing from a stock culture of *L. arabinosus* 17-5 into a tube containing 10 ml. of Bacto-Micro Inoculum Broth. Following incubation for 24 hours at 35–37°C., the cells are centrifuged, under aseptic conditions, and the supernatant liquid decanted. The cells are resuspended in 10 ml. sterile isotonic sodium chloride. The cell suspension is then diluted 1–100 with sterile isotonic sodium chloride. The suspension should be just faintly cloudy. One drop of this suspension is then used to inoculate each of the assay tubes.

It is essential that a standard curve be set up for each separate assay since conditions of autoclaving, temperature of incubation, etc., which influence the standard curve readings, cannot be duplicated exactly from time to time. The standard curve is obtained by using calcium pantothenate at levels of 0.0, 0.02, 0.04, 0.06, 0.08, 0.1, 0.12 and 0.2 microgram per assay tube (10 ml.). Bacto-Pantothenate Assay Medium may be used for both turbidimetric and acidimetric analysis. Turbidimetric readings should be made after 18–24 hours at 35–37°C. Acidimetric determinations are made after 72 hours incubation at 35–37°C. We have found the most effective assay range, using Bacto-Pantothenate Assay Medium, to be between 0.02 microgram and 0.12 microgram calcium pantothenate.

The concentrations of calcium pantothenate required for the preparation of the standard curve may be prepared by dissolving 0.1 gram of calcium pantothenate in 1000 ml. of distilled water, giving a stock solution of 100 micrograms per ml. Dilute the stock solution by adding 1 ml. to 99 ml. of distilled water. This solution is further diluted by adding 4 ml. to 96 ml. distilled water to give the final solution. Use 0.0, 0.5, 1.0, 1.5, 2.0, 2.5, 3.0 and 5 ml. of this final solution per tube. The stock solution of calcium pantothenate used for preparing the standard curve is stable for 2 months when stored at 2–6°C. under toluene.

To rehydrate the basal medium, suspend 75 grams of Bacto-Pantothenate Assay Medium in 1000 ml. distilled water, and heat to boiling for 2–3 minutes. The slight precipitate which forms should be evenly distributed by shaking. Five (5) ml. of the medium are added to each tube in the preparation of the tubes for the standard curve and to each tube containing material under assay. For the assay, each tube must contain 5 ml. of rehydrated medium, increasing amounts of the standard or the unknown and sufficient distilled water to give a total volume of 10 ml. per tube. The tubes are then autoclaved for 10 minutes at 15 pounds pressure (121°C.). Oversterilization of the medium will give unsatisfactory results.

One hundred grams of Bacto-Pantothenate Assay Medium will make 2.6 liters of final medium.

¹ J. Biol. Chem., 156:21:1944.

BACTO-BIOTIN ASSAY MEDIUM (B419)

Bacto-Biotin Assay Medium has the same composition as Bacto-Pantothenate Assay Medium described immediately above, except that biotin has been omitted and 0.002 g. calcium pantothenate included.

Bacto-Biotin Assay Medium is a complete dehydrated medium for the assay of biotin. It is free from biotin but contains all the other factors necessary for the growth of *Lactobacillus arabinosus* 17-5 ATCC 8014. The addition of biotin in specified increasing concentrations gives a growth response by *L. arabinosus* 17-5 which may be measured acidimetrically or turbidimetrically.

The following procedure is recommended for the use of Bacto-Biotin Assay Medium:

Stock cultures of the test organism, *L. arabinosus* 17-5, are prepared by stab inoculation of Bacto-Micro Assay Culture Agar. After 24–48 hours incubation at 35–37°C., the tubes are stored in the refrigerator. Transplants are made at monthly intervals, in triplicate.

Inoculum for assay is prepared by subculturing from a stock culture of *L. arabinosus* 17-5 to 10 ml. of Bacto-Micro Inoculum Broth. After 16–24 hours incubation at 35–37°C., the cells are centrifuged under aseptic conditions, and the supernatant liquid decanted. The cells are resuspended in 10 ml. sterile isotonic sodium chloride solution. The cell suspension is then diluted 1–100 with sterile isotonic sodium chloride. One drop of this latter suspension is then used to inoculate each of the assay tubes (10 ml.).

It is essential that a standard curve be constructed each time an assay is run, since conditions of autoclaving, temperature of incubation, etc., which influence the standard curve readings, cannot be duplicated exactly from time to time. A standard curve is obtained by using biotin at levels of 0.0, 0.025, 0.05, 0.1, 0.2, 0.3, 0.4, 0.5 and 1.0 millimicrogram per assay tube (10 ml.).

The concentrations of biotin required for the preparation of the standard curve may be prepared by dissolving 0.1 gram of biotin in 1000 ml. of distilled water (100 micrograms per ml.). Dilute this stock solution by adding 2 ml. to 98 ml. of distilled water. This solution is diluted by adding 1 ml. to 999 ml. distilled water giving a solution of 2 millimicrograms of biotin per ml. This solution is further diluted by adding 5 ml. to 95 ml. distilled water giving a final solution of 0.1 millimicrogram of biotin per ml. Use 0.0, 0.25, 0.5, 1.0, 2, 3, 4 and 5 ml. of this final solution. The last tube is prepared by adding 0.5 ml. of the standard solution containing 2 millimicrograms of biotin per liter. The stock solution of biotin used for preparing the standard curve is stable for 2 months when stored at 2–6°C. under toluene.

Bacto-Biotin Assay Medium may be used for both turbidimetric and acidimetric analyses. Turbidimetric readings should be made after 16–20 hours at 35–37°C. Acidimetric determinations are made after 72 hours incubation at 35–37°C. The most effective assay range, using Bacto-Biotin Assay Medium, has been found to be between 0.025 millimicrogram and 0.5 millimicrogram biotin.

To rehydrate the medium, suspend 75 grams of Bacto-Biotin Assay Medium in 1000 ml. distilled water, and heat to boiling for 2–3 minutes. The slight precipitate which forms should be evenly distributed by shaking. Five (5) ml. of the medium are added to each tube in the preparation of the tubes for the standard curve and to each tube containing material under assay. For the assay each tube must contain 5 ml. of rehydrated medium, increasing amounts of the standard or the unknown, and sufficient distilled water to give a total volume of 10 ml. per tube. The tubes are then autoclaved for 10 minutes at 15 pounds pressure (121°C.). Oversterilization of the medium will give unsatisfactory results.

One hundred grams of Bacto-Biotin Assay Medium will make 2.6 liters of final medium.

BACTO
B_{12} ASSAY MEDIUM USP (B457)
DEHYDRATED

Bacto-Vitamin Free		Biotin	0.000008 g.
Casamino Acids	15 g.	Niacin	0.002 g.
		p-Aminobenzoic Acid, Difco	0.002 g.
Bacto-Dextrose	40 g.	Calcium Pantothenate	0.001 g.
Bacto-Asparagine	0.2 g.	Pyridoxine Hydrochloride	0.004 g.
Sodium Acetate	20 g.	Pyridoxal Hydrochloride	0.004 g.
Ascorbic Acid	4 g.	Pyridoxamine Hydrochloride	0.0008 g.
l-Cystine, Difco	0.4 g.	Folic Acid	0.0002 g.
dl-Tryptophane	0.4 g.	Monopotassium Phosphate	1 g.
Adenine Sulfate	0.02 g.	Dipotassium Phosphate	1 g.
Guanine Hydrochloride	0.02 g.	Magnesium Sulfate	0.4 g.
Uracil	0.02 g.	Sodium Chloride	0.02 g.
Xanthine	0.02 g.	Ferrous Sulfate	0.02 g.
Riboflavin	0.001 g.	Manganese Sulfate	0.02 g.
Thiamine Hydrochloride	0.001 g.	Sorbitan Monooleate Complex	2 g.

Bacto-B_{12} Assay Medium USP is prepared according to the formula given in the United States Pharmacopeia.[1] It is free from Vitamin B_{12} but contains all the other factors necessary for the growth of *Lactobacillus leichmannii* ATCC 7830. The addition of Vitamin B_{12} to this medium in specified increasing concentrations gives a growth response by the test organism which may be measured acidimetrically or turbidimetrically.

The following procedure, or the procedure specified by USP is recommended for the preparation of the inoculum for the assay of Vitamin B_{12} using Bacto-B_{12} Assay Medium USP:

Stock cultures of *L. leichmannii* 7830 are prepared by stab inoculation of 3 or more tubes of Bacto-Micro Assay Culture Agar. Transfers should be made bimonthly for stock culture. Before using a culture in the assay, make at least 10 successive transfers of the culture in Bacto-Micro Assay Culture Agar in a two-week period. Incubate 24–48 hours at 35–37°C. Prepare fresh stab cultures every second day and do not use them for preparing the inoculum if more than 4 days old. Inoculum for assay is prepared by subculturing from a 24–48 hour stock culture of *L. leichmannii* 7830 to 10 ml. of Bacto-Micro Inoculum Broth. After 16–24 hours incubation at 35–37°C., the cells are centrifuged under aseptic conditions and the supernatant liquid decanted. Suspend the cells from this culture in 10 ml. of sterile B_{12} Assay Medium USP in single strength, prepared by dissolving 4.75 grams of Bacto-B_{12} Assay Medium USP in 100 ml. of distilled water. Centrifuge and decant the supernatant liquid. Again, suspend the cells in 10 ml. of the medium, centrifuge and decant the supernatant liquid. Repeat this process a third time. Finally, resuspend the cells in 10 ml. of the sterile single strength medium. Add 0.1 ml. of this suspension to 10 ml. of sterile suspension medium and mix. The cell suspension so obtained is the inoculum. Inoculate each tube aseptically with one drop of the inoculum. The use of such a diluted inoculum gives more uniform results than a heavier inoculum.

It is essential that a standard curve be constructed each time an assay is run, since conditions of autoclaving, temperature of incubation, etc., which influence the standard curve readings, cannot be duplicated exactly from time to time. A standard curve is obtained by using Bacto-B_{12} Assay Medium USP with levels of 0.0, 0.01, 0.02, 0.03, 0.04, 0.05, 0.06, 0.07, 0.08, 0.09, 0.1 and 0.25 millimicrograms Vitamin B_{12} per assay tube (10 ml.) for the turbidimetric and acidimetric determinations. Determinations are made in triplicate.

Using Bacto-B_{12} Assay Medium USP the most effective range has proved to be between 0.01 millimicrograms and 0.1 millimicrograms.

The concentration of Vitamin B_{12} required for the preparation of the standard curve may be prepared by adding the contents of one ampul containing 20 micrograms per ml. (1 ml.) in 99 ml. of 25 per cent alcohol in distilled water giving the stock solution of 200 millimicrograms per ml. Further dilutions are made as follows:

A. Add 1 ml. stock solution to 99 ml. distilled water
   (1 ml. = 2 millimicrograms)
B. Add 2.5 ml. of A to 97.5 ml. distilled water
   (1 ml. = 0.05 millimicrograms).
C. Add 1 ml. of A to 99 ml. distilled water
   (1 ml. = 0.02 millimicrograms).

Use 0.0, 0.5, 1.0, 1.5, 2.0, 2.5, 3.0, 3.5, 4.0, 5 ml. dilution C per tube and for the last tube use 5 ml. dilution B. If preferred, Vitamin B_{12} may be supplied in the form of a 0.1 per cent trituration of crystalline Vitamin B_{12} with mannitol (1 gram = 1 mg. Vitamin B_{12}). Dissolve 0.2 grams in 1000 ml. distilled water to obtain the stock solution of 200 millimicrograms per ml. The stock solution of Vitamin B_{12} is stable for 2 months if stored at 2–6°C. under toluene.

Acidimetric determinations are made electrometrically using pH 7.0 as the end point after 72 hours incubation at 30–37°C., but held constant to within 0.5°. We recommend an incubation temperature of 35–37°C. Turbidimetric determinations are made after 20–24 hours incubation. The standard curve is then constructed from the values obtained.

To rehydrate the basal medium, dissolve 85 grams of Bacto-B_{12} Assay Medium USP in 1000 ml. of distilled water, and heat to boiling for 2–3 minutes. The slight precipitate which forms should be evenly distributed by shaking. Five (5) ml. of the medium are added to each tube in the preparation of the tubes for the standard curve and to each tube containing material under assay. For the assay, each tube must contain 5 ml. of rehydrated medium, increasing amounts of the standard or the unknown and sufficient distilled water to give a total volume of 10 ml. per tube. Tubes are sterilized by autoclaving for 5 minutes at 15 lbs., pressure (121°C.). Overheating of the medium will give unsatisfactory results.

One hundred grams of Bacto-B_{12} Assay Medium USP will make 2.1 liters final medium.

[1] Pharmacopeia of the United States, Third Supplement, XIV, Revision:15:1951.

BACTO
C. S. VITAMIN B_{12} AGAR (B399)
DEHYDRATED

Bacto-Vitamin Free		Calcium Pantothenate	0.002 g.
Casamino Acids	10.0 g.	Niacin	0.002 g.
Bacto-Soytone, Vitamin Free	5.0 g.	Pyridoxine	0.004 g.
Bacto-Dextrose	20.0 g.	Pyridoxal	0.004 g.
Sodium Acetate	12.0 g.	Biotin	0.00000001 g.
Ribose Nucleic Acid	1.0 g.	dl-Tryptophane	0.2 g.
Sodium Thioglycollate, Difco	1.7 g.	Potassium Sulfate	20.0 g.
l-Cystine, Difco	0.2 g.	Monopotassium Phosphate	1.0 g.
Adenine Sulfate	0.0176 g.	Dipotassium Phosphate	1.0 g.
Guanine Hydrochloride	0.0124 g.	Magnesium Sulfate	0.4 g.
Uracil	0.01 g.	Sodium Chloride	0.02 g.
Xanthine	0.01 g.	Ferrous Sulfate	0.02 g.
Folic Acid	0.001 g.	Manganese Sulfate	0.02 g.
Riboflavin	0.002 g.	Sorbitan Monooleate Complex	1.0 g.
Thiamine Hydrochloride	0.002 g.	Bacto-Agar	15.0 g.

Bacto-C. S. Vitamin B_{12} Agar is prepared according to the formula given by Cohen and Bennett.[1] This medium is suggested for the assay of Vitamin B_{12} with *Lactobacillus leichmannii* 4797 ATCC as the test organism. The addition of a solution of crystalline Vitamin B_{12} in specified increasing amounts to cylinders or disks placed on this medium produces proportionately larger zones of growth by *L. leichmannii* 4797.

The following procedure is recommended for the use of Bacto-C. S. Vitamin B_{12} Agar:

Stock cultures of the test organism, *L. leichmannii* 4797, are prepared by stab inoculation of Bacto-Micro Assay Culture Agar. Following incubation at 35–37°C. for 24–48 hours, the tubes are kept in the refrigerator. Transplants are made at two-week intervals. Inoculum for assay is prepared by subculturing from a stock culture of *L. leichmannii* 4797 into a tube containing 10 ml. of Bacto-Micro Inoculum Broth. Following incubation for 16–24 hours at 35–37°C., the cells are centrifuged, under aseptic conditions, and the supernatant liquid decanted. The cells are resuspended in 10 ml. sterile isotonic sodium chloride, centrifuged, the supernatant liquid discarded and made up to 10 ml. volume with sterile isotonic sodium chloride. Under aseptic conditions 10 ml. of washed cells are added per 1000 ml. of sterile melted Bacto-C. S. Vitamin B_{12} Agar at 45–50°C. Into each of 4 sterile flat bottom petri dishes (95 mm.) are poured 25 ml. of the inoculated medium and allowed to solidify. When the surface is dry 6 sterile penicillin assay cups or 13 mm. filter paper disks are distributed evenly on the surface of the medium.

For the preparation of the standard, prepare sterile solutions of Vitamin B_{12} containing 0.05, 0.1, 0.2, 0.4, 0.8 and 1.6 micrograms per ml. Use 0.2–0.3 ml. of the standard B_{12} solutions per cup. When paper disks are used saturate the pads with 0.1 ml. of the above solutions under aseptic conditions. The use of a syringe and needle or a capillary pipette is suggested as a convenience in restricting the solutions to the pad. One or more duplicate plates per test may be employed using 4 to 6 disks per plate and modifying the concentration of Vitamin B_{12} as desired. Using Bacto-C. S. Vitamin B_{12} Assay Medium experience has shown that the most effective assay range is between 0.1 microgram and 0.8 microgram.

The concentrations of Vitamin B_{12} required for the preparation of the standard curve may be prepared by dissolving 1.6 g. of a 0.1 per cent trituration of crystalline Vitamin B_{12} with mannitol (1 gram = 1 mg. Vitamin B_{12}) in 1000 ml. distilled water. This is the stock solution A containing 1.6 micrograms per ml. To obtain solution B containing 0.8 micrograms dilute 10 ml. of A with 10 ml. of distilled water. To obtain solution C containing 0.4 micrograms dilute 10 ml. of B with 10 ml. distilled water. To obtain solution D containing 0.2 micrograms dilute 10 ml. of C with 10 ml. distilled water. To obtain solution E containing 0.1 micrograms dilute 10 ml. of D with 10 ml. distilled water. To obtain solution F containing 0.05 micrograms dilute 10 ml. of E with 10 ml. distilled water. These solutions are stable for 2 months when stored at 2–6°C. under toluene.

In determining the Vitamin B_{12} content of unknown materials, the assay samples are appropriately diluted and similarly applied. In the assay of some preparations, better defined, clearer cut zones may be obtained by the addition of 0.5 to 1.0 per cent of sodium chloride to Bacto-C. S. Vitamin B_{12} Agar, since added sodium chloride, with some unknown samples, makes the assay more specific for vitamin B_{12}. Sodium chloride, under these conditions, must be added to the medium in preparing the standard curve. Incubate inoculated plates at 35–37°C. for 24 hours and measure size of zone of growth produced. The diameter of the growth zone is indicative of the amount of Vitamin B_{12} present.

To rehydrate the medium, suspend 90 grams Bacto-C. S. Vitamin B_{12} Agar in 1000 ml. of cold distilled water. Heat to boiling to dissolve the medium completely. Distribute in flasks and sterilize in the autoclave for 15 minutes at 15 pounds pressure (121°C.).

One hundred grams of Bacto-C. S. Vitamin B_{12} Agar are sufficient for 1.1 liters of medium.

[1] Paper read at American Chemical Society, Philadelphia, 1950.

BACTO
FOLIC ACID ASSAY MEDIUM (B318)
DEHYDRATED

Bacto-Vitamin Free		Riboflavin	0.002 g.
Casamino Acids	12 g.	Niacin	0.002 g.
Bacto-Dextrose	40 g.	p-Aminobenzoic Acid, Difco	0.0002 g.
Sodium Citrate	20 g.	Biotin	0.0000008 g.
l-Cystine, Difco	0.2 g.	Calcium Pantothenate	0.0004 g.
dl-Tryptophane	0.2 g.	Dipotassium Phosphate	1 g.
Adenine Sulfate	0.02 g.	Monopotassium Phosphate	1 g.
Guanine Hydrochloride	0.02 g.	Magnesium Sulfate	0.4 g.
Uracil	0.02 g.	Sodium Chloride	0.02 g.
Thiamine Hydrochloride	0.002 g.	Ferrous Sulfate	0.02 g.
Pyridoxine Hydrochloride	0.004 g.	Manganese Sulfate	0.02 g.

Bacto-Folic Acid Assay Medium is a complete dehydrated medium for the assay of folic acid. It is free from folic acid but contains all the other factors necessary for the growth of *Streptococcus lactis R.* 8043 ATCC (*Streptococcus fecalis R.*). The addition of folic acid in specified increasing concentrations gives a growth response by *S. lactis R.* 8043 after 18 hours incubation at 35–37°C. which may be measured turbidimetrically. Bacto-Folic Acid Assay Medium is prepared according to the formula described by Capps, Hobbs and Fox,[1] modified by the use of sodium citrate instead of sodium acetate.

The following procedure for the preparation of the inoculum and performance of the test is recommended for the assay of folic acid using Bacto-Folic Acid Medium:

Stock cultures of *S. lactis R.* 8043 are prepared by stab inoculation of the Bacto-Micro Assay Culture Agar. Following incubation at 35–37°C. for 24–48 hours, the tubes are stored in the refrigerator. Transplants are made at monthly intervals. Inoculum for assay is prepared by subculturing from a stock culture of *S. lactis R.* 8043 into a tube containing 10 ml. of the Bacto-Micro Inoculum Broth. After 24 hours incubation at 35–37°C., the cells are centrifuged, under aseptic conditions, and the supernatant liquid decanted. The cells are resuspended in 10 ml. of sterile isotonic sodium chloride. The cell suspension is then diluted 1–100 with sterile isotonic sodium chloride. The suspension should be just faintly cloudy. One drop of this latter suspension is then used to inoculate each of the assay tubes.

It is essential that a standard curve be constructed each time an assay is run, since conditions of autoclaving, temperature of incubation, etc., which influence the standard curve readings, cannot be duplicated exactly from time to time. A standard curve is obtained by using the folic acid at levels of 0.0, 0.001, 0.002, 0.004, 0.006, 0.008, 0.009 and 0.01 microgram per assay tube (10 ml.). The concentrations of folic acid required for the construction of the standard curve may be prepared by dissolving 0.1 gram folic acid in 1000 ml. of distilled water (100 micrograms per ml.). Add 0.05N sodium hydroxide drop by drop to effect complete solution of the folic acid, being careful not to get more alkaline than pH 7.0. Dilute the stock solution by adding 1 ml. to 999 ml. distilled water. This solution is diluted further by adding 4 ml. to 96 ml. distilled water. Use 0.0, 0.25, 0.5, 1.0, 1.5, 2.0, 2.25 and 2.5 ml. of this final solution per tube. The stock solution of folic acid used for preparing the standard curve is stable for 2 months when stored at 2–6°C. under toluene.

Following inoculation, tubes are incubated at 35–37°C. for 18–24 hours and placed in the refrigerator for 15–30 minutes in order to stop growth. The growth can then be measured by any suitable nephelometric method, and the curve constructed from the values obtained. Acidimetric determinations of growth have not been found satisfactory. Using Bacto-Folic Acid Assay Medium, we have found the most effective assay range to be between the levels of 0.002 and 0.01 microgram folic acid per tube (10 ml.).

To rehydrate the basal medium, suspend 75 grams of Bacto-Folic Acid Assay Medium in 1000 ml. distilled water, and heat to boiling for 2–3 minutes. The slight precipitate which forms should be evenly distributed by shaking. Five (5) ml. of the medium are added to each tube in the preparation of the tubes for the standard curve and to each tube containing material under assay. For the assay, each tube must contain 5 ml. of rehydrated medium, increasing amounts of the standard or the unknown and sufficient distilled water to give a total volume of 10 ml. per tube. The tubes are autoclaved for 10 minutes at 15 pounds pressure (121°C.). Do not sterilize longer than specified above. One hundred grams of Bacto-Folic Acid Assay Medium will make 2.6 liters of final medium.

[1] J. Bact., 55:869:1948.

BACTO
PYRIDOXINE ASSAY MEDIUM (B324)
DEHYDRATED

Saccharose, Difco	30 g.
Biotin	0.000008 g.
Ammonium Tartrate	10 g.
Sodium Dihydrogen Citrate	4 g.
Monopotassium Phosphate	5 g.
Magnesium Sulfate	1 g.
Sodium Chloride	0.2 g.
Calcium Chloride	0.2 g.
Ferric Chloride	0.01 g.
Zinc Sulfate	0.004 g.

Bacto-Pyridoxine Assay Medium is a complete dehydrated medium for the microbiological assay of pyridoxine. It is patterned after the medium described by Stokes, Larsen, Woodward and Foster[1] and modified by Barton-Wright[2]. Bacto-Pyridoxine Assay Medium is free from pyridoxine but contains all other factors necessary for growth of *Neurospora sitophila* 299 ATCC 9276. The addition of pyridoxine, in specified concentrations, gives increasing growth response by *N. sitophila* 299 which may be determined gravimetrically.

The test is run according to the method described by Stokes, Larsen, Woodward and Foster[1] and modified by Barton-Wright.[2] Remove one loop of spores from a 48-hour culture of *N. sitophila* 299 on Bacto-Neurospora Culture Agar and suspend in 100 ml. sterile saline. Add one drop of this spore suspension to each flask. Incubate at 30°C. for 5 days. At the end of the incubation period steam the flasks at 100°C. for 5 minutes. Remove all the mycelium from the flask using a stiff wire needle or glass rod, press dry between paper towels, and roll into a small pellet. Dry the pellets at 100°C. for 2 hours in a vacuum. A glazed porcelain spot plate is convenient for handling the mycelium during drying and weighing. A standard curve is then constructed from the weights obtained and the unknown determined by interpolation.

It is essential that a standard curve be constructed each time as assay is run since conditions of autoclaving, temperature of incubation, etc., which influence the standard curve readings, cannot be duplicated exactly from time to time. The standard curve is obtained by using pyridoxine at levels of 0.0, 0.2, 0.4, 0.6, 0.8 and 1.0 microgram per assay flask (10 ml.). Using Bacto-Pyridoxine Assay

Medium the most effective assay range has proved to be between 0.2 and 0.8 microgram pyridoxine.

The concentrations of pyridoxine required for the preparation of the standard curve may be prepared by dissolving 0.1 gram of pyridoxine in 1000 ml. of distilled water, giving a stock solution of 100 micrograms per ml. Dilute the stock solution by adding 1 ml. to 499 ml. distilled water. Use 0.0, 1.0, 2, 3, 4 and 5 ml. per tube. This stock solution of pyridoxine used for preparing the standard curve is stable for 2 months when stored at 2–6°C. under toluene.

To rehydrate the basal medium, dissolve 50 grams of Bacto-Pyridoxine Assay Medium in 1000 ml. of distilled water. Distribute in 5 ml. quantities in 50 ml. Erlenmeyer flasks. Five (5) ml. of the medium are added to each flask in the preparation of the flasks for the standard curve and to each flask containing material under assay. For the assay, each flask must contain 5 ml. of rehydrated medium, increasing amounts of the standard or the unknown and sufficient distilled water to give a total volume of 10 ml. per flask. Sterilize in the autoclave for 15 minutes at 15 pounds pressure (121°C.). The flasks are then ready for inoculation. Oversterilization of the medium will give unsatisfactory results.

One hundred grams of Bacto-Pyridoxine Assay Medium will make 4 liters of final medium.

[2] J. Biol. Chem., 150:17:1943.   [a] Analyst, 70:283:1945.

BACTO

CHOLINE ASSAY MEDIUM   (B460)
DEHYDRATED

Saccharose, Difco	40 g.
Ammonium Nitrate	2 g.
Biotin	0.00001 g.
Potassium Sodium Tartrate	11.4 g.
Monopotassium Phosphate	2 g.
Magnesium Sulfate	1 g.
Sodium Chloride	0.2 g.
Calcium Chloride	0.2 g.
Sodium Borate	0.0007 g.
Ammonium Molybdate	0.0005 g.
Ferrous Sulfate	0.0011 g.
Cuprous Chloride	0.0003 g.
Manganese Sulfate	0.00011 g.
Zinc Sulfate	0.0176 g.

Bacto-Choline Assay Medium is a complete dehydrated medium for the microbiological assay of choline. It is a slight modification of the medium described by Horowitz and Beadle.[1] Bacto-Choline Assay Medium is free from choline but contains all the other factors necessary for the growth of Neurospora crassa 34486 ATCC. The addition of choline in specified increasing concentrations gives a growth response by N. crassa 34486 which may be determined gravimetrically.

The following procedure for the preparation of the inoculum and performance of the test is recommended for the assay of choline using Bacto-Choline Assay Medium:

Remove one loop of spores from a 48-hour culture of N. crassa 34486 on Bacto-Neurospora Culture Agar and suspend in 100 ml. sterile saline. Add one drop of this spore suspension to each flask. Incubate at 25°C. for 3 days. At the end of the incubation period, steam the flasks at 100°C. for 5 minutes. Remove all the mycelium from the flask using a stiff wire needle or glass rod, press dry between paper towels, and roll into a small pellet. Dry the pellets at 100°C. in a vacuum oven for 2 hours. A glazed porcelain spot plate is convenient for handling the mycelium during drying and weighing. Weigh to the nearest 0.5 mg. A standard curve is then constructed from the weights obtained and the unknown determined by interpolation. In the assay for choline, 125 ml. Erlenmeyer flasks containing a total volume of 20 ml. medium each are used.

It is essential that a standard curve be constructed each time an assay is run since conditions of autoclaving, temperature of incubation, etc., which influence the standard curve readings, cannot be duplicated exactly from time to time. The standard curve is obtained by using choline at levels of 0.0, 2.5, 5.0, 10, 20, 30, 40 and 50 micrograms per assay flask (20 ml.). Using Choline Assay Medium the most effective assay range has proved to be between 2.5 and 30 micrograms choline.

The concentration of choline required for the preparation of the standard curve may be prepared by dissolving 1.0 gram choline in 1000 ml. distilled water. This is the stock solution (1000 micrograms per ml.). Dilute the stock solution by adding 1 ml. to 99 ml. distilled water. Use 0.0, 0.5, 1.0, 2, 3, 4, and 5 ml. per tube. The stock solution is stable for 2 months when stored at 2–6°C. under toluene.

To rehydrate the basal medium, dissolve 57 grams of Bacto-Choline Assay Medium in 1000 ml. of distilled water. Ten (10) ml. of the medium are added to each flask in the preparation of the flasks for the standard curve and to each flask containing material under assay. For the assay, each flask must contain 10 ml. of rehydrated medium, increasing amounts of the standard or the unknown and sufficient distilled water to give a total volume of 20 ml. per flask. Sterilize in the autoclave for 10 minutes at 15 pounds pressure (121°C.). The flasks are then ready for inoculation. Oversterilization of the medium will give unsatisfactory results.

One hundred grams of Bacto-Choline Assay Medium will make 3.5 liters of final medium.

[1] J. Biol. Chem., 150:325:1943.

BACTO
CF ASSAY MEDIUM   (B456)
DEHYDRATED

Bacto-Vitamin Free		Pyridoxine Hydrochloride ...	0.002 g.
Casamino Acids	10 g.	Pyridoxamine Hydrochloride .	0.006 g.
Bacto-Dextrose	50 g.	Pyridoxal Hydrochloride ...	0.0006 g.
Sodium Acetate	40 g.	Calcium Pantothenate	0.001 g.
Ammonium Chloride	6 g.	Riboflavin	0.001 g.
l-Cystine, Difco	0.2 g.	Nicotinic Acid	0.002 g.
Cysteine	0.2 g.	p-Aminobenzoic Acid, Difco .	0.0002 g.
dl-Tryptophane	0.2 g.	Biotin	0.000002 g.
dl-Alanine	0.2 g.	Folic Acid	0.00002 g.
Glycine	0.2 g.	Monopotassium Phosphate	1.2 g.
Adenine Sulfate	0.02 g.	Dipotassium Phosphate	1.2 g.
Guanine Hydrochloride	0.02 g.	Magnesium Sulfate	0.4 g.
Uracil	0.02 g.	Sodium Chloride	0.02 g.
Xanthine	0.02 g.	Ferrous Sulfate	0.02 g.
Thiamine Hydrochloride	0.001 g.	Manganese Sulfate	0.04 g.

Bacto-CF Assay Medium is a complete dehydrated medium for the assay of citrovorum factor. It is free from citrovorum factor but contains all the other factors necessary for the growth of *Leuconostoc citrovorum* 8081 ATCC. The addition of citrovorum factor in specified increasing concentrations gives a growth response by *L. citrovorum* 8081 which may be measured acidimetrically or turbidimetrically. Bacto-CF Assay Medium is a modification of the formula given by Sauberlich and Baumann[1] and William F. Faloon.[2]

The following procedure is recommended for the use of Bacto-CF Assay Medium:

Stock cultures of the test organism, *L. citrovorum* 8081, are prepared by stab inoculation of Bacto-Micro Assay Culture Agar. After 24–48 hours incubation at 35–37°C., the tubes are kept in the refrigerator. Transplants are made at monthly intervals, in triplicate.

Inoculum for assay is prepared by subculturing from a stock culture to 10 ml. of Bacto-Micro Inoculum Broth. After 16–24 hours incubation at 35–37°C., the cells are centrifuged under aseptic conditions, and the supernatant liquid decanted. Suspend the cells from the culture in 10 ml. of sterile isotonic sodium chloride. The cell suspension is then diluted 1–100 with sterile isotonic sodium chloride solution. One drop of this latter suspension is used to inoculate the assay tubes (10 ml.).

It is essential that a standard curve be constructed each time an assay is run, since conditions of autoclaving, temperature of incubation, etc., which influence the standard curve readings, cannot be duplicated exactly from time to time. A standard curve is obtained by using citrovorum factor at levels of 0.0, 0.6, 1.2, 1.0, 2.4, 3.0, 3.6, 4.8 and 6.0 millimicrograms per assay tube (10 ml.).

The concentration of citrovorum factor required for the construction of the standard curve may be prepared by dissolving the contents of 1 ampul leucovorin (citrovorum factor) in 1000 ml. distilled water. This is the stock solution (3000 micrograms per ml.). Dilute the stock solution by adding 4 ml. to 96 ml. distilled water. Dilute this solution further by adding 1 ml. to 99 ml. distilled water. Use 0.0, 0.5, 1.0, 1.5, 2.0, 2.5, 3.0, 4 and 5 ml. per tube. The stock solution is stable for 2 months when stored at 2–6°C. under toluene.

Bacto-CF Assay Medium may be used for both acidimetric and turbidimetric analysis. Acidimetric determinations are made after 72 hours incubation at 35–37°C. Turbidimetric readings should be made after 20–24 hours incubation at 35–37°C. The most effective assay range, using Bacto-CF Assay Medium, has been found to be between 0.6 and 4.8 millimicrograms of citrovorum factor.

To rehydrate the medium, suspend 110 grams of Bacto-CF Assay Medium in 1000 ml. distilled water, and heat to boiling for 2–3 minutes. The slight precipitate which forms should be evenly distributed by shaking. Five (5) ml. of the medium are added to each tube in the preparation of the tubes for the standard curve and to each tube containing material under assay. For the assay, each tube must contain 5 ml. of rehydrated medium, increasing amounts of the standard or the unknown, and sufficient distilled water to give a total volume of 10 ml. per tube. The tubes are then autoclaved for 10 minutes at 15 pounds pressure (121°C.). Oversterilization of the medium will give unsatisfactory results.

One hundred grams of Bacto-CF Medium will make 1.8 liters final medium.

¹ J. Biol. Chem., 176:165:1948.   ² Personal Communication, 1951.

AMINO ACID ASSAY MEDIA

Media for the microbiological assay of the amino acids, leucine, methionine, lysine and isoleucine have been prepared. A complete description of each medium is given in the individual discussions. The formulation of the media per liter is as follows:

Bacto-Dextrose	50 g.	Guanine Hydrochloride	0.02 g.
Sodium Acetate	40 g.	Uracil	0.02 g.
Ammonium Chloride	6 g.	Xanthine	0.02 g.
dl-Alanine	0.4 g.	Thiamine Hydrochloride	0.001 g.
l-Arginine Hydrochloride	0.484 g.	Pyridoxine Hydrochloride	0.002 g.
Bacto-Asparagine	0.8 g.	Pyridoxamine Hydrochloride	0.0006 g.
l-Aspartic Acid	0.2 g.	Pyridoxal Hydrochloride	0.0006 g.
l-Cystine, Difco	0.1 g.	Calcium Pantothenate	0.001 g.
l-Glutamic Acid	0.6 g.	Riboflavin	0.001 g.
Glycine	0.2 g.	Nicotinic Acid	0.002 g.
l-Histidine Hydrochloride	0.124 g.	p-Aminobenzoic Acid, Difco	0.0002 g.
dl-Phenylalanine	0.2 g.	Biotin	0.000002 g.
l-Proline	0.2 g.	Folic Acid	0.00002 g.
dl-Serine	0.1 g.	Monopotassium Phosphate	1.2 g.
dl-Threonine	0.4 g.	Dipotassium Phosphate	1.2 g.
dl-Tryptophane	0.08 g.	Magnesium Sulfate	0.4 g.
l-Tyrosine	0.2 g.	Ferrous Sulfate	0.02 g.
dl-Valine	0.5 g.	Manganese Sulfate	0.04 g.
Adenine Sulfate	0.02 g.	Sodium Chloride	0.02 g.

BACTO

LEUCINE ASSAY MEDIUM (B 21)

DEHYDRATED

The composition of Bacto-Leucine Assay Medium is as shown above, but in addition it contains 0.5 g. of l-lysine hydrochloride, 0.2 g. dl-methionine and 0.5 g. dl-isoleucine. Bacto-Leucine Assay Medium, prepared according to the formula given by Steel, Sauberlich, Reynolds and Baumann,¹ is a complete dehydrated medium for the assay of l-leucine and dl-leucine. It is free from leucine but contains all the other growth factors and amino acids necessary for the growth of *Leuconostoc mesenteroides* P-60 ATCC 8042. The addition of l-leucine or dl-leucine in specified increasing concentrations gives a growth response by *L. mesenteroides* P-60, which may be measured acidimetrically or turbidimetrically.

The following procedure is recommended for the use of Bacto-Leucine Assay Medium:

Stock cultures of the test organism, *L. mesenteroides* P-60, are prepared by stab inoculation of Bacto-Micro Assay Culture Agar. After 24–48 hours incubation at 35–37°C., the tubes are stored in the refrigerator. The transplants are made at monthly intervals, in triplicate.

Inoculum for assay is prepared by subculturing from a stock culture to 10 ml. of Bacto-Micro Inoculum Broth. After 16–24 hours incubation at 35–37°C., the cells are centrifuged under aseptic conditions, and the supernatant liquid decanted. The cells are resuspended in 10 ml. sterile isotonic sodium chloride solution. The cell suspension is diluted 5–100 with sterile isotonic sodium chloride. One drop of this latter suspension is used to inoculate each of the assay tubes (10 ml.).

It is essential that a standard curve be constructed each time an assay is run, since conditions of autoclaving, temperature of incubation, etc., which influence the standard curve readings, cannot be duplicated exactly from time to time. A standard curve is obtained by using *l*-leucine at levels of 0.0, 10.0, 20, 30, 40, 50, 60, 80 and 100 micrograms per assay tube (10 ml.). (*dl*-leucine may be used at levels of 0.0, 20.0, 40, 60, 80, 100, 120, 160 and 200 micrograms per assay tube.)

Bacto-Leucine Assay Medium may be used for both turbidimetric and acidimetric analyses. Turbidimetric readings should be made after 16–20 hours at 35–37°C. Acidimetric determinations are made after 72 hours incubation at 35–37°C. The most effective assay range, using Bacto-Leucine Assay Medium, has been found to be between 20 micrograms and 80 micrograms *l*-leucine. (20–160 micrograms of *dl*-leucine).

The concentrations of leucine required for the construction of the standard curve may be prepared by dissolving 2.0 grams of *l*-leucine (4.0 g. *dl*-leucine) in 1000 ml. distilled water giving a stock solution of 2000 micrograms of *l*-leucine per ml. Dilute the stock solution by adding 1 ml. to 99 ml. distilled water. Use 0.0, 0.5, 1.0, 1.5, 2.0, 2.5, 3.0, 4 and 5 ml. per tube. The stock solution of leucine used for preparing the standard curve is stable for 2 months when stored at 2–6°C. under toluene.

To rehydrate the medium, suspend 105 grams of Bacto-Leucine Assay Medium in 1000 ml. distilled water, and heat to boiling for 2–3 minutes. The slight precipitate which forms should be evenly distributed by shaking. Five (5) ml. of the medium are added to each tube in the preparation of the tubes for the standard curve and to each tube containing material under assay. For the assay, each tube must contain 5 ml. of rehydrated medium, increasing amounts of the standard or the unknown, and sufficient distilled water to give a total volume of 10 ml. per tube. The tubes are autoclaved for 10 minutes at 15 pounds pressure (121°C.). Oversterilization of the medium will give unsatisfactory results.

One hundred grams of Bacto-Leucine Assay Medium will make 1.9 liters of final medium.

[1] J. Biol. Chem., 177:533:1949.

BACTO
METHIONINE ASSAY MEDIUM   (B423)
DEHYDRATED

The composition of Bacto-Methionine Assay Medium is as shown above, but in addition it contains 0.5 g. *l*-lysine hydrochloride, 0.5 g. isoleucine and 0.5 g. *dl*-leucine. Bacto-Methionine Assay Medium, prepared according to the formula given by Steel, Sauberlich, Reynolds and Baumann,[1] is a complete dehydrated medium for the assay of *dl*-methionine. It is free from methionine but contains all the other growth factors and amino acids necessary for the growth of *Leuconostoc mesenteroides* P-60 ATCC 8042. The addition of *dl*-methionine in specified increasing concentrations gives a growth response by *L. mesenteroides* P-60 which may be measured acidimetrically or turbidimetrically.

The following procedure is recommended for the use of Bacto-Methionine Assay Medium:

Stock cultures of the test organism, *L. mesenteroides* P-60 are prepared by stab inoculation of Bacto-Micro Assay Culture Agar. After 24–48 hours incubation at 35–37°C., the tubes are stored in the refrigerator. Transplants are made at monthly intervals, in triplicate.

Inoculum for assay is prepared by subculturing from a stock culture to 10 ml. of Bacto-Micro Inoculum Broth. After 16–24 hours incubation at 35–37°C., the cells are centrifuged under aseptic conditions, and the supernatant liquid decanted. The cells are resuspended in 10 ml. sterile isotonic sodium chloride solution. The cell suspension is diluted 5–100 with sterile isotonic sodium chloride. One drop of this latter suspension is used to inoculate each of the assay tubes (10 ml.).

It is essential that a standard curve be constructed each time an assay is run, since conditions of autoclaving, temperature of incubation, etc., which influence the standard curve readings, cannot be duplicated exactly from time to time. A standard curve is obtained by using *dl*-methionine at levels of 0.0, 6.0, 12, 18, 24, 30, 36, 48 and 60 micrograms per assay tube (10 ml.).

The concentrations of methionine required for the preparation of the standard curve may be prepared by dissolving 1.2 grams *dl*-methionine in 1000 ml. distilled water. This is the stock solution (1200 micrograms per ml.). Dilute the stock solution by adding 1 ml. to 99 ml. distilled water. Use 0.0, 0.5, 1.0, 1.5, 2.0, 2.5, 3.0, 4 and 5 ml. per tube. The stock solution is stable for 2 months when stored at 2–6°C. under toluene.

Bacto-Methionine Assay Medium may be used for both turbidimetric and acidimetric analyses. Turbidimetric readings should be made after 16–20 hours at 35–37°C.; acidimetric determinations are made after 72 hours incubation. The most effective assay range, using Bacto-Methionine Assay Medium, has been found to be between 6 and 48 micrograms *dl*-methionine.

To rehydrate the medium, suspend 105 grams of Bacto-Methionine Assay Medium in 1000 ml. distilled water, and heat to boiling for 2–3 minutes. The slight precipitate which forms should be evenly distributed by shaking. Five (5) ml. of the medium are added to each tube in the preparation of the tubes for the standard curve and to each tube containing material under assay. For the assay, each tube must contain 5 ml. of rehydrated medium, increasing amounts of the standard or the unknown, and sufficient distilled water to give a total volume of 10 ml. per tube. The tubes are autoclaved for 10 minutes at 15 pounds pressure (121°C.). Oversterilization of the medium will give unsatisfactory results.

One hundred grams of Bacto-Methionine Assay Medium will make 1.9 liters of final medium.

[1] J. Biol. Chem., 177:533:1949.

BACTO
LYSINE ASSAY MEDIUM (B422)
DEHYDRATED

The composition of Bacto-Lysine Assay Medium is as shown above, but in addition it contains 0.2 g. of *dl*-methionine, 0.5 g. *dl*-isoleucine and 0.5 g. *dl*-leucine. Bacto-Lysine Assay Medium, prepared according to the formula given by Steel, Sauberlich, Reynolds and Baumann,[1] is a complete dehydrated medium for the assay of *l*-lysine. It is free from lysine but contains all the other growth factors and amino acids necessary for the growth of *Leuconostoc mesenteroides* P-60 ATCC 8042. The addition of *l*-lysine in specified increasing concentrations gives a linear growth response by *L. mesenteroides* P-60, which may be measured acidimetrically or turbidimetrically.

The following procedure is recommended for the use of Bacto-Lysine Assay Medium:

Stock cultures of the test organism, *L. mesenteroides* P-60 are prepared by stab inoculation of Bacto-Micro Assay Culture Agar. After 24–48 hours incubation at 35–37°C., the tubes are stored in the refrigerator. Transplants are made at monthly intervals, in triplicate.

Inoculum for assay is prepared by subculturing from a stock culture to 10 ml. of Bacto-Micro Inoculum Broth. After 16–24 hours incubation at 35–37°C., the cells are centrifuged under aseptic conditions, and the supernatant liquid decanted. The cells are resuspended in 10 ml. sterile isotonic sodium chloride solution. The cell suspension is diluted 5–100 with sterile isotonic sodium chloride. One drop of this latter suspension is used to inoculate each of the assay tubes (10 ml.).

It is essential that a standard curve be constructed each time an assay is run, since conditions of autoclaving, temperature of incubation, etc., which influence the standard curve readings, cannot be duplicated exactly from time to time. A standard curve is obtained by using *l*-lysine at levels of 0.0, 30.0, 60, 90, 120, 150, 180, 240 and 300 micrograms per assay tube (10 ml.).

The concentrations of lysine required for the preparation of the standard curve may be prepared by dissolving 6.0 grams *l*-lysine in 1000 ml. distilled water. This is the stock solution (6000 micrograms per ml.). Dilute the stock solution by adding 1 ml. to 99 ml. distilled water. Use 0.0, 0.5, 1.0, 1.5, 2.0, 2.5, 3.0, 4 and 5 ml. per tube. The stock solution is stable for 2 months when stored at 2–6°C. under toluene.

Bacto-Lysine Assay Medium may be used for both turbidimetric and acidimetric analyses. Turbidimetric readings should be made after 16–20 hours at 35–37°C.; acidimetric determinations are made after 72 hours incubation. The most effective assay range, using Bacto-Lysine Assay Medium, has been found to be between 30 micrograms and 240 micrograms of *l*-lysine.

To rehydrate the medium, suspend 105 grams of Bacto-Lysine Assay Medium in 1000 ml. distilled water, and heat to boiling for 2–3 minutes. The slight precipitate which forms should be evenly distributed by shaking. Five (5) ml. of the medium are added to each tube in the preparation of the tubes for the standard curve and to each tube containing material under assay. For the assay, each tube must contain 5 ml. of rehydrated medium, increasing amounts of the standard or the unknown, and sufficient distilled water to give a total volume of 10 ml. per tube. The tubes are autoclaved for 10 minutes at 15 pounds pressure (121°C). Oversterilization of the medium will give unsatisfactory results.

One hundred grams of Bacto-Lysine Assay Medium will make 1.9 liters of final medium.

[1] J. Biol. Chem., 177:533:1949.

BACTO
ISOLEUCINE ASSAY MEDIUM   (B437)
DEHYDRATED

The composition of Bacto-Isoleucine Assay Medium is as shown above, but in addition, it contains 0.2 g. of *dl*-methionine, 0.5 g. of *dl*-leucine and 0.5 g. *l*-lysine. Bacto-Isoleucine Assay Medium, prepared according to the formula by Steel, Sauberlich, Reynolds and Baumann,[1] is a complete dehydrated medium for the assay of *dl*-isoleucine. It is free from isoleucine but contains all the other growth factors and amino acids necessary for the growth of *Leuconostoc mesenteroides* P-60 ATCC 8042. The addition of *dl*-isoleucine in specified increasing concentrations gives a growth response by *L. mesenteroides* P-60, which may be measured acidimetrically.

The following procedure is recommended for the use of Bacto-Isoleucine Assay Medium:

Stock cultures of the test organism, *L. mesenteroides* P-60, are prepared by stab inoculation of Bacto-Micro Assay Culture Agar. After 24–48 hours incubation at 35–37°C., the tubes are stored in the refrigerator. Transplants are made at monthly intervals, in triplicate.

Inoculum for assay is prepared by subculturing from a stock culture to 10 ml. of Bacto-Micro Inoculum Broth. After 16–24 hours incubation at 35–37°C., the cells are centrifuged under aseptic conditions, and the supernatant decanted. The cells are resuspended in 10 ml. sterile isotonic sodium chloride solution. The cell suspension is diluted 5–100 with sterile isotonic sodium chloride. One drop of this latter suspension is used to inoculate the assay tubes (10 ml.).

It is essential that a standard curve be constructed each time an assay is run, since conditions of autoclaving, temperature of incubation, etc., which influence the standard curve readings, cannot be duplicated exactly from time to time. A standard curve is obtained by using *dl*-isoleucine at levels of 0.0, 12.0, 24, 36, 48, 60, 72, 96 and 120 micrograms per assay tube (10 ml.). The concentrations of isoleucine required for the construction of the standard curve may be prepared by dissolving 2.4 grams of *dl*-isoleucine in 1000 ml. distilled water. This is the stock solution (2400 micrograms per ml.). Dilute the stock solution by adding 1 ml. to 99 ml. distilled water. Use 0.0, 0.5, 1.0, 1.5, 2.0, 2.5, 3.0, 4 and 5 ml. per tube. The stock solution is stable for 2 months when stored at 2–6°C. under toluene.

Tubes are incubated at 35–37°C. for 72 hours following inoculation. The growth response is then measured by acidimetric determinations. The most effective assay range, using Bacto-Isoleucine Assay Medium, has been found to be between 12 and 96 micrograms *dl*-isoleucine.

To rehydrate the medium, suspend 105 grams of Bacto-Isoleucine Assay Medium in 1000 ml. distilled water, and heat to boiling for 2–3 minutes. The slight precipitate which forms should be evenly distributed by shaking. Five (5) ml. of the medium are added to each tube in the preparation of the tubes for the standard curve and to each tube containing material under assay. For the assay, each tube must contain 5 ml. of rehydrated medium, increasing amounts of the standard or the unknown and sufficient distilled water to give a total volume of 10 ml. per tube. The tubes are autoclaved for 10 minutes at 15 pounds pressure (121°C.). Oversterilization of the medium will give unsatisfactory results.

One hundred grams of Bacto-Isoleucine Assay Medium will make 1.9 liters of final medium.

[1] J. Biol. Chem., 177:533:1949.

BACTO-ARGININE ASSAY MEDIUM (B466)
BACTO-CYSTINE ASSAY MEDIUM (B467)
BACTO-TYROSINE ASSAY MEDIUM (B468)
BACTO-PHENYLALANINE ASSAY MEDIUM (B469)

These media have been just recently developed for the microbiological assay of Arginine, Cystine, Tyrosine and Phenylalanine. They are similar in composition to the media described immediately above, being free of the amino acid specified for assay, but containing all other growth factors and nutriments necessary for the growth of *Leuconostoc mesenteroides* P-60 ATCC 8042. The addition of the amino acid under assay in specified increasing concentrations gives a growth response by *L. mesenteroides* which may be measured acidimetrically or turbidimetrically. Complete directions for the assay is given on the package label.

To rehydrate these media, dissolve 105 grams in 1000 ml. distilled water and heat to boiling for 2–3 minutes. The slight precipitate which forms should be evenly distributed by shaking. Five (5) ml. of the medium are added to each tube in the preparation of the tubes for the standard curve and to each tube containing material under assay. For the final assay each tube must contain 5 ml. of rehydrated medium, increasing amounts of the standard or the unknown and sufficient distilled water to give a total volume of 10 ml. per tube. The tubes are autoclaved for 10 minutes at 15 pounds pressure (121°C.). Oversterilization of the medium will give unsatisfactory results.

One hundred grams of each of these media will make 1.9 liters of final medium.

BACTO
TRYPTOPHANE ASSAY MEDIUM (B327)
DEHYDRATED

Bacto-Vitamin Free			Riboflavin	0.0004 g.
Casamino Acids	12 g.		p-Aminobenzoic Acid, Difco	0.0002 g.
Bacto-Dextrose	40 g.		Niacin	0.0002 g.
Sodium Acetate	20 g.		Biotin	0.0000008 g.
l-Cystine, Difco	0.2 g.		Dipotassium Phosphate	1 g.
Adenine Sulfate	0.02 g.		Monopotassium Phosphate	1 g.
Guanine Hydrochloride	0.02 g.		Magnesium Sulfate	0.4 g.
Uracil	0.02 g.		Sodium Chloride	0.02 g.
Thiamine Hydrochloride	0.0002 g.		Ferrous Sulfate	0.02 g.
Calcium Pantothenate	0.0002 g.		Manganese Sulfate	0.02 g.
Pyridoxine Hydrochloride	0.0004 g.			

Bacto-Tryptophane Assay Medium is a complete dehydrated medium for the assay of *l*-tryptophane or *dl*-tryptophane. It is free from tryptophane but contains all the other factors necessary for the growth of *Lactobacillus arabinosus* 17-5 ATCC 8014. The addition of tryptophane in certain concentrations gives a linear growth response by *L. arabinosus* 17-5, which may be measured acidimetrically. Bacto-Tryptophane Assay Medium is prepared according to the formula described by Greene and Black.[1]

The following procedure is recommended for the assay of tryptophane using the dehydrated medium:

Stock cultures of *L. arabinosus* 17-5 are prepared by stab inoculation of Bacto-Micro Assay Culture Agar. Following incubation at 35–37°C. for 24–48 hours, the tubes are stored in the refrigerator. Transplants are made at monthly intervals. Inoculum for assay is prepared by subculturing from a stock culture of *L. arabinosus* 17-5 into a tube containing 10 ml. of Bacto-Micro Inoculum Broth. After 24 hours incubation at 35–37°C., the cells are centrifuged under aseptic conditions, and the supernatant liquid decanted. The cells are resuspended in 10 ml. of sterile isotonic sodium chloride. The cell suspension is then diluted 1–100 with sterile isotonic sodium chloride. The suspension should be just faintly cloudy. One drop of this latter suspension is then used to inoculate each of the assay tubes.

It is essential that a standard curve be constructed each time an assay is run, since conditions of autoclaving, temperature of incubation, etc., which influence the standard curve readings, cannot be duplicated exactly from time to time. A standard curve is obtained by using *l*-tryptophane at levels of 0.0, 2.0, 4, 6, 8, 10 and 12 micrograms per assay tube (10 ml.). (*dl*-tryptophane may be used at levels of 0.0, 4.0, 8, 12, 16, 20 and 24 micrograms).

The concentrations of tryptophane required for the preparation of the standard curve may be prepared by dissolving 0.1 gram of *l*-tryptophane (0.2 g. *dl*-trypto-phane) in 1000 ml. of distilled water giving a stock solution of 100 micrograms of *l*-tryptophane per ml. Dilute this stock solution by adding 4 ml. to 96 ml. distilled water. Use 0.0, 0.5, 1.0, 1.5, 2.0, 2.5, 3.0 and 5 ml. per tube. This stock solution of tryptophane used for preparing the standard curve is stable for 2 months when stored at 2–6°C. under toluene.

Following inoculation, tubes are incubated at 35–37°C. for 72 hours and are assayed by acidimetric methods. Using Bacto-Tryptophane Assay Medium, we have found the most effective assay range to be between 2 and 10 micrograms of *l*-tryptophane. (4 and 20 micrograms *dl*-tryptophane).

To rehydrate the basal medium, suspend 75 grams of Bacto-Tryptophane Assay Medium in 1000 ml. distilled water and heat to boiling for 2–3 minutes. The slight precipitate which forms should be evenly distributed by shaking. Five (5) ml. of the medium are added to each tube in the preparation of the tubes for the standard curve and to each tube containing material under assay. For the assay, each tube must contain 5 ml. of rehydrated medium, increasing amounts of the standard or the unknown and sufficient distilled water to give a total volume of 10 ml. per tube.

The tubes are sterilized by autoclaving for 10 minutes at 15 pounds pressure (121°C.). Oversterilization of the medium will give unsatisfactory results.

One hundred grams of Bacto-Tryptophane Assay Medium will make 2.6 liters of final medium.

1 J. Biol. Chem., 155:1:1944.

MEDIA FOR MYCOLOGY

THE STUDY of yeasts and molds is one of the oldest branches of microbiology. The importance of this group of microorganisms in many fields is being recognized. Particular mention may be made of the role of yeasts and molds in relation to sanitary control, in the production of antibiotics and other industrial fermentations, as the causative agents of infections in animals and plants, the deterioration of fabrics and many other applications.

The value of selective media for the initial cultivation of pathogenic fungi particularly has been demonstrated by numerous investigators. They have shown that many fungi prefer neutral or slightly alkaline rather than acid reactions for early and luxuriant growth. Earlier media for fungi generally relied on the acid reaction to make the medium less suited for the growth of many bacteria. More recently developed media and modifications use neutral or slightly alkaline reactions, antibiotics, bile salts and dyes as selective agents against bacteria without effecting the growth of fungi. The results obtained with these selective media make their consideration important by any laboratory interested in the isolation and cultivation of fungi.

Plant diseases are exceedingly important from an economic point of view. The great majority of these diseases are undoubtedly due to infections by molds, and other fungi, viruses and bacteria. For the purpose of assisting the plant pathologist and mycologist in his studies incident to the investigation and control of the plant diseases, we have developed in our laboratories a number of dehydrated culture media. The formulae chosen for this group of media have been devised and selected with the cooperation of scientists engaged in active research in problems of plant pathology. Since no universal standard formulae prevail, selections have been based on the general usefulness of the media. The developments and applications of pure culture methods from a phytopathological point of view have aroused interest in the study of systematic mycology. The use of dehydrated culture media brings into such work the development of definite standards of uniformity and comparability.

The media listed in this section are employed for the cultivation, isolation and identification of these microorganisms. Some are recommended for pathogenic fungi, while other media are primarily for the cultivation of non-pathogenic yeasts and molds.

SABOURAUD DEXTROSE AGAR (B109)
DEHYDRATED

Neopeptone, Difco	10 g.
Bacto-Dextrose	40 g.
Bacto-Agar	15 g.

Bacto-Sabouraud Dextrose Agar is a modification of the Dextrose Agar described by Sabouraud.[1] Comparative tests have shown that Neopeptone, Difco is a most satisfactory source of nitrogen for the development of fungi. It is recommended for the cultivation and growth of fungi, particularly those associated with skin infections.

The majority of molds are not pathogenic, but some are true parasites, producing a number of common diseases such as ringworm, favus and various other hair and skin lesions. Internal infections of the lung and lymphatics may also be traced to molds. Bacto-Sabouraud Dextrose Agar is particularly adapted for the cultivation and identification of such molds, especially those infecting the skin.

For the primary isolation of fungi from scales and crusts, Ch'in[2] suggests the addition of 0.015 per cent potassium tellurite, or 0.05 per cent copper sulfate to this medium in order to suppress the growth of bacteria. Emmons and Ashburn[3] used a Sabouraud Dextrose Agar containing 1 per cent Neopeptone and 2 per cent dextrose for the isolation of *Histoplasma capsulatum* from rats. Emmons and Hollaender[4] used Sabouraud Dextrose Agar prepared with Neopeptone for growing *Trichophyton gypseum asteroides* in their studies on mutation of the dermatophytes induced by ultraviolet irradiation. Robinson and Kotcher[5] used Sabouraud Dextrose Agar containing 20 units penicillin and 40 units dihydrostreptomycin hydrochloride per ml. of medium for the isolation of *Histoplasma* from dogs. Kotcher, Robinson and Miller[6] in a study of media for the recovery of *H. capsulatum* from tissues of artificially infected rats reported that the highest percentage recovery of the organism was from spleen on Sabouraud Dextrose Agar. Serowy and Jung[7] used Bacto-Sabouraud Dextrose Agar in their study of the *Microspora* and called attention to the suitability of this medium for the cultivation of *Microspora* and other pathogenic fungi, as well as the ease with which this medium may be prepared and used.

The addition of antibiotics to acid as well as neutral media for the isolation of pathogenic fungi has proven especially satisfactory. Generally 20 units penicillin and 40 micrograms streptomycin or dihydrostreptomycin per ml. medium are added to the sterile melted medium at 45–50°C. under aseptic conditions. These desired concentrations of penicillin may be readily obtained by dissolving the contents of one (1) vial of penicillin containing 100,000 units penicillin in 10 ml. sterile distilled water. Two (2) ml. of this solution are added to one liter of sterile melted medium at 45–50°C. under aseptic conditions (0.2 ml. per 100 ml. of medium). To obtain the desired concentration of streptomycin in the same medium dissolve the contents of a one gram vial of streptomycin (one million micrograms) in 10 ml. sterile distilled water. One (1) ml. of this solution is added to 9 ml. sterile distilled water to give a solution containing 10,000 micrograms streptomycin per ml. To each liter of medium are added 4 ml. of this solution to obtain 40 micrograms per ml. (0.4 ml. for 100 ml. medium).

To rehydrate the medium, suspend 65 grams of Bacto-Sabouraud Dextrose Agar in 1000 ml. of cold distilled water and heat to boiling to dissolve the medium completely. Distribute in tubes or flasks and sterilize in the autoclave for 15 minutes at 15 pounds pressure (121°C.) The final reaction of the medium will be pH 5.6.

One pound of Bacto-Sabouraud Dextrose Agar will make 6.9 liters of medium.

¹ Ann. dermatol. syphilol., 1892–1893.
² Proc. Soc. Exp. Biol. Med., 38:700:1938.
⁸ Pub. Health Reports, 63:1416:1948.
⁴ Arch. Dermatol Syphilol., 52:257:1945.
⁵ Pub. Health Reports, 66:1533:1951.
⁶ J. Bact., 62:613:1951.
⁷ Derm. Wschr., 124:665:1951.

BACTO
SABOURAUD MALTOSE AGAR (B110)
DEHYDRATED

Neopeptone, Difco .... 10 g.
Maltose, Difco .... 40 g.
Bacto-Agar .... 15 g.

Bacto-Sabouraud Maltose Agar is a modification of the formula suggested by Sabouraud.[1] Comparative tests have shown that Neopeptone, Difco is a most satisfactory source of nitrogen for the development of fungi. This medium is an excellent substrate for the propagation of molds and yeasts, particularly the parasitic fungi concerned with skin and scalp lesions.

Bacto-Sabouraud Maltose Agar, like Bacto-Sabouraud Dextrose Agar, contains no selective agent, and depends entirely on the acid reaction, pH 5.6, for the selective growth of fungi over bacteria. In the initial cultivation of fungi from specimens many investigators prefer to use a selective medium such as Bacto-Littman Oxgall Agar, as discussed on page 240 or Bacto-Brain Heart Infusion Agar as described on page 90.

Antibiotics may also be added to Sabouraud Maltose Agar to give selective media, as discussed under Bacto-Sabouraud Dextrose Agar immediately above.

The use of maltose, or the extractives of malt, in media designed for the cultivation of molds and other fungi is quite universal. Maltose is well adapted to the nutritional requirements of these organisms.

Frank[2] has used Bacto-Sabouraud Maltose Agar successfully in cultivating the causative organisms of perleche. Davidson, Dawding and Buller[3] reported that Bacto-Sabouraud Maltose Agar was a most satisfactory medium in their studies of the infections caused by *Microsporon audouini, M. lanosum* and *Trichophyton gypseum*. Davidson and Dawding[4] also used this medium in isolating *T. gypseum* from a case of tinea barbae. Serowy and Jung[5] used Bacto-Sabouraud Maltose Agar in their study of the *Microspora* and called attention to the suitability of this medium for the cultivation of *Microspora* and other pathogenic fungi, as well as the ease with which this medium may be prepared and used. A. W. Bengtson[6] observed that Sabouraud Maltose Agar could be used to advantage in the isolation and differentiation of *Pseudomonas*. On this medium the blue pyocyanin pigment is enhanced making it easy to determine pigment production thereby detecting *Pseudomonas* organisms in mixed infections. Sabouraud Dextrose Agar on the other hand, tends to elicit the production of the pink fluorescene pigment with suppression of the pyocyanin. Chapman[7] modified Sabouraud Maltose Agar in the preparation of a selective medium for the isolation and identification of *Monilia* and other fungi. The medium was prepared by adding 0.1 ml. of Tergitol 7 and 0.0025 per cent Brom Cresol Purple to Sabouraud Maltose Agar at pH 5.6. The medium was sterilized in the autoclave for 10 minutes and when cooled to 45–55°C., 0.3 ml. of Bacto-Chapman Tellurite Solution and 3 ml. of 2,3,5-triphenyltetrazolium chloride (TTC), was added. Surface of the plates were inoculated followed by incubation at 37°C. for 48 hours. Chapman reported that the Tergitol 7 inhibited all bacteria except members of the coliform group, while the potassium tellurite inhibited these organisms. *Candida albicans* pro-

240   DIFCO MANUAL

duced "off white" circular smooth entire convex to pulvinate colonies about 4 mm. in diameter. Other *Candida* produce colored colonies ranging from orange to tan to lilac, often discoloring the medium. *Saccharomyces* grew in 48 hours on the medium producing colonies somewhat resembling those of *Candida*.

To rehydrate the medium, suspend 65 grams of Bacto-Sabouraud Maltose Agar in 1000 ml. of cold distilled water and heat to boiling to dissolve the medium completely. Distribute in tubes or flasks, and sterilize in the autoclave for 15 minutes at 15 pounds pressure (121°C.). The final reaction of the medium will be pH 5.6.

One pound of Bacto-Sabouraud Maltose Agar will make 6.9 liters of medium.

[1] Ann. dermatol. syphilol., 1892–1893.
[2] Arch. Dermatol. Syphilol., 26:451:1932.
[3] Can. J. Research, 6:1:1932.
[4] Arch. Dermatol. Syphilol., 26:660:1932.
[5] Derm. Wschr., 124:665:1951.
[6] Personal Communication, 1951.
[7] Trans. New York Acad. Sci. Series II, 14:254:1952.

SABOURAUD MALTOSE BROTH   (B429)

DEHYDRATED

Neopeptone, Difco	10 g.
Maltose, Difco	40 g.

Bacto-Sabouraud Maltose Broth is a liquid medium recommended for the cultivation of fungi. It is acid in reaction and has the same formula as Bacto-Sabouraud Maltose Agar except agar is omitted. Bacto-Sabouraud Maltose Broth is also well suited for the detection of fungi in sterility test procedures.

To rehydrate the medium, dissolve 50 grams Bacto-Sabouraud Maltose Broth in 1000 ml. of distilled water. Distribute in tubes or flasks and sterilize in the autoclave for 15 minutes at 15 pounds pressure (121°C.). Final reaction will be pH 5.6.

One pound of Bacto-Sabouraud Maltose Broth will make 9 liters of medium.

SABOURAUD LIQUID MEDIUM

DEHYDRATED

Bacto-Sabouraud Liquid Medium is recommended as a liquid medium for the cultivation of fungi. This medium supports early and luxuriant growth of fungi from small inocula. A complete discussion of this medium is given on page 200. A selective liquid medium may be prepared by the addition of penicillin and streptomycin as described in the discussion on Bacto-Sabouraud Dextrose Agar page 238.

LITTMAN OXGALL AGAR   (B294)

DEHYDRATED

Bacto-Peptone	10 g.
Bacto-Dextrose	10 g.
Bacto-Oxgall	15 g.
Bacto-Agar	20 g.
Bacto-Crystal Violet	0.01 g.

Bacto-Littman Oxgall Agar with the addition of streptomycin is a selective medium for the primary isolation of fungi. It is also of especial value for the cultivation of the dermatophytes.

Littman[1] described a selective medium for the primary isolation of fungi. Crystal violet and streptomycin are used as selective bacteriostatic agents, while Bacto-Oxgall is used to restrict the spreading of fungus colonies. The medium is neutral in reaction, which favors the growth of many pathogenic fungi. The studies of Littman have indicated that this medium offers considerable promise as a diagnostic tool for the primary isolation of fungi from specimens possessing a mixed bacterial and fungal flora.

Littman has shown that his medium is especially valuable for culturing the dermatophytes. Molds and yeasts form non-spreading discrete colonies, easy to isolate in pure culture. He also suggests that the medium may be used for the following purposes: estimation of the normal fungal flora of feces, sputum and other human discharges; evaluation of human disorders of the upper and lower respiratory and gastrointestinal tract caused by fungi; single cell isolation of fungi; plate count of viable saprophytic fungi in foodstuffs and air. In a comparative study Littman[2] compared this medium with Sabouraud Dextrose Agar using a large variety of pathogenic and saprophytic fungi. On the Littman Oxgall Agar the majority of fungi tested produced colonies at the end of the first month of incubation about half the size of the colonies on Sabouraud Dextrose Agar, but equal in size after 56 days of incubation. He reported the isolation of three times as many fungi from feces, sputum, skin scrapings and hair on his medium as were isolated on Sabouraud Dextrose Agar, and four times as many pathogenic dermatophytes on the selective medium as on the Sabouraud medium. The selective oxgall agar of Littman is specified in "Diagnostic Procedures and Reagents"[3] of the American Public Health Association for the isolation of pathogenic fungi.

For inoculation, skin and nail scrapings or infected hairs are placed directly on the surface of the medium. Exudates, sputa, or fecal suspensions are spread over the surface with a sterile swab. The selectivity of the medium permits the use of a heavy inoculum without the danger of overgrowth by bacteria or saprophytic fungi. Plates are incubated at room temperature or preferably at 30°C. for four to eight days. Do not incubate at 37°C.

To rehydrate the medium, suspend 55 grams of Bacto-Littman Oxgall Agar in 1000 ml. of cold distilled water and heat to boiling to dissolve the medium completely. Distribute in flasks and sterilize in the autoclave for 15 minutes at 15 pounds pressure (121°C.). Cool to 45–50°C. and add 30 micrograms of streptomycin per ml. of medium. Dispense in 27–30 ml. amounts in sterile petri dishes 100 mm. in diameter or distribute in sterile tubes. Let stand at room temperature for 6–8 hours before inoculation. Plates or tubes of media may be kept in the refrigerator for 2–3 weeks without deterioration if placed in sealed containers to prevent evaporation. A concentration of 30 micrograms per ml. of medium may be obtained by adding 10 ml. sterile distilled water to a 1 gram (one million micrograms) bottle of streptomycin or dihydrostreptomycin. One (1) ml. of this solution is added to 9 ml. sterile distilled water to give a solution containing 10,000 micrograms streptomycin per ml. To each liter of sterile melted medium at 45–50°C. are added 3 ml. of this solution to obtain 30 micrograms per ml. (0.3 ml. for 100 ml. medium). Final reaction of the sterile medium will be pH 7.0.

One pound of Bacto-Littman Oxgall Agar will make 8.2 liters of medium.

[1] Science, 106:109:1947.
[2] Tech. Bull., Reg. Med. Tech., 18:409:1948.
[3] Diagnostic Procedures and Reagents, 3rd Edition:452:1950

BACTO
BRAIN HEART INFUSION AGAR   (B418)
DEHYDRATED

Bacto-Brain Heart Infusion Agar is recommended as a solid medium for the cultivation of fastidious pathogenic bacteria and fungi. A selective Brain Heart Infusion Agar especially recommended for the isolation of fungi is obtained by the addition of 20 units penicillin and 40 micrograms of streptomycin per ml. of sterile melted medium at 45–50°C. A method to obtain these concentrations of the antibiotics is given in the description of Bacto-Sabouraud Dextrose Agar page 238. A complete discussion of Bacto-Brain Heart Infusion Agar is given on page 90.

BACTO
MALT EXTRACT BROTH   (B113)
DEHYDRATED

Bacto-Malt Extract Broth is prepared from Bacto-Malt Extract, according to the directions given by Thom and Church.[1] It is recommended as a liquid medium for the cultivation of yeasts and molds and may be employed as a sterility test medium to detect the presence of these organisms.

The use of malt and malt extracts for the propagation of yeasts and molds is quite common. Reddish[2] described a culture medium prepared from malt extract which was a satisfactory substitute for wort. Thom and Church, following the formula of Reddish, used Bacto-Malt Extract, as a base. The carbohydrates present in such media are well suited to the growth requirements of fungi, particularly if the reaction of the media is somewhat acid. Comparative tests have shown that early and luxuriant growth will be initiated in Bacto-Malt Extract Broth from inocula of yeasts and molds as small or smaller than those required for other media, including broths prepared with honey.

For the cultivation of molds, filter paper cones may be dipped into Malt Extract Broth and sterilized in deep culture dishes containing a layer of the medium. The molds are seeded upon the moist surface of the sterile cones. Thom and Church advise a solution of 100 grams of Bacto-Malt Extract Broth in 900 ml. of distilled water.

To rehydrate the medium, dissolve 15 grams of Bacto-Malt Extract Broth in 1000 ml. of distilled water. A more nutritious medium can be obtained by using more Bacto-Malt Extract Broth per unit of water. Distribute in tubes or flasks and sterilize in the autoclave for 15 minutes at 15 pounds pressure (121°C.). The final reaction of the medium will be pH 4.7.

One pound of Bacto-Malt Extract Broth will make 30.2 liters of medium.

[1] Thom and Church: The Aspergilli, 1926.   [2] Abst. Bact., 3:6:1919.

BACTO
NEUROSPORA CULTURE AGAR
DEHYDRATED

Bacto-Neurospora Culture Agar is recommended as a neutral medium for the cultivation of fungi. A selective medium for this group of microorganisms may be prepared by the addition of penicillin and streptomycin as discussed under Bacto-Sabouraud Dextrose Agar page 238. A complete description of Bacto-Neurospora Culture Agar is given on page 214.

BACTO
MYCOLOGICAL AGAR (B405)
DEHYDRATED

Bacto-Soytone	10 g.
Bacto-Dextrose	10 g.
Bacto-Agar	15 g.

Bacto-Mycological Agar is a medium which is neutral in reaction, recommended for the cultivation of fungi. Better growth of many fungi is obtained on neutral or slightly alkaline media. This medium is also recommended for carrying stock cultures of fungi and for chlamydospore production. A selective medium for fungi may be prepared from Bacto-Mycological Agar by the addition of penicillin and streptomycin. Generally 20 units of penicillin and 40 micrograms of streptomycin per ml. of medium are added to the sterile melted medium at 45–50°C. under aseptic conditions. A method to obtain these concentrations of the antibiotics is given in the description of Bacto-Sabouraud Dextrose Agar page 238. This medium is also well suited as a Dextrose Agar for the cultivation of a large variety of saprophytic and pathogenic microorganisms.

To rehydrate the medium, suspend 35 grams of Bacto-Mycological Agar in 1000 ml. of cold distilled water. Heat to boiling to dissolve the medium completely. Distribute in tubes or flasks and sterilize in the autoclave for 15 minutes at 15 pounds pressure. Final reaction of the medium will be pH 7.0.

One pound of Bacto-Mycological Agar will make 13 liters of medium.

BACTO
MYCOLOGICAL BROTH (B406)
DEHYDRATED

Bacto-Soytone	10 g.
Bacto-Dextrose	40 g.

Bacto-Mycological Broth is a liquid medium neutral in reaction recommended for the cultivation of fungi. A selective liquid medium for fungi may be prepared by the addition of penicillin (generally 20 units per ml. medium) and streptomycin (40 micrograms per ml. medium) or other selective agents to the sterile medium at 50°C. or less under aseptic conditions. A method to obtain these concentrations of the antibiotics is given in the description of Bacto-Sabouraud Dextrose Agar page 238. Bacto-Mycological Broth is also well suited as a sterility test medium for the detection of fungi.

To rehydrate the medium, dissolve 50 grams Bacto-Mycological Broth in 1000 ml. distilled water. Distribute in tubes or flasks and sterilize in the autoclave for 15 minutes at 15 pounds pressure (121°C.). Final reaction of the medium will be pH 7.0.

One pound of Bacto-Mycological Broth will make 9.0 liters of medium.

BACTO
POTATO DEXTROSE AGAR
DEHYDRATED

BACTO
MALT AGAR
DEHYDRATED

Bacto-Potato Dextrose Agar and Bacto-Malt Agar are recommended for the cultivation of yeasts and molds and for counts of these organisms. A complete discussion of these media is given on page 64, 65.

WORT AGAR (B111)
DEHYDRATED

Bacto-Malt Extract	15	g.
Bacto-Peptone	0.78	g.
Maltose, Technical	12.75	g.
Dextrin, Difco	2.75	g.
Glycerol	2.35	g.
Dipotassium Phosphate	1	g.
Ammonium Chloride	1	g.
Bacto-Agar	15	g.

Bacto-Wort Agar is a medium prepared particularly for the cultivation of yeasts. The reaction is adjusted so that after sterilization it will be pH 4.8, which is near the optimum for most yeasts and at the same time will inhibit most bacterial growth.

The study of yeasts is one of the oldest branches of the science of microbiology, and it remains today one of the most important. A variety of processes in industry are performed by yeasts. A study of the pathogenic activities of yeasts (blastomycetes) has revealed them to be the causative organisms of such conditions as certain skin ulcers, tumors, infections of the upper and lower respiratory and gastrointestinal tract etc. As a rule, the yeasts grow well upon culture media containing dextrose or maltose, particularly if the reaction is somewhat acid. The formula of Bacto-Wort Agar closely duplicates the composition of wort, which is a favorable medium for the cultivation of yeasts. Growth-promoting qualities have been increased by the addition of salts and other nutriments.

Parfitt[1] reported satisfactory results with Bacto-Wort Agar in his study of the influence of culture media on the mold and yeast counts of butter, and in order to procure comparative yeast and mold counts he suggested that dehydrated Bacto-Whey Agar, Bacto-Malt Agar or Bacto-Wort Agar should be used.

To rehydrate the medium, suspend 50 grams of Bacto-Wort Agar in 1000 ml. of cold distilled water and heat to boiling to dissolve the medium completely. Distribute in tubes or flasks, and sterilize in the autoclave for 15 minutes at 15 pounds pressure (121°C.). The final reaction of the medium will be pH 4.8.

Due to the high acidity of the medium the heating process should be completed in as short a period of time as possible. Excessive heating of this acid medium causes a breaking down of the agar, resulting in an inability to solidify properly when cool. Normally, medium prepared from Bacto-Wort Agar is soft and is ideal for plating purposes. However, if a medium of solidity satisfactory for streaking is desired, it can be prepared by using 60 grams of Bacto-Wort Agar per 1000 ml. of water or including 5 grams Bacto-Agar.

One pound of Bacto-Wort Agar will make 9 liters of medium.

[1] J. Dairy Science, 16:141:1933.

MALT EXTRACT AGAR (B112)
DEHYDRATED

Some laboratories have used Bacto-Malt Extract Agar for the cultivation of yeasts and molds. We will continue to carry this medium in stock for those laboratories where it has been in routine use or where it is desired for comparative purposes.

BACTO
CZAPEK DOX BROTH (B338)
DEHYDRATED

Saccharose, Difco	30 g.
Sodium Nitrate	3 g.
Dipotassium Phosphate	1 g.
Magnesium Sulfate	0.5 g.
Potassium Chloride	0.5 g.
Ferrous Sulfate	0.01 g.

Bacto-Czapek Dox Broth is a liquid medium, nearly neutral in reaction, prepared from materials of known chemical composition and designed for the cultivation of fungi and bacteria capable of utilizing inorganic nitrogen. Sodium nitrate is the sole source of nitrogen, and saccharose serves as a source of carbon in this medium. Bacto-Czapek Dox Broth is a modification of the Czapek formula of Dox[1] prepared according to the directions given by Thom and Raper.[2]

Media prepared with only inorganic sources of nitrogen and chemically defined compounds as sources of carbon are useful for a variety of microbiological procedures. They are of principal value in soil microbiology, for the enrichment, cultivation and identification of soil bacteria and fungi, or for mildew resistance tests, as well as for other tests wherein a simple chemically defined medium is desired. Czapek Dox Broth will support a moderately vigorous growth of nearly all saprophytic *Aspergilli*.[2]

To rehydrate the medium, dissolve 35 grams of Bacto-Czapek Dox Broth in 1000 ml. distilled water. Distribute in tubes or flasks and sterilize in the autoclave for 15 minutes at 15 pounds pressure (121°C.). Final reaction of the medium will be pH 7.3.

One pound of Bacto-Czapek Dox Broth will make 13 liters of medium.

[1] U. S. Dept. Ag. Bur. Anim. Ind. Bull., 120:70:1910.   [2] Thom and Raper, Manual of the Aspergilli: 39:1945.

BACTO
CZAPEK SOLUTION AGAR (B339)
DEHYDRATED

Saccharose, Difco	30 g.
Sodium Nitrate	2 g.
Dipotassium Phosphate	1 g.
Magnesium Sulfate	0.5 g.
Potassium Chloride	0.5 g.
Ferrous Sulfate	0.01 g.
Bacto-Agar	15 g.

Bacto-Czapek Solution Agar is a solid neutral medium of known chemical composition with nitrate as the only source of nitrogen for the cultivation of saprophytic fungi, soil bacteria and other microorganisms. It is prepared according to the formula given by Thom and Church.[1] This medium is of value in many microbiological procedures such as the cultivation and identification of fungi, growth of soil bacteria, mildew resistance tests and others. Thom and Raper[2] state that this medium will produce a moderately vigorous growth of nearly all saprophytic *Aspergilli,* and yield characteristic mycelia and conidia useful in comparative studies.

To rehydrate the medium suspend 49 grams of Bacto-Czapek Solution Agar in 1000 ml. cold distilled water. Heat to boiling to dissolve the medium completely.

Distribute in tubes or flasks and sterilize in the autoclave for 15 minutes at 15 pounds pressure (121°C.). Final reaction of the medium will be pH 7.3.

One pound of Bacto-Czapek Solution Agar will make 9.2 liters of medium.

Thom and Church, The Aspergilli, 39:1926.   ² Thom and Raper, Manual of the Aspergilli, 39:1945.

BACTO
MILDEW TEST MEDIUM (B428)
DEHYDRATED

Sodium Nitrate .... 3 g.
Dipotassium Phosphate .... 1 g.
Magnesium Sulfate .... 0.25 g.
Potassium Chloride .... 0.25 g.
Bacto-Agar .... 10 g.

Bacto-Mildew Test Medium is recommended for use in all procedures for testing processed fabrics, threads and cordage for mildew proofing. This medium is also recommended as a solid basal medium of known chemical composition with sodium nitrate as the sole source of nitrogen to which various sources of carbon may be added to complete the medium.

To rehydrate the medium, suspend 14.5 grams of Bacto-Mildew Test Medium in 1000 ml. of cold distilled water. Heat to boiling to dissolve the medium completely. Distribute in tubes or flasks and sterilize in the autoclave for 15 minutes at 15 pounds pressure (121°C.). Final reaction of the medium will be pH 6.8.

One pound of Bacto-Mildew Test Medium will make 31.3 liters of medium.

BACTO
CORN MEAL AGAR (B386)
DEHYDRATED

Corn Meal, Infusion from .... 50 g.
Bacto-Agar .... 15 g.

Bacto-Corn Meal Agar is recommended for the production of chlamydospores by *Candida albicans* and for the cultivation of phytopathological and other fungi. The medium is prepared from an infusion of ground yellow corn, and solidified by the addition of 1.5 per cent Bacto-Agar. A similar medium, with the addition of 0.2 per cent Bacto-Dextrose, Bacto-Corn Meal Agar with Dextrose, will produce a more luxuriant growth of some fungi.

To rehydrate the medium, suspend 17 grams of Bacto-Corn Meal Agar in 1000 ml. cold distilled water and heat to boiling to dissolve the medium completely. Distribute in tubes or flasks and sterilize in the autoclave for 15 minutes at 15 pounds pressure (121°C.). Final reaction of the medium will be pH 6.0.

One pound of Bacto-Corn Meal Agar will make 26.7 liters of medium.

BACTO
CORN MEAL AGAR (B114)
with Dextrose
DEHYDRATED

Corn Meal, Infusion from .... 50 g.
Bacto-Dextrose .... 2 g.
Bacto-Agar .... 15 g.

Bacto-Corn Meal Agar with Dextrose is recommended for the cultivation of phytopathological and other fungi. It is prepared from an infusion of ground yellow corn to which is added 0.2 per cent Bacto-Dextrose and 1.5 per cent Bacto-Agar. A similar medium prepared without added dextrose, Bacto-Corn Meal Agar, is recommended for chlamydospore production by *Candida albicans*.

To rehydrate the medium, suspend 19 grams of Bacto-Corn Meal Agar with Dextrose in 1000 ml. cold distilled water and heat to boiling to dissolve the medium completely. Distribute in tubes or flasks and sterilize in the autoclave for 15 minutes at 15 pounds pressure (121°C.). Final reaction of the medium will be pH 6.0.

One pound of Bacto-Corn Meal Agar with Dextrose will make 23.8 liters of medium.

BACTO
BEAN POD AGAR   (B116)
DEHYDRATED

Green String Beans, Infusion from. .   200 g.
Bacto-Agar ....   15 g.

Bacto-Bean Pod Agar is recommended for the cultivation of phytopathological and other fungi. It is prepared from an infusion of fresh green beans, and solidified with 1.5 per cent Bacto-Agar.

Edgerton[1] reported the value of fresh green bean pod infusion in media for the cultivation of phytopathological fungi. He described a method of drying green bean pods and storing the dry bean meal so as to have it available for the preparation of media at all seasons of the year. Bacto-Bean Pod Agar prepared from fresh green beans possesses all the growth properties of fresh bean pod infusion, and eliminates the necessity of preparing and storing the desiccated bean meal.

To rehydrate the medium, suspend 22.5 grams of Bacto-Bean Pod Agar in 1000 ml. cold distilled water and heat to boiling to dissolve the medium completely. Distribute in tubes or flasks and sterilize in the autoclave for 15 minutes at 15 pounds pressure (121°C.). Final reaction of the medium will be pH 5.6.

One pound of Bacto-Bean Pod Agar will make 20.1 liters of medium.

[1] Phytopathology, 8:445:1918.

BACTO
LIMA BEAN AGAR   (B117)
DEHYDRATED

Lima Beans, Infusion from ...... 62.5 g
Bacto-Agar .... 15 g.

Bacto-Lima Bean Agar is recommended for the cultivation of phytopathological and other fungi. It is prepared from an infusion of dry lima beans, and is solidified by the addition of 1.5 per cent of Bacto-Agar. This medium possesses all the nutritive properties of an infusion of lima beans and has a final reaction of pH 5.6, making it well suited for the growth of fungi.

To rehydrate the medium, suspend 23 grams of Bacto-Lima Bean Agar in 1000 ml. cold distilled water and heat to boiling to dissolve the medium completely. Distribute in tubes or flasks and sterilize in the autoclave for 15 minutes at 15 pounds pressure (121°C.). Final reaction of the medium will be pH 5.6.

One pound of Bacto-Lima Bean Agar will make 19.7 liters of medium.

BACTO
PRUNE AGAR   (B56)
DEHYDRATED

Prunes, Infusion from .... 36 g.
Bacto-Agar .... 15 g.

Bacto-Prune Agar is recommended for the cultivation of phytopathological and other fungi. In the preparation of this medium the infusion of prunes is solidified by the addition of 1.5 per cent Bacto-Agar. The final reaction of the medium is pH 5.6, well suited for the growth of a large number and variety of fungi.

To rehydrate the medium, suspend 24 grams of Bacto-Prune Agar in 1000 ml. cold distilled water and heat to boiling to dissolve the medium completely. Distribute in tubes or flasks and sterilize in the autoclave for 15 minutes at 15 pounds pressure (121°C.). Final reaction of the medium will be pH 5.6.

One pound of Bacto-Prune Agar will make 18.9 liters of medium.

BACTO
W. L. NUTRIENT MEDIUM   (B424)
DEHYDRATED

Bacto-Yeast Extract .... 4 g.
Bacto-Casitone .... 5 g.
Bacto-Dextrose .... 50 g.
Monopotassium Phosphate .... 0.55 g.
Potassium Chloride .... 0.425 g.
Calcium Chloride .... 0.125 g.
Magnesium Sulfate .... 0.125 g.
Ferric Chloride .... 0.0025 g.
Manganese Sulfate .... 0.0025 g.
Bacto-Agar .... 20 g.
Bacto-Brom Cresol Green .... 0.022 g.

Bacto-W. L. Nutrient Medium is recommended for use in the control of brewing and industrial fermentation processes. It is prepared according to the formula described by Green and Gray.[1,2] The nutrient medium permits the development of the yeast. Also, in those instances in which the number of yeast cells is comparatively small, certain bacteria can be detected. A similar medium, Bacto-W. L. Differential Medium, containing actidione as a selective agent inhibits the development of yeast and molds but permits unrestricted growth of bacteria. Gray[3] in a discussion on the microbiological control for beer quality describes in detail the value of these two media and the type of information they are able to give.

The microbiological population of beers is an important factor in the scientific control of brewing and other fermentation industries. Direct microscopic counts do not give sufficient or specific information. In their study of various fermentation processes, Green and Gray pointed out the inadequacy of the microscopic count in fermentation control procedures and made an exhaustive study of the method of examination of worts, beers and liquid yeast and similar fermentation products. The application of their method to other fermentation industries was also shown by these authors. Two media were developed, one containing no selective agent, and the other, a differential medium, containing, as a selective agent, the antibiotic actidione, having the ability to inhibit the development of yeasts without in any way interfering with the development of bacteria generally encountered in beers. Experimental results indicated that yeasts grew as well on their nutrient medium in the absence of the selective agent, as on the conventional hopped wort agar.

Green and Gray[2] reported that counts of viable baker's yeast may be made on the Nutrient Medium at pH 5.5. If the reaction is adjusted to pH 6.5, the count of baker's and distiller's yeast may be made. The differential medium at pH 5.5 permits a reliable count of the bacteria generally encountered in brewing. If the plates of this medium be incubated under anaerobic conditions, then estimations of beer cocci and lactic rods will be obtained. Aerobic incubation gives an estimation of the acetic acid rods and termobacteria (very small rods occurring in wort as described by Linder in about 1900 as *Termobacterium lutescens, iridescens* and *erythrinum*) etc., present in the sample.

For the analysis of baker's yeast and alcohol fermentation mashes the reaction of the Differential Medium is adjusted to pH 6.5. Plates containing dilutions of baker's yeast are incubated aerobically, whereas those from alcoholic fermentation mashes are incubated anaerobically under an atmosphere of carbon dioxide. With the alcoholic fermentation mashes, roll tubes containing 15 ml. of medium may be used and, unlike the plates, the roll tubes may be incubated aerobically instead of anaerobically. In preparing media for the estimation of the number of bacteria from alcohol mashes, markedly increased growth will be obtained if the medium be rehydrated in a diluted clarified canned tomato juice, using 400 ml. of the juice with 600 ml. of distilled water per liter.

In making microbial counts using these media the temperature and time of incubation will vary depending on the various materials under investigation. Temperatures of 25°C. are generally employed with brewing materials, and 30°C. for baker's yeast and alcohol fermentation mash analyses. Incubating periods run from 2 to 7 days, depending on the flora encountered. Incubation periods from 10 to 14 days may be used in some cases.

To rehydrate the medium, suspend 80 grams of Bacto-W. L. Nutrient Medium in 1000 ml. cold distilled water and heat to boiling to dissolve the medium completely. Distribute in tubes or flasks and sterilize in the autoclave for 15 minutes at 15 pounds pressure (121°C.). Final reaction of the medium is pH 5.5. The Nutrient Medium with a final reaction of pH 6.5 is prepared by adding sodium carbonate according to directions given on the label of each bottle.

One pound of Bacto-W. L. Nutrient Medium will make 5.6 liters of medium.

[2] Paper read at Am. Soc. of Brewing Chemists Meeting, Detroit, May, 1950.
[2] Wallerstein Lab. Comm., 13:357:1950.
[3] Wallerstein Lab. Comm., 14:169:1951.

BACTO
W. L. DIFFERENTIAL MEDIUM (B425)
DEHYDRATED

Bacto-W. L. Differential Medium has the same composition as Bacto-W. L. Nutrient Medium described above except for the addition of 0.004 g. of actidione per liter. This medium permits unrestricted growth of bacteria and inhibits the development of yeast and molds.

To rehydrate the medium, suspend 80 grams of Bacto-W. L. Differential Medium in 1000 ml. cold distilled water and heat to boiling to dissolve the medium completely. Distribute in tubes or flasks and sterilize in the autoclave for 15 minutes at 15 pounds pressure (121°C.). Final reaction of the medium is pH 5.5. The Differential Medium with a final reaction of pH 6.5 is prepared by adding sodium carbonate according to directions given on the label of each bottle. Avoid overheating or repeated re-melting of the Differential Medium.

One pound of Bacto-W. L. Differential Medium will make 5.6 liters of medium.

MEDIA FOR
THE CLASSIFICATION OF YEASTS

These media have been prepared according to the formulae of Wickerham[1,2,3,4,5] and are recommended for use in classifying yeast according to the following criteria suggested by him.
1. Colonial characteristics and cell morphology using Bacto-Yeast Morphology Agar.
2. Carbon assimilation using Bacto-Yeast Nitrogen Base.
3. Nitrogen assimilation using Bacto-Yeast Carbon Base.
4. Vitamin requirements using Bacto-Vitamin Free Yeast Base.
These media will be considered separately, and the composition of each medium is given on the following page.

BACTO
YEAST MORPHOLOGY AGAR (B393)
DEHYDRATED

Colonial characteristics and cell morphology are determined by a modified Dalmau technique using Bacto-Yeast Morphology Agar. This medium is composed of ingredients of known composition prepared according to the formula suggested by Wickerham.

The following technique has been suggested by Wickerham for the determination of typical colonial characteristics and cell morphology.

Following sterilization, pour the sterile medium into plates to a depth of about 1.5 mm. Allow the plates to stand at room temperature for one or two days before using to be assured of a dry surface. Inoculation is made using the Dalmau plate technique, as described by Wickerham and Rettger[1]. Briefly, this method consists of making a single streak inoculation near one side of the plate (as from the relative positions 10 o'clock to 2 o'clock). The inoculum should be light and taken from a slant culture. In addition to the single streak inoculation, two point inoculations are made near the other sides of the plate (as at positions 4 o'clock and 8 o'clock). A central section of the streak inoculation and one of the point inoculations are covered with cover glasses. With forceps, remove cover glasses from absolute alcohol, drain momentarily, and burn off the excess alcohol by passing over a low flame. When the cover glass has cooled, place one edge on the agar and allow the cover glass to fall across the central portion of the inoculated streak and a second cover glass over one point inoculation. The plate is incubated six or seven days at 25°C. and then observed, using the high-dry objective. This is an excellent method for studying the hyphae of filamentous yeasts.

To rehydrate the medium, suspend 35 grams of Bacto-Yeast Morphology Agar in 1000 ml. of cold, distilled water. Heat to boiling to dissolve the medium completely. Distribute in tubes or flasks and sterilize in the autoclave for 15 minutes at 15 pounds pressure (121°C.). The final reaction of the medium will be pH 4.5.

Composition of Media

Formula Ingredients per Liter	Bacto Yeast Morphology Agar	Bacto Yeast Nitrogen Base (for Carbon Assimilation Tests)	Bacto Carbon Base (for Nitrogen Assimilation Tests)	Bacto Vitamin Free Yeast Base (for vitamin requirement test)
Nitrogen Sources				
Ammonium Sulfate	3.5 g.	5 g.	None	5 g.
Bacto-Asparagine	1.5 g.	None	None	None
Carbon Source				
Bacto-Dextrose	10 g.	None	10 g.	10 g.
Amino Acids				
l-Histidine Monohydrochloride	10 mg.	10 mg.	1 mg.	10 mg.
dl-Methionine	20 mg.	20 mg.	2 mg.	20 mg.
dl-Tryptophane	20 mg.	20 mg.	2 mg.	20 mg.
Vitamins				
Biotin	2 mcg.	2 mcg.	2 mcg.	None
Calcium Pantothenate	400 mcg.	400 mcg.	400 mcg.	None
Folic Acid	2 mcg.	2 mcg.	2 mcg.	None
Inositol	2000 mcg.	2000 mcg.	2000 mcg.	None
Niacin	400 mcg.	400 mcg.	400 mcg.	None
p-Aminobenzoic Acid, Difco	200 mcg.	200 mcg.	200 mcg.	None
Pyridoxine Hydrochloride	400 mcg.	400 mcg.	400 mcg.	None
Riboflavin	200 mcg.	200 mcg.	200 mcg.	None
Thiamine Hydrochloride	400 mcg.	400 mcg.	400 mcg.	None
Compounds supplying trace elements				
Boric Acid	500 mcg.	500 mcg.	500 mcg.	500 mcg.
Copper Sulfate	40 mcg.	40 mcg.	40 mcg.	40 mcg.
Potassium Iodide	100 mcg.	100 mcg.	100 mcg.	100 mcg.
Ferric Chloride	200 mcg.	200 mcg.	200 mcg.	200 mcg.
Manganese Sulfate	400 mcg.	400 mcg.	400 mcg.	400 mcg.
Sodium Molybdate	200 mcg.	200 mcg.	200 mcg.	200 mcg.
Zinc Sulfate	400 mcg.	400 mcg.	400 mcg.	400 mcg.
Salts				
Potassium Phosphate Monobasic	1 g.	1 g.	1 g.	1 g.
Magnesium Sulfate	0.5 g.	0.5 g.	0.5 g.	0.5 g.
Sodium Chloride	0.1 g.	0.1 g.	0.1 g.	0.1 g.
Calcium Chloride	0.1 g.	0.1 g.	0.1 g.	0.1 g.
Bacto-Agar	18	None	None	None
Amount of final medium from 100 grams dehydrated medium	2.8 liters	14.9 liters	8.5 liters	5.9 liters

BACTO
YEAST NITROGEN BASE   (B392)
DEHYDRATED

Media for carbon assimilation tests may be prepared by adding various sources of carbon to Bacto-Yeast Nitrogen Base. Wickerham[1,2,3,4,5] reported that some strains of yeast require the presence of certain vitamins for the assimilation of carbon. Bacto-Yeast Nitrogen Base is a suitable medium for such studies.

For these demonstrations the tubes of media are inoculated *very* lightly, then placed at 25°C. After 6 to 7 days of incubation, and again at 20 to 24 days, the tubes are shaken to suspend growth, then they are placed against a white card bearing lines approximately ¾ of a millimeter wide. The lines are drawn with India ink. If the lines cannot be seen through the culture, or if the lines appear as diffuse, broad bands, the test is positive. If the lines are distinguishable as such, the test is negative. The two observations indicate which reactions occur rapidly and which occur latently.

The medium should be filter sterilized in 10X strength for best results. This is accomplished by suspending 6.7 grams of Bacto-Yeast Nitrogen Base and 5 grams of dextrose or an equivalent amount of other carbohydrate in 100 ml. of distilled water. It may be necessary to warm the distilled water slightly to effect complete solution of some of the carbohydrates. This 10X strength solution is then filter sterilized. The 10X strength sterile medium is kept in the refrigerator and used as needed. The final medium is prepared by pipetting, under aseptic conditions, 0.5 ml. into 4.5 ml. of sterile distilled water in 16 mm. cotton stoppered tubes. The required number of such water blanks are prepared and autoclaved in advance. After receiving the 10X strength solution, the tubes are shaken and are then ready for inoculation.

Some laboratories may prefer to filter sterilize the basal medium and the carbohydrate solution separately. To accomplish this, dissolve 6.7 grams of Bacto-Yeast Nitrogen Base in 100 ml. distilled water and filter sterilize. Distribute in 0.5 ml. amounts in sterile 16 mm. cotton stoppered tubes. Dissolve sufficient carbon compound under test for 100 ml. (0.5 gram dextrose) in 90 ml. of distilled water. Filter sterilize. The final medium is prepared by adding 4.5 ml. of the sterile carbohydrate solution to each 0.5 ml. of the sterile basal medium under aseptic conditions and mixing thoroughly by shaking. Final reaction of the basal medium will be pH 4.5.

BACTO
YEAST CARBON BASE   (B391)
DEHYDRATED

The ability of yeasts to assimilate nitrogen[1,2,3,4,5] is determined by adding various nitrogen sources to Bacto-Yeast Carbon Base and inoculating with the test organisms. The inclusion of vitamins in this base was found necessary by Wickerham as an aid for the utilization of nitrogen-containing compounds by certain yeasts which cannot assimilate these compounds in the absence of vitamins. Bacto-Yeast Carbon Base is a suitable medium for such studies.

Yeasts which have grown on a rich medium may carry a reserve of nitrogen in the form of protein. Possible errors due to this reserve are eliminated by making two serial transfers in the complete medium. When the first transfer is seven days old, the culture is shaken and one loopful is transferred to a second tube of the complete medium containing the same source of nitrogen. If a positive test is obtained when the second culture is seven days old, the organism under test assimilates this particular nitrogen source.

The medium should be filter sterilized in 10X strength for best results. This is accomplished by dissolving 11.7 grams of Bacto-Yeast Carbon Base and the nitrogen sources as desired in 100 ml. of distilled water. It may be necessary to warm the distilled water slightly to effect complete solution. This 10X strength solution is then filter sterilized. The 10X strength sterile medium is kept in the refrigerator and used as needed. The final medium is prepared by pipetting 0.5 ml. into 4.5 ml. of sterile distilled water in a 16 mm. cotton stoppered tube. The required number of such water blanks are prepared and autoclaved in advance. After receiving the 10X strength solution, the tubes are shaken, and are then ready for inoculation.

At present, the most important nitrogen-containing compound being used for nitrogen assimilation studies is potassium nitrate. This medium may be prepared by dissolving 0.78 gram potassium nitrate in 100 ml. distilled water containing 11.7 grams of Bacto-Yeast Carbon Base.

Some laboratories may prefer to filter sterilize the basal medium and nitrogen source solution separately. To accomplish this, dissolve 11.7 grams of Bacto-Yeast Carbon Base in 100 ml. distilled water and filter sterilize. Distribute in 0.5 ml. amounts in sterile 16 mm. cotton stoppered tubes. Dissolve sufficient source of nitrogen for 100 ml. (0.078 gram potassium nitrate) in 90 ml. of distilled water. Filter sterilize. The final medium is prepared by adding 4.5 ml. of the sterile nitrogen solution to each 0.5 ml. of the sterile basal medium under aseptic conditions and mixing thoroughly by shaking. The final reaction of the basal medium will be pH 4.5.

BACTO

VITAMIN FREE YEAST BASE (B394)

DEHYDRATED

Vitamin requirements of yeast may be determined by adding various vitamins to Bacto-Vitamin Free Yeast Base. This base contains sufficient nitrogen and carbon sources to permit growth of yeast after the addition of the required vitamins, as described by Wickerham.[1,2,3,4,5]

Because the inoculum may carry a large supply of vitamin reserve, it is necessary to make two serial transfers in a medium containing either no vitamins or the particular combination to be tested. When the first transfer is seven days old, the culture is shaken and one loopful is transferred to a second tube of medium having the same combination of vitamins. This second tube is likewise incubated for seven days. If growth occurs, the yeast does not require an exogenous source of whatever vitamins are absent from the medium.

The medium should be filter sterilized in 10X strength for best results. This is accomplished by dissolving 16.7 grams Bacto-Vitamin Free Yeast Base in 100 ml. of distilled water containing the desired vitamins. It may be necessary to warm the distilled water slightly to effect complete solution. This 10X strength solution is then filter sterilized. The sterile 10X strength solution is kept in the refrigerator and used as needed. The final medium is prepared by pipetting, under aseptic conditions, 0.5 ml. into 4.5 ml. of sterile distilled water in 16 mm. cotton stoppered tubes. The solutions are mixed thoroughly by shaking and are then ready for inoculation.

Some laboratories may prefer to filter sterilize the basal medium and the desired vitamins separately. To accomplish this, dissolve 16.7 grams of Bacto-Vitamin Free Yeast Base in 100 ml. distilled water and filter sterilize. Distribute

in 0.5 ml. amounts in sterile 16 mm. cotton stoppered tubes. Filter sterilize
sufficient amounts of the desired vitamins for 100 ml. of the final medium in
90 ml. of distilled water. The final medium is prepared by adding 4.5 ml. of the
sterile vitamin solution to each 0.5 ml. of the sterile basal medium under aseptic
conditions and mixing thoroughly by shaking. The final reaction of the basal
medium will be pH 4.5.

¹ U. S. Dept. Ag. Tech. Bull., No. 1029:1951.   ⁴ J. Bact., 56:363:1948.
² J. Tropical Med. Hyg., 42:176:1939.   ⁵ J. Bact., 46:501:1943.
⁸ J. Bact., 52:293:1946.

Ingredients of Culture Media

THE CHOICE of the ingredients to be used is most important for the successful preparation of microbiological culture media. Superior products will yield superior media and will lessen the time-consuming labor incident to their preparation.

The ingredients listed in this section are prepared expressly for use in making microbiological culture media. Each product is carefully tested for its usefulness and suitability for the purpose for which it is intended.

PEPTONES, DIFCO
ENZYMATIC HYDROLYSATES

PEPTONE prepared expressly for bacteriological purposes was first introduced by Difco Laboratories in 1914 after many years of preliminary study. The first of our bacteriological peptones to be produced was Bacto-Peptone. This was followed several years later by Proteose Peptone, Difco, and in more recent years other peptones have been added to the group. Since no one peptone is satisfactory for all microbiological purposes each of these peptones is particularly suitable for some special purpose or possesses singular characteristics which distinguish it from other peptones. For this reason it has been the consistent policy of Difco Laboratories to keep unchanged the method of preparation of its bacteriological peptones once these products have become established. Slight modifications or changes in method might readily result in products possessing entirely different nutritive properties. Bacto-Peptone and other Difco peptones are prepared today in the same manner as when first developed. Users of Difco peptones are, therefore, assured of products prepared in a uniform manner at all times.

It is not improbable that increased knowledge of the minutiae of bacterial metabolism may make it necessary to prepare additional specialized peptones in the future, since the formula of a Difco peptone is never modified after once being adopted. For this reason Difco Laboratories is continuing its investigation, in cooperation with other bacteriologists, to develop new products which will meet the new demands. To this end, not only are extensive studies inaugurated and carried on by Difco Laboratories, but many more are conducted in conjunction with bacteriologists throughout the world, and we extend to all our active cooperation to aid in the development of the peptones necessary to meet the problems encountered in this field.

It has been our consistent effort to make available, to the bacteriologist, products which are eminently fitted and suitable for specific purposes in view. Only when these preparations have been tested by extensive and impartial investigation in the hands of laboratory workers are they released for general use.

Difco peptones may be relied upon for biochemical studies, particularly fermentation reactions because of their freedom from fermentable substances which would interfere with the accuracy of such determinations.

Practical experience, concerned not only with the complexities of bacterial

255

metabolism and nutrition, but also with the difficulties attendant upon the separation, classification and recognition of bacterial species by means of specific cultural reactions, have long demonstrated that no single peptone can be equally suitable for all the varied ends in view. Indole production, maintenance of growth, maximum production of soluble toxins, etc., are all definitely influenced by the nature and character of the peptone and the other nitrogenous constituents of the culture medium.

Recognizing the essential importance and great practical value of these facts in relation to bacteriological investigations, Difco Laboratories has for many years engaged in a consistent and progressive study of this problem, the fruits of which are represented in the group of products briefly described below. These products are the results of original, intensive investigations, checked and corroborated by extensive practical trials in the hands of experienced bacteriologists before such materials are released for distribution. It is believed that they represent a definite advance in practical bacteriology and that they cover, as fully as is possible at present, the field of peptones in their relation to microbiology.

BACTO-PEPTONE   (B118)

Bacto-Peptone, first introduced in 1914, has long since become the universal standard peptone for the preparation of bacteriological culture media. Countless studies which have been published during the intervening years specify the use of Bacto-Peptone and constant reference to its use is currently being made in bacteriological literature.

When Bacto-Peptone was originally developed it was first subjected to trial in the routine bacteriological examination of water and milk, and was shown to be well suited for these purposes. It has continually been recommended as the peptone to be employed for culture media preparation in "Standard Methods of Water Analysis" and is at the present time included in the Ninth Edition.[1] It is similarly specified for use in a number of special studies of milk and other dairy products. [2,3] Bacto-Peptone, furthermore, is also suggested for general use in the preparation of culture media in "Standard Methods"[4] of the Division of Laboratories and Research of the New York State Department of Health.

Bacteriological literature abounds with an increasing number of references to the use of Bacto-Peptone, not only for the preparation of general culture media, but also for those employed in special research studies. Marbé and Olariu[5] have employed Bacto-Peptone in combination with Proteose Peptone in their medium for the elaboration of toxin by *Corynebacterium diphtheriae*. Veldee[6] also employed a combination of these two peptones in his medium for cultivating streptococcus for scarlet fever toxin. He states that his medium gives a toxin of uniformly high potency and that it is particularly suitable for the preparation of purified and tannic acid precipitated toxin. Bacto-Peptone is also used in culture media for studies of the intestinal bacteria,[7 to 15] streptococci,[16 to 24] pneumococci,[25] lactobacilli,[26] anaerobes[27,28,29] and the fungi.[30,31] It has been suggested for use in media for the *Brucella*,[32,33] but is now superseded by Bacto-Tryptose for this purpose. Bacto-Peptone is also specified in media used in studies of bacterial metabolism,[34] studies of disinfectants and determinations of phenol coefficients,[35] studies of bacterial luminosity,[36] and the reduction of nitrates.[37] Although it has been suggested for use in media for detection of hydrogen sulfide production[38] its use for this purpose has been supplanted by Bacto-Tryptone and Proteose Peptone. Similarly, for pigment production, Proteose Peptone or Bacto-Tryptone is more satisfactory than Bacto-Peptone as recommended in earlier papers.[39,40]

In a study by Morton, Smith and Leberman[41] Bacto-Peptone was reported to be superior to other peptones in a medium recommended for the isolation and cultivation of pleuropneumonia-like organisms.

This list is by no means complete or exhaustive but it suffices to indicate the wide range of usefulness of Bacto-Peptone. In addition to the references mentioned many other citations are to be found in the literature.

Bacto-Peptone contains nitrogen in a form which is readily available for bacterial growth requirements. It has a high peptone and amino acid content and only a negligible quantity of proteoses and more complex nitrogenous constituents. Bacto-Peptone is completely soluble in water and yields sparklingly clear solutions in the concentrations usually employed for culture media. From the very first, Bacto-Peptone has been standardized to a definite hydrogen ion concentration of pH 7.0 in a one per cent solution, as generally employed in culture media.

A typical quantitative analysis of Bacto-Peptone is given on page 265.

[1] Standard Methods for the Examination of Water and Sewage, 9th Edition: 184:1946.
[2] Bull. 524, N. Y. Agr. Exp. Sta., 1924.
[3] J. Dairy Science, 16:277:1933.
[4] Standard Methods, Div. Labs. Res. N. Y. Dept. Health, 1927.
[5] Compt. rend. soc. biol., 118:1673:1935.
[6] Public Health Reports, 53:909:1938.
[7] J. Infectious Diseases, 24:260:1919.
[8] J. Infectious Diseases, 28:384:1921.
[9] J. Bact., 11:359:1926.
[10] Abst. Bact., 6:34:1922.
[11] J. Bact., 29:349:1935.
[12] J. Bact., 32:329:1936.
[13] J. Infectious Diseases, 58:225:1936.
[14] J. Am. Water Works Assoc., 30:808:1938.
[15] J. Am. Water Works Assoc., 30:1821:1938.
[16] J. Bact., 7:449:1922.
[17] J. Infectious Diseases, 39:186:1926.
[18] J. Lab. Clin. Med., 17:530:1931–32.
[19] J. Lab. Clin. Med., 15:662:1929–30.
[20] J. Exp. Med., 50:617:1929.
[21] J. Bact., 25:527:1938.
[22] Sixth Annual Year Book (1935–1936) p. 159. Suppl., Am. J. Pub. Health, 26:No. 3:1936.
[23] J. Infectious Diseases, 63:122:1938.
[24] J. Infectious Diseases, 62:138:1938.
[25] J. Path. Bact., 39:323:1934.
[26] Am. J. Pub. Health, 28:759:1938.
[27] Proc. Soc. Exp. Biol. Med., 26:88:1928–29.
[28] J. Bact., 20:85:1930.
[29] J. Immunol., 18:141:1930.
[30] J. Infectious Diseases, 54:35:1934.
[31] Phytopathology, 24:1153:1934.
[32] Sixth Annual Year Book (1935–1936) p. 118. Suppl. Am. J. Pub. Health, 26:No. 3:1936.
[33] Sixth Annual Year Book (1935–1936) p. 193. Suppl., Am. J. Pub. Health, 26:No. 3:1936.
[34] J. Infectious Diseases, 15:417:1914.
[35] Am. J. Pub. Health, 14:1043:1924.
[36] J. Gen. Physiol., 8:89:1925.
[37] J. Bact., 19:261:1930.
[38] J. Bact., 9:235:1924.
[39] Biochem. J., 30:1323:1936.
[40] J. Bact., 32:533:1936.
[41] Am. J. Syphilis Gonorrh. Venereal Diseases, 35:361:1951.

PROTEOSE PEPTONE, DIFCO (B120)

Proteose Peptone is particularly adapted for use in culture media for the production of various bacterial toxins. This peptone is the result of extensive investigations which had their inception in the fact, developed by practical experience, that no one peptone was equally useful for all the varied phenomena included in the biological and biochemical reactions produced by bacteria. As an illustration of this fact the work carried out on the production of diphtheria toxin may be cited. Excellent, and indeed luxuriant, growth of *Corynebacterium diphtheriae* may be obtained in the usual Veal Infusion Medium containing Bacto-Peptone, but toxin production is exceedingly slight. Accordingly, over a period of six years the full time of bacteriologists and chemists in our laboratories was devoted to a study of all phases of diphtheria toxin production before Proteose Peptone was selected as the most satisfactory peptone for this purpose.

While the exact chemical composition of diphtheria toxin is still unknown, many factors influencing its production have been established. During the early work on the development of Proteose Peptone and while studying the production of diphtheria toxin, Bunker[1,2,3] recognized the importance of a correctly buffered peptone, the necessity of the optimum initial reaction of the toxin broth, and the limiting hydrogen ion concentration within which potent toxin could be harvested with a reasonable degree of certainty. For example, diphtheria toxin is produced under practical conditions only when the organism grows as a film on the surface of liquid media. Media supporting such growth are, therefore, essential. According to Robinson and Rettger[4] the toxin factors are probably supplied by the proteoses and polypeptides. Gibbs and Rettger[5] have shown that in sugar-free media toxin production occurs only when proteoses are present. Toxin production, therefore, is definitely dependent upon the composition of the peptones present in the medium.

Hazen and Heller[6] have shown that diphtheria toxin of high Lf can be produced in a "bob veal" infusion medium containing 2 per cent Proteose Peptone, 0.15 per cent dextrose and 0.3 per cent maltose. Pope[7] has also used Proteose Peptone in his semi-synthetic media for diphtheria toxin production, and Bayne-Jones[8] was able to obtain a diphtheria toxin having more than 300 M.L.D. per milliliter in a synthetic medium to which he added 2 per cent Proteose Peptone. Semi-synthetic media containing Proteose Peptone have also been employed by Kirkbride, Berthelsen and Clark[9] and by Wadsworth and Wheeler.[10]

Proteose Peptone quickly became established as a suitable peptone for use in the production of diphtheria toxin, and it is now employed almost universally in the biological laboratories engaged in the preparation of diphtheria toxin for antitoxin, toxin-antitoxin and toxoid. In addition to the references already cited, mention should also be made of the work of Hewitt,[11] Bunney[12] and Povitsky, Eisner and Jackson.[13]

Proteose Peptone is also valuable in the elaboration of other bacterial toxins as well as that of *C. diphtheriae*. Kirkbride and Wheeler[14] used this peptone successfully for the production of scarlet fever toxin, and Veldee[15] has shown that a combination of Proteose Peptone and Bacto-Peptone with inorganic salts is an excellent medium for elaboration of scarlet fever toxin of uniformly high potency. Nelson[16] used Proteose Peptone for elaboration of toxin by *Clostridium botulinum,* Kneeland and Dawes[17] for that of the pneumococcus, and Hanks and Rettger[18] that of *Salmonella pullorum.*

Proteose Peptone is a satisfactory nutriment for the propagation of many bacteria as may be seen from the work of Chapman, Lieb, Berens and Curcio,[19] and Dolman and Wilson[20] on the pathogenic staphylococci, Eldering and Kendrick[21] on *Hemophilus pertussis,* Tittsler and Lisse[22] on *S. pullorum,* and Scott[23] on *Pasteurella multocida.* This peptone, furthermore, is a valuable ingredient of culture media designed for such special biological reactions as the methyl red and Voges-Proskauer tests,[24,25] bacterial fluorescence[26] and pigment production.[27] Many factors account for the suitability of Proteose Peptone for cultivating the fastidious types of bacteria; among them are the availability of its nitrogenous components and its buffer range. These factors also aid in establishing favorable conditions for maintaining the virulence of the cultures and for the elaboration of bacterial by-products.

A method for the *in vitro* testing for virulence of *C. diphtheriae* was described by Elek[28] and also a modification of this method was given by King, Frobisher and Parsons.[29] King, Frobisher and Parsons[30] and Frobisher, King and Parsons[31] continuing their studies on the *in vitro* test for virulence of *C. diphtheriae* simplified their basal medium, and a comparative study of peptones showed Proteose Peptone to give the most satisfactory results. Handley[32] described a selective medium for the identification and isolation of *C. diphtheriae,* and in an exhaustive study of available peptones found that Proteose Peptone, Difco was more suitable than any other peptone tried for the preparation of his medium. Mc-Vickar[33] in a study of the factors important for the growth of *Histoplasma capsulatum* reported that of the 18 peptones used, Proteose Peptone, Difco gave the best growth of the organisms.

A typical quantitative analysis of Proteose Peptone, Difco is given on page 265.

[1] Abst. Bact., 1:31:1917.
[2] Abst. Bact., 2:10:1918.
[3] Abst. Bact., 4:106:1919.
[4] J. Med. Research, 36:357:1917.
[5] J. Immunol., 13:323:1927.
[6] J. Bact., 23:195:1932.
[7] Brit. J. Exp. Path., 13:218:1932.
[8] Bayne-Jones: A Textbook of Bacteriology, 1066:1934.
[9] J. Immunol., 21:1:1931.
[10] J. Infectious Diseases, 55:123:1934.
[11] Biochem. J., 24:983:1930.
[12] J. Immunol., 20:71:1930.
[13] J. Infectious Diseases, 52:246:1933.
[14] J. Immunol., 11:477:1926.
[15] Public Health Reports, 53:909:1938.
[16] J. Infectious Diseases, 41:9:1927.
[17] J. Exp. Med., 55:735:1932.

[18] J. Immunol., 22:283:1932.
[19] J. Bact., 33:533:1937.
[20] J. Immunol., 35:13:1938.
[21] Am. J. Pub. Health, 26:506:1936.
[22] J. Immunol., 15:105:1928.
[23] J. Bact., 20:9:1930.
[24] Standard Methods for the Examination of Water and Sewage, 9th Edition:230:1946.
[25] Pure Culture Study of Bacteria, 2:No. 4:1934.
[26] J. Bact., 23:135:1932.
[27] J. Bact., 29:223:1935.
[28] Brit. Med. J., 1:493:1948.
[29] Am. J. Pub. Health, 39:1314:1949.
[30] Am. J. Pub. Health, 40:704:1950.
[31] Am. J. Clin. Path., 21:282:1951
[32] J. Hygiene, 47:102:1949.
[33] J. Bact., 62:137:1951.

PROTEOSE PEPTONE NO. 2, DIFCO (B121)

The development of new peptones designed for specific purposes frequently leads to their use in new fields of investigation. Thus, Proteose Peptone No. 2, which is similar in type to Proteose Peptone, was originally developed in our studies on peptones for use in production of diphtheria toxin. Although well adapted for this purpose, it was never used extensively because Proteose Peptone, either in a semi-synthetic medium or in a veal infusion base, became established as a superior peptone in media used for diphtheria toxin production.

Interest in Proteose Peptone No. 2 was revived by the work of Bunney and Thomas[1] in their study of diphtheria toxin production in semi-synthetic media. These workers describe the preparation of a uniformly constant, infusion-free medium composed of Proteose Peptone, Proteose Peptone No. 2, dextrose, maltose and sodium acetate. This medium was reported as supporting a consistently good yield of toxin. The work of Bunney and Thomas followed soon after that of Marbé and Olariu[2] who used Bacto-Peptone and Proteose Peptone for a similar purpose.

[1] J. Immunol., 31:95:1936.   [2] Compt. rend. soc. biol., 118:1673:1935.

PROTEOSE PEPTONE NO. 3, DIFCO (B122)

Investigating Proteose Peptone No. 2 for various purposes we developed another modification of Proteose Peptone that proved to be excellent for the cultivation of many organisms. This peptone was designated as Proteose Peptone No. 3. Studies of the nutritive requirements of fastidious organisms have demonstrated that a 2 per cent solution of Proteose Peptone No. 3 with 0.05 per cent dextrose satisfactorily replaces the meat infusion-peptone portion of culture media. The dextrose is added to supply a uniform amount of utilizable carbohydrate to replace the variable amount of muscle sugars present in infusions from meat. The use of Proteose Peptone No. 3 in this manner eliminates all of the laborious processes of trimming, chopping and infusing meat. For example, a medium superior to Douglas Agar enriched with whole blood as employed by Carpenter,[1,2] is prepared by mixing equal volumes of an autoclaved 2 per cent solution of Bacto-Hemoglobin with an autoclaved agar medium composed of 4 per cent Proteose Peptone No. 3, 0.1 per cent dextrose, 1 per cent sodium chloride, 1 per cent disodium phosphate and 3 per cent agar. Chocolate Agar prepared according to this formula is satisfactory for the isolation of *Neisseria gonorrhoeae* from gonococcal infection in the male and female. In 2 per cent concentration Proteose Peptone No. 3 is an excellent carrying fluid for suspending suspected gonococcal specimens. The suitability of Proteose Peptone No. 3 in the preparation of media for the isolation of *N. gonorrhoeae* from all types of gonococcal infection is amply demonstrated by the many references to the use of this peptone for this purpose. Among others Peizer and Steffen,[3] Bucca,[4] Morton and Leberman,[5] Landy and Gerstung,[6] Lankford and Skaggs[7] and the "Diagnostic Procedures and Reagents"[8] of the American Public Health Association used Proteose Peptone No. 3 in media for gonococcal studies. Continued study of the nutritional requirements of gonococci has shown that a small percentage are exacting in their growth requirements. Chocolate Agars, prepared with Bacto-Proteose No. 3 Agar and Bacto-Hemoglobin, enriched with Bacto-Supplement A or Bacto-Supplement B, have proved excellent for the isolation of all types of *N. gonorrhoeae*. The method for the isolation of this organism is discussed in detail under Bacto-Proteose No. 3 Agar, page 116, or Bacto-G C Medium Base, page 122.

Proteose Peptone No. 3 is well suited for the preparation of media for cultivation of *Corynebacterium diphtheriae*. This peptone is employed in the preparation of Bacto-Dextrose Proteose No. 3 Agar, as discussed on page 147, for isolation of the diphtheria bacillus. Levin[9] used Proteose Peptone No. 3 in media for the isolation of meningococci and the diphtheria bacillus.

This peptone is well suited for the growth of a large variety of organisms including streptococci, staphylococci, meningococci, pneumococci, anaerobes and aerobes. In addition to the media listed above it is employed in Bacto-Phenol Red Carbohydrate Media discussed on page 187, 189, Bacto-Purple Broth Media, page 189, 190, and other fermentation media, Bacto-A C Broth and Bacto-A C Medium, pages 201 and 202.

[1] Seventh Annual Year Book (1936–37) p. 125. Suppl., Am. J. Pub. Health, 27:No. 3:1937.
[2] Bull. Genitoinfectious Diseases, Mass. Dept. Pub. Health, 2:No. 9:1938.
[3] Venereal Disease Inform., 23:224:1942.
[4] J. Bact., 46:153:1943.
[5] U. S. Naval Med. Bull., 43:409:1944.
[6] J. Immunol., 51:269:1945.
[7] Arch. Biochem., 9:265:1946.
[8] Diagnostic Procedures and Reagents, 3rd Edition:119:1950.
[9] J. Bact., 46:235:1943.

BACTO-TRYPTONE   (B123)

Bacto-Tryptone was developed in our search for a peptone particularly suitable for the elaboration of indole by bacteria. Tests for the presence or absence of indole as a by-product of bacterial metabolism are of definite value in the identification and classification of bacteria. However, unless the culture medium in which the organisms are grown can be relied upon to support indole production uniformly, the results of the test are misleading and fallacious as shown by Tilley.[1]

Indole production is dependent upon the presence of the tryptophane group in the medium,[2,3,4] Bacto-Tryptone is exceptionally well suited for use in tests for indole production because it is rich in this form of nitrogen. Strong indole tests are possible after incubation of the cultures for 15 or 16 hours in a 1 per cent solution of Bacto-Tryptone. The reaction, furthermore, will remain strong even when cultures are incubated for 4–5 days. The advantages of securing a positive indole test, particularly after a relatively short incubation period, are obvious. "Standard Methods for the Examination of Water and Sewage"[5] of the American Public Health Association and the American Water Works Association, and "Pure Culture Study of Bacteria"[3] of the Society of American Bacteriologists, specify the use of Bacto-Tryptone in demonstrating the presence of indole.

A complete discussion of the methods for the determination of indole is given under Bacto-Tryptone on page 53.

Investigation of the usefulness of Bacto-Tryptone in other fields has demonstrated a number of industrial applications. The National Canners Association, in its "Bacterial Standards for Sugar,"[6] specified the use of Tryptone media for the detection of the organisms causing "flat sour" spoilage of canned goods and also for detecting the presence of "sulfide spoilage" organisms in sugar.[7]

In his studies of the thermophilic bacteria of milk, Prickett[8] developed a medium containing Bacto-Tryptone which possessed excellent growth-stimulating properties for these organisms. Bowers and Hucker[9] also demonstrated the advantages of culture media containing this peptone for propagating bacteria from milk. An extensive survey of the use of the Bowers and Hucker medium for plate counts of milk has been summarized by Yale.[10] A modification of this medium, still utilizing Bacto-Tryptone as the peptone, was originally recommended in "Standard Methods for the Examination of Dairy Products,"[11] Seventh Edition, 1939, of the American Public Health Association for standard plate counts of milk. The report of Abele[12] analyzes in detail the results of extensive comparative studies made with Tryptone Glucose Extract Milk Agar, and the former standard Nutrient Agar. The use of the Tryptone medium has been continued since its original introduction as a medium for the plate count of milk, and is specified in the current Ninth Edition of "Standard Methods for the Examination of Dairy Products."[13] The usefulness of Bacto-Tryptone as an ingredient of culture media for the examination of milk is further shown by its use in the medium for the total bacterial plate count of certified milk[14] in which medium it may be employed alone or in conjunction with Proteose Peptone.

Among the many other uses for Bacto-Tryptone that may be mentioned, McClung[15] in a study of anaerobic bacteria utilized a 1 per cent solution of Tryptone as a basal medium for studying the physiological characteristics of Clostridia. These organisms grew sparsely in the medium containing only Tryptone, but developed rapidly in the presence of a utilizable source of carbon. Thus profuse growth and also increase in hydrogen ion concentration served as criteria for the utilization and fermentation of the test compound by these organisms. Spray[16] utilized Tryptone for the propagation of anaerobes and McCoy[17] prepared the antigens for her serological studies of the Clostridia in a 1 per cent Tryptone Medium containing 0.5 per cent dextrose. Bowers and West[18] used Tryptone in their studies on the streptococci and pneumococci and Moberly[19] employed this peptone for the cultivation of Lactobacillus acidophilus. Pringsheim and Pringsheim[20] reported that Bacto-Tryptone renders the growth of Porphyridium cruentum more vigorous and lasting. The best liquid medium for the growth of this organism is sea water plus one half volume of Beijerinck solution with 0.2 per cent added Bacto-Tryptone. In 3–4 weeks a dense red mucilaginous growth is formed.

A typical quantitative analysis of Bacto-Tryptone is given on page 265.

[1] Am. J. Pub. Health, 11:834:1921.
[2] J. Bact., 25:623:1933.
[3] Pure Culture Study of Bacteria, 5:No. 3:1947.
[4] Centr. Bakt., I Abt., 76:1:1915.
[5] Standard Methods for the Examination of Water and Sewage, 9th Edition:230:1946.
[6] Bacterial Standards for Sugar, 1935.
[7] J. Assoc. Official Agr. Chem., 21:457:1938.
[8] Tech. Bull., 147, N. Y. State Agr. Exp. Sta., 1928.
[9] Tech. Bull., 228, N. Y. State Agr. Exp. Sta., 1935.
[10] Am. J. Pub. Health, 28:148:1938.
[11] Standard Methods for the Examination of Dairy Products, 7th Edition:21:1939.
[12] Am. J. Pub. Health, 29:821:1939.
[13] Standard Methods for the Examination of Dairy Products, 9th Edition:93:1948.
[14] Methods and Standards for the Production of Certified Milk, 1953–54.
[15] J. Bact., 29:189:1935.
[16] J. Bact., 32:135:1935.
[17] J. Bact., 34:321:1937.
[18] Am. J. Pub. Health, 26:880:1936.
[19] Zentr. Bakt., II Abt. Orig., 96:329:1937.
[20] J. Ecology, 37:57:1949.

BACTO-TRYPTOSE　(B124)

In the course of a series of studies on the growth requirements of the *Brucella,* a peptone which was particularly suited for these organisms was developed. This peptone was designated as Bacto-Tryptose. In the absence of meat infusion, Bacto-Tryptose is recommended for use in an agar medium with sodium chloride and dextrose for the propagation of all types of *Brucella.*[1] With suitable dyes this medium also proved satisfactory for the isolation and differentiation of *Brucella* strains. Many of the irregular results obtained on liver infusion media are eliminated by the use of culture media containing Bacto-Tryptose.

Subsequent investigation of the nutritive properties of Bacto-Tryptose demonstrated that culture media prepared with this peptone were superior to the meat infusion peptone media employed for cultivation of the streptococci, pneumococci, meningococci and other fastidious pathogenic bacteria. A 2 per cent solution of Bacto-Tryptose with 0.05 per cent dextrose to replace muscle sugars, is an excellent substitute for the infusions plus peptones generally employed in culture media for the propagation of many of the organisms which grow with difficulty even on infusion media. Other ingredients are added as usual to this solution to make the complete medium.

An agar medium prepared with 2 per cent Bacto-Tryptose and 0.5–0.8 per cent sodium chloride, without tissue infusion, is an excellent general culture medium and base for Blood Agar. This peptone is excellently suited for the preparation of a base for Blood Agar as was reported by Casman.[2,3]

A medium containing 2 per cent Bacto-Tryptose, 0.5 per cent sodium chloride, 0.3 per cent disodium phosphate and 0.2 per cent dextrose may be used as a liquid medium for blood culture work. A discussion of Bacto-Tryptose Phosphate Broth is given on page 100. Excellent growth of many fastidious organisms occurs in this liquid medium. As in the case with other liquid substrates, the medium is greatly improved by the addition of 0.1 per cent agar. A medium consisting of 1 per cent Bacto-Tryptose, 0.5 per cent sodium chloride and 0.1 per cent disodium phosphate is an excellent base free from carbohydrate to which a suitable indicator and appropriate sugars may be added for studying the fermentation reactions of the pathogenic bacteria.

Tryptose has proved of value in media for the detection of coliform bacteria. Darby and Mallmann[4,5] developed a Lauryl Tryptose Broth that gave a high colon index and could be used as a presumptive as well as a confirmatory test for members of the coliform group. This medium was investigated by Levine,[6] McCrady[7] and Perry and Hajna[8] and is recommended for use in the standard tests for the coliform group as specified in "Standard Methods for the Examination of Water and Sewage"[9] of the American Public Health Association. A complete discussion of this medium is given under Bacto-Lauryl Tryptose Broth on page 39. Perry and Hajna used Bacto-Tryptose in their modified Eijkman Lactose Medium for the differentiation of *Escherichia coli* from other coliform bacteria. This medium is discussed on page 44 under Bacto-Eijkman Lactose Medium.

The usefulness of Bacto-Tryptose in a large variety of bacteriological studies is demonstrated by the many references to it in the literature. Among these may be cited those of Schneiter et al.[10] and Wells et al.[11] in the bacteriological examination of air, Pike[12] and Parker and Callen[13] in their studies of media for the isolation of streptococci and many others.

Bacto-Tryptose was employed in preparing the media used in Castaneda's double medium method[14] for the isolation of *Brucella* from the blood. A detailed description of this method is given on page 111 under the discussion of Bacto-Tryptose Agar.

Schuhardt, Rode, Foster and Oglesby,[15] by special techniques, demonstrated that a few of the numerous samples of Bacto-Tryptose which had been in his laboratory exhibited some toxicity for certain *Brucella abortus* strains used in his laboratory. The particular samples of Bacto-Tryptose possessing this characteristic had absorbed moisture and had undergone chemical change. Schuhardt[16] in a discussion of this observation stated that "the ease of neutralization of this toxic factor by blood, serum, agar and other substances tends to make the practical significance of the toxicity relatively minor. We probably would not have encountered it had we not been doing extensive tests on the *in vitro* effect of sulfonamides on *Brucella* using decimal dilution inocula." The high productivity of Bacto-Tryptose Agar, and Bacto-Tryptose used clinically for the isolation and cultivation of *Brucella* attests to its value for the primary cultivation of *Brucella* as well as other fastidious organisms.

A typical analysis of Bacto-Tryptose is given on page 265.

[1] Huddleson: Brucellosis in Man and Animals, 14:1939.
[2] J. Bact., 43:33:1942.
[3] Am. J. Clin. Path., 17:281:1947.
J. Am. Water Works Assoc., 31:689:1939.
[4] Am. J. Pub. Health, 31:127:1941.
[5] Am. J. Pub. Health, 31:351:1941.
[6] Am. J. Pub. Health, 33:1199:1943.
[7] Am. J. Pub. Health, 34:735:1944.

[9] Standard Methods for the Examination of Water and Sewage, 9th Edition:193:1946.
[10] Am. J. Hyg., 40:136:1944.
[11] Am. J. Pub. Health, 36:324:1946.
[12] Am. J. Hyg., 41:211:1945.
[13] J. Bact., 46:343:1943.
[14] Proc. Soc. Expl. Biol. Med., 64:114:1947.
[15] J. Bact., 57:1:1949.
[16] Personal Communication, 1949.

NEOPEPTONE, DIFCO (B119)

Neopeptone is an enzymatic protein digest especially adapted for the preparation of media to be used in the propagation of organisms usually considered difficult to cultivate *in vitro*. Neopeptone has been shown to be particularly well suited to the growth requirements of many delicate and fastidious bacteria.

Dubos[1] obtained growth of pneumococci from small inocula using media prepared with Neopeptone. According to Dawson and his associates[2,3,4] the use of Neopeptone facilitates the development of mucoid colonies of the hemolytic streptococci. Long and Bliss[5] consider Neopeptone to have definite advantages over other peptones in media for the cultivation of the minute beta hemolytic streptococci. Neopeptone media were also utilized by Lancefield[6] in her work on the classification of the streptococci.

In addition to these studies, Neopeptone has been used with satisfaction for the propagation of many other pathogenic organisms. Parker[7] used Neopeptone media for the pneumococcus, and Bailey[8] employed it in her medium for differentiation of the gonococcus and meningococcus from other *Neisseria*. Spray[9] used Neopeptone in his media for classification of the sporulating anaerobes, Hobby[10] employed it in her study of the diphtheria bacilli, and Eldering and Kendrick[11] reported good results with this peptone in cultivating *Hemophilus pertussis*. Krumwiede[12] used Neopeptone in media for cultivation of group A streptococci. Engley and Snyder[13] cultivated *Pasteurella tularensis* in media prepared with Neopeptone. Casman,[14] in a comparison of peptones used in the preparation of fresh beef infusion agar for Blood Agar, reported Neopeptone to be best suited for inclusion in the infusion base.

This peptone has proved to be of decided value in media for the cultivation of pathogenic fungi. Growth of these microorganisms is rapid and colonial formation uniform and typical for the various types. Bacto-Sabouraud Dextrose Agar and Bacto-Sabouraud Maltose Agar, prepared with Neopeptone, are discussed on pages 238–240.

A typical quantitative analysis of Neopeptone, Difco, is given on page 265.

[1] J. Exp. Med., 52:331:1930.
[2] Proc. Soc. Exp. Biol. Med., 31:594:1934.
[3] Science, 80:296:1934.
[4] J. Infectious Diseases, 62:138:1938.
[5] J. Exp. Med., 60:619:1934.
[6] Proc. Soc. Exp. Biol. Med., 38:473:1938.
[7] J. Exp. Med., 67:667:1938.

[6] J. Bact., 34:645:1937.
[9] J. Bact., 32:135:1936.
[10] J. Infectious Diseases, 57:186:1935.
[11] Am. J. Pub. Health, 26:506:1936.
[12] J. Bact., 46:117:1943.
[13] J. Bact., 51:573:1946.
[14] Am. J. Clin. Path., 17:281:1947.

BACTO-CASITONE (B259)

Bacto-Casitone is a pancreatic digest of casein, conforming to the specifications given by the National Institute of Health[1] and the U. S. Pharmacopeia.[2] It is recommended for use in the preparation of media for sterility testing according to the National Institute of Health,[1] "The compilation of Tests and Methods of Assay for Antibiotic Drugs,"[3] Federal Security Agency, Food and Drug Administration, National Formulary,[4] and the U. S. Pharmacopeia.[5] It is also recommended for the preparation of media where an enzymatic hydrolyzed casein is desired, as for example the liquid medium for the cultivation of *Mycobacterium tuberculosis* as described by Dubos and Middlebrook.[6]

Bacto-Casitone is readily soluble in distilled water giving a clear nearly colorless solution, neutral in reaction. It has a high tryptophane content making it satisfactory for the detection of indole production.

[1] National Institute of Health Circular: Culture Media for the Sterility Test, 2nd Revision: February 5, 1946.
[2] Pharmacopeia of the United States, XIV Revision:875:1950.
[3] The compilation of Tests and Methods of Assay for Antibiotic Drugs, Federal Security Agency, Food and Drug Administration.
[4] National Formulary, 9th Edition:768:1950.
[5] Pharmacopeia of the United States, XIV Revision:758:1950.
[6] Am. Rev. Tuber., 56:335:1947.

BACTO-PEPTONIZED MILK (B35)

Bacto-Peptonized Milk, as the name implies, is a skim milk digest. Inasmuch as this product contains carbohydrates as well as nitrogenous materials it is considered as a complete medium. Bacto-Peptonized Milk is discussed in detail on page 75.

BACTO-SOYTONE (B436)

Bacto-Soytone is an enzymatic hydrolysate of soybean meal prepared under controlled conditions especially for use in microbiological procedures. It is recommended for use in media for the cultivation of a large variety of organisms, including fungi, and is also used in media for microbiological assay. This peptone contains the naturally occurring carbohydrate of the soybean and is suitable in all microbiological procedures wherein carbohydrates are not objectionable. Bacto-Soytone is completely soluble in distilled water in concentrations generally employed and forms clear solutions with a neutral reaction.

BACTO-PROTONE (B125)

Bacto-Protone was developed in response to a demand for a product high in proteoses which could be used in preparing varying combinations of proteoses, peptones and amino acids in studies of bacterial metabolism. About 85 per cent of the nitrogen in Bacto-Protone is precipitated by saturation with ammonium sulfate, thus indicating a high content of proteoses. Until pure primary or secondary proteoses are available Bacto-Protone forms the nearest and most useful substitute.

Being low in readily utilizable nitrogen Bacto-Protone does not, by itself, support good growth of bacteria. Its usefulness lies in combination with more readily available forms of nitrogen. W. E. Bunney has suggested its use as a diluent for maintaining the potency of diluted diphtheria toxin for use in the Schick test. Studies undertaken by the New York State Health Department[1] indicate that marked stability of the toxin dilutions was secured when Bacto-Protone was used.

A typical quantitative analysis of Bacto-Protone is given below.

[1] N. Y. State Health Dept., 54th Annual Report:72:1933.

TYPICAL ANALYSES OF PEPTONES

Peptone	Bacto-Peptone	Proteose Peptone, Difco	Bacto-Tryptone	Bacto-Tryptose	Neopeptone, Difco	Bacto-Protone
Per Cent						
Total Nitrogen	16.16	14.37	13.14	13.76	14.33	15.41
Primary Proteose N	0.06	0.60	0.20	0.40	0.46	5.36
Secondary Proteose N	0.68	4.03	1.63	2.83	3.03	7.60
Peptone N	15.38	9.74	11.29	10.52	10.72	2.40
Ammonia N	0.04	0.00	0.02	0.01	0.12	0.05
Free Amino N (Van Slyke)	3.20	2.66	4.73	3.70	2.82	1.86
Amide N	0.49	0.94	1.11	1.03	1.23	....
Mono-amino N	9.42	7.61	7.31	7.46	7.56	....
Di-amino N	4.07	4.51	3.45	3.98	4.43	....
Tryptophane	0.29	0.51	0.77	0.64	0.73	1.03
Tyrosine	0.98	2.51	4.39	3.45	4.72	2.99
Cystine (Sullivan)	0.22	0.56	0.19	0.38	0.39	0.27
Organic Sulfur	0.33	0.60	0.53	0.57	0.63	0.45
Inorganic Sulfur	0.29	0.04	0.04	0.04	0.09	0.16
Phosphorus	0.22	0.47	0.97	0.72	0.19	0.27
Chlorine	0.27	3.95	0.29	2.77	0.84	0.38
Sodium	1.08	2.84	2.69	2.77	0.45	0.30
Potassium	0.22	0.70	0.30	0.50	0.85	0.06
Calcium	0.058	0.137	0.096	0.117	0.198	0.263
Magnesium	0.056	0.118	0.045	0.082	0.051	0.057
Manganese	nil	0.0002	nil	0.0001	nil	nil
Iron	0.0033	0.0056	0.0104	0.0080	0.0041	0.0023
Ash	3.53	9.61	7.28	8.45	3.90	2.50
Ether Soluble Extract	0.37	0.32	0.30	0.31	0.30	0.31
Reaction, pH	7.0	6.8	7.2	7.3	6.8	6.7

pH 1 per cent solution in distilled water after autoclaving 15 minutes at 121°C.

HYDROLYSATES, ACID

BACTO-CASAMINO ACIDS (B230)

Bacto-Casamino Acids is acid hydrolyzed casein recommended for use in the production of diphtherial toxin and other biological products. Hydrolysis is carried on until all the nitrogen in the casein is converted to amino acids or other compounds of relative chemical simplicity. Bacto-Casamino Acids is prepared according to the method described by Mueller and Miller[1] and Mueller and Johnson.[2] This product has a satisfactory sodium chloride content for diphtheria toxin production[1,3] and has had all but the last traces of iron removed. Bacto-Casamino Acids is also particularly well suited for nutritional studies, microbiological assays, the preparation of so called "synthetic" or chemically defined media and media used for sulfonamide inhibitor studies.

Mueller[3] prepared diphtheria toxin in a medium containing a casein hydrolysate as the source of nitrogen. It was shown that the high sodium chloride content was the limiting factor in the amount of toxin that could be produced in this medium. Mueller and Miller[1] described a method of reducing the sodium chloride content of the hydrolyzed casein and also for reducing the iron content to a minimum. Using this hydrolyzed casein supplemented with inorganic salts, growth accessory factors, cystine, maltose and an optimum amount of iron, 100 flocculating units per ml. of diphtheria toxin were prepared. Bacto-Casamino Acids duplicates this especially treated hydrolyzed casein. Complete detailed directions for the preparation of diphtheria toxin are given by these authors.[1]

Using this hydrolyzed casein, Bacto-Casamino Acids, Mueller and Miller[4] determined the growth requirements for *Clostridium tetani*. Morton and Gonzalez[5] employed Bacto-Casamino Acids in the medium used to study the site of formation of diphtheria toxin. They obtained diphtheria toxin of high potency using the method described by Mueller and Miller.[1]

Bacto-Casamino Acids has also been used in media for the testing of disinfectants. Wolf[6] used Bacto-Casamino Acids or Bacto-Casamino Acids, Technical in the preparation of his disinfectant test medium. Klarman and Wright[7] used Bacto-Casamino Acids in the semi-synthetic medium for testing disinfectants described by them. Logan, Tytell, Danielson and Griner[8] employed Bacto-Casamino Acids in the preparation of the medium used for maintaining stock cultures for the elaboration of *Clostridium perfringens* alpha toxin. Straus, Dingle and Finland[9] employed a medium containing Bacto-Casamino Acids in their study of the mechanism of sulfonamide bacteriostasis.

Bacto-Casamino Acids also is well suited for use in media for microbiological assay. A description of these media with references is given on page 216 to 230. Bird, Bressler, Brown, Campbell and Emmett[10] employed Bacto-Casamino Acids in the medium for the assay for folic acid using *Lactobacillus casei* as the test organism. This casein hydrolysate has been used with excellent results in media for the cultivation of *Hemophilus pertussis* according to the method described by Hornibrook[11] and by Verwey, Thiele and Sage.[12]

The following is an approximate analysis of Bacto-Casamino Acids:

Total Nitrogen	10 per cent
Sodium Chloride	14 per cent
Ash	20 per cent
P as PO4	2 per cent
Iron, 3 grams Bacto-Casamino Acids	15 micrograms

[1] J. Immunol., 40:21:1941.
[2] J. Immunol., 40:33:1941.
[3] J. Immunol., 37:103:1939.
[4] J. Bact., 43:763:1942.
[5] J. Immunol., 45:63:1942.
[6] J. Bact., 49:463:1945.
[7] Soap and Sanitary Chemicals, 21:113:1945.
[8] J. Immunol., 51:317:1945.
[9] J. Immunol., 42:331:1941.
[10] J. Biol. Chem., 159:631:1945.
[11] Public Health Reports, 54:1847:1939.
[12] J. Bact., 54:71:1947.

BACTO-CASAMINO ACIDS, TECHNICAL (B231)

Bacto-Casamino Acids, Technical is acid hydrolyzed casein. The hydrolysis is carried out as in the preparation of Bacto-Casamino Acids, but the sodium chloride and iron content of this product have not been decreased to the same extent. Bacto-Casamino Acids Technical is recommended for use in culture media where amino acid mixtures are required for a nitrogen source and the sodium chloride content need not be low. It is particularly valuable in studying the growth requirements of bacteria.

Bacto-Casamino Acids, Technical is prepared according to the method suggested by Mueller[1] for use in the preparation of diphtheria toxin in a medium containing nitrogen substances of chemical composition similar to amino acids in simplicity. Later it was shown that the sodium chloride of the hydrolysate was the limiting factor in the production of diphtheria toxin and a method is described by Mueller and Miller[2] for the reduction of this material in the hydrolysate, see Bacto-Casamino Acids discussed above.

Casein hydrolysates prepared according to Mueller's method[1] have been used for many purposes. Tetanus toxin of high potency was produced by Mueller and Miller[3] in a simple medium using this hydrolysate.

Favorite and Williams[4] used a casein hydrolysate prepared according to the method of Mueller[1] for the production of staphylococcus enterotoxin and alpha hemolysin. Mueller and Hinton[5] used Bacto-Casamino Acids, Technical in a medium for primary isolation of the gonococcus and meningococcus. Bacto-Casamino Acids, Technical was used in agar-free media for the isolation of *Neisseria* and also in a tellurite medium for the isolation of *Corynebacterium,* described by Levin.[6] Wolf[7] used Bacto-Casamino Acids or Bacto-Casamino Acids, Technical in the preparation of a medium for the testing of disinfectants. Mueller and Miller[8] used Bacto-Casamino Acids, Technical in their Tellurite Serum Agar for a selective medium for diphtheria. This casein hydrolysate has been used with excellent results in media for the cultivation of *Hemophilus pertussis* according to the method described by Hornibrook[9] and by Verwey, Thiele and Sage.[10]

The following is an approximate analysis of Bacto-Casamino Acids, Technical:

Total Nitrogen	8 per cent
Sodium Chloride	37 per cent
Ash	39 per cent

[1] J. Immunol., 37:105:1939.
[2] J. Immunol., 40:21:1941.
[3] Proc. Soc. Exp. Biol. Med., 43:389:1940.
[4] J. Bact., 41:305:1941.
[5] Proc. Soc. Exp. Biol. Med., 48:330:1941.
[6] J. Bact., 46:233:1943.
[7] J. Bact., 49:463:1945.
[8] J. Bact., 51:743:1946.
[9] Public Health Reports, 54:1847:1939.
[10] J. Bact., 54:71:1947.

BACTO-VITAMIN FREE CASAMINO ACIDS

As the name implies, Bacto-Vitamin Free Casamino Acids is acid hydrolyzed casein, free from vitamins. It is recommended for use in microbiological assay media and in studies on the growth requirements of microorganisms. A description of these media with references is given on page 216 to 230. Sarett[1] used Bacto-Vitamin Free Casamino Acids as the acid hydrolyzed casein in his studies on *p*-aminobenzoic acid and pteroylglutamic acid as growth factors for *Lactobacilli*.

Bacto-Vitamin Free Casamino Acids is readily soluble in distilled water yielding a clear colorless solution. The following is a typical analysis of Bacto-Vitamin Free Casamino Acids:

Total Nitrogen .... 7 per cent
Sodium Chloride .... 38 per cent
Ash .... 41 per cent

[1] J. Biol. Chem., 171:265:1947.

AMINO ACIDS

A DISCUSSION of the amino acids most commonly used is given here. Additional amino acids are available as required. Difco amino acids are pure and recommended as standards for chemical and microbiological procedures as well as for use in media of chemically defined composition for nutritional studies.

BACTO-ASPARAGINE (B144)

Bacto-Asparagine is *l*-asparagine of exceptional purity. It is recommended as a particularly useful ingredient of synthetic culture media employed in studies of bacterial nutrition.

Asparagine is used as a source of organic nitrogen of known chemical composition. It is readily available for bacterial energy and growth when used in culture media. Bacto-Asparagine is widely employed in media for the mass cultivation of *Mycobacterium tuberculosis* for use in the preparation of tuberculin for the detection and eradication of tuberculosis. Asparagine has also been used in recent investigations for the growth of tubercle bacilli as reported by Dubos and Davis,[1] and others.

[1] J. Exp. Med., 83:409:1946.

dl-ALANINE, DIFCO (B182)

Alanine has been used occasionally in culture media as a source of nitrogen in studies of the metabolism of various organisms. *dl*-Alanine, Difco is a highly purified amino acid suitable for use in studies of this type.

l-CYSTINE, DIFCO (B184)

Cystine is used extensively in synthetic culture media, particularly those employed in studies of bacterial metabolism. Davis and Ferry[1] devised a cystine medium for use in their studies on diphtheria toxin production, and Duval[2] employed a cystine medium for propagation of *Mycobacterium leprae*. Shaw[3] and Rhamy[4] used cystine media for the cultivation of *Pasteurella tularensis*. Cystine is employed in the media specified by the National Institute of Health,[5] for the sterility testing of biologicals, for sterility testing as specified in the Pharmacopeia[6] and National Formulary[7] and for the sterility testing of antibiotics according to the method of the Food and Drug Administration.[8]

l-Cystine, Difco is a highly purified amino acid recommended for use in the preparation of culture media.

[1] J. Bact., 4:217:1919.
[2] J. Exp. Med., 12:649:1910.
[3] Zentr. Bakt., I Abt. Orig., 118:216:1930.
[4] Am. J. Clin. Path., 3:121:1933.
[5] National Institute of Health Circular: Culture Media for the Sterility Test, 2nd Revision: Feb. 5, 1946.

[6] Pharmacopeia of the United States, XIV Revision:758:1950.
[7] National Formulary, 9th Edition:778:1950.
[8] Compilation of Tests and Methods of Assay for Antibiotic Drugs, Federal Security Agency, Food and Drug Administration.

l-TRYPTOPHANE, DIFCO (B188)

Tryptophane is an amino acid, essential for the growth of many microorganisms. Tryptophane is utilized by bacteria in the elaboration of indole and has, therefore, been employed in media devised for testing for indole production.

Since tryptophane is destroyed by acid hydrolysis, synthetic media employing acid hydrolysates or chemically pure amino acid mixtures as sources of nitrogen, require the addition of tryptophane for the growth of most bacteria.

l-TYROSINE, DIFCO (B189)

Tyrosine is an amino acid which has been used occasionally in the preparation of culture media.

EXTRACTS

BACTO-BEEF EXTRACT (B126)

Infusions of meat were first generally employed together with peptone as nutriments in culture media. Later it was found that for many routine procedures beef extract gave fully as good results and had the decided advantages of greater ease of preparation, greater uniformity and economy. A medium composed of beef extract, peptone and agar has been one of the most generally used media in bacteriological procedures.

Bacto-Beef Extract is prepared and standardized for use in microbiological culture media, where it is generally used to replace infusions of meat. It is standard in its composition and reaction, and does not require adjustment of reaction or filtration. For many years beef extract media have been recommended as standard for use in the routine bacteriological examination of water, milk and other materials where it is important to have media of uniform composition.

Bacto-Beef Extract may be relied upon for biochemical studies, particularly fermentation reactions because of its freedom from fermentable substances which would interfere with the accuracy of such determinations.

In culture media, Bacto-Beef Extract is usually employed in concentrations of 0.3 per cent as in the standard media recommended for water and for milk analysis.[1,2] Concentrations may vary slightly according to the requirements of individual formula, but do not often exceed 0.5 per cent. In 0.3 per cent concentration Bacto-Beef Extract forms brilliantly clear solutions, rich in the nutriments required for bacterial metabolism. After autoclave sterilization this solution has a reaction of pH 6.8.

In the fields of special research Bacto-Beef Extract has been employed in media by a number of investigators. Bedell and Lewis[3] used it in their medium for the study of the non-sporulating anaerobes of the intestinal tract, and Tittsler and Sandholzer[4] employed it in carbohydrate broths for studying the cultural characteristics of the *Escherichia-Aerobacter* intermediates. Hutner[5] used a medium containing Bacto-Beef Extract as a stock broth in his study of the nutritional needs of the streptococci. Kent[6] also employed Bacto-Beef Extract in a medium for culturing *Agrobacterium tumefaciens* in studying the specific bacteriophage of this organism. Countless other references to the use of this product are to be found in bacteriological literature.

1 Standard Methods for the Examination of Water and Sewage, 9th Edition:1946.
2 Standard Methods for the Examination of Dairy Products, 9th Edition:1948.
3 J. Bact., 36:567:1938.
4 J. Bact., 29:349:1935.
5 J. Bact., 35:429:1938.
6 Phytopathology, 27:871:1937.

BACTO-YEAST EXTRACT   (B127)

Bacto-Yeast Extract is the water soluble portion of autolyzed yeast. The autolysis is carefully controlled to preserve the naturally occurring B-complex vitamins. Bacto-Yeast Extract is prepared and standardized for bacteriological use. It is an excellent stimulator of bacterial growth and is used in culture media in place of, or as an adjuvant to, beef extract. In concentrations of 0.3–0.5 per cent, as it is generally employed, it forms sparklingly clear solutions with a reaction of pH 6.6.

Bacto-Yeast Extract has been used advantageously in culture media for studies of the bacteria in milk and other dairy products. Its usefulness for this purpose is attested in such reports as those of Prickett[1] on the thermophilic and thermoduric bacteria of milk. Since publication of this work, Bacto-Yeast Extract has been used with increasing frequency in the study of the bacterial flora of milk. Among the references to its use for this purpose are those of Hucker and Hucker[2] on the number and type of bacteria in commercially prepared infant foods, Breed et al.[3] on methods for the examination of thermophiles in dry milk and Downs and his associates[4] on methods for the study of these organisms in evaporated and condensed milk. Bowers and Hucker[5] have also studied the effect of Bacto-Yeast Extract in media employed for counting bacteria in milk. An increasing number of references to Bacto-Yeast Extract is to be found in bacteriological literature. Hutner[6] used this product in a stock broth for the streptococci. Nelson and Werkman[7] have used Bacto-Yeast Extract as an ingredient of the medium they employed for cultivation of *Lactobacillus brevis*. Werkman and his associates[8,9,10,11] have used Bacto-Yeast Extract media for propagating organisms of the propionic acid group. Partansky and McPherson[12] used Bacto-Yeast Extract in combination with Bacto-Malt Extract, and Bacto-agar for the growth of molds in their laboratory method for testing the mold resistant properties of oil paints.

Pringsheim and Robinow[13] in their studies on the cultivation of *Caryophanon latum* reported very good growth of the organism in agar media containing Bacto-Yeast Extract. Some batches of laboratory made autolysates of Bakers yeast gave excellent results but others were unsatisfactory. They were able to rely on a medium prepared with 0.5 per cent Bacto-Yeast Extract and 0.5 per cent Bacto-Peptone, which was very favorable for isolation and maintenance of the culture. In a survey of ingredients for a medium for the standard plate count for dairy products, Buckbinder and associates[14] compared various yeast extracts and showed that media prepared with Bacto-Yeast Extract gave a higher count than similar media prepared with other yeast extracts.

Bacto-Yeast Extract is an excellent source of B-complex vitamins and is often used to supply these factors in bacteriological culture media. For example, Snell and Strong[15] used Bacto-Yeast Extract for the preparation of the yeast supplement in their medium for riboflavin assay. It has proved to be a valuable ingredient of media used for carrying stock cultures and for preparation of inocula of

Lactobacilli for microbiological assay of vitamins. This product is also of value in the assay of antibiotics.[16,17]

[1] Tech. Bull. 147, N. Y. Agr. Exp. Sta., 1928.
[2] Tech. Bull. 153, N. Y. Agr. Exp. Sta., 1929.
[3] J. Dairy Science, 15:383:1932.
[4] J. Dairy Science, 18:647:1935.
[5] Am. J. Pub. Health, 24:396:1934.
[6] J. Bact., 35:429:1938.
[7] J. Bact., 31:603:1936.
[8] J. Bact., 36:201:1938.
[9] Biochem. J., 32:1262:1938.

[10] Biochem. J., 31:349:1937.
[11] J. Bact., 31:595:1936.
[12] Ind. Eng. Chem., Anal. Edition:12:443:1940.
[13] J. Gen. Microbiol., 1:267:1947.
[14] Pub. Health Reports:66:327:1951.
[15] Ind. Eng. Chem., Anal. Edition:11:346:1939.
[16] J. Bact., 47:199:1944.
[17] Science, 98:69:1943.

BACTO-MALT EXTRACT (B186)

Bacto-Malt Extract is a useful ingredient of culture media designed for the propagation of yeasts and molds. This product was used by Thom and Church[1] in the preparation of "wort" medium as originally described by Reddish.[2] Bacto-Malt Extract Broth, as discussed on page 242, is a complete dehydrated medium and duplicates the medium of Thom and Church.

Bacto-Malt Extract is employed in the preparation of Bacto-Malt Agar, a widely used medium for the detection and isolation of yeast and molds from dairy products, food and other materials. This medium is discussed in detail on page 65. Partansky and McPherson[3] used Bacto-Malt Extract, in conjunction with Bacto-Yeast Extract and Bacto-Agar for the cultivation of molds in their laboratory method for testing mold resistant properties of oil paints.

[1] Thom and Church: The Aspergilli, 1926.
[2] Abst. Bact., 3:6:1919.
[3] Ind. Eng. Chem., Anal. Edition:12:443:1940.

ENRICHMENTS

THE ENRICHMENTS described in this section are used with liquid or solid basal media to give the complete formulation. The enrichments are of such a nature that they cannot be sterilized with the base medium but must be added under aseptic conditions. Some of the enrichments are sterilized in the autoclave following rehydration while others are supplied as sterile solutions of thermolabile complexes. Some contain a selective agent producing a medium designed for the isolation or cultivation of a certain group of microorganisms. Care must be taken to use the selective enrichments with the exact base medium specified since the selective agent is standardized with the designated medium and the use of a different base would not give the desired results.

BACTO-HEMOGLOBIN (B136)

Bacto-Hemoglobin, prepared from beef blood, is a convenient, readily available enrichment, which may be sterilized in the autoclave. It is prepared according to the procedure described by Spray[1] and is recommended for use in media for the cultivation of *Neisseria gonorrhoeae, Hemophilus influenzae, H. ducreyi, Pasteurella tularensis,* streptococci, pneumococci, etc.

Bacto-Protose No. 3 Agar and Bacto-G C Medium Base enriched with Bacto-Hemoglobin and Bacto-Supplement A or Bacto-Supplement B are recommended for the cultural isolation of the gonococcus from all types of gonococcal infections in the male or female. The technique for this procedure is given in detail on pages 116 and 122. The medium suggested for the cultural detection of the gonococcus by "Diagnostic Procedures and Reagents"[2] of the American Public Health Association is Bacto-G C Medium Base enriched with Bacto-Hemoglobin and Bacto-Supplement B. These media may also be recommended for the isolation of H. influenzae and H. ducreyi. For the isolation of P. tularensis a medium prepared with Bacto-Hemoglobin and Bacto-Cystine Heart Agar, as discussed on page 91, is recommended.

Solutions of Bacto-Hemoglobin have the advantage of being sterilizable in the autoclave. Bacto-Hemoglobin is used solely as an enrichment, and cannot be employed as an indicator of hemolysis. For use as an enrichment in media, 2 grams of Bacto-Hemoglobin are dissolved in 100 ml. of distilled water. This solution is best prepared by placing 2 grams of Bacto-Hemoglobin in a dry flask and adding 100 ml. cold distilled water while the flask is being agitated vigorously. The hemoglobin suspension is shaken intermittently for 10–15 minutes to break up all aggregates and effect complete solution. It is sterilized in the autoclave for 15 minutes at 15 pounds pressure (121°C.). The sterile solution is added, in equal proportions, to sterile double strength medium. When agar media are prepared it is important to cool the melted agar and the hemoglobin solution to 50–60°C. before the solutions are mixed, and the mixture should be agitated to insure a perfect suspension of hemoglobin throughout the medium. Agar media enriched with Bacto-Hemoglobin are similar to Chocolate Agar in appearance. Broth media may be enriched in the same manner except that the temperature of the mixture may be disregarded.

[1] J. Lab. Clin. Med., 16:166:1930.   Diagnostic Procedures and Reagents, 3rd Edition:30:107:1950.

BACTO-BEEF BLOOD   (B137)

Bacto-Beef Blood is whole beef blood which has been desiccated and powdered. It is an enrichment, capable of being sterilized in the autoclave, duplicating the dilute whole blood (Preparation No. 3) as described by Spray[1] for use in the cultivation of hemoglobinophilic organisms. Bacto-Beef Blood is used solely as an enrichment for culture media. It cannot be employed as an indicator of hemolysis.

Bacto-Proteose No. 3 Agar as discussed on page 116, enriched with Bacto-Beef Blood, is well suited for propagation of the hemophilic bacteria. This enriched medium possesses excellent growth-promoting properties. For the cultivation of the gonococcus, however, Bacto-Hemoglobin should be employed as the enrichment.

When Bacto-Beef Blood is first dissolved in water it has the appearance of laked blood. After it has been autoclaved there is a tendency for the soft coagulum to settle. It is, therefore, advisable to maintain an even dispersion by gentle agitation of the flask when the sterilized solution is added to the medium. After addition of the solution to an agar medium, the mixture should be agitated to secure an even suspension of the blood in the medium as described below. Agar media enriched with Bacto-Beef Blood are similar to Chocolate Agar in appearance.

Bacto-Beef Blood is prepared for use by dissolving 2 grams of the powder in 100 ml. of distilled water. It is then sterilized in the autoclave for 15 minutes at 15 pounds pressure (121°C.). To prepare a chocolate or enriched agar, mix equal parts sterile beef blood solution and sterile melted double strength agar, under aseptic conditions. The temperature of both solutions should be between 50–60°C. at the time of mixing and they should be gently agitated to insure a perfect suspension of the blood in the medium without the formation of air bubbles. Broth media may be enriched in the same manner except that the temperature of the mixing may be disregarded.

1 J. Lab. Clin. Med., 16:166:1930.

BACTO-BEEF BLOOD SERUM (B138)

Bacto-Beef Blood Serum is a dehydrated powdered form of fresh beef blood serum. In a 10 per cent solution it is equivalent to fresh serum.

Bacto-Beef Blood Serum is a useful aid to bacteriologists who have occasional use for serum media. The use of this product eliminates all the disagreeable and time-consuming procedures attendant upon the preparation of fresh serum. Bacto-Beef Blood Serum may be employed with excellent success in the preparation of many serum media. When it is used in plain 10 per cent solution or as an ingredient of Loeffler Medium it forms firm, smooth, white slants upon heat coagulation.

The Beef Blood Penetration Test of the Institute of Paper Chemistry in their Institute Tentative Method No. 522, November, 1941, specifies the use of a 10 per cent solution of Bacto-Beef Blood Serum in distilled water adjusted to pH 6.6 with a 5 per cent solution of phosphoric acid for the performance of their test.

BACTO-BEEF SERUM (B260)

Bacto-Beef Serum is filter sterilized fresh normal beef serum. It is recommended as an enrichment for use in bacteriological culture media, and in other procedures requiring beef serum. Bacto-Beef Serum is supplied in packages of one-half dozen and one dozen ampuls of 10 ml. each.

BACTO-HORSE SERUM (B261)

Bacto-Horse Serum is prepared from normal horse serum. It is filter sterilized and is recommended for use as an enrichment in bacteriological culture media and in other procedures requiring horse serum. Bacto-Horse Serum is supplied in packages of one-half dozen and one dozen ampuls of 10 ml. each.

BACTO-HORSE SERUM SALINE 1-6 (B262)

Bacto-Horse Serum Saline 1-6 is normal horse serum diluted 1 to 6 with saline. It is filter sterilized and is especially recommended for use in the cultivation of *Endamoeba histolytica* according to the procedure discussed on page 97. Bacto-Horse Serum Saline 1-6 is supplied in packages of one-half dozen and one dozen ampuls of 10 ml. each.

BACTO-ASCITIC FLUID (B135)

Bacto-Ascitic Fluid is prepared from serous fluids removed aseptically from the peritoneal cavity of a number of individuals. It is filter sterilized and packaged aseptically. The finished product is subjected to regular sterility tests and found to be free from demonstrable organisms. It is not guaranteed, however, to be free from filterable forms of viruses.

Bacto-Ascitic Fluid is used as an enrichment for culture media. The usual proportion for use is one 10 ml. ampul of Bacto-Ascitic Fluid for each 20 or 30 ml. of sterile medium. To prevent coagulation of the ascitic fluid, the medium should be cooled to 45–50°C. before the enrichment is added. Agar media should be prepared with concentrations of agar sufficiently high to allow for dilution of the media with the fluid. In order to prevent contamination, great care should always be taken to observe aseptic precautions when Bacto-Ascitic Fluid is added to culture media. The enriched media should always be incubated to insure their sterility before they are used.

Bacto-Ascitic Fluid is supplied in packages of one-half dozen or one dozen ampuls of 10 ml. each.

BACTO-DUBOS MEDIUM SERUM (B292)

Bacto-Dubos Medium Serum is filter sterilized fresh beef serum to which is added 7.5 per cent Bacto-Dextrose. Bacto-Dubos Medium Serum is prepared for use in the preparation of a liquid medium for the rapid cultivation of *Mycobacterium tuberculosis* as discussed on page 108 and 105 under Bacto-TB Broth Base and Bacto-Dubos Broth Base. Bacto-Dubos Medium Serum is supplied in packages of one-half dozen and one dozen tubes of 20 ml. each.

BACTO-DUBOS MEDIUM ALBUMIN (B309)

Bacto-Dubos Medium Albumin is a filter sterilized 5 per cent solution of albumin fraction V from bovine plasma in normal saline and contains 7.5 per cent Bacto-Dextrose. Bacto-Dubos Medium Albumin is prepared especially for use in the preparation of a liquid medium for the rapid cultivation of *Mycobacterium tuberculosis,* giving readily dispersible growth as discussed on page 108 and 105 under Bacto-TB Broth Base and Bacto-Dubos Broth Base. Bacto-Dubos Medium Albumin is a filter sterilized solution supplied in packages of one-half dozen and one dozen tubes of 20 ml. each.

BACTO-DUBOS OLEIC SERUM COMPLEX (B376)

Bacto-Dubos Oleic Serum Complex is a sterile liquid enrichment for use with Bacto-Dubos Oleic Agar Base for the preparation of a medium for the isolation and cultivation of *Mycobacterium tuberculosis.* This enrichment is similar to Bacto-Dubos Oleic Albumin Complex, prepared according to the directions given by Dubos and Middlebrook,[1] except that normal beef serum is used instead of albumin fraction V.

The complete medium is prepared by adding 20 ml. of Bacto-Dubos Oleic Serum Complex and 5,000 to 10,000 units of penicillin (25 to 50 units per ml. medium) to 180 ml. of sterile rehydrated Bacto-Dubos Oleic Agar Base at 50–55°C. under aseptic conditions. A description of the medium is given on page 107, Bacto-Dubos Oleic Agar Base. The desired concentration of penicillin may be readily obtained by dissolving the contents of one vial of penicillin containing 100,000 units in 10 ml. sterile distilled water. One-half (0.5) ml. (5,000 units) is added to 200 ml. of the sterile medium at 50–55°C. under aseptic conditions to obtain a concentration of 25 units per ml. medium (1 ml. to give

50 units per ml. medium). The enriched medium is then mixed to obtain an even distribution of all components, and distributed into tubes or plates as desired. When solidified in tubes or plates, it is ready for surface inoculation.

Bacto-Dubos Oleic Serum Complex is supplied in packages of one-half dozen tubes of 20 ml. each.

[1] Am. Rev. Tuberculosis, 56:334:1942.

BACTO-DUBOS OLEIC ALBUMIN COMPLEX (B375)

Bacto-Dubos Oleic Albumin Complex is a sterile liquid enrichment for use with Bacto-Dubos Oleic Agar Base for the preparation of a medium for the isolation and cultivation of *Mycobacterium tuberculosis,* as described by Dubos and Middlebrook.[1] The enrichment consists essentially of a 0.05 per cent solution of alkalinized oleic acid in a 5 per cent solution of albumin fraction V in normal saline (0.85 per cent sodium chloride solution).

A discussion of the complete medium is given under Bacto-Dubos Oleic Agar Base, page 107. The medium is prepared by adding 20 ml. of Bacto-Dubos Oleic Albumin Complex and 5,000 to 10,000 units of penicillin (25 to 50 units per ml. medium) to 180 ml. of sterile rehydrated Bacto-Dubos Oleic Agar Base at 50–55°C. under aseptic conditions. The desired concentration of penicillin may be readily obtained by dissolving the contents of one vial of penicillin containing 100,000 units in 10 ml. sterile distilled water. One-half (0.5) ml. (5,000 units) is added to 200 ml. of the sterile medium at 50–55°C. under aseptic conditions to obtain a concentration of 25 units per ml. medium (1 ml. to give 50 units per ml. medium). The enriched medium is then mixed to obtain an even distribution of all components, and distributed into tubes or plates as desired. When solidified in tubes or plates, it is ready for surface inoculation.

Bacto-Dubos Oleic Albumin Complex is supplied in packages of one-half dozen tubes of 20 ml. each.

[1] Am. Rev. Tuberculosis, 56:334:1942.

BACTO-PEIZER TB MEDIUM ENRICHMENT (B401)

Bacto-Peizer TB Medium Enrichment is prepared according to the formula described by Peizer and Schecter,[1] and is used with Bacto-Peizer TB Medium Base for the preparation of a medium for the isolation and cultivation of *Mycobacterium tuberculosis.* The enrichment consists of fresh egg yolk, glycerol, dextrose and malachite green as a selective agent. A complete discussion of the medium is given on page 110. Bacto-Peizer TB Medium Enrichment is packaged in 29 ml. amounts, sufficient for the preparation of 129 ml. of complete medium. It is supplied in packages of one-half dozen vials.

[1] Am. J. Clin. Path., 20:682:1950.

BACTO-PPLO SERUM FRACTION (B441)

Bacto-PPLO Serum Fraction is a sterile solution recommended as an enrichment in media for the cultivation of PPLO (pleuropneumonia-like organisms). It is employed in 1 per cent concentration in Bacto-PPLO Agar and Bacto-PPLO Enrichment Broth as discussed on pages 89 and 82. Bacto-PPLO Serum

Fraction has also been used for the propagation, stabilization and maintenance of the *Treponemes in vitro*.

Bacto-PPLO Serum Fraction is the partially purified serum fraction required for growth by the pleuropneumonia-like organisms described by Smith and Morton.[1] It has the advantage over sera or ascitic fluid in that only 1 per cent is required for enriching broth or solid media for culturing PPLO and does not exhibit the inhibitory effect which normal sera has upon some PPLO strains.

Bacto-PPLO Serum Fraction was shown by Rose and Morton[2] to replace effectively the serum or albumin fractions commonly employed in the cultivation of avirulent *Treponemes*.

[1] J. Bact., 61:395:1951.   [2] Am. J. Syphilis Gonorrh. Venereal Diseases, 36:1:1952.

BACTO-SUPPLEMENT B   (B276)

Bacto-Supplement B is a sterile yeast concentrate for use in supplementing media for culturing fastidious microorganisms with exacting growth requirements. It is particularly recommended for use in Chocolate Agar, prepared from Bacto-G C Medium Base or Bacto-Proteose No. 3 Agar and Bacto-Hemoglobin, employed in the cultural diagnosis of gonococcal infections. It is also recommended for use as an enrichment in both solid and liquid media for the isolation and propagation of *Hemophilus influenzae* as described by Neter.[1,2] This supplement, with crystal violet added (Bacto-Supplement A), may be recommended for the preparation of selective enriched media for these organisms.

Bacto-Supplement B is processed to preserve both the thermolabile and thermostable growth accessory factors of fresh yeast, including glutamine, coenzyme (v factor), cocarboxylase and other growth factors for the most exacting strains of *Neisseria gonorrhoeae* and *H. influenzae*. It also contains the hematin or x factor required by *H. influenzae*.

Bacto-Supplement B is used in one per cent concentration in either solid or liquid media. It is added aseptically after the medium has been sterilized in the autoclave and cooled below 50°C.

The use of this enrichment in media is discussed in detail under Bacto-G C Medium Base, page 122, Bacto-Proteose No. 3 Agar, page 116 and Bacto-Brain Heart Infusion, page 77.

Bacto-Supplement B is supplied in packages of six bottles of 5 ml. each.

[1] Science, 106:350:1947.   [2] J. Bact., 54:70:1947.

BACTO-SUPPLEMENT A   (B246)

Bacto-Supplement A is a sterile yeast concentrate containing crystal violet as a selective agent for use in supplementing media for culturing fastidious microorganisms with exacting growth requirements. It is particularly recommended for use in Chocolate Agar prepared from Bacto-Proteose No. 3 Agar or Bacto-G C Medium Base and Bacto-Hemoglobin employed in the cultural diagnosis of gonococcal infections. It is also suggested for use as a selective enrichment in solid media containing Bacto-Hemoglobin for the isolation and propagation of *Hemophilus influenzae*.

Bacto-Supplement A is processed to preserve both the thermolabile and thermostable growth accessory factors, including glutamine, coenzyme (v factor), cocarboxylase, and other growth factors for the most exacting strains of *Neisseria gonorrhoeae* and *H. influenzae*. It also contains the hematin or x factor required by *H. influenzae*. In addition, this enrichment contains crystal violet which suppresses growth of many of the common contaminants on the final medium. In gonococcal isolations, these contaminants, if permitted to develop, may interfere with the growth and detection of the gonococcus.

Bacto-Supplement A is used in one per cent concentration in either solid or liquid media containing Bacto-Hemoglobin. It is added aseptically after the medium has been sterilized in the autoclave and cooled below 50°C.

The use of this enrichment in media is discussed in detail under Bacto-G C Medium Base, page 122 and Bacto-Proteose No. 3 Agar, page 116.

Bacto-Supplement A is supplied in packages of six bottles of 5 ml. each.

BACTO-CHAPMAN TELLURITE SOLUTION (B291)

Bacto-Chapman Tellurite Solution is a 1 per cent solution of potassium tellurite prepared and standardized especially for use with Bacto-Mitis Salivarius Agar, as discussed on page 154. The final medium is prepared by adding exactly 1.0 ml. to 1000 ml. of sterile melted Mitis Salivarius Agar at 50–55°C., mixing thoroughly and pouring into plates at once to obtain the proper selectivity. The resulting selective medium duplicates that described by Chapman.[1,2] It permits the isolation of *Streptococcus mitis*, *S. salivarius* and enterococci from grossly contaminated specimens, other organisms generally being inhibited. Bacto-Chapman Tellurite Solution is also used in the preparation of PPLO Enrichment Broth as discussed on page 82.

Bacto-Chapman Tellurite Solution is supplied in packages of six ampuls of 5 ml. each. The solution must be stored in a glass stoppered container free from organic matter.

[1] Am. J. Digestive Diseases, 13:105:1946.　　　　[2] Trans. N. Y. Acad. Sciences, 10:45:1947.

BACTO-TELLURITE BLOOD SOLUTION (B139)

Bacto-Tellurite Blood Solution is defibrinated beef blood to which one per cent potassium tellurite has been added. This mixture is prepared expressly for use in the isolation of *Corynebacterium diphtheriae*. To 100 ml. sterile medium prepared from Bacto-Dextrose Proteose No. 3 Agar (as discussed on page 147), are added 5 ml. Bacto-Tellurite Blood Solution with aseptic precautions. This mixture is heated to 75–80°C. until it takes on the appearance of Chocolate Agar, then cooled to 50°C., poured into previously sterilized petri dishes, and allowed to solidify. The surface of the medium is streaked with the suspected diphtheritic material and the plates are then incubated at 35–37°C. for 24–48 hours.

Surface colonies of *C. diphtheriae* on the Tellurite Agar are black in color, slightly raised, and may have entire or irregular margins. Most contaminating organisms fail to grow on the complete medium due to its inhibitory action.

Bacto-Tellurite Blood Solution is not sterile, and cannot be recommended for use except as described above. The tellurite present prevents growth of microorganisms and, during the heating at 75–80°C. in preparation of the medium, contaminating organisms are killed or are inhibited by the potassium tellurite during the incubation period. It is recommended that plates be inoculated the same day as prepared.

Bacto-Tellurite Blood Solution is supplied in single bottles or in packages of six bottles of 25 ml. each.

BACTO-MUELLER TELLURITE SERUM (B266)

Bacto-Mueller Tellurite Serum is a sterile selective enrichment used in the preparation of the tellurite plating medium described by Mueller and Miller[1] for the isolation of *Corynebacterium diphtheriae*. It is prepared according to the directions given by the authors and contains lactate, pantothenate, beef serum and potassium tellurite, as a selective agent. To prepare the complete medium, add 25 ml. of Bacto-Mueller Tellurite Serum to 1000 ml. of sterile Bacto-Mueller Tellurite Base at 50°C. under aseptic conditions. Mix thoroughly avoiding formation of air bubbles and distribute 20 ml. into sterile 95 mm. plates. The resultant medium is transparent. A complete discussion of this medium is given on page 149 under Bacto-Mueller Tellurite Base.

Bacto-Mueller Tellurite Serum is supplied in single bottles or in packages of six bottles of 25 ml. each.

[1] J. Bact., 51:743:1946.

ENZYMES

IN THIS SECTION are included enzymes generally used for the preparation of Bacteriological culture media. We are pleased to present several new enzyme preparations for microbiological and clinical laboratory procedures, including Bacto-Penase, a potent Penicillinase, Bacto-Chicken Pancreas, for the liberation of folic acid for microbiological assay, Bacto-Trypsin 1%, for Hemagglutination, Bacto-Lysozyme and Bacto-Lysozyme Substrate.

PANGESTIN, DIFCO, 1:75 (B150)
(*Pancreatic Enzymes*)

Pangestin is an active preparation of pancreatic enzymes. It is strongly amylolytic, proteolytic, and lipolytic. It is also free from starch and sugar. One part of Pangestin, Difco, 1:75 will digest 75 parts of cooked potato starch under the conditions of the U.S.P. test for amylase in pancreatin and will also digest 75 parts of casein under conditions of the U.S.P. test for trypsin in pancreatin. The optimum reaction for pancreatic amylase is pH 7.1, for pancreatic trypsin it is pH 7.8, and for pancreatic lipase it is pH 8.0.

Pangestin, Difco, 1:75 is available in 500, 100 or 25 gram quantities.

PEPSIN, DIFCO, 1:10,000 (B151)

Pepsin is employed in the preparation of culture media solely because of its ability to break down protein materials. One part of Pepsin, Difco, 1:10,000 will digest 10,000 parts of freshly coagulated egg albumen under the conditions of the U.S.P. test for pepsin. Pepsin acts best at a reaction of pH 1.8.

Pepsin, Difco, 1:10,000 is available in 500, 100 or 25 gram quantities.

PAPAIN, DIFCO (B253)

Papain, Difco, is prepared from the fruit of the papaya (*Carica papaya*). It is recommended as a source of proteolytic enzyme of vegetable origin for the digestion of meat and other protein materials. Papain has also been used in treating red blood cells in blood grouping work by Kuhns and Bailey.[1] Papain, Difco is tested by and meets the National Formulary[2] specification for papain in that 0.1 gram digests 2.0 g. Bacto-Beef suspended in 50 ml. distilled water in 2 hours at 52°C. Digestion with Papain may be carried out at an acid or alkaline reaction, but is most active at pH 6.0–6.5 at 52°C.

Asheshov,[8] in a description of the preparation of bacteriological culture media using papain, stated that this enzyme was relatively heat stable, being most active at 60–70°C. Temperatures above 70°C. diminished the rate of digestion and activity stopped at 80°C.; best digestion was obtained at pH 7.0 and at a temperature of 60–65°C.

Papain, Difco is available in 500, 100 or 25 gram quantities.

[1] Am. J. Clin. Path., 20:1067:1950.   [3] Can. J. Pub. Health, 32:468:1941.
[2] National Formulary, Eighth Edition:371:1946.

RENNIN, DIFCO (B287)

Rennin, Difco is a desiccated enzyme obtained from the glandular layer of the stomach of the calf. It is used for the enzymatic coagulation of milk. Rennin, Difco conforms in every respect to the National Formulary standards for this material.

Rennin, Difco is available in 500, 100 and 25 gram quantities.

TRYPSIN, DIFCO, 1:250 (B152)

Trypsin is used in the preparation of culture media to break down proteins into simpler compounds which are more readily available for bacterial nutrition. One part Trypsin, Difco, 1:250 will digest 250 parts of casein under the conditions of the U.S.P. test for trypsin in pancreatin. Trypsin acts best at pH 7.8.

Trypsin, Difco, 1:250 has been used in the digestion of sputum and other body fluids in the isolation of *Mycobacterium tuberculosis* and other acid-fast bacilli. Haynes,[1] using this method in comparison with the Hanks flocculation method, reported 11 per cent more positive specimens with trypsin concentration. The technique is easily performed and requires a minimum of time. Trypsin, Difco, 1:250 has proven especially useful for treating red blood cells to increase their specificity in hemagglutinating systems with anti-Rh sera and other blood group antibodies. A method that has been employed successfully for treating the red cells with the enzyme is described by Wheeler, Luhby and Scholl.[2,3] Wiener and Katz[4] also found Trypsin, Difco, 1:250 to be well suited for the preparation of red cells for Rh studies. Such trypsin-modified cells are extremely sensitive indicators for the detection of anti-Rh and other blood group antibodies. Agglutination reactions with such cells are specific, easily read, immediate and unlikely to show failure of agglutination or prozones. The complete prepared reagent for Rh testing is discussed on page 280 under Bacto-Trypsin 1% for Hemagglutination. Rosenthal, Dameleshak and Brukhardt[5] used Trypsin, Difco, 1:250 in treating red blood cells in their study of cells in acquired hemolytic anemia. Morris[6] used Trypsin, Difco, 1:250 in his study of hemagglutination by murine encephalomyelitis virus. He reported that virus which failed to agglutinate human group O erythrocytes at 20°C. did so in the presence of trypsin. Additional uses of Trypsin in the microbiological laboratory are given under Bacto-Trypsin page 280.

Trypsin, Difco, 1:250 is available in 500, 100 or 25 gram quantities.

[1] J. Lab. Clin. Med., 27:806:1942.   [3] J. Immunol., 65:39:1950.
[2] Paper presented at a Symposium on Serology   [4] J. Immunol., 66:51:1951.
    of Blood Groups, American Association of Im-   [5] Am. J. Clin. Path., 21:635:1951.
    munologist, 1949.   [6] J. Immunol., 68:97:1952.

BACTO-TRYPSIN (B153)

Bacto-Trypsin is a filter sterilized and carefully standardized desiccation of tryptic enzymes. It is rehydrated by the addition of sterile distilled water. Bacto-Trypsin is recommended for the neutralization of the antitryptic power of serum and also for use in blood culture.

Wright first made the observation that, in the treatment of suppurating wounds, there may be a stage at which the infecting organisms grow luxuriantly and that this stage was coincident with the lysis of the leucocytes. This destruction of the white blood cells sets free the tryptic enzymes which neutralize the antitryptic power of the blood and permits growth of the invading organisms. By utilizing this principle Douglas and Colebrook[1] evolved a method for blood culture work which has been satisfactory.

Owen[2] recommended Trypsin-Beef Tea as an ideal medium for blood culture. His medium consisted of 10 ml. Bacto-Trypsin added aseptically to 90 ml. sterile Beef Broth. Typhoid and other organisms tend to show early and luxuriant growth in this medium. An alternative method consisted of collecting the blood in sterile tubes containing 0.5 ml. Bacto-Trypsin per milliliter of blood. The blood and trypsin are mixed, incubated at 35–37°C. for a short period and the mixture is then smeared directly upon agar media.

For tryptic digests of protein for the preparation of culture media, use Trypsin, Difco, 1:250 as discussed above. For Rh Blood Grouping use Bacto-Trypsin 1% for Hemagglutination described below or Bacto-Trypsin, Difco, 1:250 discussed above.

Bacto-Trypsin is supplied in packages of one half dozen and one dozen vials of 10 ml. each.

[1] Lancet, 2:181:1916.　　　　　　　　　　[2] J. Lab. Clin. Med., 2:198:1916–17.

BACTO-TRYPSIN 1% (B454)
for Hemagglutination

Bacto-Trypsin 1% for Hemagglutination is a carefully standardized water soluble trypsin preparation designed especially for conditioning erythrocytes for Rh determinations and other hemagglutination tests.

Hubener[1] and Thomsen[2] first showed that enzymes present in certain bacterial filtrates could activate latent red cell agglutinogens. Friendenreich[3] referred to this type of reaction as "T agglutination". Burnet, McCrae and Stone[4] observed that filtrates from *Vibrio cholerae* modified the virus hemagglutination of human red cells. Pickles[5] discovered that such *V. cholerae* treated cells became specifically agglutinable in saline dilutions of "incomplete" anti-Rh sera. Morton and Pickles[6] noted that trypsin behaved similarly to culture filtrates in increasing the sensitivity and specificity of red cells sensitized with "incomplete" antibody and also that it enhanced the specific agglutination of other hemagglutinins in the absence of any detectable antibody of the "incomplete" type. The authors used the beneficial effect of trypsin on erythrocytes as the basis for an improved test for Rh sensitization.

Wheeler, Luhby and Scholl[7,8] and Wheeler and Taylor[9] studied the effect of trypsin and other enzymes on cells employed in Rh determinations and found trypsin to be particularly suitable for conditioning erythrocytes for such tests. The titers of anti-Rh sera were greater when determined with the trypsin-modified cell technique than were those obtained with the albumin-tube technique and in many cases the sensitivity of the titrations equalled that of the indirect

Coombs test. The prozones commonly experienced in titrations using untreated cells in albumin solutions, were completely eliminated when trypsin-modified cells were employed. Wheeler[10] found Trypsin, Difco, 1:250 and Bacto-Trypsin 1% to be eminently satisfactory for use in treating erythrocytes employed in Rh determinations. The latter preparation was preferable because of its greater purity, ready solubility and ease of solution. Wiener and Katz[11] in their studies on the use of enzyme-treated red cells in tests for Rh sensitization found that the use of trypsinated red cells was a sensitive and specific method for testing Rh-Hr antibodies and antibodies of other specificities. Enzyme-treated cells gave more sensitive results in tests for Rh sensitization than other standard tests hitherto introduced and equalled them in specificity. The titers obtained using trypsinated erythrocytes were four or five times as high as by the albumin plasma conglutination technique. In no case of Rh sensitization did the test with enzyme-treated cells fail to demonstrate the presence of Rh antibodies although in several of these cases the other tests were negative. Furthermore, the trypsinated cell technique was observed to be a reliable method for demonstrating autosensitization even in the absence of clinical manifestations. These authors used Trypsin, Difco, 1:250 and noted no damage to any of the hemagglutinogen loci by this enzyme.

Unger, Tortora and Mappi[12] in their isoimmunization studies in rabbits used Trypsin, Difco, 1:250 for conditioning the erythrocytes and observed that the trypsinated cell method was more sensitive than either the saline agglutination or albumin plasma methods for the detection of isoantibodies. Rosenfield and Vogel[13] studied the effect of trypsinated erythrocytes on the identification of hemagglutinins. They confirmed Wheeler's observations that the prozone phenomenon obtained with certain high titer sera in albumin is not observed with optimally trypsin-treated erythrocytes. They found trypsinated cells to be sensitive to agglutination by extremely small amounts of Rh antibody. Like Wiener and Katz[11] these authors did not encounter an instance of sensitization to Rh-Hr that was not detectable by this technique. This fact makes the enzyme technique just as valuable in routine tests for Rh sensitization as the indirect antiglobulin test. Rosenfield and Vogel also observed that trypsin treatment of the cells influenced the A and B factors so that agglutination was of better avidity and the titration values were higher than in saline. The O factor was not changed. The M and N factors were largely destroyed by enzyme activity. The S factor was enhanced by trypsin treatment. The Fy^a (Duffy) factor was destroyed by enzyme treatment. Trypsin improved the Le^a and Le^b agglutination. Trypsin was also found to accentuate hemolysin activity upon the red cells treated with this enzyme. Trypsin enhanced agglutination with Anti-P sera. Agglutinogen for cold autoagglutinins was altered by enzyme treatment resulting in higher titration values for cold agglutinins in general and a wider thermal amplitude. They recommended careful standardization of the technique of treating cells with trypsin so as to avoid false positive reactions. Rosenthal, Damelshak and Brukhardt[14] used Trypsin, Difco 1:250 in treating red blood cells in their study of cells in acquired hemolytic anemia. Morris[15] used Trypsin, Difco 1:250 in his study of hemagglutination by murine encephalomyelitis virus. He reported that virus which failed to agglutinate human group O erythrocytes at 20°C. did so in the presence of trypsin. Bacto-Trypsin 1% is ideally suited for these determinations.

Bacto-Trypsin 1% for Hemagglutination is reconstituted by adding 10 ml. Bacto-Hemagglutination Buffer to each 10 ml. vial. The resultant solution is sparklingly clear and equivalent in tryptic activity to a 1 per cent solution of Trypsin, Difco, 1:250. The reaction of the final solution will be pH 7.2. The reconstituted solution should be kept refrigerated at 2–6°C. or colder until used. Bacto-Trypsin 1% for Hemagglutination when reconstituted is used according to the methods described by Wheeler, Luhby and Scholl,[7,8] Wiener and Katz[11] or by Rosenfield and Vogel.[13]

Bacto-Trypsin 1% for Hemagglutination is supplied in packages of ten vials of 10 ml. each.

[1] Ztschr. Immunitats Exper. Therap., 45:223: 1925.
[3] Ztschr. Immunitats Exper. Therap., 52:85: 1927.
[8] The Thomsen Hemagglutination Phenomenon, Levin & Munksgaard, 1930.
[4] Brit. J. Exp. Path., 27:228:1946.
[5] Nature, 158:880:1946.
[6] Nature, 159:779:1947.
[7] Symposium on Serology of Blood Groups. Am. Assoc. Immunol., 1949.

[8] J. Immunol., 65:39:1950.
[9] Am. Assoc. Blood Banks, 1951.
[10] Personal Communication, 1951.
[11] J. Immunol., 66:51:1951.
[12] The Laboratory Digest, 15:5:1951.
[13] New York Academy of Sciences, 13:213:1951.
[14] Am. J. Clin. Path., 21:635:1951.
[15] J. Immunol., 68:97:1952.

BACTO-HEMAGGLUTINATION BUFFER   (B454D)

Bacto-Hemagglutination Buffer, prepared according to the formula of Wheeler, Luhby and Scholl,[1] is a desiccation consisting of sodium chloride, disodium phosphate and potassium dihydrogen phosphate. It is recommended for the preparation of isotonic buffered saline for use in hemagglutination studies. It is especially recommended for rehydrating Bacto-Trypsin 1% and for suspending and washing red cells preparatory for hemagglutination.

Bacto-Hemagglutination Buffer is rehydrated by dissolving 8.6 grams in 1000 ml. distilled water. The resultant solution is isotonic for blood cells and has a pH of 7.3.

Bacto-Hemagglutination Buffer is conveniently packaged in vials containing 8.6 grams, sufficient for one liter, and supplied in boxes of ten vials.

[1] J. Immunol., 65:39:1950.

INVERTASE FOR ANALYTICAL USE   (B154)

Invertase for Analytical Use is an enzymatic extract of yeast cells. It is packaged in ampuls of 10 ml. each of a standardized extract, 5 ml. of which will cause complete inversion of 50 ml. of a 10 per cent sucrose solution in one hour at room temperature. Invertase for Analytical Use is most active at a reaction of pH 4.4–4.6. The K value of Invertase Analytical is K (A.O.A.C.)=0.1.

Invertase for Analytical Use is supplied in packages of one-half dozen and one dozen ampuls of 10 ml. each.

BACTO

CHICKEN PANCREAS   (B459)

DEHYDRATED

Bacto-Chicken Pancreas is standardized desiccated chicken pancreas used in the enzymatic liberation of folic acid from its conjugated state. It is prepared according to the method described by the Official Agricultural Chemists.[1] Bacto-Chicken Pancreas, is recommended for use in techniques requiring this enzyme, among which the following may be cited:

Official Methods of Analysis of the Association of Official Agricultural Chemists,[2] Methods of Vitamin Assay,[3] Sreenivasan, Harper and Elvehjem,[4] Burkholder, McVeigh and Wilson,[5] Mimms and Laskowski,[6] Bird, Bressler, Brown, Campbell and Emmett[7] and Laskowski, Mimms and Day.[8]

Bacto-Chicken Pancreas is supplied in 10 gram packages.

[1] A.O.A.C., Seventh Edition:785:1950.
[2] A.O.A.C., Seventh Edition:786:1950.
[3] The Association of Vitamin Chemists, Inc., Second Edition:231:1951.
[4] J. Biol. Chem., 177:117:1949.

[5] Arch. of Biochem., 7:287:1945.
[6] J. Biol. Chem., 160:493:1945.
[7] J. Biol. Chem., 159:631:1945.
[8] J. Biol. Chem., 157:731:1945.

BACTO-PENASE (B345)

Bacto-Penase is a potent sterile thermolabile biological extract capable of neutralizing the antibiotic properties of all known types of penicillin. It is non-toxic to microorganisms and, therefore, particularly well suited for use in media for culturing bacteria from blood and other body fluids containing penicillin and for estimating penicillin levels in such fluids.[1,2] "Diagnostic Procedures and Reagents"[3] recommend that a penicillin inactivator, penicillinase, be included in media for culturing organisms from blood of patients under penicillin therapy. Bacto-Penase is ideally suited for this purpose. It is also satisfactory for use in the sterility testing of penicillin and products containing penicillin and for ascertaining the microbial counts on penicillin-containing products. Bacto-Penase or Bacto-Penase Concentrate is recommended as a penicillinase for use in all official procedures for the sterility testing of penicillin as specified by the U. S. Government.[4] Most laboratories prefer to use Bacto-Penase Concentrate in such procedures.

One (1) ml. of Bacto-Penase will inactivate 50,000 units or more of penicillin as indicated by the following test procedure:

Prepare dilutions of Bacto-Penase of 1:2, 1:3, 1:4, 1:5, 1:6, 1:7, 1:8, 1:9 and 1:10 in sterile distilled water. Add 1 ml. of each dilution to a series of test tubes containing 15 ml. of Bacto-Fluid Thioglycollate Medium. Add 1.0 ml. of a solution of penicillin containing 5000 units per ml. to each tube and allow to remain at room temperature for two hours. Inoculate each tube with 1.0 ml. of a 24-hour broth culture of *Micrococcus pyogenes* var. *aureus* P209 diluted 1:1000 and incubate at 37°C. for 24 hours. Determine the highest dilution permitting growth in this period and multiply this dilution of Bacto-Penase by 5000. This will give the actual units of penicillin that 1.0 ml. of Bacto-Penase will inactivate.

M. pyogenes var. *aureus* P209 will show growth in 18–24 hours in 15 ml. of Bacto-Fluid Thioglycollate Medium or Bacto-Brain Heart Infusion with PAB and Agar containing 50,000 units of penicillin and 1 ml. of Bacto-Penase. Suitable controls show that less than 3 units of penicillin per 15 ml. of medium inhibit growth completely in the absence of Bacto-Penase, and that Bacto-Penase is not inhibitory to the growth of microorganisms. The maximum efficiency of Bacto-Penase against penicillin will be obtained if the reacting substances are contained in small volumes.

In culturing blood or other body fluids containing penicillin it is recommended that 1 ml. of Bacto-Penase be added to each 100 ml. or less of sterile Bacto-Brain Heart Infusion with PAB or Bacto-Brain Heart Infusion with PAB and Agar. This will assure inactivation of the maximum amount of penicillin that would be present in 10 ml. of blood or other body fluid. A medium so prepared will also inactivate sulfonamides and up to 1000 units of streptomycin introduced with the inoculum.

The sterility of penicillin is determined by adding the test sample to sterile Bacto-Fluid Thioglycollate Medium containing Bacto-Penase and incubating the tubes at 35–37°C. for 4 days. The test is performed in tubes containing 15 ml. of medium. At least 1 ml. of Bacto-Penase for each 50,000 units of penicillin to be tested should be incorporated in 15 ml. of sterile Bacto-Fluid Thioglycollate Medium under aseptic conditions. The medium containing Bacto-Penase must not be heated. Most laboratories find it more convenient to use Bacto-Penase Concentrate for sterility testing. The sterility testing of penicillin products for yeasts and molds is accomplished by adding the test samples to Bacto-Sabouraud Liquid Medium and incubating for 5 days at room temperature. The sterility testing of products for yeasts and molds which have high concentrations of penicillin may require the addition of Bacto-Penase Concentrate to the medium.

Bacto-Penase is stable when stored at refrigerator temperatures. At normal room temperature slow deterioration of Bacto-Penase does occur, and for that reason this product, or media prepared with it, should be stored at 2–6°C.

Bacto-Penase is regularly supplied in packages of one-half dozen tubes of 20 ml. each.

1 Science, 101:365:1945.
2 Science, 102:355:1945.
3 Diagnostic Procedures and Reagents, Third Edition:55:1950.
4 Compilation of Regulations for Tests and Methods of Assay and Certification of Antibiotic Drugs, Federal Security Agency, Food and Drug Administration.

BACTO-PENASE CONCENTRATE (B346)

Bacto-Penase Concentrate is a highly potent sterile thermolabile biological extract possessing the capacity to neutralize the antibiotic properties of all known types of penicillin. It is non-toxic to microorganisms and is therefore, particularly satisfactory for use in the sterility testing of penicillin or products containing penicillin, and in ascertaining the microbial counts on penicillin-containing products. Bacto-Penase Concentrate is recommended as a penicillinase for use in all official procedures for the sterility testing of penicillin as specified under the regulations promulgated by the U. S. Government.[1] Bacto-Penase Concentrate may be used in media for culturing organisms from blood and other body fluids containing penicillin, and for estimation of penicillin levels in such fluids, but for these purposes Bacto-Penase is recommended.

One ml. of Bacto-Penase Concentrate will inactivate 500,000 units of penicillin, as indicated by the following test procedures:

Prepare dilutions of Bacto-Penase Concentrate of 1:2, 1:3, 1:4, 1:5, 1:6, 1:7, 1:8, 1:9 and 1:10 in sterile distilled water. Add 1 ml. of each dilution to a series of test tubes containing 15 ml. of Bacto-Fluid Thioglycollate Medium. Add 1 ml. of a solution of penicillin containing 50,000 units per ml. to each tube and allow to remain at room temperature for two hours. Inoculate each tube with 1 ml. of a 24-hour broth culture of *Micrococcus pyogenes* var. *aureus* P209 diluted 1 to 1000 and incubate at 35–37°C. for 24 hours. Determine the highest dilution permitting growth in this period, and multiply this dilution of Bacto-Penase Concentrate by 50,000. This will give the actual units of penicillin that Bacto-Penase Concentrate will inactivate.

The sterility of penicillin is determined by adding the test sample to sterile Bacto-Fluid Thioglycollate Medium containing Bacto-Penase Concentrate and incubating the tubes at 35–37°C. for 4 days. The test is performed in tubes containing 15 ml. of medium. At least 1 ml. of Bacto-Penase Concentrate for each 500,000 units of penicillin to be tested should be incorporated in 15 ml. of sterile Bacto-Fluid Thioglycollate Medium under aseptic conditions. The medium containing Bacto-Penase Concentrate must not be heated. Bacto-Penase Concentrate is recommended for testing the sterility of 50,000 units or larger amounts of penicillin, while Bacto-Penase may be used for the sterility testing of smaller amounts of penicillin.

The sterility testing of penicillin products for yeasts and molds is accomplished by adding the test samples to Bacto-Sabouraud Liquid Medium and incubating for 5 days at room temperature. The sterility testing of products for yeasts and molds which have high concentrations of penicillin may require the addition of Bacto-Penase Concentrate to the medium.

When employed in media such as Bacto-Brain Heart Infusion with PAB and Agar for culturing blood or other body fluids containing penicillin, it is recommended that Bacto-Penase Concentrate be used in a concentration to give a final unitage of 100 units or more per ml. of medium.

Bacto-Penase Concentrate is stable when stored at refrigerator temperatures. At normal room temperature slow deterioration of Bacto-Penase Concentrate does occur, and for that reason this product, or media prepared with it, should be stored at 2–6°C.

Bacto-Penase Concentrate is regularly supplied in packages of one-half dozen tubes of 20 ml. each or packages of one-half dozen bottles of 100 ml. each.

[1] Compilation of Regulations for Tests and Methods of Assay and Certification of Anti-biotic Drugs, Federal Security Agency, Food and Drug Administration.

BACTO-LYSOZYME (B465)
BACTO-LYSOZYME SUBSTRATE (B461)
BACTO-LYSOZYME BUFFER (B464)

Bacto-Lysozyme is a crystalline enzyme prepared from fresh egg white, containing sufficient Bacto-Lysozyme Buffer to give a solution of pH 6.2 when rehydrated with distilled water. Bacto-Lysozyme Substrate is a dried standardized irradiated culture of *Micrococcus lysodeikticus* recommended for use in the turbidimetric assay of Lysozyme activity of body fluids, extracts from animal tissues and other materials suspected of containing this enzyme. It is supplied with sufficient Bacto-Lysozyme Buffer to give a suspension of pH 6.2 when rehydrated with distilled water. Bacto-Lysozyme Buffer, rehydrated in distilled water is a phosphate solution at pH 6.2 used in the test. The test employs the principles of Fleming,[1] Goldsworthy and Florey,[2] Boasson[3] and Hartsell and Smolelis.[4] A detailed discussion of the test is available upon request.

[1] Proc. Roy. Soc. (London), B, 93:306:1922.   [3] J. Immunol., 34:281:1938.
[2] Brit. J. Exp. Path., 11:192:1930.   [4] J. Bact., 58:731:1949.

BILE PRODUCTS
BACTO-OXGALL (B128)

Bacto-Oxgall is a dehydrated fresh bile, prepared especially for use in making bile media. It is manufactured from large quantities of fresh bile by rapid evaporation of the water content. The use of Bacto-Oxgall insures a regular source of supply independent of the slaughterhouse, and assures a degree of uniformity impossible to obtain with fresh materials, eliminating the uncertainty of variable results. The equivalent of fresh bile is attained in a 10 per cent solution of Bacto-Oxgall.

Bacto-Oxgall is recommended for use in the preparation of media for the detection and propagation of intestinal organisms. Specifically, a large number of bile-containing media have been devised for use in the bacteriological examination of water. Bacto-Oxgall is most frequently used in the preparation of culture media for water analysis. The Ninth Edition of "Standard Methods for the Examination of Water and Sewage"[1] recommends Brilliant Green Lactose Bile Broth as discussed on page 37, for confirming positive presumptive tests of coliform bacteria in water. In this text Brilliant Green Lactose Bile Agar, as discussed on page 52, is described as a selective agar medium for the direct plate count of the coliform group. Bacto-Oxgall is recommended as an ingredient of both these media. Brilliant Green Lactose Peptone Bile 2 per cent is also approved in "Standard Methods for the Examination of Dairy Products"[2] for detecting the presence of coliform bacteria in milk.

Solutions of Bacto-Oxgall, added to broth cultures of pneumococci, produce lysis of the cells, and can therefore be used in bile solubility tests for differentiating pneumococci from the bile-insoluble streptococci. The general procedure of the bile solubility test is to add one part of a sterile 10 per cent solution of Bacto-Oxgall to nine or ten parts of culture. Evans[3] and McKinney[4] have used Bacto-Oxgall for this purpose. Greey[5] reported excellent results using dry Bacto-Oxgall sprinkled directly on Blood Agar plates. According to this procedure pneumococcus colonies are dissolved and disappear entirely, but leave evidence of their presence by means of the fixed blood cells in the clear medium. Colonies of *Streptococcus viridans* are not dissolved or otherwise altered. Bacto-Oxgall is also used in solution for the enrichment of blood cultures.

Bacto-Oxgall has been used in the preparation of a selective medium for fungi. Littman[6] described an agar medium for the isolation of pathogenic fungi, employing Bacto-Oxgall, crystal violet and streptomycin as inhibiting agents for bacteria. A complete discussion of this medium is given on page 240.

[1] Standard Methods for the Examination of Water and Sewage, 9th Edition, 1946.
[2] Standard Methods for the Examination of Dairy Products, 9th Edition, 1948.
[3] J. Bact., 31:423:1936.
[4] J. Bact., 27:373:1934.
[5] J. Infectious Diseases, 64:206:1939.
[6] Science, 106:109:1947.

BACTO-BILE SALTS (B129)

Bacto-Bile Salts was originally developed for use in the Lactose Bile Salt Agar of MacConkey,[1] one of the best known of the plating media for the isolation of organisms of the colon-typhoid group. As originally described by MacConkey, the medium was a peptone lactose, or glucose, agar containing 0.5 per cent sodium glycocholate. Bacto-Bile Salts fulfilled the requirements of the original sodium glycocholate. However, in recent studies, we have developed Bacto-Bile Salts No. 3 which has been found to be more suitable than the Bacto-Bile Salts previously employed in the MacConkey Agar.

Bacto-Bile Salts has proven particularly valuable in the preparation of Bacto-Tetrathionate Broth. This medium is discussed on page 157.

Bacto-Bile Salts is readily soluble in distilled water and is neutral in reaction. It may, therefore, be used in preparing media without adjustment of reaction or filtration.

[1] J. Hyg., 5:333:1905.

BACTO-BILE SALTS NO. 3 (B130)

Bacto-Bile Salts No. 3 is a modification of Bacto-Bile Salts and is prepared especially for use in Bacto-MacConkey Agar, Bacto-S S Agar and Bacto-Violet Red Bile Agar. In our investigations on these media we found that the Bacto-Bile Salts gave a somewhat heavy precipitate around lactose fermenting colonies, which, under certain conditions, made it difficult to detect colonies of the pathogenic lactose non-fermenters. Bacto-Bile Salts No. 3 obviates this fault, giving a clearer medium and also reducing the precipitation around the coliform colonies, thus facilitating the detection of lactose non-fermenting colonies. A complete discussion of these media, using Bacto-Bile Salts No. 3, is given on pages 131, 134, and 61, respectively.

Bacto-Bile Salts No. 3 is readily soluble in distilled water and is neutral in reaction. It may, therefore, be used in preparing media without adjustment of reaction or filtration.

SODIUM TAUROCHOLATE, DIFCO (B278)

Sodium Taurocholate, Difco is the sodium salt of a conjugated bile acid used generally in bacteriological culture media for the isolation and cultivation of members of the enteric group. Like whole bile, it has the cultural characteristic of inhibiting the growth of Gram-positive organisms and spore forming bacteria, without inhibiting the development of Gram-negative bacilli.

Sodium Taurocholate, Difco contains about 75 per cent sodium taurocholate along with other naturally occurring salts of bile acids. It is readily soluble in distilled water forming a clear amber solution, neutral in reaction.

SODIUM DESOXYCHOLATE, DIFCO (B248)

Sodium Desoxycholate, Difco is the sodium salt of desoxycholic acid. It is used in bacteriological culture media and in the pneumococcus bile solubility test. Sodium desoxycholate is readily soluble in distilled water, giving a clear colorless solution neutral in reaction.

Sodium desoxycholate, like bile and other bile salts when used in bacteriological culture media, is inhibitive to Gram-positive cocci and spore forming organisms but is not inhibitory to Gram-negative enteric bacilli. Since sodium desoxycholate is a salt of a highly purified bile acid it is used in culture media in lower concentrations than is naturally occurring bile.

Leifson[1] described media for the enumeration of coliform organisms from milk, water, sewage, etc., and for the isolation of enteric pathogens using sodium desoxycholate to inhibit Gram-positive organisms. He also prepared a selective medium using sodium desoxycholate and sodium citrate for the isolation of intestinal pathogens. Coliform as well as Gram-positive organisms are inhibited on this Desoxycholate Citrate Agar. Bacto-Desoxycholate Agar and Bacto-Desoxycholate Citrate Agar, prepared with sodium desoxycholate, are discussed on pages 63 and 138, respectively.

Sodium desoxycholate is also used in 10 per cent concentration in the bile solubility test for pneumococci.

[1] J. Path. Bact., 40:581::1935.

DEHYDRATED MEATS
FOR INFUSIONS

BACTO-BEEF (B131)

Bacto-Beef is desiccated powdered fresh lean beef. It is prepared especially for use in making beef infusion media. Large quantities of beef are processed at one time in order to secure a uniform and homogenous product. The nutritive qualities of the fresh beef are retained in Bacto-Beef and may be preserved in the infusions prepared from it. Media prepared from Bacto-Beef are superior to beef extract media and are equal to infusion media made from market beef.

The equivalent of 500 grams of fresh lean beef is secured from 100 grams of Bacto-Beef. An excellent infusion, however, can be prepared by using 50 grams of Bacto-Beef per 1000 ml. of distilled water. This mixture is infused at 50°C. for one hour. It is then heated to boiling for a few minutes to coagulate some of the proteins and is filtered. Peptone and the other ingredients of the medium are then added to the filtrate. After adjustment of the reaction to pH 7.5–7.8 and subsequent boiling for a few minutes there will be a further coagulation which should be removed by filtration before the medium is sterilized.

Infusion media prepared from Bacto-Beef have been recommended for use in the microbial examination of butter.[1] Herrold[2] has also used an infusion from Bacto-Beef in preparing Blood Agar for primary cultivation of the gonococcus. Bacto-Beef is used in the National Formulary[3] specifications in determining the proteolytic activity of papain.

[1] J. Dairy Science, 16:289:1933.
[2] J. Infectious Diseases, 42:79:1928.
[3] National Formulary, Eighth Edition:371:1946.

BACTO-BEEF HEART FOR INFUSIONS (B132)

Bacto-Beef Heart for Infusions is prepared from fresh beef heart tissue and is particularly recommended for preparing heart infusion media. Bacto-Beef Heart for Infusions is processed from large quantities of raw material, retaining all the nutritive and growth-stimulating properties of the fresh tissues.

One hundred grams of Bacto-Beef Heart for Infusions are the equivalent of 500 grams of fresh heart tissue. Generally, excellent infusions can be prepared using 50 grams of Bacto-Beef Heart for Infusions per 1000 ml. of distilled water. For best results infuse at 50°C. for 1 hour, then heat to boiling for a few minutes to coagulate some of the proteins, and filter. Peptone and the other ingredients of the medium should then be added to the filtrate, the reaction adjusted to pH 7.5–7.8, and the medium boiled and filtered before sterilizing.

Bacto-Beef Heart for Infusions is recommended for the preparation of St. John's Medium[1] for the cultivation of *Endamoeba histolytica* by Brown in "Diagnostic Procedures and Reagents"[2] of the American Public Health Association. Morton, Smith and Leberman[3] used Bacto-Beef Heart for Infusions in a medium recommended for the cultivation and isolation of Pleuropneumonia-like organisms.

Bacto-Beef Heart for Infusions is not to be confused with Bacto-Beef Heart (for antigens) as discussed on page 315. The latter product is prepared for an entirely different purpose and is not interchangeable with Bacto-Beef Heart for Infusions.

[1] Am. J. Trop. Med., 12:301:1932.   [3] Am. J. Syphilis Gonorrh. Venereal Diseases,
[2] Diagnostic Procedures and Reagents, 3rd Edi-   35:361:1951.
tion:417:1950.

BACTO-LIVER (B133)

Bacto-Liver is prepared from large quantities of carefully trimmed fresh beef liver and is recommended for use in preparing liver infusion media. The nutritive factors of fresh liver tissue are retained in infusions prepared from Bacto-Liver.

The equivalent of 500 grams of fresh liver is obtained with 135 grams of Bacto-Liver. An excellent infusion can be prepared by using 75, or even 50, grams of Bacto-Liver per 1000 ml. of distilled water. The latter concentration is recommended for media for general culture purposes. The infusion is made by warming the mixture to 50°C. and holding it at this temperature with frequent agitation for one hour. The mixture is heated to boiling for a few minutes to coagulate a portion of the proteins, and is filtered. Peptone and other ingredients of the medium are then added to the filtrate. After adjustment of the reaction to pH 7.5–7.8 and subsequent boiling, there will be a further coagulation which should be removed by filtration before the medium is sterilized.

BACTO-VEAL (B134)

Bacto-Veal is desiccated powdered fresh lean veal, retaining the growth-promoting properties of the fresh tissue, and is recommended for use in the preparation of veal infusion media.

Eighty-five grams of Bacto-Veal are the equivalent of 500 grams of fresh lean veal. An excellent infusion can be prepared by using 50 grams of Bacto-Veal per 1000 ml. of distilled water, but larger quantities may be used if desired. Bacto-Veal should be infused at 50°C. for 1 hour, then heated to boiling for a few minutes to coagulate some of the proteins, and filtered. Peptone and the other ingredients may then be added to the filtrate and the reaction adjusted to pH 7.5–7.8. The medium is boiled and filtered before sterilization.

Veal Broth for the preparation of diphtheria toxin can be prepared by infusing 80 grams of Bacto-Veal in 1000 ml. of distilled water at 38°C. for 1 hour. To remove the muscle sugars the infusion is then inoculated with a vigorously growing culture of *Escherichia coli* and incubated overnight at room temperature. After heating to 85°C. and filtering, 20 grams of peptone and 5 grams of sodium chloride are added and the reaction adjusted to pH 8.0. The medium is then boiled for 5 minutes, filtered and the filtrate distributed in 100 ml. amounts in 300 ml. Erlenmeyer flasks and sterilized in the autoclave for 15 minutes at 15 pounds pressure (121°C.). The sterile medium is inoculated with an 18-hour culture of *Corynebacterium diphtheriae* which has been previously acclimated to the medium. A potent toxin can usually be harvested after incubation at 36°C. for 4–7 days.

SOLDIFYING AGENTS

BACTO-AGAR (B140)

The introduction of agar-agar as a solidifying agent for culture media was an important step in the advancement of the science of bacteriology. Credit for the use of agar for this purpose is generally given to Fannie Hesse.[1,2] Agar media have made possible many of the advances of bacteriology, for the use of these solid media paved the way for our present day methods of pure culture isolation and study.

Bacto-Agar is a purified agar from which the extraneous matter, pigmented portions, and salts are reduced to a minimum. Bacto-Agar is available in the form of fine, light-colored granules, which are convenient for weighing and handling. It is usually employed in solid culture media in concentrations of 1–2 per cent. Recently the use of small quantities of agar (0.05–0.3 per cent) in media has become quite general for the determination of motility and the growth of anaerobes and micro-aerophiles. The addition of such amounts of agar to liquid media, as discussed under Bacto-Brain Heart Infusion on page 77, permits all degrees of oxygen tension to exist and thus aids in the development of many fastidious aerobic and anaerobic organisms.

The value of the use of small quantities of agar in media for sterility testing was pointed out by Falk, Bucca and Simmons[3] and has been incorporated in the thioglycollate medium for sterility testing of biologics and antibiotics by official procedures.[4,5,6,7]

[1] Hueppe: Die Methoden der Bakterienforschung, 1891.
[3] J. Bact., 37:485:1939.
[3] J. Bact., 37:121:1939.
[4] National Institute of Health Circular: Culture Media for the Sterility Test, 2nd Revision, Feb. 25, 1946.

[5] Compilation of Regulations for Tests and Methods of Assay and Certification of Antibiotic Drugs, Federal Security Agency, Food and Drug Administration.
[6] Pharmacopeia of the United States, XIV Revision:758:1950.
[7] National Formulary, 9th Edition:768:1950.

SPECIAL AGAR (NOBLE) (B142)

Special Agar (Noble) is a carefully washed agar, free from all impurities which would interfere with its efficiency when employed in the preparation of Noble's[1] Cyanide Citrate Agar, for the direct plating and counting of the coli-aerogenes group. It is prepared according to the procedure suggested by Noble and each lot is tested for its usefulness in the preparation of his medium. Noble and Tonney[2] specify the use of Special Agar (Noble) as an ingredient of their Brilliant Green Lactose Bile Agar for the direct plate count of the coliform group in water. The medium, Bacto-Brilliant Green Bile Agar, is discussed on page 52.

[1] J. Am. Water Works Assoc., 19:182:1928.   [2] J. Am. Water Works Assoc., 27:108:1935.

BACTO-GELATIN (B143)

Gelatin was first employed as a solidifying agent for bacteriological culture media by Koch in 1881. This innovation paved the way for the future of the science although gelatin media were soon replaced by others containing agar as the solidifying material.

Bacto-Gelatin is a high grade gelatin in granular form for convenience in handling. This granular form of gelatin is readily soluble in warm water. Solutions of Bacto-Gelatin are light in color and sparklingly clear in appearance. They generally require no adjustment of reaction when used in culture media, as in the Nutrient Gelatin described in "Standard Methods of Water Analysis" of the American Public Health Association. In a 12 per cent concentration Bacto-Gelatin has a melting point between 28 and 30°C. and a reaction of pH 6.8.

The use of Bacto-Gelatin in culture media for studies of gelatinolysis (elaboration of gelatinolytic enzymes) by bacteria is recommended by the Committee on Bacteriological Technic[1] of the Society of American Bacteriologists. Levine and Carpenter[2] and Levine and Shaw[3] also employed Bacto-Gelatin in the media used in their studies of gelatin liquefaction. Garner and Tillett[4] used culture media prepared with Bacto-Gelatin in their study of the fibrinolytic activity of hemolytic streptococci.

The formula for Nutrient Gelatin as given in "Standard Methods" specifies the use of 12 per cent gelatin. Other formulae may call for larger or smaller quantities of gelatin or for combinations of gelatin and agar.

[1] Pure Culture Study of Bacteria, 4:No.3:1936.
[2] J. Bact., 8:297:1923.
[3] J. Bact., 9:225:1924.
[4] J. Exp. Med., 60:255:1934.

CARBOHYDRATES, POLYHYDRIC ALCOHOLS, AND GLUCOSIDES

CARBOHYDRATES, polyhydric alcohols, glucosides and salts of organic acids are extensively employed in culture media as a source of energy for bacteria and, more particularly, for differentiating genera and identifying species. The ability of an organism to attack a particular carbohydrate is a definite characteristic of bacterial species and under controlled conditions remains constant for the organism throughout generations of cultivation on media.

These carbohydrates, polyhydric alcohols, glucosides and salts of organic acids are prepared with the utmost care to eliminate admixtures, other sugars or contaminating materials. They are standardized to the highest known degree of purity, having in view the consensus of authority concerning their respective properties. In addition to the carbohydrates described below we also prepare filter sterilized solutions of a selected number of carbohydrates. These solutions are prepared in 10 per cent concentration and are discussed on page 293.

BACTO-DEXTROSE (B155)

Bacto-Dextrose is a specially prepared dextrose (d-glucose) of unusual purity, recommended for use as a readily available source of energy for bacteria and also for fermentation studies. It is free from all other sugars and from starch, proteins, alcohol and heavy metals. In appearance it is a pure white crystalline powder. Its specific rotation lies between +52.5 and +52.76.

Bacto-Dextrose is widely used in studies of the fermentative processes of bacteria. In fluid media it is usually employed in a concentration of 0.5 per cent, but in solid media it may be used in higher concentrations. Dextrose media also have a distinct value in the rejuvenation of cultures because this carbohydrate is readily assimilated by most bacteria. As small an amount of dextrose as 0.05

per cent added to a carbohydrate-free medium causes a definite increase in the rate of growth of many microorganisms.

BACTO-LACTOSE (B156)

Bacto-Lactose is a highly purified disaccharide, recommended for use in the study of the fermentation reactions of bacteria. It is free from dextrose as determined by culture of *Salmonella typhosa* and controlled by determinations of changes in hydrogen ion concentration. It contains no trace of casein or other proteins, starch, alcohol or heavy metals. Its specific rotation is +52.4 with 0.5° tolerance.

Lactose media are of distinct value for the presumptive test for coliform bacteria in water and milk. Many of the differential media used for identification of organisms of the colon-typhoid-dysentery group also contain this carbohydrate either alone or in combination with other fermentable substances. In fluid media, lactose is usually employed in a concentration of 0.5 per cent, but in solid media higher concentrations may be used.

ADDITIONAL COMPOUNDS

In addition to the above we also prepare the following purified carbohydrates, polyhydric alcohols, glucosides and salts of organic acids. These are especially suited for bacteriological culture media.

Adonitol (Adonite) (B157)
Aesculin (B158)
l-Arabinose (B159)
Cellobiose (B160)
Dextrin (B161)
Dextrose (d-Glucose, see Bacto-Dextrose) (B155)
Dulcitol (Dulcite) (B152)
d-Galactose (B163)
Glycerol (B282)
i-Inositol (B164)
Inulin (B165)

Invert Sugar Syrup (B166)
Lactose (see Bacto-Lactose) (B156)
Levulose (d-Fructose, from Inulin) (B167)
Maltose (B168)
Maltose, Technical (B169)
d-Mannitol (Mannite) (B170)
d-Mannose (B171)
Melezitose (B172)
Melibiose (B173)
Raffinose (B174)

Rhamnose (Isodulcitol) (B175)
Saccharose (Sucrose) (B176)
Salicin (B177)
Soluble Starch (B178)
Sodium Hippurate (B330)
d-Sorbitol (Sorbite) (B179)
Trehalose (B180)
d-Xylose (B181)

CARBOHYDRATE SOLUTIONS IN AMPULS

Carbohydrate solutions, sterilized by filtration, are prepared for the use of laboratories desiring fermentation media in which the carbohydrate has not been heat sterilized. These carbohydrates are ampuled in 10 ml. amounts, each ampul containing 1 gram of the carbohydrate in sterile solution. Carbohydrate solutions in ampuls are convenient and economical when small quantities of fermentation media are required.

For the preparation of carbohydrate media, the basic sugar-free medium is prepared and sterilized as usual. The desired carbohydrate solution is then added aseptically and the medium is dispensed into sterile containers with aseptic precautions. To prepare a medium containing one per cent of the carbohydrate the contents of one ampul are added to 90 ml. of medium; to prepare a medium with 0.5 per cent of the carbohydrate, the contents of one ampul are added to 190 ml. of the sterile sugar-free base. The final medium should always be incubated before use to insure its sterility.

In conjunction with these solutions reference should be made to Bacto-

Phenol Red Broth Base, Bacto-Phenol Red Agar Base, Bacto-Purple Broth Base and Bacto-Purple Agar Base as discussed on pages 186–190. The following carbohydrate solutions are supplied in packages of one-half dozen or one dozen ampuls of 10 ml. each:

Dextrose Solution 10% (B155A)   Maltose Solution 10% (B168A)
Galactose Solution 10% (B163A)   Mannitol Solution 10% (B170A)
Glycerol Solution 10% (B282A)   Saccharose Solution 10% (B176A)
                Lactose Solution 10% (B156A)

DYES AND INDICATORS

DYES AND INDICATORS are essential to the preparation of most differential culture media. In such media the dyes may act as bacteriostatic agents, as inhibitors of growth or as indicators of changes in the degree of acidity or alkalinity of the substrate. It is obvious, therefore, that only dyes of known purity and known dye content should be used in the preparation of media.

Great care is necessary in the preparation of differential or selective media, even with dyes standardized by the most modern methods. All ingredients of the medium must be used in the amounts specified in the formula and the reaction of the medium must be adjusted with extreme care in order to obtain proper results. Certain of the dyes listed in this section are identified by their Color Index number (C.I. No.) according to "Color Index" of the Society of Dyers and Colourists, 1924. The actual dye content of each dye is shown on each label.

BACTO-BASIC FUCHSIN (B191)
For Endo Agar and Other Basic Fuchsin Media

Bacto-Basic Fuchsin (C.I. No. 676) is certified for use in culture media and for the general histological and bacteriological staining by the Commission on Standardization of Biological Stains.

Bacto-Basic Fuchsin is recommended for the preparation of Endo Agar and other basic fuchsin media. In Endo Agar this dye is partially decolorized with sodium sulfite. On this medium lactose fermenting organisms form red colonies and change the color of the surrounding medium from faint pink to red; typical *Escherichia coli* colonies, in addition to being red in color, generally exhibit a brilliant metallic sheen. Organisms not fermenting lactose form uncolored colonies which do not alter the appearance of the medium.

In Tryptose Agar, discussed on page 111, Bacto-Basic Fuchsin may be employed in a concentration of 1:100,000 for differentiation of strains of *Brucella*. In Bacto-Fuchsin Lactose Broth, discussed on page 41, the dye is present in a concentration of 1:66,000.

BACTO-BRILLIANT GREEN (B192)
For Brilliant Green Media

Bacto-Brilliant Green (C.I. No. 662) is certified for use in culture media by the Commission on Standardization of Biological Stains.

Bacto-Brilliant Green is recommended for use in preparing the Brilliant

Green Bile Media described in "Standard Methods for the Examination of Water and Sewage"[1] and "Standard Methods for the Examination of Dairy Products."[2] This dye, in the proper concentration in media, exhibits the desired selectivity, being inhibitive to Gram-positive non-confirming organisms, permitting the unrestricted development of the colon-aerogenes group.

[1] Standard Methods for the Examination of Water and Sewage: 9th Edition, 1946.   [2] Standard Methods for the Examination of Dairy Products, 8th Edition, 1941.

BACTO-CRYSTAL VIOLET (B193)
(GENTIAN VIOLET)

Bacto-Crystal Violent (C.I. No. 681) is certified for use in bacteriological culture media by the Commission on Standardization of Biological Stains.

Crystal violet and its impure form, gentian violet, have long been used in culture media because of their selective inhibitory action toward the Gram-positive bacteria. Although Bacto-Crystal Violet has a wide range over which it is not significantly toxic to the Gram-negative bacteria and is still definitely bacteriostatic toward the Gram-positive organisms, it should be used with extreme care to preserve the proper ratio of dye to medium and to maintain the correct reaction.

In Tryptose Agar, discussed on page 111, Bacto-Crystal Violet may be used in a concentration of 1:700,000 for isolation of *Brucella* strains from infected milk. Bacto-Crystal Violet is employed in Bacto-Supplement A, a selective enrichment for gonococci and meningococci. A complete discussion of this supplement is given on page 276 or under Bacto-Proteose No. 3 Agar, page 116, and Bacto-G C Medium Base, page 122.

BACTO-EOSIN Y (B194)

Bacto-Eosin Y (C.I. No. 768) is certified for use in bacteriological culture media by the Commission on Standardization of Biological Stains.

Bacto-Eosin Y is recommended for use in conjunction with Bacto-Methylene Blue in the preparation of Eosin Methylene Blue Agar according to the Levine formula[1] as specified in "Standard Methods for the Examination of Water and Sewage"[2] or in accordance with the formula of Holt-Harris and Teague.[3] These media are discussed in detail on pages 35 and 133.

[1] Bull. 62, Iowa Eng. Exp. Sta., 1921.   [3] J. Infectious Diseases, 18:596:1916.
[2] Standard Methods for the Examination of Water and Sewage, 9th Edition:187:1946.

BACTO-METHYLENE BLUE (B195)

Bacto-Methylene Blue (C.I. No. 922) is certified for use in bacteriological culture media and for all other purposes by the Commission on Standardization of Biological Stains.

Bacto-Methylene Blue is recommended for use in conjunction with Bacto-Eosin Y in the preparation of Eosin Methylene Blue Agar according to the Levine formula[1] as specified in "Standard Methods for the Examination of Water and Sewage,"[2] or in accordance with the formula of Holt-Harris and Teague.[3] These media are discussed in detail on pages 35 and 133.

[1] Bull. 62 Iowa Eng. Exp. Sta., 1921.   [3] J. Infectious Diseases, 18:596:1916.
[2] Standard Methods for the Examination of Water and Sewage, 9th Edition:187:1946.

BACTO-THIONIN (B196)

Bacto-Thionin (C.I. No. 920) is recommended for use in preparing the thionin medium employed in the differentiation of *Brucella* types. In Tryptose Agar, as discussed on page 111, Bacto-Thionin may be used for the differentiation of *Brucella* in a concentration of 1:200,000. Upon Thionin Tryptose Agar *Brucella melitensis* and *B. suis* grow readily while *B. abortus* fails to develop.

SULFONPHTHALEIN AND OTHER INDICATORS

In selecting this group of indicators[1,2] we have chosen those generally employed in most laboratories. The use of these indicators in the preliminary adjustment of culture media reactions, or as indicators of bacterial metabolism in the media themselves, is well-known and needs no further explanation. These indicators have been subjected to both bacteriological and chemical assay. They are non-toxic in the concentration usually employed in media, and indicate color changes at various reactions as shown below.

[1] Clark: The Determination of Hydrogen Ions, 1928.
[2] Pharmacopeia of the United States, XIV:970: 1950.

INDICATORS SHOWING PREPARATION, pH RANGES AND COLOR CHANGES

	A*	pH Range	pK	Color Acid Alkali
Bacto-Cresol Red (acid) (B204)......... (o-Cresolsulfonphthalein)	26.2	0.2–1.8	—	Red-Yellow
Bacto-Meta Cresol Purple (acid) (B205).. (m-Cresolsulfonphthalein)	26.2	1.2–2.8	1.51	Red-Yellow
Bacto-Thymol Blue (acid) (B202)........ (Thymolsulfonphthalein)	21.5	1.2–2.8	1.5	Red-Yellow
Bacto-Brom Phenol Blue (B199)......... (Tetrabromophenolsulfonphthalein)	14.9	3.0–4.9	3.98	Yellow-Blue
Bacto-Brom Cresol Green (B200)........ (Tetrabromo-o-cresolsulfonphthalein)	14.3	3.8–5.4	4.67	Yellow-Blue
Bacto-Brom Cresol Purple (B201)........ (Dibromo-o-cresolsulfonphthalein)	18.5	5.2–6.8	6.3	Yellow-Purple
Bacto-Brom Thymol Blue (B202)........ (Dibromothymolsulfonphthalein)	16.0	6.0–7.6	7.0	Yellow-Blue
Bacto-Phenol Red (B203).............. (Phenolsulfonphthalein)	28.2	6.8–8.4	7.9	Yellow-Red
Bacto-Cresol Red (alkaline) (B204)...... (o-Cresolsulfonphthalein)	26.2	7.2–8.8	8.3	Yellow-Red
Bacto-Meta Cresol Purple (alkaline) (B205) (m-Cresolsulfonphthalein)	26.2	7.4–9.0	8.32	Yellow-Purple
Bacto-Thymol Blue (alkaline) (B206).... (Thymolsulfonphthalein)	21.5	8.0–9.6	8.9	Yellow-Blue

*A—ml. 0.01N NaOH required per 0.1 g. indicator. Dilute to 250 ml. with distilled water for 0.04 per cent solution for use as indicator for colorimetric pH determinations.

	pH Range	Color Acid Alkali	Preparation
Methyl Red (B207)....	4.4– 6.0	Red-Yellow	0.1 g. in 300 ml. ethanol and dilute to 500 ml. with distilled water
Neutral Red (B208)....	6.8– 8.0	Red-Yellow	0.1 g. in 60 ml. ethanol make up to 100 ml.
Litmus, Pure (B209)....	4.5– 8.3	Red-Blue	1.0 g. in 100 ml. water
Phenolphthalein (B210).	8.3–10.0	Colorless-Red	1.0 g. in 60 ml. ethanol and make up to 100 ml. with ethanol.

BIOCHEMICALS

p-AMINOBENZOIC ACID, DIFCO   (B240)

p-Aminobenzoic acid is recommended for use in liquid culture media for the prevention of bacterial stasis due to any sulfonamide drug. It should be added to all liquid media used for blood cultures of patients under sulfonamide therapy, and in the culture of exudates or other materials containing sulfonamide compounds. As pointed out by Lockwood[1] and McLeod[2] most culture media normally contain some sulfonamide inhibitors which generally are not sufficient to neutralize completeiy the sulfonamides likely to be encountered. The addition of 5 mg. of p-aminobenzoic acid to 100 ml. of medium will more than suffice to neutralize the bacteriostatic effect of 1.5 mg. per cent sulfonamide drug. This quantity of p-aminobenzoic acid is not toxic to fastidious pathogens even though the inocula contain only a few organisms. The report of Janeway[3] shows the value of p-aminobenzoic acid in culture media wherever sulfonamides are encountered.

[1] J. Immunol., 35:155:1938.   [3] J. Am. Med. Assoc., 116:941:1941
[2] J. Exp. Med., 72:217:1940.

p-AMINODIMETHYLANILINE MONOHYDRO-CHLORIDE, DIFCO   (B249)

p-Aminodimethylaniline Monohydrochloride, Difco (dimethyl-p-phenylenediamine hydrochloride) is recommended for use in the detection of oxidase production by microorganisms. Its practical application in the bacteriological laboratory was first described by Gordon and McLeod[1] who employed this reagent as an aid in differentiating colonies of oxidase-producing microorganisms from those not elaborating this enzyme. These authors found the oxidase test to be particularly helpful in the detection of *Neisseria gonorrhoeae* colonies growing among colonies of extraneous organisms in the primary culture of gonococcal exudates on Chocolate Agar. Since its introduction for this purpose p-aminodimethylaniline monohydrochloride has been widely adopted for use in the cultural diagnosis of gonorrhoea.[2,3] Oxidase positive colonies flooded or sprayed with p-aminodimethylaniline monohydrochloride turn pink within a minute or two and darken to become black. Oxidase negative colonies do not change color. *p*-Aminodimethylaniline monohydrochloride is used in 1 per cent concentration in distilled water. The solution should be prepared on the same day it is to be used. However, if kept longer, it should be refrigerated and then warmed before use. In no case should the solution be used if more than 5 days old or if a precipitate is present. A complete discussion of the use of this reagent is given under Bacto-Proteose No. 3 Agar and Bacto-G C Medium Base, pages 116 and 122, for use of the oxidase test in the cultural diagnosis of gonococcal infections.

Tetramethyl *p*-phenylenediamine hydrochloride may also be used in exactly the same way as the dimethyl reagent. The tetramethyl compound has the disadvantage of sometimes coloring the surrounding medium and is much more expensive than the dimethyl.

[1] J. Path. Bact., 31:185:1928.
[2] Seventh Annual Year Book (1936–37) p. 133. Suppl., Am. J. Pub. Health, 27:No. 3:1937.

[3] Diagnostic Procedures and Reagents, 3rd Edition:107:1950.

p-AMINODIMETHYLANILINE OXALATE, DIFCO (B329)

p-Aminodimethylaniline Oxalate, Difco, is recommended for the detection of oxidase production by microorganisms. It has the advantage over the monohydrochloride salt in that it is more stable in the powdered form and also in solution. The oxidase reagent is prepared by dissolving 1 gram of *p*-Aminodimethylaniline Oxalate, Difco in 100 ml. distilled water by heating gently. This solution is used to flood plates in determining the oxidase reaction. Positive colonies assume a pink color, finally turning to maroon and black. Carpenter[1] reported that the dry crystalline oxalate salt is more stable than the monohydrochloride salt. No change was observed after six months storage. Aqueous solutions were also more stable. Both salts showed about the same toxicity for microorganisms. The oxalate salt is slightly less soluble in cold distilled water, but solution is hastened by warming gently. Carpenter[2] further stated the oxalate salt possesses the additional advantages over the monohydrochloride in that it does not form the marked black precipitate on Chocolate Agar sometimes observed with the use of the monohydrochloride, especially when freshly prepared solutions are not employed.

[1] Science, 105:649:1948.

[2] Diagnostic Procedures and Reagents, 3rd Edition:107:1950.

SODIUM THIOGLYCOLLATE, DIFCO (B233)

Sodium thioglycollate or thioglycollic acid is recommended for use in liquid culture media for testing the sterility of biological and other materials containing heavy metal compound preservatives, such as the mercurials. The active sulfhydryl group annuls the toxicity of the metallic preservatives, thus permitting the development of any viable organisms present and, further, behaves similarly to glutathione, cysteine and the alkali sulfides in being able to lower the oxidation-reduction potential of the medium. This principle was first described by Trenkmann[1] who showed that the presence of an alkali sulfide induced "aerobic growth of anaerobic organisms".

Quastel and Stephenson[2] showed likewise that cysteine and thioglycollic acid made possible the growth of anaerobes through the lowering of the oxidation-reduction potential of the medium. Brewer[3,4] combined the principle of lowering the oxidation-reduction potential with Hitchen's[5] method of adding 0.05 to 0.1 per cent agar to the medium for the growth of anaerobes. Such a combination was found particularly useful as a sterility test medium for biological containing mercurial preservatives, since the sodium thioglycollate neutralizes the toxic effect of any mercurial carried over with the inoculum, while the agar provides anaerobic conditions necessary for growth.

Since sodium thioglycollate is toxic for some organisms, especially with inocula containing very few organisms, it is recommended that no more of the sodium thioglycollate be added to the medium than is required for mercurial neutralization. Sodium thioglycollate in 0.05 per cent concentration is specified in the thioglycollate media of the National Institute of Health[6] for sterility testing. These media are discussed under Bacto-Fluid Thioglycollate Medium and Bacto-N.I.H. Thioglycollate Broth on pages 195 and 198. Bacto-Brewer Anaerobic Agar, discussed on page 126, contains sodium thioglycollate, and is employed as a solid medium for the cultivation of anaerobes.

[1] Centr. Bakt. I Abt., 23:1038:1898.
[2] Biochem. J., 20:1125:1926.
[3] J. Bact., 39:10:1940.
[4] J. Am. Med. Assoc., 115:598:1940.

[5] J. Infectious Diseases, 29:390:1921.
[6] National Institute of Health Circular: Culture Media for Sterility Test, 2nd Revision, Feb. 5, 1946.

THIOGLYCOLLIC ACID, DIFCO (B250)

Thioglycollic Acid, Difco is recommended for use in media designed for the cultivation of organisms in the presence of mercurial salt preservative. It may also be used for the preparation of media of a low Eh. In the preparation of media for the sterility testing of biologicals, thioglycollic acid or sodium thioglycollate may be employed. A complete discussion of these media is given under Bacto-Fluid Thioglycollate Medium page 195 and Bacto-N.I.H. Thioglycollate Broth page 198.

UREA, DIFCO (B190)

Urea, Difco is purified urea recommended for the preparation of bacteriological culture media. The ability of an organism to hydrolyze urea is often a salient characteristic in its identification. The use of Urea Broth and Urea Agar Base for the identification of enteric organisms is discussed in detail on pages 170 and 171.

POTASSIUM TELLURITE, DIFCO (B384)

Potassium Tellurite, Difco is recommended for use as a selective agent in media for the isolation and differentiation of diphtheria bacilli. It has also been used as a selective agent in media designed for isolation of streptococci and the enrichment and isolation of pleuropneumonia-like organisms. Potassium Tellurite, Difco is readily soluble and well suited for use in media requiring this chemical, as each batch is checked to determine its inhibitive properties. Bacto-Chapman Tellurite Solution as discussed on page 277 is prepared with Potassium Tellurite. A complete description of the media using this selective agent is given under Bacto-PPLO Enrichment Broth, page 82 and Mitis Salivarius Agar, page 154.

MISCELLANEOUS INGREDIENTS

BACTO-EGG ALBUMEN, COAGULATED (B147)
BACTO-EGG YOLK, COAGULATED (B148)
BACTO-WHOLE EGG, COAGULATED (B149)

At the suggestion of, and in cooperation with, R. S. Spray, we have prepared Bacto-Egg Albumen, Coagulated; Bacto-Egg Yolk, Coagulated; and Bacto-Whole Egg, Coagulated. In his extensive studies on the use of egg for the cultivation and differentiation of anaerobic bacteria Spray[1] used these dehydrated egg products with excellent results.

Bacto-Egg Albumen, Coagulated is free from all traces of egg yolk. Bacto-Egg Yolk, Coagulated is similarly free from traces of egg albumen, while Bacto-Whole Egg, Coagulated, as the name indicates, contains both of these materials. All three are prepared for use by making a suspension of 0.5 gram of material in 10 ml. of distilled water or Nutrient Broth in a test tube. Spray has also found that a solution of Bacto-Tryptone was distinctly advantageous as a diluent for these materials. The suspensions are sterilized by autoclaving for 15 minutes at 15 pounds pressure (121°C.). After sterilization the media will have a reaction of pH 7.2 and will present a loosely flocculent appearance with a layer of fluid above the solid material.

The tubes are inoculated deeply by loop or pipette. Characteristic reactions indicative of proteolysis are produced by most anaerobes. The addition of reduced iron or lead acetate to the media greatly intensifies the blackening of the media produced by the action of proteolytic organisms.

[1] J. Lab. Clin. Med., 18:512:1932–33.

BACTO-ISOELECTRIC CASEIN (B145)

Bacto-Isoelectric Casein is a protein of exceptional purity, prepared by repeated precipitation of casein at its isoelectric point. This casein of more than ordinary purity is recommended for use in routine bacteriological culture media and also for the most exacting special procedures. It is suitable for the Fuld Gross method for the determination of tryptic activity. Bacto-Isoelectric Casein is quickly and completely soluble in a concentration of 1–2 per cent in a slightly alkaline solution.

Sodium caseinate is readily prepared by suspending Bacto-Isoelectric Casein in water for a few minutes and then making the suspension slightly alkaline with sodium hydroxide. This alkaline condition should be maintained until solution is complete. When prepared in this manner the solution of Bacto-Isoelectric Casein is light in color and only lightly opalescent.

CASEIN PURIFIED, DIFCO (B336)

Casein Purified is recommended for all procedures requiring a casein of high purity. Repeated precipitation and washing of casein at the isoelectric point produces a purified casein of uniform quality. Casein Purified is soluble in dilute solutions of sodium hydroxide forming the sodium salt.

CASEIN TECHNICAL, DIFCO (B337)

Casein Technical is a technical grade of this protein recommended for use in the preparation of culture media, and in other techniques not requiring a purified product.

SODIUM CASEINATE, DIFCO (B187)

Sodium Caseinate is a valuable ingredient of many culture media. It has frequently been referred to as "Nutrose". Sodium Caseinate, Difco is a purified product recommended for use in all media in which "Nutrose" or sodium caseinate has been employed.

EGG ALBUMEN SOLUBLE, DIFCO (B255)
WHOLE EGG SOLUBLE, DIFCO (B254)

Egg Albumen Soluble and Whole Egg Soluble are desiccated egg albumen and whole egg, respectively. They are available to bacteriologists who may desire to use such products for the preparation of culture media or for studies of bacterial metabolism. Egg Albumen Soluble and Whole Egg Soluble when rehydrated in 13.5 per cent concentration will give the equivalent of the original form of these products.

BACTO-RICE POWDER (B146)

Bacto-Rice Powder was prepared at the suggestion of L. R. Cleveland and is recommended for use in the propagation of *Endamoeba histolytica*. Cleveland and his co-workers[1,2,3] have given detailed descriptions of the methods they employed for the cultivation of this organism on a medium prepared from Bacto-Liver Infusion Agar with rice powder. Their method is discussed in detail under Bacto-Endamoeba Medium, page 97. Essentially, this procedure is to cover each slant of the medium with fresh horse serum-saline solution and to add sterile rice powder to each tube prior to inoculation with the organism. Bacto-Rice powder is sterilized in a dry heat oven at 160°F. for one hour. Scorching must be prevented.

[1] Arch. Protistenkunde, 70:223:1930.   [2] Am. J. Hyg., 12:606:1930.
[3] Science, 72:149:1930.

Tissue Culture Media
Reagents, Difco

As in the field of dehydrated culture media for Bacteriology and Mycology, Difco Laboratories has pioneered in the preparation of dehydrated reagents for *in vitro* propagation and maintenance of tissue cells. The task of preparing and distributing these highly specialized products was undertaken at the request of the Tissue Culture Association. Each of these reagents, before being released for distribution, is tested and certified for use in tissue culture by the Central Laboratory of the Tissue Culture Association. They are applicable to the slide, roller tube and flask culture techniques commonly employed for propagation and study of tissue cells *in vitro*. All desiccated reagents are dried from the frozen state to preserve, unaltered, the properties of the original material. The reagents currently available are those commonly employed for culturing tissue cells, maintaining tissue banks, and for the propagation of Viruses. Additional reagents will be made available as required for these and other procedures related to tissue culture.

TC CHICKEN PLASMA (B354)

TC Chicken Plasma is sterile desiccated whole chicken plasma certified for use in culturing tissue cells *in vitro*. It is prepared from selected disease-free cockerels 4–8 months old and is packaged in 5 ml. quantities.

TC Chicken Plasma is reconstituted to its original volume by adding, aseptically, 4.5 ml. sterile TC Reconstituting Fluid or TC Triple Distilled Water to each bottle. The Reconstituting Fluid may be added conveniently with a sterile 5 ml. syringe. Solution of the material is accelerated by gentle end-over-end rotation of the bottle. Do not shake. Allow 30 minutes for complete solution of the desiccated plasma.

The reconstituted plasma is alkaline in reaction due to loss of carbon dioxide in the desiccation process and requires adjustment with carbon dioxide to pH 7.2–7.4 if a normal clotting time is desired. Adjustment of the reaction with carbon dioxide to pH 7.2–7.4 accelerates the clotting time when Embryo Extract and tissue explants are added. The adjustment of the reaction of the reconstituted plasma is best accomplished by first adding TC Phenol Red Solution 1% to the plasma to give a final Phenol Red concentration of 0.002 per cent, (add 1 ml. TC Phenol Red Solution 1% to 9 ml. TC Triple Distilled Water, then add 0.1 ml. of resultant Phenol Red Solution to 5 ml. of reconstituted Chicken Plasma) and then introducing carbon dioxide to bring the reaction to pH 7.2–7.4. Three methods of introducing carbon dioxide that have given good results are outlined:

1. Transfer the reconstituted TC Chicken Plasma containing 0.002 per cent Phenol Red to a clean, dry, sterile cotton stoppered or loosely capped test tube. Place the tube in a beaker or container of sufficient depth so that the walls extend one or more inches above the mouth of the tube. Introduce carbon dioxide into the beaker to displace the air and then cover the beaker with paper or suitable cover. Gently agitate the plasma in the tube occasionally to bring all parts of the solution in contact with the carbon dioxide. Observe color change in

301

the indicator from cerise alkaline reaction to reddish orange almost neutral reaction. Reasonable care should be exercised to prevent overacidification as this will tend to coagulate the plasma spontaneously. When the indicator color change begins to turn from cerise to reddish orange, double check the pH by removing a drop of the plasma aseptically and transferring it to a few drops of distilled water to which indicator has been added on a spot plate or in a test tube. The recheck of the reaction by the test tube or spot plate method is essential because indicators do not always give true color changes in undiluted protein solutions. Failure to adjust the reaction of Chicken Plasma may give prolonged clotting times. For example, undiluted Chicken Plasma containing 0.002 per cent Phenol Red may give a color reaction indicative of pH 7.2 whereas the true reaction as determined by dilution in a test tube or spot plate may be pH 8.0 or greater. Also, color reactions with Phenol Red in undiluted plasma indicative of pH 7.2 reaction may actually be more acid by the test tube dilution and spot plate methods. When the reaction has been adjusted to pH 7.2–7.4, stopper tightly to prevent escape of carbon dioxide. Store in refrigerator at 2–6°C. if not used immediately. Storage for periods longer than one week is not recommended.

2. Transfer the reconstituted plasma containing Phenol Red to a clean, dry sterile tube. Bubble sterile carbon dioxide or a mixture of sterile carbon dioxide and nitrogen through the solution until the cerise color changes to reddish orange. Recheck pH by test tube or spot plate as outlined above. Adjust final reaction to pH 7.2–7.4.

3. Same as method #2 except blow sterile alveolar air through the plasma solution to give pH 7.2–7.4 using precautions stated above.

It has been our observation that Embryo Extracts diluted with Balanced Salt Solutions containing calcium in levels comparable with TC Balanced Salt Solution (Earle's BSS) give a faster clotting rate and a firmer coagulum with TC Chicken Plasma than do extracts prepared with a lower calcium content.

TC CHICK EMBRYO EXTRACT EE_{100} (B355)

TC Chick Embryo Extract EE_{100} is sterile desiccated whole, undiluted Chick Embryo Extract certified for use in tissue culture procedures requiring embryo extract. It is prepared from selected eleven-day old chick embryos, and is packaged in 2 ml. quantities.

TC Chick Embryo Extract EE_{100} is reconstituted by adding, aseptically, 2.0 ml. of TC Reconstituting Fluid or TC Triple Distilled Water to the 2 ml. bottle. When the contents of the bottle have uniformly combined with the water, they are diluted further as desired with TC Balanced Salt Solution. A 20 per cent Embryo Extract, EE_{20}, has been found to be useful in tissue culture procedures. This concentration is obtained by adding 4 volumes (8 ml.) of TC Balanced Salt Solution to the reconstituted Embryo Extract EE_{100}. The Reconstituting Fluid and the Balanced Salt Solution may be added conveniently by means of a sterile syringe and needle.

The diluted Embryo Extract EE_{20}, or other desired concentration, is allowed to stand at 35–37°C. for 30–60 minutes to obtain maximum solution of the nutrients. Solution of the desiccated material is accelerated by gentle end-over-end rotation of the bottle. Do not shake. A small portion of the desiccated Embryo Extract may remain in suspension. This insoluble residue should be removed by centrifugation of the bottle for 10 minutes at 2500–3000 rpm. The supernatant liquid is now ready for use. Unused portions of the diluted Embryo Extract should be stored in tightly stoppered containers in the refrigerator (2–6°C.). Storage of the reconstituted TC Chick Embryo Extract for periods longer than one week, even though refrigerated, is not recommended.

It has been our observation that Embryo Extracts diluted with Balanced Salt

Solutions containing calcium in levels comparable with TC Balanced Salt Solution (Earle's BSS) give a faster clotting rate and a firmer coagulum with TC Chicken Plasma than do extracts prepared with a lower calcium content.

TC CHICK EMBRYO (B470)

TC Chick Embryo is sterile whole minced Chick Embryo dried from the frozen state and certified for use in tissue culture procedures requiring chick embryo extract. It is prepared from selected eleven-day old chick embryos and is packaged in 2 ml. quantities.

TC Chick Embryo is prepared for use by adding 2 ml. TC Reconstituting Fluid or TC Triple Distilled Water to each vial to wet the desiccated embryo tissue thoroughly. Four volumes (8 ml.) TC Balanced Salt Solution are then added to each bottle. The solids are suspended by rotating the bottles gently in an end-over-end motion. Do not shake. The suspension is warmed to 35–$37°C$. for 30–60 minutes with occasional rotation to resuspend the solids. The bottles are then centrifuged at 2500–3000 rpm for 5 minutes to sediment the particulate matter following which, the supernatant is drawn off aseptically and transferred to a clean sterile container. The resultant extract is a 20 per cent Chick Embryo Extract, EE_{20}, and is ready for use. Unused portions of the extract should be stored at 2–$6°C$. Storage of the extract for periods longer than one week are not recommended.

It has been our observation that Embryo Extracts diluted with Balanced Salt Solutions containing calcium in levels comparable with TC Balanced Salt Solution (Earle's BSS) give a faster clotting rate and a firmer coagulum with TC Chicken Plasma than do extracts prepared with a lower calcium content.

TC BEEF EMBRYO EXTRACT EE_{100} (B396)

TC Beef Embryo Extract EE_{100} is sterile desiccated undiluted Beef Embryo Extract certified for use in tissue culture procedures requiring mammalian embryo extract. It is prepared from fresh bovine embryos 60–90 days of age and is packaged in 2 ml. quantities.

TC Beef Embryo Extract EE_{100} is reconstituted to its original volume by adding, aseptically, 2.0 ml. TC Reconstituting Fluid or TC Triple Distilled Water to each bottle. When the contents of the bottle has uniformly combined with the liquid it is then diluted further as desired with TC Balanced Salt Solution. A 20 per cent Embryo Extract, EE_{20}, has been found useful in tissue culture procedures. This concentration is obtained by adding four volumes (8 ml.) of TC Balanced Salt Solution to the reconstituted Embryo Extract EE_{100}. The Reconstituting Fluid and Balanced Salt Solution may be added conveniently by means of a sterile syringe and needle.

The diluted Embryo Extract EE_{20}, or other desired concentration, is allowed to stand at 35–$37°C$. for 30–60 minutes to obtain maximum solution of the nutrients. Solution of the desiccated material is accelerated by gentle end-over-end rotation of the bottle. Do not shake. A small portion of the desiccated Embryo Extract may remain in suspension. This insoluble residue should be removed by centrifugation of the bottle for 10 minutes at 2500–3000 rpm. The supernatant liquid is now ready for use. Unused portions of the diluted Embryo Extract should be stored in tightly stoppered containers in the refrigerator at 2–$6°C$. Storage of the reconstituted TC Beef Embryo Extract for periods longer than one week, even though refrigerated, is not recommended.

It has been our observation that Embryo Extracts diluted with Balanced Salt Solutions containing calcium in levels comparable with TC Balanced Salt Solution (Earle's BSS) give a faster clotting rate and a firmer coagulum with TC Chicken Plasma than do extracts prepared with a lower calcium content.

TC BEEF EMBRYO   (B471)

TC Beef Embryo is sterile whole minced Beef Embryo dried from the frozen state and certified for use in tissue culture procedures requiring beef embryo extract. It is prepared from beef embryos 60–90 days of age and is packaged in 2 ml. quantities.

TC Beef Embryo is prepared for use by adding 2 ml. TC Reconstituting Fluid or TC Triple Distilled Water to each vial to wet the desiccated embryo tissue thoroughly. Four volumes (8 ml.) TC Balanced Salt Solution are then added to each bottle. The solids are suspended by rotating the bottles gently in an end-over-end motion. Do not shake. The suspension is warmed to 35–37°C. for 30–60 minutes with occasional rotation to resuspend the solids. The bottles are then centrifuged at 2500-3000 rpm for 5 minutes to sediment the particulate matter following which, the supernatant liquid is drawn off aseptically and transferred to a clean sterile container. The resultant extract is a 20 per cent Beef Embryo Extract, EE_{20}, and is ready for use. Unused portions of the extract should be stored at 2–6°C. Storage of the extract for periods longer than one week are not recommended.

It has been our observation that Embryo Extracts diluted with Balanced Salt Solutions containing calcium in levels comparable with TC Balanced Salt Solution (Earle's BSS) give a faster clotting rate and a firmer coagulum with TC Chicken Plasma than do extracts prepared with a lower calcium content.

TC CORD SERUM, HUMAN   (B356)

TC Cord Serum, Human is sterile desiccated whole human cord serum certified for use in culturing tissue cells *in vitro*. It is obtained from blood from the placenta at childbirth. Each preparation is from the pooled sera from 25 or more placentae. It is packaged in 5 ml. quantities.

TC Cord Serum, Human is reconstituted to its original volume by adding, aseptically, 4.5 ml. TC Reconstituting Fluid or TC Triple Distilled Water to each bottle. Solution of the material is accelerated by gentle end-over-end rotation of the bottle. Do not shake. When solution is complete, it is ready for use. Unused portions of the reconstituted TC Cord Serum, Human should be kept in tightly stoppered containers in the refrigerator at 2–6°C. Storage of the reconstituted TC Cord Serum, Human for periods longer than one week, even though refrigerated, is not recommended.

The Reconstituted TC Cord Serum, Human is alkaline in reaction due to loss of carbon dioxide in the desiccation process and if desired may be adjusted to pH 7.2–7.4 in an atmosphere of carbon dioxide as described for the adjustment of Chicken Plasma page 301.

TC HORSE SERUM   (B357)

TC Horse Serum is sterile desiccated whole, pooled horse serum certified for use in culturing tissue cells *in vitro*. It is obtained from blood from fasted, healthy, lean geldings, and is packaged in 5 ml. quantities.

TC Horse Serum is reconstituted for use by adding, aseptically, 4.5 ml. TC Reconstituting Fluid or TC Triple Distilled Water to each bottle. The Reconstituting Fluid may be added conveniently with a sterile syringe and needle. Solution of the material is accelerated by a gentle end-over-end rotation of the bottle. Do not shake. When solution is complete, the serum is ready for use. Unused portions of the reconstituted TC Horse Serum should be kept in tightly stoppered containers in the refrigerator at 2–6°C. Storage of the reconstituted TC Horse Serum for periods longer than one week, even though refrigerated, is not recommended.

The reconstituted TC Horse Serum is alkaline in reaction due to loss of carbon dioxide in the desiccation process and if desired may be adjusted to pH 7.2–7.4 in an atmosphere of carbon dioxide as described for the adjustment of Chicken Plasma page 301.

TC ASCITIC FLUID (B472)

TC Ascitic Fluid is sterile, pooled, whole human ascitic fluid certified for use in tissue culture procedures. It is obtained from cirrhotic patients, free from bile salts, and is packaged in 10 ml. ampuls. TC Ascitic Fluid has a reaction of pH 6.9–7.0 and requires adjustment to 7.2–7.4 before being used as a nutrient for tissue cells. Adjustment is made by adding sterile sodium bicarbonate solution or by diluting the Ascitic Fluid with TC Balanced Salt Solution and agitating the mixture gently to drive off some of the carbon dioxide. TC Phenol Red Solution 1% may be added to the Ascitic Fluid in a concentration of 0.002 per cent as an indicator of reaction. (Add, aseptically, 0.02 ml. TC Phenol Red Solution 1% to 10 ml. Ascitic Fluid.)

TC BEEF SERUM ULTRAFILTRATE (B473)

TC Beef Serum Ultrafiltrate is a protein-free solution containing 0.001 per cent Phenol Red indicator. It is prepared by the ultrafiltration of beef serum through a colloidion membrane filter to remove all protein and preserve filterable growth accessory factors. It is certified for use in tissue culture and is recommended for all procedures requiring serum ultrafiltrate. TC Beef Serum ultrafiltrate is especially suited as a basal substrate for culturing tissue cells, maintaining tissue banks, propagating viruses and for maintaining the viability and motility of *Treponema pallida* for the Treponema Immobilization test. It is packaged in 50 ml. quantities in glass sealed ampuls.

TC HORSE SERUM ULTRAFILTRATE (B474)

TC Horse Serum Ultrafiltrate is a protein-free solution containing 0.001 per cent Phenol Red indicator. It is prepared by the ultrafiltration of horse serum through a colloidion membrane filter to remove all protein and preserve filterable growth accessory factors. It is certified for use in tissue culture and is recommended for all procedures requiring serum ultrafiltrate. TC Horse Serum ultrafiltrate is especially suited as a basal substrate for culturing tissue cells, maintaining tissue banks, propagating viruses and for maintaining the viability and motility of *Treponema pallida* for the Treponema Immobilization test. It is packaged in 50 ml. quantities in glass sealed ampuls.

TC BALANCED SALT SOLUTION (B351)

TC Balanced Salt Solution is a sterile balanced salt solution certified for use in tissue culture procedures. It is prepared according to the formula of Earle,[1] and has the following composition:

Sodium Chloride	6.8 g.
Potassium Chloride	0.4 g.
Calcium Chloride	0.2 g.
Magnesium Sulfate	0.2 g.
Sodium Phosphate Monobasic	0.125 g.
Bacto-Dextrose	1. g.
Sodium Bicarbonate	2.2 g.
Triple Distilled Water	1,000 ml.

TC Balanced Salt Solution is stabilized by adjustment of the reaction to pH 7.0 with carbon dioxide during preparation. It can readily be adjusted to pH 7.2–7.4 by permitting carbon dioxide to escape after removal from the bottle. TC Phenol Red Solution 1% may be added to the TC Balanced Salt Solution in 0.002 per cent concentration as an indicator of reaction. (Add, aseptically, 0.2 ml. TC Phenol Red Solution 1% to 100 ml. Balanced Salt Solution). TC Balanced Salt Solution is packaged in 100 ml. bottles.

[1] Nat. Cancer Inst., 4:167:1943.

TC RECONSTITUTING FLUID (B352)

TC Reconstituting Fluid is sterile, triple distilled water saturated with carbon dioxide and is certified for use in tissue culture procedures. It is packaged in 100 ml. quantities. It is used for reconstituting desiccated tissue culture reagents where a lower pH is desired than obtainable through use of TC Triple Distilled Water.

TC TRIPLE DISTILLED WATER (B353)

TC Triple Distilled Water is sterile and certified for use in tissue culture procedures. It is the distillate from triple distillation of water in an all-Pyrex still and is packaged in 100 ml. bottles.

TC Triple Distilled Water is recommended as a reconstituting fluid for tissue culture reagents and for the preparation of Balanced Salt Solution and other media.

TC PHENOL RED SOLUTION 1% (B358)

TC Phenol Red Solution 1% is sterile and certified for use as an indicator of pH in tissue culture procedures. It is employed in tissue culture media in concentrations of 0.001–0.002 per cent. For judging the pH of very small volumes of media, (1–2 ml.), the concentration of phenol red should be 3–5 times that given above, as suggested under the discussion of TC Chicken Plasma as given on page 301. TC Phenol Red Solution is packaged in 1 ml. ampuls and supplied in boxes of 6 ampuls.

METHODS OF TISSUE CULTURE

BRIEF outlines for the use of Difco tissue culture media reagents by the common methods of tissue culture are given below. These directions apply generally for any type of animal tissue; however, special investigation may be required to determine the optimal conditions for culturing a given tissue. Proportions of the various reagents given in the discussion may be varied to meet individual requirements.

Slide Culture

The sterile tissue to be cultured should be placed on a clean sterile glass surface and cut into appropriate sized explants while immersed in balanced salt solution (pH 7.4). The following sizes are usually suitable for the specified tissue:

minced tissues	0.5–1.0 mm.
embryonic tissues	1.0 mm.
adult tissues	1.5 mm.
adult skin	2.0 mm.

Further rinsing of the explants in balanced salt solution may be done if desired. Add one drop of TC Chicken Plasma to a cover-glass, followed by one drop of TC Embryo Extract EE_{20}. Larger amounts may be used in the same ratio if desired. Mix the two with a spatula and spread over an area having a diameter of 1 cm. Add two or three explants and separate them by about equal distances. Cover with a well slide and set aside to clot. Later, seal the coverglass to the well slide with melted paraffin or a mixture of 5 parts paraffin and 1 part yellow vaseline.

More diffuse and extensive cell migration may be encouraged by diluting the plasma before using with an equal or double volume of TC Balanced Salt Solution. Incubate the slide culture at 37°C., observe and continue culture in accordance with standard procedures.

Roller Tube Culture

Prepare explants as for slide cultures and place them in a small volume of nutrient solution in a well-slide or petri dish. The nutrient may consist of various proportions of TC Balanced Salt Solution, TC Horse Serum, or TC Cord Serum, Human and TC Embryo Extract EE_{20} (5 parts of Balanced Salt Solution, 3 parts serum and 2 parts embryo extract is satisfactory for general purposes). Place 2 drops of whole TC Chicken Plasma (50 per cent plasma is also satisfactory) in a 16x150 mm. tube and rotate until bottom third or half of tube is coated. With a pipette place 4 or 5 explants on the uncoated area near the top of the tube and remove excess nutrient from around explants with a Pasteur pipette. Then with pipette transfer individual explants to plasma coated surface. After about 10 minutes, stopper tubes and place them in the roller drum in the 37°C. incubator for 2 hours. The nutrient medium (mentioned above) should now be added in 0.5 ml. volumes to each tube and the tubes returned to roller drum in the incubator. Incubate at 37°C., observe and continue culture in the usual manner.

Flask Culture

Prepare explants in TC Balanced Salt Solution. Explants may be made considerably larger for culture in flasks than for slide or roller tube cultures. While the conventional size of the explants has approximated 1x1x1 mm., Earle has used explants ranging from 0.5x1x2 mm. to 0.5x3x2 mm. In other cases he has substituted cell suspensions for the explants.

To a 35 mm. flask (Carrel type) add 0.3 ml. of TC Chicken Plasma, either whole or diluted to 50 or even 25 per cent with TC Balanced Salt Solution, and spread over bottom of flask. This is then increased in volume to 1 ml. by introducing 0.6 ml. of TC Balanced Salt Solution and 0.1 ml. of TC Embryo Extract EE_{20}. Add explants and orient them. Stopper flasks and set aside to clot. Incubate for 1–2 hours to give firm clot, then add 0.5 ml. of nutritional mixture as described under Roller Tube Culture.

Detailed methods of tissue culture may be found in texts such as those listed below:

Parker, Methods of Tissue Culture
Paul B. Hoeber, Inc., 1938, 1950.

White, Handbook of Plant Tissue Culture
Ronald Press Company, 1943.

Cameron Tissue Culture Technique
Academic Press, Inc., 1950.

Pomerat, Methods in Medical Research Section IV, 1951
Year Book Publishers, 1951.

Serological Reagents
for Diagnosis of Syphilis

THE EXACTING technique of serological diagnostic methods requires carefully prepared and standardized materials. The reagents listed in this section are prepared for the diagnosis of syphilis by means of the complement-fixation and precipitation tests. Each preparation of Bacto-Beef Heart, or Bacto-Kahn Beef Heart, is tested and approved for the preparation of antigens, before release. The complete antigens for the diagnosis of syphilis are prepared in strict accordance with the published methods. Before distribution each lot of antigen is tested and approved for its sensitivity and specificity by the author serologist or by a laboratory designated by him for that purpose. Thus, users of Bacto-Antigens are assured of the most satisfactory reagent for the performance of the various tests.

Complete antigens prepared with purified cardiolipin and lecithin are described in this section. These antigens are in exact agreement with the formula given by the author serologists using cardiolipin and lecithin prepared according to the directions given by Pangborn. Additional cardiolipin-lecithin reagents will be prepared as required. The cardiolipin is prepared under license from the New York State Health Department.

Additional antigens and reagents for syphilology are available and descriptions will be given upon request.

REAGENTS FOR
COMPLEMENT-FIXATION TESTS

BACTO-KOLMER IMPROVED ANTIGEN (B304)

Bacto-Kolmer Improved Antigen is prepared according to the directions given by Kolmer and Lynch.[1] It consists of an alcoholic extract of acetone and ether extracted Bacto-Beef Heart, fortified with 0.4 per cent Bacto-Cholesterol. In the Kolmer simplified and quantitative complement-fixation tests for syphilis, these authors[2] report this antigen to give the same sensitivity as cardiolipin antigen (Kolmer); the specificity of the antigens with sera and spinal fluids of presumably normal nonsyphilitic individuals was found to be equal.

[1] Am. J. Clin. Path., 10.731.1940.
[2] Texas State J. Med., 44:312:1948.

BACTO-KOLMER IMPROVED ANTIGEN (B305)
(REENFORCED)

Bacto-Kolmer Improved Antigen (Reenforced) is prepared according to the formula described by Kolmer and Lynch.[1] In the preparation of this antigen Bacto-Beef Heart is extracted with acetone followed by ether and then with

309

alcohol. The alcoholic extract of the tissue is fortified with 0.4 per cent Bacto-Cholesterol and the ether-soluble, acetone-insoluble lipoids of the Bacto-Beef Heart. The antigenic sensitivity of this antigen is similar to that of an antigen prepared with 0.03 per cent cardiolipin, 0.05 per cent lecithin and 0.6 per cent cholesterol when used in the Kolmer simplified and quantitative complement-fixation tests for syphilis;[2] the specificity of the antigens with sera and spinal fluids of presumably normal nonsyphilitic individuals was reported to be equal. The sensitivity of Bacto-Kolmer Improved Antigen (Reenforced) is slightly increased over that of Bacto-Kolmer Improved Antigen.

[1] Am. J. Clin. Path., 18:731:1948.
[2] Texas State J. Med., 44:312:1948.

BACTO-EAGLE WASSERMANN (B214) ANTIGEN

Bacto-Eagle Wassermann Antigen was developed by Eagle[1,2] for use in his modification of the Wassermann reaction. It is an alcoholic extract of Bacto-Beef Heart reenforced with Bacto-Cholesterol. This antigen, when tightly stoppered, retains its reactivity indefinitely at room temperature.

[1] J. Lab. Clin. Med., 22:300:1936.
[2] Eagle: Laboratory Diagnosis of Syphilis, 144:1938.

BACTO-B.J.L. WASSERMANN ANTIGEN (B234)

Bacto-B.J.L. Wassermann Antigen is prepared according to the procedure described by Boerner, Jones and Lukens[1]. The antigen is an alcoholic extract of Bacto-Beef Heart to which is added Bacto-Cholesterol. In the authors' technique, the time and cost of performing the test is greatly reduced without loss of specificity.[2,3] It is suitable for quantitative as well as qualitative tests. The antigen is stable when stored in tightly stoppered bottles at room temperature.

[1] Am. J. Clin. Path., 9:13:1939.
[2] Arch. Derm. Syph., 41:32:1940.
[3] Am. J. Clin. Path., 10:282:1940.

BACTO-ANTISHEEP HEMOLYSIN (B217)
(AMBOCEPTOR)

The epochal discovery of Bordet concerning the lysis of erythrocytes by immunized serum is the foundation upon which the indicator system of the complement-fixation test is built.

Bacto-Antisheep Hemolysin (Amboceptor) is prepared by the method of Kilduffe.[1] It is a highly potent antisheep rabbit serum preserved with glycerol. It is exceptionally stable and may be stored in the refrigerator for periods of 12 months or more without loss of activity if kept properly stoppered.

[1] J. Lab. Clin. Med., 10:582:1924-25

BACTO-COMPLEMENT (B383)

Bacto-Complement is fresh guinea pig serum dried from the frozen state. It is prepared by pooling sera of a large number of mature, well-nourished guinea pigs. It will retain its potency for a minimum of one year if kept at −5°C. (the freezing chamber of the refrigerator). The pooling of the large numbers of sera as used in the preparation of Bacto-Complement eliminates the possibility of non-specific reactions with antigens used in the complement-fixation test.

Bacto-Complement is reconstituted by adding 5 ml. of Bacto-Complement Reconstituting Fluid, using a clean sterile syringe to make the transfer. Rotate the bottle to effect complete solution of the complement. This solution will retain its potency for two to three weeks if stored in the freezing compartment of the refrigerator. After thawing the frozen solution, avoid unnecessary exposure to room temperature.

Bacto-Complement is recommended for use in all complement-fixation tests. Variables encountered in performing these tests necessitate that the complement be titered just prior to use with the same reagents employed in the test.

It has been shown that the use of a satisfactory saline is of utmost importance in the performance of complement-fixation tests. In many localities the use of tap water for the preparation of saline is preferred over distilled water. The titer of complement is often improved by incorporating 0.1 gram of magnesium chloride or magnesium sulfate per liter of tap or distilled water saline, resulting in more clear-cut complement-fixation reactions.

Bacto-Complement is supplied in 5 ml. amounts in vials. Each vial is accompanied with 5 ml. of Bacto-Complement Reconstituting Fluid.

REAGENTS FOR PRECIPITATION TESTS

BACTO-KAHN STANDARD ANTIGEN (B218)

Precipitation tests during the past thirty years have gained in interest and use as diagnostic agents in syphilis. The Kahn test, described in 1923, was the first practical precipitation test to gain wide usage. It is readily performed, rapid and accurate.

Bacto-Kahn Standard Antigen is prepared according to Kahn's directions[1,2,3] and is a highly sensitive and specific reagent. Each lot is standardized to the same standard degree of sensitivity and specificity. No lot is released without approval from Dr. Kahn's laboratory. The antigen is stable and should be kept tightly stoppered in the dark at room temperature. Bacto-Kahn Standard Antigen is used in the standard and quantitative Kahn procedures with serum and spinal fluid and is also used in the Universal Reaction of Kahn.[4,5]

[1] Kahn: The Kahn Test, A Practical Guide, 76:1928.
[2] Kahn: Technique of the Standard Kahn Test, Univ. Mich. Press, 39:1944.
[3] Kahn: Serology with Lipid Antigen, 271:1950.
[4] Kahn: Serology with Lipid Antigen, 1 and 24:1950.
[5] Kahn: An Introduction to Universal Serologic Reaction in Health and Disease, 1951.

BACTO-KAHN SENSITIZED ANTIGEN   (B219)

Bacto-Kahn Sensitized Antigen is prepared in strict accordance with the procedure outlined by Kahn.[1,2,3,4] It is an especially sensitive and stable antigen. Each lot is carefully standardized and is rechecked under the personal supervision of Dr. Kahn. This antigen is used in the Kahn presumptive procedures with serum and spinal fluid. To prevent fluctuations in the titer, this antigen should be kept tightly stoppered, in the dark, at about 21°C. (not below room temperature).

[1] Kahn: The Kahn Test, A Practical Guide, 143:1928.
[2] Kahn: Technique of the Standard Kahn Test, Univ. Mich. Press, 39:1944.
[3] Am. J. Clin. Path., 17:130:1947.
[4] Am. J. Clin. Path., 17:770:1947.

BACTO-EAGLE FLOCCULATION   (B220)
ANTIGEN

The flocculation technique developed and modified by Eagle[1,2,3,4] is a relatively simple and highly accurate diagnostic test for syphilis. Eagle's research on the sterols led him to use a combination of corn germ sterol and cholesterol in the antigen for his flocculation test. With these sensitizing agents he secured large crystalline aggregates in positive sera, which made the reaction easier to read.

Bacto-Eagle Flocculation Antigen is a sensitive and satisfactory reagent for use in the Eagle flocculation technique. It is diluted for use according to the titer shown on the label. The antigen is stable when stored at room temperature. As described by Eagle[3,4] this same antigen is used in both the "macro" and "micro" modification of his flocculation technique.

[1] J. Lab. Clin. Med., 17:787:1932.
[2] J. Lab. Clin. Med., 22:300:1936.
[3] Am. J. Syphilis, 22:22:1938.
[4] Eagle: Laboratory Diagnosis of Syphilis, 215:1937.

BACTO-HINTON INDICATOR   (B221)

The Hinton Glycerol Cholesterol Reaction for the detection of syphilis is recommended for its accuracy and simplicity. For the actual reading of the test only one tube need be considered. Like all other serological diagnostic tests, however, the success of this test depends upon the sensitivity of the reagents used as well as rigid adherence to the details of the technique.

Bacto-Hinton Indicator is the cholesterolized heart extract used in Hinton's[1] Glycerol Cholesterol Reaction for syphilis, and also in "A Modification of the Hinton Test applied to Spinal Fluid" by Davies.[2] This extract has been prepared according to the directions given by Hinton and is also recommended for use in the "micro" and "capillary" serological tests as described by Davies.[3]

This indicator is stable when it is stored, tightly stoppered, at room temperature. In the event that the cholesterol precipitates, the indicator is warmed to redissolve the cholesterol before diluting it with salt solution for use in the performance of the test.

Each lot of Bacto-Hinton Indicator is tested in Dr. Hinton's laboratory and is not released for distribution until his approval is received.

[1] J. Lab. Clin. Med., 18:198:1932–33.
[2] Am. J. Clin. Path., 7:240:1937.
[3] J. Lab. Clin. Med., 22:959:1936–37.

BACTO-B.J.L. FLOCCULATION (B235)
ANTIGEN

Bacto-B.J.L. Flocculation Antigen is prepared according to the directions given by Boerner, Jones and Lukens.[1] It is an alcoholic extract of Bacto Beef Heart. It is stored in the dark in a tightly stoppered bottle at room temperature. Bacto-B.J.L. Flocculation Antigen is satisfactory for the performance of the microscopic and macroscopic flocculation tests described by these authors. Their technique has the advantage of simplicity, reproducibility and a desirable degree of sensitivity and specificity.

[1] Am. J. Clin. Path., Tech. Sup., 4:141:1940.

CARDIOLIPIN ANTIGENS
BACTO-V D R L ANTIGEN (B388)

Bacto-V D R L Antigen is a cardiolipin-lecithin antigen for the V D R L Slide and Tube Test Procedures used in the serological diagnosis of syphilis.

Bacto-V D R L Antigen is prepared according to the directions given by Harris, Rosenberg, and Riedel,[1] and consists of cardiolipin, cholesterol and lecithin dissolved in absolute ethyl alcohol. Cardiolipin and lecithin are prepared according to directions given by Pangborn.[2,3,4,5]

Buffered saline used in dilution of the Bacto-V D R L Antigen is prepared according to the directions given by Harris, Rosenberg, and Riedel.[1]

Bacto-V D R L Antigen is used in the techniques as given in detail in the Manual of Serologic Tests for Syphilis, Federal Security Agency, Public Health Service, Division of Venereal Disease.[6]

Bacto-V D R L Antigen is supplied in 5 ml. units. Each unit consists of 5 ml. antigen and 50 ml. Buffered Saline for diluting the antigen in preparing the emulsion for the VDRL Slide and Tube Test Procedures for the serological diagnosis of syphilis.

[1] J. Venereal Disease Inform., 27:169:1946.
[2] Proc. Soc. Exp. Biol. Med., 48:484:1941.
[3] J. Biol. Chem., 143:484:1942.
[4] J. Biol. Chem., 153:343:1944.
[5] J. Biol. Chem., 161:71:1945.
[6] J. Venereal Disease Inform., Supplement No. 22, 1949.

BACTO-KAHN CARDIOLIPIN ANTIGEN (B404)

Bacto-Kahn Cardiolipin Antigen is prepared according to the directions given by Kahn and McDermott[1] and Kahn[2] and consists of cardiolipin, lecithin and cholesterol in absolute ethyl alcohol. The cardiolipin and lecithin are prepared according to the directions given by Pangborn.[3,4,5,6] The amount of lecithin present may vary slightly to give a suitable antigen; however, generally the antigen consists essentially of 0.1 per cent cardiolipin, 1.0 per cent lecithin, and 0.025 per cent cholesterol.

Bacto-Kahn Cardiolipin Antigen is recommended for use in conjunction with standard Kahn antigen in the performance of the Kahn Standard Test with serum and spinal fluids as well as quantitative procedures in accordance with the directions given by Kahn.[2] This antigen may also be used in a microflocculation procedure as described by Kahn and McDermott.[1] Each batch of Bacto-Kahn Cardiolipin Antigen is tested and approved in Dr. Kahn's laboratory to assure an antigen of the correct specificity and sensitivity.

A complete discussion of the Kahn Cardiolipin Antigen and its use in the serological diagnosis of syphilis is given in "Serology with Lipid Antigen with Special Reference to Kahn and Universal Reactions" by Kahn.[2]

Bacto-Kahn Cardiolipin Antigen is supplied in 5 ml. bottles.

[1] Am. J. Clin. Path., 18:364:1948.
[2] Kahn, Serology with Lipid Antigen, p. 159, 164, 259, 263, and 283, 1950.
[3] Proc. Soc. Biol. Med., 48:484:1941.
[4] J. Biol. Chem., 143:484:1942.
[5] J. Biol. Chem., 153:343:1944.
[6] J. Biol. Chem., 161:71:1945.

BACTO-KOLMER CARDIOLIPIN   (B438)
ANTIGEN

Bacto-Kolmer Cardiolipin Antigen is used in the Kolmer Complement Fixation Test for Syphilis as described by Kolmer and Lynch.[1] It consists of a solution of purified cardiolipin, lecithin and cholesterol (0.03 per cent cardiolipin, 0.05 per cent lecithin and 0.6 per cent cholesterol) in absolute ethyl alcohol in the optimum combination to give maximum sensitivity consistent with specificity in tests with sera and spinal fluids. Cardiolipin and lecithin are prepared according to directions given by Pangborn.[2,3,4,5]

Bacto-Kolmer Cardiolipin Antigen is tested and approved by Dr. Kolmer's laboratory before release, assuring an antigen of the proper sensitivity and specificity. The dose to employ as given on the label was determined by a method of antigenic titration described by Kolmer and Boerner.[6]

This method determines the "optimum dose" instead of "antigenic units," and the dose as given on the label is the optimum amount to use. It corresponds to 10 to 20 antigenic units by the older method of titration. The titration should be checked before use. If employed for any other method, the titrations should be conducted, and the dose determined, in accordance with the method employed. The dilution should be prepared in quantities sufficient for one day's use, and a new dilution made daily.

Bacto-Kolmer Cardiolipin Antigen is supplied in 5 ml. bottles.

[1] J. Venereal Disease Inform., 29:166:1948.
[2] Proc. Soc. Exp. Biol. Med., 48:484:1941.
[3] J. Biol. Chem., 143:484:1942.
[4] J. Biol. Chem., 153:343:1944.
[5] J. Biol. Chem., 161:71:1945.
[6] Kolmer and Boerner, Approved Laboratory Technic, 4th Edition:679:1945.

BACTO-HINTON CARDIOLIPIN   (B440)
INDICATOR

Bacto-Hinton Cardiolipin Indicator is prepared according to the directions given by Hinton, Stuart and Grant[1] consisting of purified cardiolipin, lecithin and cholesterol in absolute ethyl alcohol. The cardiolipin and lecithin are prepared according to the directions given by Pangborn.[2,3,4,5]

Bacto-Hinton Cardiolipin Indicator is recommended for the regular Hinton qualitative and quantitative tests. Each batch of Bacto-Hinton Cardiolipin Antigen is tested and approved by Dr. Hinton's laboratory before being released for distribution.

Bacto-Hinton Cardiolipin Indicator is supplied in 5 ml. bottles.

[1] Am. J. Syphilis Gonorrh. Venereal Diseases, 33:587:1949.
[2] Proc. Soc. Biol. Med., 48:484:1941.
[3] J. Biol. Chem., 143:484:1942.
[4] J. Biol. Chem., 153:343:1944.
[5] J. Biol. Chem., 161:71:1945.

REAGENTS FOR PREPARATION OF ANTIGENS

BACTO-BEEF HEART (B222)

The discovery that alcoholic extracts of normal organs would act as antigens for tests for syphilis and that the antigenic principles were associated with lipoids, has resulted in much experimentation and research. The first description of the preparation of desiccated heart muscle and its use for the extraction of phosphatides belongs to Rubow.[1] This method for the preparation of dried tissue was improved by Erlandsen.[2] Dried heart muscle was employed by Neymann and Gager[3] in 1917 for the preparation of Wassermann test antigen. In 1922, Kolmer[4] described the technique of desiccating beef heart for use in the antigen employed in his modification of the complement-fixation test for syphilis. Many extracts of desiccated beef heart tissues are now employed as the source of the necessary antigenic lipoidal substances for use in both complement-fixation and flocculation tests.

Bacto-Beef Heart is a desiccated and powdered fresh beef heart tissue, trimmed free from fat, possessing highly polytropic properties as each lot represents the heart muscle of not less than several hundred animals. It has not been treated with any solvent other than water. It contains a minimum of fat and moisture. The production at one time of large quantities of Bacto-Beef Heart assures a polytropic material, yielding extracts which are only slightly hemolytic and anti-complementary and at the same time highly antigenic. Each lot is tested and approved for its sensitivity and specificity by the laboratory designated for that purpose by the author-serologists for use in the preparation of the following antigens which are listed alphabetically:

B. J. L. Flocculation Antigen	Hinton Indicator
B. J. L. Wassermann Antigen	Kline Antigen
Eagle Flocculation Antigen	Kolmer Improved Antigen
Eagle Wassermann Antigen	Kolmer Improved Antigen (Reenforced)

Bacto-Beef Heart has also been recommended for use in the preparation of the antigens used in such other tests for the diagnosis of syphilis as those of Mazzini,[5] Rosenthal[6] and Rytz.[7,8] It is also used in alcoholic[9] and cholesterolized antigen.[10] Bacto-Beef Heart is not recommended for the preparation of the antigens used for the Kahn tests. Bacto-Kahn Beef Heart as discussed on page 316, is recommended for the preparation of Kahn Standard Antigen and Kahn Sensitized Antigen.

Bacto-Beef Heart should be stored in the refrigerator at 2–6°C. to secure the most satisfactory antigens.

A description of the preparation of the more widely used antigens employing Bacto-Beef Heart is available upon request.

[1] Arch. exp. Path. Pharmakol., 52:173:1905.
[2] Zeit. physiol. Chem., 51:71:1907.
[3] J. Immunol., 2:573:1917.
[4] Am. J. Syphilis, 6:76:1922.
[5] Am. J. Clin. Path., 9:163:1939.
[6] Proc. Soc. Exp. Biol. Med., 27:61:1929.
[7] J. Lab. Clin. Med., 21:934:1936.
[8] J. Lab. Clin. Med., 22:1186:1937.
[9] Kolmer: Infection, Immunity, and Biologic Therapy, 455:1924.
[10] Kolmer: Infection, Immunity, and Biologic Therapy, 456:1924.

BACTO-KAHN BEEF HEART   (B223)

Bacto-Kahn Beef Heart[1,2,3,4,5] is recommended particularly for the preparation of antigens for use in the Kahn tests for the diagnosis of syphilis and for use in the Kahn Universal Reaction. Dried beef heart, even when stored in the refrigerator, may undergo changes which render it unsatisfactory for use in preparing antigens for the Kahn procedures, although it continues to be satisfactory for use in the preparation of other antigens. Bacto-Kahn Beef Heart is prepared specifically for use in the preparation of Kahn antigens. No lot is released for distribution until it has been found satisfactory for the preparation of Kahn Standard Antigen and Kahn Sensitized Antigen in Dr. Kahn's laboratory. Bacto-Kahn Beef Heart should be stored in the refrigerator at all times.

The antigens employed in the Kahn tests are stable. For that reason Bacto-Kahn Beef Heart should be converted into antigen as soon as the material has been received from our laboratories. A description of the method of preparation of Kahn Standard Antigen and Kahn Sensitized Antigen is available upon request.

[1] Kahn: The Kahn Test, A Practical Guide, Chapter 3:1928.
[2] Kahn: Technique of the Standard Kahn Test, Univ. Mich. Press, p. 39, 1944.
[3] Kahn: The Kahn Test, A Practical Guide, Chapter 4:1928.
[4] Am. J. Clin. Path., 17:117:1947.
[5] Kahn, Serology with Lipid Antigen, 271:1950.

BACTO-CHOLESTEROL   (B224)

Bacto-Cholesterol is prepared especially for cholesterolizing antigens. It is of the highest purity and is ash free.

The addition of pure cholesterol to reenforce antigens was first recommended by Sachs.[1] By this means, antigens are rendered more sensitive without increasing their anticomplementary or hemolytic powers.

Bacto-Cholesterol is also recommended for use as a standard in blood cholesterol and other cholesterol determinations.

[1] Klin. Wochschr., Berlin, 48:2066:1911.

BACTO-CORN GERM STEROL   (B225)

Bacto-Corn Germ Sterol is a highly purified reagent which was developed in cooperation with Dr. Eagle for use as a sensitizing agent in the antigen for his tests.

This sterol is used in conjunction with Bacto-Cholesterol by Eagle[1] in the antigen for his flocculation technique for syphilis. In positive sera the crystalline aggregates are large and readily lend themselves to detection.

[1] J. Lab. Clin. Med., 17:787:1932.

KAHN OVERSENSITIVE CORRECTION SOL'N.   (B448)
KAHN UNDERSENSITIVE CORRECTION SOL'N.   (B449)

Bacto-Kahn Oversensitive Correction Solution and Bacto-Kahn Undersensitive Correction Solution are used for the correction of oversensitive and undersensitive alcoholic extracts of Bacto-Kahn Beef Heart in the preparation of Kahn Standard Antigen and Kahn Sensitized Antigen as described by Wheeler, Brandon and Kahn[1,2] and Wheeler and Brandon.[3]

[1] Am. J. Clin. Path., 17:117:1947.
[2] Am. J. Clin. Path., 17:130:1947.
[3] Am. J. Clin. Path., 17:770:1947.

Diagnostic Reagents

BACTO-THROMBOPLASTIN (B226)

Bacto-Thromboplastin is stabilized, desiccated rabbit brain substance for use in determining the prothrombin time of bloods from patients with obstructive jaundice, hepatitis, cirrhosis, hepatic neoplasia, biliary fistula, colitis, cholangitis, hemorrhagic disease of the newborn, and other conditions wherein hypoprothrombinemia is suspected. It is particularly recommended for use in following prothrombin activity in patients on dicoumarol, tromexan or other anticoagulant therapy. It is applicable to the procedures described by Quick,[1,2,3] Smith, Warner and Brinkhouse,[4] the bedside test of Smith et al.[5], the micro-prothrombin test of Kato,[6] and Kato and Poncher,[7] the dilute plasma technique of Campbell, Smith, Roberts and Link,[8] Shapiro, Sherwin, Redish and Campbell,[9] Shapiro[10] and its extensions[11,12,13,14] and is recommended for all tests requiring a potent thromboplastin. Bacto-Thromboplastin has given exceptionally good results in the preparation of the Two-Stage Reagent for the quantitative determination of prothrombin concentration as described by Ware and Seegers.[15]

Quick Prothrombin Time Test[2]

Reagents:

1. Bacto-Thromboplastin

   Empty the contents of one ampul Bacto-Thromboplastin into a clean dry test tube. Add 4.0 ml. of 0.85 per cent sodium chloride solution. Mix lightly to suspend and wet all particles. Incubate the mixture in a water bath at 45–48°C., for 10 minutes, during which time gently twirl the tube momentarily at three-minute intervals to resuspend the solids. Avoid excessive agitation as this will yield an unsatisfactory heavy milky extract.

   Place a thin layer of absorbent cotton over the wide end of a clean dry pipette. Insert the covered end into the tube containing the incubated thromboplastin mixture and carefully lower it through the suspension to the bottom of the tube keeping the end of the pipette pressed firmly against the cotton. Withdraw as much extract as possible through the cotton by gentle suction and transfer the filtered extract to a clean container. The filtered extract should be opalescent without particles. Some laboratories may prefer to use the extract without filtration. In such cases it is best to employ a pipette with a wide tip orifice.

   The Thromboplastin Extract should be used within six hours following preparation. Unused portions of the Thromboplastin Extract should be frozen solidly in the freezing compartment of the refrigerator, thawed and reincubated for 5 minutes at 37°C. before being used in the test. Extract properly frozen will retain full potency for at least three months. Repeated thawing and freezing of the extract is not recommended. Accordingly, if the extract is prepared for stock use it should be distributed in amounts of approximately one day's usage or single test dose (0.1 ml.) and then frozen and stored as recommended above. In such cases the amount required for a day's use or one test can then be withdrawn from the freezer, thawed and reincubated as specified.

2. Bacto-Sodium Oxalate 0.1 Molar or dissolve 1.34 grams of anhydrous reagent grade sodium oxalate in 100 ml. of distilled water.

317

3. Bacto-Calcium Chloride 0.02 Molar or dissolve 0.222 gram of anhydrous reagent grade calcium chloride in 100 ml. distilled water.
4. Bacto-Sodium Chloride 0.85 per cent or dissolve 0.85 gram reagent grade sodium chloride in 100 ml. distilled water.

Procedure:

Obtain 4.5 ml. of blood by venipuncture and immediately mix it with 0.5 ml. of sodium oxalate solution. Within one-half hour centrifuge the oxalated blood to separate the plasma from the formed elements.

Place the tubes containing thromboplastin extract and the tubes containing calcium chloride solution in the 37°C. water bath to bring them to this working temperature.

Transfer 0.1 ml. of plasma to a small dry serologic tube supported by a rack in the 37°C. water bath. Add 0.1 ml. thromboplastin extract and twirl the tube to mix the contents. After the tube has been in the water bath a few seconds, add 0.1 ml. calcium chloride solution by blowing it forcibly into the mixture and simultaneously start the stop watch. Keep the tube in the water bath and shake it lightly until within a few seconds of the expected clotting time; then by gently tilting the tube in a horizontal position observe the formation of the clot or fibrin web which is the end point.

Many laboratories may prefer to use the following loop technique. Immediately upon the addition of the calcium chloride solution and starting of the stop watch, insert a clean iron, nichrome or platinum wire with a terminal loop about 1/8″ in diameter into the tube and stir thoroughly. Draw the loop from the back of the tube to the front through the plasma-thromboplastin-calcium chloride mixture at the rate of 2 sweeps per second, and observe the time at which the clot forms. When the clot forms it will usually adhere to the loop and is easily recognizable. Stop the watch at the first evidence of the clot and record the time required for the plasma to clot after adding the calcium chloride to the plasma-thromboplastin mixture. This is the prothrombin time.

The time elapsing between the addition of calcium chloride and the end point is the prothrombin time. The test should be run in duplicate or triplicate to obtain the minimum clotting time.

Some laboratories find it helpful to check the prothrombin time of the test plasma diluted with an equal volume of 0.85 per cent sodium chloride solution as well as the whole plasma. Where such a dilution of the test plasma is made, this must be taken into consideration when interpolating the prothrombin activity.

For determining the prothrombin activity of a patient's plasma by the Quick method it is desirable to construct a prothrombin activity curve for a given thromboplastin using several normal human plasmas. The following is a typical example:

This is a typical prothrombin activity curve constructed with Bacto-Thromboplastin using normal human plasmas. It was constructed by running prothrombin time tests on 10, 20, 30, 40, 60 and 100 per cent plasma of normal individuals, and plotting the prothrombin time against per cent prothrombin employed. The indicated concentration of plasmas used were obtained by diluting the normal plasmas with 0.85 per cent sodium chloride solution.

The prothrombin activity of the blood to be tested is obtained by determining the prothrombin time of the whole plasma, locating this time on the prothrombin activity curve and, by means of the curve, converting the prothrombin time to the per cent of prothrombin activity.

A curve is submitted with each lot of Bacto-Thromboplastin to serve as a guide for laboratories using Bacto-Thromboplastin according to the method of Quick.

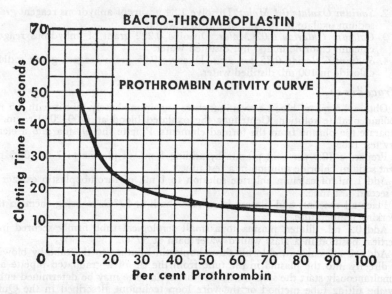

BACTO-THROMBOPLASTIN

PROTHROMBIN ACTIVITY CURVE

Clotting Time in Seconds / Per cent Prothrombin

However, variability in prothrombin times obtained by different technicians makes it imperative that the technician running the test construct a curve with two or more normal plasmas using a given thromboplastin to make sure his or her values correspond with the guide. Otherwise, the technician must construct his own prothrombin activity curve using three or more normal human plasmas. Interpretation:

When Bacto-Thromboplastin is used in the Quick prothrombin time test, clot formation is obtained in 12–14 seconds with normal plasma. The quantitative relationship between the prothrombin content of plasma and its clotting time as obtained by the Quick test is discussed in detail by Quick[16],[17],[18] and in the "Manual for Prothrombin and Blood Clotting Determinations for Laboratory Technicians" published by the Newton Health Department, Newton, Massachusetts.

Safe and effective limits of prothrombin activity in controlled dicoumarol therapy are discussed by: Allen, Barker and Waugh,[19] Wright and Prandoni,[20] Butsch and Stewart,[21] Echstam,[22] Evans,[23] Barker, Cramer, Hurn and Waugh,[24] Peters, Guyther and Brambel,[25] Barker, Hines, Kvale and Allen,[26] Allen[27] and in leaflets descriptive of dicoumarol and its clinical application published by the licensees of dicoumarol, Eli Lilly and Company,[28] Abbott Laboratories[29] and E. R. Squibb and Company.[30]

The necessity of repeated prothrombin determinations in following and determining the dosage in anticoagulant therapy has been emphasized by Wellman and Allen.[31] Bacto-Thromboplastin is eminently suited for this control procedure.

Link-Shapiro Dilute Plasma Technique[8],[9],[10]

Reagents:

1. *Thromboplastin Extract.* Prepare thromboplastin extract as described for the Quick technique and dilute with an equal volume of sodium chloride 0.85 per cent.

2. *Sodium Oxalate 0.1 Molar.* Dissolve 1.34 grams of anhydrous reagent grade
   sodium oxalate in 100 ml. of distilled water.
3. *Calcium Chloride 0.02 Molar.* Dissolve 0.222 gram of anhydrous reagent
   calcium chloride in 100 ml. distilled water.
4. *Sodium Chloride 0.85 per cent.* Dissolve 0.85 gram reagent grade sodium
   chloride in 100 ml. distilled water.

Procedure:

Obtain 4.5 ml. of blood by venipuncture and immediately mix it with 0.5 ml.
sodium oxalate solution. Centrifuge the oxalated blood at 1700–2000 r.p.m. to
separate the plasma from the formed elements. Pipette the plasma into a clean,
dry test tube.

Prepare a 12.5 per cent plasma by adding 1 ml. of plasma to 7 ml. 0.85 per
cent sodium chloride solution in a test tube.

Add 1 ml. of calcium chloride solution to 1 ml. of thromboplastin extract in
a second test tube.

Place all reagents and plasma in a water bath at 37°C. to bring them to this
working temperature.

Add 0.1 ml. diluted plasma to a small serological tube firmly secured in a
vertical position in a glass walled water bath at 37°C.

Add 0.2 ml. calcium chloride-thromboplastin mixture to the tube by blowing
it directly into the plasma in the tube from the tip of a graduated pipette and
simultaneously start the stop watch. Prothrombin time may be determined either
by the tilting tube method or the wire loop technique described in the Quick
Prothrombin Time Technique discussed above.

Stop the watch at the first evidence of the clot and record the time required
for the plasma to clot after adding the thromboplastin-calcium chloride mixture.
This is the prothrombin time of the dilute plasma. Standard values for diluted
normal human plasma lie between 35–42 seconds. Two or more known normal
plasma diluted similarly to the plasma under test should be run as controls. The
prothrombin time of whole plasma may be performed by using this same technique, but omitting the dilution of the plasma.

Complete details for prothrombin time determinations by the Smith Bedside[4]
and Kato Micro Prothrombin Test[6,7] are available upon request.

Precautions—factors influencing prothrombin time:

1. Storage temperature of desiccated Bacto-Thromboplastin in ampuls.
   Bacto-Thromboplastin, kept properly refrigerated below 6°C., will retain
   its potency for years. At room temperature, 22–23°C., there may be a slight
   reduction in potency after one or two months. Storage temperature higher
   than 25°C., will accelerate destruction of the active thromboplastin principle.
2. Reagents.
   The calcium chloride, sodium chloride and sodium oxalate used in the
   various prothrombin time tests should be anhydrous and of reagent grade.
   Prolonged clotting times obtained with Bacto-Thromboplastin have been
   traced most frequently to a faulty calcium chloride reagent. A calcium
   chloride solution either more or less concentrated than that indicated for
   use in the Quick technique may prolong the clotting time. Anhydrous
   calcium chloride is hygroscopic, and absorbs moisture from the atmosphere. Compensation for the moisture content must be taken into consideration when preparing the 0.02M solution.
3. Thromboplastin Extract.
   Thromboplastin extracts that are deeply opaque or milky may give pro-

longed clotting times. Deeply opaque or dense thromboplastin extracts result through excessive agitation of the suspension during the extraction period and may give unsatisfactory results. Unfiltered extracts which are not deeply opaque even though they contain gross particles of brain tissue generally give satisfactory results.

4. Temperature for Extraction of the Thromboplastin.
   A temperature of 45–48°C., for 10 minutes is most satisfactory. Temperatures in excess of 50°C., will cause deterioration of the thromboplastin principle. The optimum temperature for performing the prothrombin time test is 36–38°C.

5. Aging of Thromboplastin Extract.
   Thromboplastin extract is subject to deterioration. There should be no loss of potency of the extract if used within 6 hours after its preparation. Prolonged aging results in a gradual loss in potency. Extracts held over from one day to another should be frozen solid to retard deterioration. These frozen extracts should be thawed and incubated for 5 minutes at 37°C., before being used. Extracts properly frozen will retain full potency for at least two weeks. Repeated thawing and freezing of the extract is not recommended.

6. Age of Plasma at Time of Test.
   Fresh plasma should be used in running the test. Plasmas allowed to stand at room temperature or ice box temperature for more than 2–3 hours may give clotting times slightly higher than does fresh plasma.

7. Calcium Chloride Addition.
   Usually if the thromboplastin extract is allowed to remain in contact with the plasma for 30 seconds before the calcium chloride is added, the clotting time is shortened in comparison with that obtained if the calcium chloride is added immediately following the addition of the extract. Either procedure is satisfactory if adhered to consistently. Our curve is based upon the addition of calcium chloride a few seconds after the addition of the thromboplastin extract.

8. Cleanliness of Glassware.
   Soaps and other detergents used in cleaning glassware must be completely removed by rinsing. Frequently glassware appears optically clean but remains chemically contaminated with adsorbed soap or detergent. These materials interfere with prothrombin procedures as reported by Lehmann.[32] He also stated that results will still be irregular if the container in which the blood has been collected is not chemically clean.

9. Ionic Contamination.
   Metallic ions present in excess in the distilled water used in making the saline for extraction of the thromboplastin may lead to prolonged clotting times. Water from copper stills or water which has been in contact with copper vessels may contain enough copper to be detrimental.

10. Agitation of Plasma-Thromboplastin-Calcium Chloride Mixture.
    Failure to mix thoroughly the reagents with the plasma at the time of addition may result in a prolonged clotting time. Also, excessive agitation of the plasma-thromboplastin-calcium chloride mixture will often prolong the clotting time.

11. Silicone coated apparatus.
    Some laboratories prefer to use syringes, needles and glassware that have been coated with silicone for handling blood for prothrombin time determinations. Where silicone coated glassware is used, the prothrombin time will be slightly prolonged over that normally obtained with uncoated glassware. According to Quick,[33] one should use 0.01 Molar Calcium Chloride

solution for running prothrombin times of plasma collected and handled in silicone coated glassware.

12. Time of drawing blood.

Blood drawn for prothrombin determinations should be taken previous to meal time and not directly after meals. High lipid content of plasma following ingestion of high fat food materials may prolong the clotting time.

13. Effect of Salicylates and other drugs.

Aspirin and other salicylates, as well as caffeine as shown by Link,[34] when ingested may influence the clotting mechanism by prolonging the prothrombin time.

[1] J. Biol. Chem., 109:lxxiii:1935.
[2] J. Am. Med. Assoc., 110:1658:1938.
[3] J. Hem., 4:1281:1949.
[4] J. Exp. Med., 66:801:1937.
[5] J. Am. Med. Assoc., 113:380:1939.
[6] Am. J. Clin. Path., 10:147:1940.
[7] J. Am. Med. Assoc., 114:749:1940.
[8] J. Biol. Chem., 138:1:1941.
[9] Proc. Soc. Exp. Biol. Med., 50:85:1942.
[10] Exp. Med. Surgery, 2:103:1944.
[11] Proc. Soc. Exp. Biol. Med., 52:12:1943.
[12] Proc. Soc. Exp. Biol. Med., 53:218:1943.
[13] Arch. Surgery, 50:137:1945.
[14] Am. J. Clin. Path., 17:405:1947.
[15] Am. J. Clin. Path., 19:471:1949.
[16] J. Am. Med. Assoc., 114:1342:1940.
[17] Am. J. Clin. Path., 19:1016:1949.

[18] Quick, The Physiology and Pathology of Hemostasis, 1951.
[19] J. Am. Med. Assoc., 120:1009:1942.
[20] J. Am. Med. Assoc., 120:1015:1942.
[21] J. Am. Med. Assoc., 120:1025:1942.
[22] Minnesota Med., 27.455:1944.
[23] New England J. Med., 230:131:1944.
[24] Surgery, 17:207:1945.
[25] J. Am. Med. Assoc., 130:398:1946.
[26] Minnesota Med., 29:250:1946.
[27] J. Am. Med. Assoc., 134:323:1947.
[28] Dicumarol Leaflet, Eli Lilly & Co.
[29] Dicumarol Leaflet, Abbott Laboratories.
[30] Dicumarol Leaflet, E. R. Squibb & Sons.
[31] Proc. Mayo Clinic, 26:257:1951.
[32] Lancet, Vol. I, (XXIV):1133:1950.
[33] Personal Communication, 1950.
[34] Chicago Med. Bull., 51:53:1948.

BACTO-SODIUM CHLORIDE 0.85 per cent   (B379)

Bacto-Sodium Chloride 0.85 per cent is recommended for use in all prothrombin techniques requiring 0.85 per cent sodium chloride solutions. It is prepared with reagent grade sodium chloride and triple distilled water.

Bacto-Sodium Chloride 0.85 per cent is supplied in bottles of 100 ml. in packages of 6.

BACTO-SODIUM OXALATE 0.1 MOLAR   (B377)

Bacto-Sodium Oxalate 0.1 Molar is recommended for use in all prothrombin techniques requiring 0.1 Molar sodium oxalate solutions. It is prepared with anhydrous, reagent grade sodium oxalate in triple distilled water.

Bacto-Sodium Oxalate 0.1 Molar is supplied in 25 ml. bottles in packages of 6.

BACTO-CALCIUM CHLORIDE   (B378)
0.02 MOLAR

Bacto-Calcium Chloride 0.02 Molar is recommended for use in all prothrombin techniques requiring 0.02 Molar solutions of calcium chloride. It is prepared with anhydrous, reagent grade calcium chloride and triple distilled water.

Bacto-Calcium Chloride 0.02 Molar is supplied in 5 ml. and 25 ml. bottles in packages of 6.

BACTO-PROTHROMBIN 2 STAGE (B407)
REAGENT

Bacto-Prothrombin 2 Stage Reagent is a desiccated reaction mixture dried from the frozen state, prepared according to the specifications of Ware and Seegers,[1] for use in the two-stage procedure for the quantitative determination of prothrombin concentration and Ac globulin. The two-stage prothrombin concentration determination, as the name implies, is carried out in two steps. The fibrinogen is first removed from the plasma under test by adding thrombin. The clot which forms is defibrinated and the resulting fluid allowed to stand for a short time for destruction of the added thrombin by the antithrombin present in the serum. The second step consists of measuring quantitatively the unaltered prothrombin in the fibrinogen-free plasma. This is accomplished by adding Bacto-Prothrombin 2 Stage Reagent and Bacto-Ac Globulin to the fibrinogen-free plasma to convert the prothrombin to thrombin and subsequently measuring the thrombin activity on a standardized solution of fibrinogen. A thrombin unit is that amount of thrombin which will clot 1 ml. of standardized fibrinogen solution in 15 seconds under conditions imposed by the two-stage analysis. One unit of thrombin is derived from each unit of prothrombin. Therefore, the prothrombin unitage is the same as that of the thrombin. Complete details of the two-stage procedure for measuring prothrombin concentration are outlined by Ware and Seegers.[1]

Bacto-Prothrombin 2 Stage Reagent is supplied in vials of 10 ml. which are rehydrated by adding 10 ml. 0.6 per cent sodium chloride solution. Bacto-Prothrombin 2 Stage Reagent as well as the resulting solution should be refrigerated when not in use.

Bacto-Ac Globulin is also available for use in conjunction with Bacto-Prothrombin 2 Stage Reagent in the two-stage procedure for the quantitative determination of prothrombin concentration.

[1] Am. J. Clin. Path., 19:471:1949.

BACTO-Ac GLOBULIN (B447)

Bacto-Ac Globulin is desiccated beef serum dried from the frozen state prepared according to the specifications of Ware and Seegers,[1] for use as a source of accelerator globulin in the two stage procedure for the quantitative determination of prothrombin. It is recommended for use in conjunction with Bacto-Prothrombin 2 Stage Reagent for the total conversion of prothrombin to thrombin.

Bacto-Ac Globulin is rehydrated by adding 2 ml. sterile distilled water to each vial to give a solution comparable with fresh beef serum. The reconstituted Ac Globulin is further diluted with 0.05 per cent sodium chloride solution to give a final concentration of 1·600 as used in the two stage prothrombin concentration test of Ware and Seegers. Bacto-Ac Globulin as well as the solution should be stored in the refrigerator at 2–6°C.

Bacto-Ac Globulin is supplied in 2 ml. vials in packages of 6.

[1] Am. J. Clin. Path., 19:471:1949.

BACTO-PROTHROMBIN FREE (B445)
BEEF PLASMA

Bacto-Prothrombin Free Beef Plasma is prepared according to the method of Quick[1,2,3] for use in the prothrombin consumption tests and for diluting human plasma for prothrombin time determinations according to the method of Rosenfield and Tuft.[4]

To rehydrate Bacto-Prothrombin Free Beef Plasma, add 4.5 ml. distilled water and rotate gently in an end over end motion to effect solution without generating excessive air bubbles. The reconstituted plasma is equivalent to freshly prepared deprothrombinized beef plasma. Bacto-Prothrombin Free Beef Plasma as well as the reconstituted plasma should be stored in the refrigerator at 2–6°C.

Bacto-Prothrombin Free Beef Plasma is supplied in 5 ml. vials in packages of 6.

[1] Blood, 4:1281:1949.
[2] Am. J. Clin. Path., 19:1016:1949.
[3] Quick, The Physiology and Pathology of Hemostasis, 142:1951.
[4] Am. J. Clin. Path., 17:405:1947.

BACTO-PROTHROMBIN FREE (B446)
RABBIT PLASMA

Bacto-Prothrombin Free Rabbit Plasma is prepared according to the method of Quick[1,2,3] for use in the prothrombin consumption test. It may also be used for diluting plasmas for prothrombin time determinations by the method described by Rosenfield and Tuft.[4]

To rehydrate Bacto-Prothrombin Free Rabbit Plasma, add 4.5 ml. distilled water to each 5 ml. vial. Rotate gently in an end over end motion to effect solution without generating excessive air bubbles. The reconstituted plasma is equivalent to freshly prepared deprothrombinized rabbit plasma. Bacto-Prothrombin Free Rabbit Plasma as well as the reconstituted plasma should be stored in the refrigerator at 2–6°C.

Bacto-Prothrombin Free Rabbit Plasma is supplied in 5 ml. vials in packages of 6.

[1] Blood, 4:1281:1949.
[2] Am. J. Clin. Path., 19:1016:1949.
[3] Quick, The Physiology and Pathology of Hemostasis, 142:1951.
[4] Am. J. Clin. Path., 17:405:1947.

BACTO-CEPHALIN CHOLESTEROL (B238)
ANTIGEN

Bacto-Cephalin Cholesterol Antigen is recommended for use in the Hanger flocculation test[1,2] for determining the index of disturbance of the liver parenchyma. It is a stable desiccation consisting of 1 part especially prepared sheep brain cephalin and 3 parts Bacto-Cholesterol.

The Hanger flocculation test is regarded as an index of inflammatory and certain other forms of degenerative disturbances of the liver parenchyma, and does not necessarily parallel hepatic function tests. Cephalin cholesterol emulsions, properly prepared, are not flocculated by sera from normal individuals but are flocculated by sera from patients with active disturbance of the liver parenchyma. The degree of flocculation parallels the severity of active liver disease and may, therefore, be employed prognostically in estimating the degree and persistence of the active process. Jaundice due to biliary obstruction usually may be distinguished from hepatogenous jaundice by this flocculation test.

Since its introduction in 1938 the Hanger flocculation test has won the unanimous approval and acceptance of its many investigators. The publications of Rosenberg,[3] Rosenberg and Soskin,[4] Phole and Stewart,[5] Mateer, Baltz, Marion, Hollands and Yagle,[6] Nadler and Butler,[7] Lawson and Englehardt,[8] Yardumian and Weisband,[9] and Mateer, Baltz, Marion and MacMillin[10] express the high regard which the authors have for the test and characterize it as a valuable adjunct to the other tests in the study of hepatic dysfunction.

Kopp and Solomon,[11] Mirshy and Von Brecht[12] and Lippencott, Ellerbrook, Hesselbrock, Gordon, Gottlieb and Marbel[13] obtained positive cephalin cholesterol flocculation reactions with sera from malarial patients. Guttman, Potter, Hanger, Moore, Pierson and Moore[14] confirmed these observations with sera from malarial infected patients and found the changes in the blood to simulate those in acute hepatitis—hypoalbumenemia, decreased capacity of the serum albumin fraction to inhibit the flocculating action of gamma globulin, and an increase in the globulin content of serum in this disease. In malaria infection, the formation of serum protein was more profoundly deranged than many other functions ascribed to the liver and these changes were well demonstrated by a series of cephalin cholesterol flocculation tests.

Mateer, Baltz, Steele, Brouwer and Colvert[15] in their studies on chronic subclinical impairment of the liver, regarded the cephalin cholesterol flocculation test as the most satisfactory single screening test available to detect cases of early hepatic impairment. Mateer, Baltz, Comanduras, Steele and Brouwer[16] recommended the cephalin cholestrol flocculation test as (a) the best of all screening tests to detect early hepatic impairment in subclinical cases and preoperative cholelithiasis cases; (b) valuable in chronic hepatitis and cirrhosis cases, and (c) extremely helpful in detecting residual impairment in post-icteric repair stage of acute hepatitis, and helpful in early stages.

The Hanger flocculation test when properly executed is extremely simple and reliable. It is a more sensitive index of hepatic disturbance than many of the functional studies and gives by far the best correlation with clinical observations. Because of its simplicity, as well as its reliability and efficiency, the flocculation test is advocated as an ideal routine test for determining active disease of the liver.

Preparation of the Test Antigen

The test antigen is prepared from the desiccated material in the following manner:

1. Add 5 ml. of anesthetic ether per unit bottle to effect solution of the contents. If turbidity persists, add one drop of distilled water to obtain a clear solution. This solution constitutes the stock ether antigen of Hanger and is stable for months if kept tightly stoppered to prevent evaporation.

2. The final test antigen is prepared by adding (slowly and with stirring) 1 ml. of the stock ether antigen solution to 35 ml. of distilled water warmed to 65–70°C. and then heating slowly to boiling. The mixture is allowed to simmer until the final volume is reduced to 30 ml. During the heating, all coarse granular clumps should be dispersed, resulting in a stable, milky, translucent emulsion from which all traces of ether are driven off. The antigen is cooled to room temperature and then is ready for use. The liquid emulsion when properly prepared and stored in the refrigerator at 2–6°C. is stable.

Excessive bacterial contamination of the test antigen emulsion or of the serum-saline-antigen test mixture may give rise to falsely positive flocculation. This may, be overcome by using clean, dry, sterile glassware in which to prepare and store the emulsion and in which to perform the test. The addition of sodium ethyl mercuri-thiosalicylate (Merthiolate), in a concentration of 1:10,000 to the test antigen emulsion and to the saline used for diluting the serum, has given good results. The antigen emulsion should be stored at refrigerator temperature, 2–6°C., when not in use.

Performance of the Hanger Flocculation Test

The Hanger flocculation test is performed by adding 1 ml. of the aqueous lipoid emulsion to a test tube (preferably a centrifuge tube) containing 0.2 ml. of the patient's serum diluted with 4 ml. of 0.85 per cent sodium chloride. After thorough shaking and stoppering with cotton, the tube is allowed to stand undisturbed in the dark at room temperature (20–25°C.) and a notation is made at the end of 24 and 48 hours as to the amount of flocculation and precipitation that has taken place. With normal human sera the emulsion remains as a stable homogeneous suspension, but with sera from patients with diffuse hepatitis the lipoid material tends to flocculate or precipitate to the bottom of the tube. A ++++ reaction indicates a complete precipitation leaving the supernatant liquid water-clear. Gradations of the reaction between negative and ++++ are designated in terms of +, ++ and +++. No test should be regarded as negative until 48 hours have elapsed without flocculation.

Neefe and Reinhold[17] discovered that the cephalin cholesterol flocculation reaction was influenced by light and that this photosensitivity gave rise to falsely positive reactions with normal sera. Hanger[18] and Mateer[15,19] confirmed Neefe's and Reinhold's observations. Their findings suggested that the test antigen emulsion and the serum should be protected from light and that the serum-saline-antigen test mixture should be incubated in the dark at room temperature (20–25°C.). Higher or lower incubation temperatures are not indicated. The patient's serum should not be diluted until the test is to be performed.

A rapid Cephalin Cholesterol Flocculation Test using centrifugation has been described by Moloney, Donovan and Whoriskey.[20] While less sensitive than the regular Hanger test, the centrifugation technique is rapid, permitting the reading of the test within a few minutes. Saifer and Zymaris[21] have described an easily performed accurate photometric microprocedure for the quantitative determination of electrophoretically pure gamma globulin (Cohn's Fraction II) in the range of 100 to 1,000 micrograms of protein using Bacto-Cephalin Cholesterol Antigen in the presence of Hayem's solution.

Bacto-Cephalin Cholesterol Antigen is supplied in 5 ml. bottles in packages of 6. Each bottle or unit is sufficient for the preparation of 5 ml. of stock ether antigen and 150 ml. of the final test antigen.

[1] Trans. Assoc. Am. Physicians, 53:148:1938.
[2] J. Clin. Invest., 18:261:1939.
[3] Arch. Surgery, 43:231:1941.
[4] Am. J. Digestive Diseases, 8:421:1941.
[5] J. Clin. Invest., 20:241:1941.
[6] Am. J. Digestive Diseases, 9:13:1942.
[7] Surgery, 11:732:1942.
[8] New Orleans Med. Surgical J., 95:60:1942.
[9] Am. J. Clin. Path., 13:383:1943.
[10] J. Am Med. Assoc., 121:723:1943.
[11] Am. J. Med. Sci., 205:90:1943.
[12] Science, 99:20:1944.
[13] J. Clin. Invest., 24:616:1945.
[14] J. Clin. Invest., 24:296:1945.
[15] J. Am. Med. Assoc., 133:909:1947.
[16] Gastroenterology, 8:52:1947.
[17] Science, 100:83:1944.
[18] Personal Communication, 1944.
[19] Personal Communication, 1944.
[20] Am. J. Clin. Path., Tech. Supp., 18:568: 1948.
[21] J. Clin. Investigation, 31:1:1952.

BACTO-THYMOL TURBIDITY REAGENT (B328)

Bacto-Thymol Turbidity Reagent is recommended for use in the Maclagan thymol turbidity test and its modifications for indicating hepatic parenchymal impairment. It is a barbital buffered saturated thymol solution with a reaction of pH 7.55, prepared according to the method described by Maclagan,[1] and the modification of Mateer et al.[2,3]

It was observed by Maclagan,[1] that a turbidity or precipitate formed in a buffered saturated thymol solution when serum from patients with certain types of liver disease was added to it. The degree of turbidity paralleled closely the severity of parenchymatous hepatic impairment and provided a quantitative measure of the extent of the damage done. Clinical tests indicated the thymol turbidity reaction to be a valuable indicator of liver dysfunction particularly in infective hepatitis and cirrhosis. Findings were negative or only weakly positive in obstructive jaundice.

Clinical studies employing the thymol turbidity test and other tests used for detecting hepatic impairment have been reported by Watson and Rappaport,[4] Neefe,[5] Neefe and Reinhold[6] and Mateer et al.[2,3,7] These authors have all assigned the thymol turbidity test a significant place as an adjunct in studying liver disease. Their results parallel, to a degree, those obtained with the cephalin cholesterol flocculation reaction; however, significant differences in positivity and sensitivity displayed by the two tests on the same sera indicate that the chemical mechanisms of the tests are different.

In a study of the sensitivity and value of the thymol turbidity and thymol flocculation tests Mateer et al.[2,3] showed that the buffer solution with a reaction of pH 7.55, gave more satisfactory results than at pH 7.8 as originally suggested by Maclagan, and could be used for acute as well as chronic cases. With this slightly more acid thymol buffer solution they reported that the sensitivity of the test was greatly increased and that no false positives were obtained. In addition, the modified solution was of equal value in chronic cases and for following the progress of acute impairment. Mateer's observation of the greater sensitivity of the thymol turbidity reagent at pH 7.55 has been confirmed by Neefe[8] et al. Bacto-Thymol Turbidity Reagent is prepared according to the modification suggested by Mateer et al.[2,3] with a reaction of pH 7.55.

Procedure:

Measure 0.05 ml. of unheated serum into a dry tube and add 3 ml. of Bacto-Thymol Turbidity Reagent. Allow to stand for one-half to one hour, and examine in a comparator with a black line on a white background against the turbidity standards of Kingsbury et al.[9] Bacto-Kingsbury Turbidity Standards are now available. If the turbidity exceeds the 100 mg. per cent standard, dilute with a further measured volume of buffer as required. The result is expressed in arbitrary units equal to the appropriate standard divided by ten with allowance for dilution. The standard dilution is 1–60, so that if the final dilution is 1–120 and the mixture then matches the 70 mg. per cent tube, the result is 14 units.

$$\text{Expressed as a formula: Units} = \frac{\text{Standard tube reading} \times \text{final dilution of serum}}{600}$$

Normal limits are 0 to 4 units. Tubes showing positive results, as evidenced by turbidity within one hour, if held overnight usually show flocculation. This flocculation may also be used as a measure of hepatic damage.[3,5] The reaction is inhibited by heating to 56°C. for 30 minutes, so that inactivated sera cannot be used. The turbidity standards referred to are those in common use for urine protein estimation. They should be checked every few months against diluted serum of known protein content as recommended by Kingsbury[9]. Also, a photoelectric method for measuring the turbidity quantitatively in this test has been described by Shank & Hoagland.[10]

Occasionally a slight turbidity or a light flocculent precipitate forms in the reagent upon long standing. This slight turbidity in no way interferes with the result obtained; however, if any flocculent be present, it should be removed by filtration through ash-free filter paper into chemically clean receptacles. The reagent should be stored in the refrigerator at 2–6°C.

Bacto-Thymol Turbidity Reagent is supplied in 25 ml. bottles in packages of 6.

[1] Brit. J. Exp. Path., 25:234:1944.
[2] Gastroenterology, 8:52:1947.
[3] J. Am. Med. Assoc., 133:909:1947.
[4] J. Lab. Clin. Med., 30:983:1945.
[5] Gastroenterology, 7:1:1946.
[6] Gastroenterology, 7:393:1946.
[7] Cyclopedia of Med., 1947.
[8] Am. J. Med., 8:60:1950.
[9] J. Lab. Clin. Med., 11:981:1926.
[10] J. Biol. Chem., 162:133:1946.

BACTO-KINGSBURY STANDARDS   (B349)

Bacto-Kingsbury Standards are prepared according to the specifications of Kingsbury, Clark, Williams and Post[1] for use in the Maclagan Thymol Turbidity Test and in the estimation of urinary albumin. The set consists of seven standards, corresponding to 5, 10, 20, 30, 40, 50 and 75 per cent albumin as published by Kingsbury et al.[1] These standards are especially recommended for use with Bacto-Thymol Turbidity Reagent (see page 327) in the Maclagan test[2] and modifications[3,4] indicating hepatic parenchymal impairment.

[1] J. Lab. Clin. Med., 11:981:1926.
[2] Brit. J. Expl. Path., 25:234:1944.
[3] Gastroenterology, 8:52:1947.
[4] J. Am. Med. Assoc., 133:909:1947.

PHENOLSULFONPHTHALEIN AMPULS, DIFCO   (B221)
FOR RENAL FUNCTION TEST

Phenolsulfonphthalein Ampuls, Difco contain a carefully prepared solution for determining renal functional activity. Each ml. of the solution contains 0.006 grams (1/10 grain) of the dye in the form of its monosodium salt. The ampuls contain sufficient solution to allow the withdrawal of one ml. Phenolsulfonphthalein Ampuls, Difco conform to the specifications for Phenolsulfonphthalein Injection as given in the U. S. Pharmacopeia.

When phenolsulfonphthalein, in the form of its sodium salt, is injected either intramuscularly or intraveneously, a large percentage is normally excreted in the urine within a comparatively short time. This observation by Abel and Rowntree[1] has been used by Rowntree and Geraghty[2] as the basis of a most accurate test for the functional activity of the kidney. This test is universally known as a renal function test.

After intramuscular injection the first traces of dye begin to appear in the urine in 5–10 minutes and the normal kidney will excrete from 60–80 per cent of the total amount injected within 2 hours.

After intravenous administration the excretion of the phenolsulfonphthalein is normally more rapid; 35–45 per cent being eliminated in 15 minutes, 50–65 per cent in 30 minutes, and 65–80 per cent during the first hour.

If the initial appearance of the phenolsulfonphthalein in the urine is delayed, or the amount excreted is below normal, an impairment of renal function is indicated. The degree of dysfunction may be estimated by the proportionate amount excreted. The functional efficiency of each kidney may be determined by catheterizing each ureter and collecting the excretions separately.

For the performance of the test, exactly 1 ml. of the solution containing 6 mg. of phenolsulfonphthalein is carefully withdrawn from a Phenolsulfonphthalein Ampul, Difco, by means of an accurately graduated syringe. This solution is injected either intramuscularly or intravenously, aseptic technique being observed throughout. (*Note: More than 1 ml. has been placed in each ampul in order that exactly 1 ml. may be easily withdrawn*). To insure copious excretion of urine, the patient is given 200–400 ml. of water 20–30 minutes before the beginning of the test. If this precaution is not taken, a late appearance of phenolsulfonphthalein in the urine may be due to lack of excretion. The patient's bladder must be emptied, preferably by catherization, the time noted, and 1 ml. of phenolsulfonphthalein solution injected. When the injection is made intramuscularly, the most suitable site is in the lumbar region. The area surrounding the point of injection must be free from edema. If the patient is catheterized the urine may be allowed to drain into a test tube containing a drop of 25 per cent sodium hydroxide solution and the time noted for the appearance of phenolsulfonphthalein denoted by the first faintly pink tinge. In patients having no obstruction to the free passage of urine, the catheter may now be withdrawn. If there is no urinary obstruction and the passing of the catheter be disagreeable or inconvenient, it may be omitted, in which case the first appearance of the dye in the urine is not noted. When the phenolsulfonphthalein is administered intramuscularly, the patient is instructed to void into a suitable receptacle at the end of 70 minutes and again into another receptacle at the end of the second hour. If the injection is made intravenously, it is customary for the urine to be collected at the end of 15 minutes, 30 minutes or 1 hour.

The amount of phenolsulfonphthalein in the urine may be estimated by making the sample alkaline with a sufficient quantity of 25 per cent sodium hydroxide solution, diluting to 1 liter, and after filtering, if necessary, comparing the depth of color with that of a standard solution. When the color is faint, it is advisable to dilute to only 500 ml., in which case the result should be divided by 2.

If the comparison is made by means of the ordinary biological colorimeter, it is customary to use a 50 per cent standard, prepared by diluting 0.5 ml. of the same solution used for injection, to 1 liter, after the addition of a few drops of 25 per cent sodium hydroxide solution to insure the development of the full alkaline color. If this standard solution is kept in a cool place and not exposed to strong light, it will keep for several months.

The depth of color may be also conveniently, but less accurately, estimated by placing a small quantity of the diluted alkaline sample in a tube or vial and comparing the depth of color with similar tubes or vials containing amounts of alkaline phenolsulfonphthalein corresponding to 5, 10, 15, 20, 25, 30, 35, 40, 45, 50, 60, 80 and 100 per cent. The 100 per cent standard is prepared by diluting 1 ml. of solution from a Phenolsulfonphthalein Ampul, Difco, and a few drops of 25 per cent sodium hydroxide solution to 1 liter. The other standards are made by appropriate dilution of the 100 per cent standard.

Complete details of the phenolsulfonphthalein renal function test will be found in the references of the original articles as given below and also in such texts as "Manual of Clinical Laboratory Methods" by Cummer, "Diagnostic Methods" by Webster, "Approved Laboratory Technic" by Kolmer, Spaulding and Robinson and other similar texts.

[1] J. Pharmacol., 1:231:1909.
[2] J. Pharmacol., 1: 579:1910.

BACTO-COAGULASE PLASMA   (B286)

Bacto-Coagulase Plasma is a desiccated plasma recommended for the determination of coagulase production by staphylococci. The coagulase test is generally accepted as affording the best single criterion of potential pathogenicity of staphylococci. The use of plasma dried on filter paper was first suggested by Chapman.[1] Foley[2] also described a method for the desiccation of rabbit plasma for use in the coagulase test.

The ability of staphylococci to produce coagulase, an enzyme capable of clotting plasma, was first reported by Loeb[3] in 1903. Daranyi[4] indicated the practical significance of this test, and since then numerous investigators have studied this reaction to determine its relationship to the pathogenicity of staphylococci. Chapman, Berens, Peters and Curcio[5] in a study of coagulase and hemolysin production by staphylococci, showed that strains producing coagulase were usually pathogenic regardless of their hemolytic or chromogenic properties. Hallman[6] used coagulase production as a means of differentiating pathogenic from nonpathogenic staphylococci isolated from the nares of a large number of individuals. Cruickshank[7] recommended that coagulase production be used as a test for the pathogenicity of the staphylococci. Chapman, Berens, Nilson and Curcio[8] stated that coagulase production was the most reliable single test for the differentiation of pathogenic from nonpathogenic staphylococci. Fairbrother[9] concluded that coagulase is formed only by pathogenic staphylococci and constitutes an important criterion for the classification of these organisms into pathogenic and nonpathogenic strains. Moss, Squires and Pitts[10] also showed the importance of coagulase production in the determination of the pathogenicity of staphylococci. Many other reports have been made showing the value of this test for the differentiation of pathogenic from nonpathogenic staphylococci.

The coagulase test may be performed using the tube method or the slide technique. Chapman, Berens and Stiles[11] described a tube coagulase test using a 1–3 dilution of fresh plasma. Incubation of the plasma and emulsified culture was at 37°C. and readings were made at one hour intervals for four hours. Generally, rabbit plasma has been used in the various tests. Human plasma and human whole blood have also been employed. Chapman[12] compared the value of human plasma and human whole blood with rabbit plasma for testing the coagulating power of staphylococci. He reported that rabbit plasma clotted more rapidly and more firmly than did the human plasma or whole blood. Whole human blood, however, clotted more easily than did the corresponding plasma. Chapman[13] noted that not all human bloods were satisfactory and that other factors also enter into a satisfactory coagulase test. There must be sufficient culture, grown under satisfactory conditions, to react with a satisfactory plasma or whole blood. Conditions that give a satisfactory coagulase test for the determination of pathogenicity are discussed by Chapman.[14-17] Evans[18] used Bacto-Coagulase Plasma and the tube technique in his studies of coagulase positive staphylococci. He reported the 19 coagulase positive staphylococci comprised a rather homogenous group. They fermented mannitol under anaerobic conditions and were able to grow in a synthetic medium devoid of biotin.

Bacto-Coagulase Plasma is well suited for the coagulase test. An outline for the performance of the test follows:

Dissolve the contents of one ampul (100 mgs.) in 3.0 ml. of distilled water. Place 0.5 ml. of the plasma solution in a Wassermann tube supported in a rack. Add two drops of a 16–24 hour Bacto-Brain Heart Infusion culture of the organism under test, or two drops of a Bacto-Brain Heart Infusion suspension of a 16–24 hour culture on a slant of Heart Infusion Agar. Incubate at 37°C. Most coagulase positive staphylococci will clot Bacto-Coagulase Plasma within one hour. A second reading should be made, however, after three hours incubation at 37°C., before the organism can be regarded as coagulase negative. Any degree of clotting, however slight, is considered positive.

Bacto-Coagulase Plasma is satisfactory for the slide technique as reported by Chapman[15] and Moss.[19] It is also satisfactory for the slide test as described by Cadness-Graves, Williams, Harper and Miles,[20] discussed by Needham, Ferris and Spink.[21] This technique is particularly useful for presumptive identification or screen test for coagulase positive staphylococci in large scale bacteriological surveys. This test is performed by preparing a homogeneous suspension of a suspected colony in a drop of water on a slide with a minimum of spreading. Mix a large loop of rehydrated Bacto-Coagulase Plasma with the suspension. Coagulase positive staphylococci will produce macroscopic clumping within 5–15 seconds. Delayed clumping is not indicative of a positive test. Morphological confirmation by the Gram stain is made simultaneously.

Bacto-Coagulase Plasma is stable when stored in the refrigerator. The plasma solution prepared from Bacto-Coagulase Plasma may be kept in the refrigerator for several days without loss of potency. It is not satisfactory for use, however, if gross contamination occurs. After being kept in the refrigerator the plasma solution is cold enough to delay clotting for 10–15 minutes. This delay can be prevented by warming the plasma solution to 37°C. before use. *Caution: Bacto-Coagulase Plasma must be kept in the refrigerator in order to preserve its stability.*

1 J. Bact., 41:431:1941.
2 Science, 95:416:1942.
3 J. Med. Res., 10:407:1903.
4 Zentr. Bakt. I Abt. Orig., 99:74:1926.
5 J. Bact., 28:343:1934.
6 Proc. Soc. Exp. Biol. Med., 36:789:1937.
7 J. Path. Bact., 45:295:1937.
8 J. Bact., 35:311:1938.
9 J. Path. Bact., 50:83:1940.
10 Am. J. Clin. Path., 11:857:1941.
11 J. Bact., 41:431:1941.

12 J. Bact., 47:211:1944.
13 J. Bact., 50:119:1945.
14 J. Bact., 50:234:1945.
15 Trans. N. Y. Academy Sciences, 9:52:1946.
16 J. Bact., 52:151:1946.
17 J. Bact., 53:367:1947.
18 J. Bact., 55:793:1948.
19 Personal Communication.
20 Lancet, 1:736:1945.
21 Am. J. Clin. Path., Tech. Supp., 9:83:1945.

BACTO-SENSITIVITY DISKS (B403)

Bacto-Sensitivity Disks are sterile paper disks containing known amounts of the more commonly employed antibiotics and other therapeutic agents. They are recommended as a rapid, practical, clinically accurate and inexpensive means of determining the relative sensitivity of microorganisms to these therapeutic agents. Bacto-Sensitivity Disks are especially valuable in selecting the antibiotics effective against chronic or persistent infections refractory to primary antibiotic therapy. Three concentrations of each antibiotic are available, indicating if the microorganism is very sensitive, moderately sensitive, slightly sensitive or resistant. With proper interpretation the bacterial susceptibilities as determined with these Disks give the clinician a qualitative *in vitro* measure of sensitivity equal to that of any other procedure with less effort and often without the added time necessary for pure culture isolation as in the test tube method. Bacto-Sensitivity Disks are available containing three concentrations of Aureomycin, Bacitracin, Chloromycetin®*, Dihydrostreptomycin, Penicillin, Polymyxin B (Aerosporin®**), Streptomycin and Terramycin.

The use of paper disks in testing the potency of penicillin and other bacterio-

* Chloramphenical: Parke, Davis and Company.

** Polymyxin B: Burroughs Wellcome and Company.

static or bactericidal materials has been described by numerous investigators. Likewise, many investigators have used this technique to determine the resistance or susceptibility of microorganisms to antibiotics or other inhibitory substances. Morley[1] dried sulfathiazole and penicillin on paper disks for determining the sensitivity of wound bacteria to these materials. O'Toole[2] reported that this method proved to be simple and economical. She suggested modifications making the test suitable for determining the sensitivity of various species of microorganisms in the routine laboratory and gave tables showing the stability of the dried disks, and also the size of zones produced by various concentrations of penicillin, streptomycin and sulfathiazole. Bondi, Spaulding, Smith and Dietz[3] described a method for the rapid determination of the susceptibility of microorganisms to penicillin and other antibiotics stressing that this method can be used at the time of primary isolation, thereby eliminating the time required for pure culture isolation and identification prior to selecting the antibiotic for treatment. They saturated sterile disks with solutions of the antibiotic and placed them on the surface of Blood Agar plates immediately after inoculation with clinical specimens. Kolmer, Spaulding and Robinson[4] described the paper disk technique of determining susceptibility of bacteria to antibiotics. They pointed out that the method is a practical, simple and a rapid means of estimating sensitivity. Many modifications of these and similar tests are in current use to determine the resistance or sensitivity of microorganisms to antibiotics and other therapeutic agents.

The use of antibiotics in the treatment of many infectious diseases is an established procedure. The sensitivity of groups of many pathogenic bacteria to the various antibiotics and other therapeutic agents is known, and infections caused by these microorganisms usually respond to treatment with the designated antibiotic. However, the clinician frequently finds that an infection is not responding as expected to a specific treatment. In such cases he must accurately and rapidly determine the most effective antibiotic to use to overcome the infection. If treatment is not effective against the organism, there is danger of the possible sensitization of a patient to an antibiotic or other therapeutic agent which may be required at some future date. It is also possible to increase the resistance of microorganisms to these materials if ineffective dosages are used in treatment.

Determination of susceptibility of microorganisms to various antibiotics has, shown a wide variation in individual strains. The publications of Finland, Frank and Wilcox[5,6,7,8] clearly show a wide range of sensitivity between different species or groups of organisms. Barber and Rozwadowska-Dowzenko[9] reported that the proportion of staphylococci isolated from hospital patients resistant to penicillin increased from 14 per cent in 1946 to about 60 per cent in 1948. Davison[10] suggested that penicillin blood levels in 1949 had to be 15 times higher than in 1946 in order to inhibit the growth of 80 per cent of the Gram-positive cocci found in nasal exudates. The more sensitive organisms are killed by inadequate dosage of penicillin while the more resistant strains survive, becoming progressively more resistant. Miller and Sherlock-Hubbard[11] reported that over the seven year period, 1945–1951, the resistance of pathogenic staphylococci to penicillin had increased markedly. In addition during the last two years comparative resistance to the broad spectrum antibiotics on the part of the usually sensitive organisms has increased. Increased resistance of the tubercle bacillus to streptomycin was also shown. The clinician must rely on the laboratory for the determination of the sensitivity of microorganisms in cases where prompt response is not obtained with the usual antibiotic therapy. The use of Bacto-Sensitivity Disks supplies this information for all the more commonly employed antibiotics with a minimum of laboratory time.

Sweeney, Davis and Barnes[12] used Bacto-Sensitivity Disks to determine the susceptibility of 10 *Shigella* strains and one *Proteus* strain to bacitracin, dihydro-streptomycin, penicillin, chloromycetin and terramycin. They reported this method could be used to determine if an organism is sensitive, moderately sensitive or resistant and concluded that the test was adaptable to a field laboratory or mobile unit. Christensen and Lipsett[13] reported that Bacto-Sensitivity Disks could be satisfactorily used to show the relative sensitivity of a variety of microorganisms to six antibiotics, using Bacto-Heart Infusion Agar, with or without blood as a test medium. Mitchell, Arnold and Lett[14] used Bacto-Sensitivity Disks in their study of the sensitivity of *Pseudomonas aeruginosa* isolated from external otitis. They reported this method as a quick aid to the physician in his choice of therapy, since the test could be run directly, using the specimen as inoculum. Spaulding and Anderson[15] called attention to the necessity for the determination of the susceptibility of microorganisms to various antibiotics in treating certain types of infections. They described and evaluated a disk technique which is readily performed and within the scope of any laboratory capable of culturing clinical material. The test gives information which is a valuable and often an indispensable guide to successful treatment of severe, refractory or relapsing infections. They state that disks are presently available that may be transferred directly to the inoculated plate and are admirably suited to the needs of the clinical laboratory. Bacto-Sensitivity Disks are of this type, containing known amounts of the various antibiotics, thus eliminating the need of making standardized solutions of the antibiotics.

Pike, Schulze and McCullough[16] using Bacto-Tryptose Agar and Bacto-Sensitivity Disks determined the sensitivity of *Mima polymorpha*, isolated from a patient, and reported prompt recovery upon administration of the selected antibiotic. Lind and Swanton[17] reported that the Disk method of determining whether an organism is sensitive to one or more antibiotics is reliable, relatively inexpensive, rapid and when used as a guide to therapy is of definite value to the physician and patient. Trafton and Lind[18] in a study of urinary infections pointed out that sensitivity testing by the Disk method permitted a rapid, accurate and inexpensive determination of the susceptibility of microorganisms to the various antibiotics. They suggested that physicians should be encouraged to use these tests routinely and reported clinical data showing that the Disk method gives a fairly reliable guide to prognosis when selecting an antibiotic. Fusillo and Kuhns,[19] using Bacto-Sensitivity Disks described a method for antibiotic sensitivity testing using one concentration of each antibiotic with a single plate of medium to give the entire antibiotic sensitivity spectrum thereby saving time, media and equipment. Broom, Martineau and Young[20] used Bacto-Sensitivity Disks in determining the sensitivity of organisms in their evaluation study of the Disk Method in treating 100 clinical cases. Their results showed the indispensability of sensitivity testing from the clinical standpoint and demonstrated the practicability of the disk technique in routine diagnosis. Koch and Bourgeois[21] reported increased resistance of staphylococci to penicillin as well as aureomycin and terramycin. They used Bacto-Sensitivity Disks in determining the resistance of staphylococci and showed that the Disk Method correlated in every instance with results obtained by the two fold tube dilution technique. Gould and Bowie[22] in a study of the determination of bacterial sensitivity to antibiotics reported the Disk technique to be more accurate than "ditch and cylinder" methods, and less tedious. They pointed out that the serial dilution tube method is much more laborious than the Disk method, and subject to more errors. Closely similar results were obtained when the Disk method was carried out in parallel with the serial dilution tube method and reported that the Disk technique is as accurate as the more complicated tube dilution method for all purposes. They expressed their results as "sensitive, relatively resistant and resistant," and stated this suffices for clinical purposes. Since *in vivo* sensitivities cannot be accurately gauged from *in vitro* levels of sensitivity, mathematical expressions of these might even be misleading.

There have been some interpretations in the literature to indicate that the tube dilution method of determining sensitivity is the only accurate procedure and that the Disk method does not present the desired information. Continued widespread use of the Disk Technique and proper interpretation of results have demonstrated the clinical accuracy, efficiency and reliability of this procedure. The tube dilution method is applicable in research procedures and in cases where quantitative determinations are required and where proper consideration can be made of resistant variants and other factors. The tube dilution method because of the time and materials involved is not suitable for routine diagnostic work, and has not offered any advantages over the Disk method in clinical procedures.

The results obtained with Bacto-Sensitivity Disks, as with other sensitivity tests similarily conducted, are of a qualitative rather than a quantitative nature. The many variables that enter into a test of this type such as the size of the inoculum, type of growth of the organism, amount of inoculum on the plate, thickness of the medium, incubation conditions, diffusion rate of the antibiotic, rate of deterioration of the antibiotic during incubation, preclude its quantitative nature. Sensitivities are to be determined by the presence of and not entirely by the diameter of the zone of inhibition around the disks. Organisms showing a zone of inhibition around the disk with the smallest concentration of the antibiotic would be considered very sensitive to that antibiotic; an organism showing no zone around the lowest, but a zone around the intermediate disk would be classed as sensitive or moderately sensitive, while a zone around only the highest concentration disk would indicate that the organism is but slightly sensitive to the antibiotic. Resistant organisms produce no zone of inhibition even around the disk containing the highest concentration. As was pointed out by Jawetz in a personal communication, the information obtained by the use of Sensitivity Disks is not only important as an aid in determining which antibiotic may be effective against a specific infection, but also which antibiotics are ineffective. He stressed that knowledge of the resistance and sensitivity of an organism is equally important in saving time and expense in treatment.

Information of this type has proven to be invaluable to the clinician under practical conditions in selecting the most appropriate antibiotic for treating infections. It is stressed that the differences in the diameters of the zones of inhibition obtained with like concentrations of the various antibiotics do not necessarily indicate their relative therapeutic efficiency. The rate of diffusion of the various therapeutic agents from the disks and through the medium influence the diameter of the zone of inhibition. Howe[23] in a study of sensitivity testing using paper disks considered only the presence or absence of bacterial growth and gave no attention to the diameter of the zone of inhibition.

The importance of culture media in sensitivity testing has been shown by many investigators. Repeated comparative tests in our laboratory have shown that Bacto-Heart Infusion Agar, with or without added blood, is well suited for the plating medium, producing excellent growth of a large variety of pathogenic microorganisms. Hemolytic reactions on this medium containing blood are typical, being an added advantage in diagnostic work. Tryptic soy media have been employed in sensitivity testing but we have found no advantage in their use. Waisbren, Carr and Dunnett[24] reported inhibition of activity with certain antibiotics using media of this type. Bacto-Brain Heart Infusion is recommended as a liquid medium for obtaining a rapid profuse growth of the test organism to be used for inoculating the Heart Infusion Agar employed in the disk plate technique of sensitivity testing. This medium also was employed in a turbidimetric assay method suitable for an antibiotic screen test using a large variety of test organisms by Joslyn and Galbraith.[25]

Performance of the Test

Bacto-Sensitivity Disks are sterile and should be removed from the vials using aseptic technique. Antibiotics are differentiated by the color of the disk and concentrations are identified by the markings on each disk. The vials should be tightly stoppered when not in use, and stored in the refrigerator at 2–6°C.

The sensitivity test may be performed on plates of medium inoculated with either the isolated organism or the pathological material containing these organisms as suggested by Bondi, Spaulding, Smith and Dietz.[3] Wood[26] suggested the inoculation of duplicate plates with the specimens, placing the sensitivity disks on one and using the second plate for the primary isolation of the etiological agent. With either of these procedures, often the antibiotic of choice can be determined prior to the isolation and identification of the organism.

Plates of Bacto-Heart Infusion Agar, with or without added blood, are prepared. These are inoculated either by smearing or streaking with a heavy suspension of the test organism or clinic specimen containing the causative organism, to obtain confluent or solid growth. Excessive moisture is to be avoided. Immediately following the inoculation of the medium, Bacto-Sensitivity Disks are placed on the surface spaced about 3–4 cm. apart. Use a flamed tweezer in removing the disks from the vial so as not to contaminate the remaining disks. Plates are incubated at 35–37°C. for 12 hours or until growth develops, and then examined for zones of inhibition of growth. It is recommended that in any case the etiological agent be isolated since mixed cultures may not always give dependable sensitivities.

Heavy inoculation of plates permits more rapid sensitivity determinations with the possibility of earlier treatment. Experience has demonstrated that with some organisms plates so inoculated have shown definite zones of inhibition within 5–6 hours after inoculation. Generally 5–6 sensitivity disks can be placed on a regular 95 mm. petri plate. Some laboratories may prefer to use large size petri plates (140 mm.) permitting the testing of the sensitivity of an organism to a larger number of antibiotics or therapeutic agents. Crowding of disks is to be avoided.

If desired, a base and "seed layer" technique may be employed. For this purpose, pour 15 to 20 ml. of sterile Bacto-Heart Infusion Agar in sterile 95 mm. plates and allow to solidify (use 60 ml. for 140 mm. plates). The inoculum is incorporated in sterile melted Bacto-Heart Infusion Agar with or without blood at 45°C. This inoculated seed agar is poured on the base layer and distributed evenly over the surface by tilting the plate to give a thin "seed layer" inoculation. The disks are placed on the surface of this layer after it has solidified.

The sensitivity of tubercle bacilli can be determined using Bacto-Sensitivity Disks in combination with Bacto-Peizer TB Medium Base and Bacto-Peizer TB Medium Enrichment. The medium used in this test is prepared according to the formula described by Peizer and Schecter.[27] This procedure has been compared with other methods and found to be as accurate and less time consuming than other techniques presently in use.

The method for determining the sensitivity of the tubercle bacillus to therapeutic agents using Bacto-Sensitivity Disks is essentially similar to the determination of sensitivities of other organisms. Either the pure culture or the clinic specimen, such as treated sputum, spinal fluid, urine, etc., provided these contain a moderate number of acid-fast organisms, Gaffky III or IV, may be used for the inoculation. The complete medium is prepared from Bacto-Peizer TB

Medium Base and Bacto-Peizer TB Medium Enrichment. The medium is poured into sterile plates or flat wide-mouth bottles and allowed to solidify. A heavy suspension of the organism or the clinic specimen is smeared on the surface of the medium and the Bacto-Sensitivity Disks, dihydrostreptomycin or streptomycin 1, 10 and 100 mcg., are placed on the surface about 3 cm. apart. The plates are incubated for 48 hours and then sealed with either cellophane tape or melted paraffin and incubation continued at 35–37°C. Tubercle bacilli are frequently isolated and their sensitivities determined in 10–14 days; some strains may require up to 6–8 weeks incubation for suitable growth. Sensitivity of the organisms to the antibiotic is indicated by the presence of zones of inhibition surrounding the disks.

Interpretation

A moderate zone of inhibition around the lowest concentration of one or more antibiotics would classify the organism as being sensitive to any or all of these antibiotics even though there may be a difference in zone size. Resistant organisms are not inhibited in the maximum concentration of the antibiotic while very sensitive strains show marked zones of inhibition even in the lowest concentrations. In the case of very sensitive strains, one may obtain zones of inhibition around the disk containing the lowest concentration nearly as large as those obtained around the higher concentrations, due to the diffusion characteristics of the test.

Results of this technique cannot necessarily be expressed in terms of the tube dilution method. The presence of zones of inhibition of growth around the disks indicates that the organism is sensitive to the antibiotic. The diameter of the zone is dependent not only upon the sensitivity of the organism but also upon the diffusability of the antibiotic and other factors which may limit the availability of the antibiotic to the organism in the medium.

Hemolytic properties of microorganisms must be considered when using plates of Blood Agar for the test. Growth of hemolytic organisms is characterized by a lysed, cleared or discolored background with the presence of colonies, while zones of inhibition leave the medium unchanged (no hemolysis). Upon longer incubation the hemolysin produced by the organism may diffuse toward the disk, giving a cleared zone, without growth, around the periphery of the zone of inhibition. The true zone of inhibition on Blood Agar includes both the unchanged non-hemolytic as well as the hemolytic areas showing no bacterial growth.

Frequently one will observe isolated colonies growing within the zone of inhibition. These represent resistant variants of the strain or culture, under test. The appearance of several such resistant colonies in the zone of inhibition does not indicate the true resistance of the culture which is demonstrated by the zone of inhibition of growth. Bacto-Sensitivity Disks thus permit the isolation of resistant variants from a culture.

Bacto-Sensitivity Disks are stable for one year when stored in the refrigerator at 2–6°C.

Bacto-Sensitivity Disks are available in vials of 25 disks each. They are supplied in complete sets and as replacement packages. A complete set (B403) consists of 1 vial each of three concentrations of the more commonly used antibiotics.

Antibiotic	Color	Plain	Marking ∴	=
Aureomycin	Yellow	10 mcg.	30 mcg.	60 mcg.
Bacitracin	Brown	2 units	10 units	20 units
Chloromycetin	Grey	10 mcg.	30 mcg.	60 mcg.
Dihydrostrepto-mycin	Pink	1 mcg.	10 mcg.	100 mcg.
Penicillin	Green	0.5 unit	1 unit	10 units
Polymyxin B (Aerosporin)	Blue	5 mcg. (50 units)	10 mcg. (100 units)	30 mcg. (300 units)
Terramycin	Terra-cotta	10 mcg.	30 mcg.	60 mcg.

Sets are also available consisting of one vial each of the lowest (B403A), intermediate (B403B) or highest (B403C) concentration of each therapeutic agent.

Replacement packages consist of six vials of any one concentration of any antibiotic.

Streptomycin (white disks) in concentrations of 1.0, 10 and 100 mcg. are available also in replacement packages.

[1] J. Path. Bact., 57:379:1945.
[2] Am. J. Med. Tech., 12:251:1946.
[3] Am. J. Med. Sciences, 213:221:1947.
[4] Approved Laboratory Technique, 5th Edition:557:1951.
[5] J. Lab. Clin. Med., 35:188:1950.
[6] J. Lab. Clin. Med., 35:205:1950.
[7] Am. J. Clin. Path., 20:325:1950.
[8] Am. J. Clin. Path., 20:335:1950.
[9] Lancet, 2:641:1948.
[10] Laryngoscope, 60:131:1950.
[11] Can. J. Pub. Health, 43:35:1952.
[12] Navy Med. Research Inst. Research Report, Project NM 005 048, 04.13.
[13] News Letter S.A.B., 17:15:1951. Paper read at Mich. Branch S.A.B. Mtg. April, 1951.
[14] Laryngoscope, 61:649:1951.
[15] J. Am. Med. Assoc., 147:1336:1951.
[16] Am. J. Clin. Path., 21:1094:1951.
[17] J. Antibiotics and Chemotherapy, 2:30:1952.
[18] J. Urol. In Press.
[19] Med. Technicians Bull., 3:7:1952.
[20] Bact. Proceedings, Boston, p. 120:1952.
[21] Antibiotics and Chemotherapy, 2:229:1952.
[22] Edinburgh Med. J., 59:178:1952.
[23] Surg. Gynecol. Obstet., 9:669:1950.
[24] Am. J. Clin. Path., 21:884:1951.
[25] J. Bact., 59:711:1951.
[26] Personal Communication, 1950.
[27] Am. J. Clin. Path., 20:682:1950.

BACTO-CONCENTRATION DISKS, PENICILLIN (B452)
BACTO-SUBTILIS SPORE SUSPENSION (B453)

Bacto-Concentration Disks, Penicillin are used to determine the penicillin level of milk, serum, plasma, urine and other body fluids. Concentrations of from 0.05 to 5 units penicillin per ml. may be determined by this method. The Concentration Disks contain known measured amounts of penicillin to correspond to 0.05, 0.1, 0.25, 0.5, 1.0, 2.5 and 5.0 units per ml. Disks containing Bacto-Penase are supplied to identify the bactericidal agent as penicillin. The test employs a standardized medium (Bacto-Whey Agar), a standardized inoculum (Bacto-Subtilis Spore Suspension), and when the conditions of the test are adhered to, accurate determinations can be made.

Churchill and Frank[1,2] used the Concentration Disks, Penicillin to detect penicillin in milk. They compared the phosphatase method, growth coagulation method and the Disk method and reported the superiority of the Disk method. Kosikowsky,[3] in a systematic testing of inhibitory substances in milk reported that under optimum conditions concentrations of penicillin as low as 0.05 unit per ml. were detected. Detailed discussion of Bacto-Concentration Disks is available upon request.

[1] Paper read at Mich. Branch S.A.B. Mtg. April 1951. [2] In Press. [3] J. Dairy Science, 35:533:1952.

Miscellaneous Products

DEHYDRATED MEDIA IN SPECIAL PACKAGES

FOR THE convenience of the user, we have prepared a series of dehydrated media in small packages. Each bottle contains sufficient dehydrated medium for 1 liter or 100 ml. "Standard Methods Media" are packaged in amounts sufficient for 1 liter; other media for 100 ml.

These packages of dehydrated media are recommended for use in laboratories where humidity is high or in laboratories where there is occasional need for a small quantity of medium.

The special packages of dehydrated media are securely sealed to prevent the absorption of moisture. Unopened vials will keep for long periods of time without lumping or deterioration.

The following media are packaged in amounts sufficient for 1 liter in boxes of six:

Bacto-Brilliant Green Bile 2% (B7)   Bacto-Lactose Broth (B4)
Bacto-Endo Agar (B6)   Bacto-Nutrient Agar (B1)
Bacto-Levine E.M.B. Agar (B5)   Bacto-Nutrient Broth (B3)
Bacto-Formate Ricinoleate Broth (B9) Bacto-Tryptone Glucose Extract Agar (B2)

The following media are packaged in amounts sufficient for 100 ml. in boxes of six:

Bacto-Brain Heart Infusion (B32)   Bacto-Phenol Red Lactose Broth (B94)
Bacto-Heart Infusion Agar (B44)   Bacto-Phenol Red Maltose Broth (B96)
Bacto-Heart Infusion Broth (B38)   Bacto-Phenol Red Mannitol Broth (B97)
Bacto-Phenol Red Agar Base (B98)   Bacto-Phenol Red Saccharose Broth (B95)
Bacto-Phenol Red Broth Base (B92)   Bacto-Russell Double Sugar Agar (B84)
Bacto-Phenol Red Dextrose Broth (B93)

PREPARED MEDIA IN TUBES AND BOTTLES

FOR THE bacteriologist who requires only a few tubes or bottles of media or who does not have readily available facilities for the preparation of media, we prepare a series of media in tubes, ready for use. This group of prepared media in tubes offers still another convenience to bacteriologists since some of the media do not lend themselves to dehydration.

Upon request media of any desired formula will be prepared and supplied in tubes or bottles.

These media are put up in regular sized tubes fitted with a tightly sealed screw cap. No cotton plugs are used. The media are freshly prepared, and are examined for sterility before being released. Culture media in tubes should be stored in sealed cans to prevent evaporation, and under these conditions should give good results indefinitely. Agar media should be melted and allowed to resolidify in a slanted position or placed in a warm water bath for several minutes to provide a fresh moist surface prior to inoculation. Media containing blood, ascitic fluid, antibiotics or other thermolabile materials, should not be heated prior to use.

We supply the following media in tubes, packed in boxes of one dozen or one-half dozen tubes each:

B1000T	Ascitic Agar	B88T	Lead Acetate Agar
B1001T	Blood Agar	B5T	Levine E.M.B. Agar
B1013T	Bovine TB Medium	B294T	Littman Oxgall Agar
B37T	Brain Heart Infusion	B70T	Loeffler Blood Serum
B37AT	Brain Heart Infusion with PAB	B1017T	Lowenstein-Jensen Medium
		B50T	North Gelatin Agar
B37BT	Brain Heart Infusion with PAB and Agar	B1T	Nutrient Agar
		B3T	Nutrient Broth
B1002T	Chocolate Agar	B11T	Nutrient Gelatin
B1012T	Chocolate Tellurite Agar	B400T	Peizer TB Medium
B1003T	Cystine Hemoglobin Agar	B1015T	Penase Ascites Medium
B67T	Dextrose Agar	B1010T	Petragnani Medium
B63T	Dextrose Broth	B1011T	Petroff Egg Medium
B1006T	Dorset Egg Medium	B13T	Potato Dextrose Agar
B385TA	Dubos Albumin Broth	B1014T	Root Canal Medium
B373T	Dubos Oleic Agar	B84T	Russell Double Sugar Agar
B385T	Dubos Serum Broth	B109T	Sabouraud Dextrose Agar
B256T	Fluid Thioglycollate Medium	B110T	Sabouraud Maltose Agar
B1007T	Glucose Ascites Medium	B247T	Snyder Test Agar
B1008T	Glycerol Agar	B291T	TB Serum Broth
B44T	Heart Infusion Agar	B64T	Tryptose Agar
B1016T	Lash Serum Medium		

BACTO-DIPHTHERIA CULTURE TUBES (B1004T) AND OUTFITS (B1005T)

The advantages of early diagnosis in suspected cases of diphtheria require no enumeration. As an emergency aid at times when delay may be of serious consequence, we have prepared a Bacto-Diphtheria Culture Outfit which consists of a Bacto-Diphtheria Culture Tube (an hermetically sealed and sterilized Loeffler Blood Serum slant) and a sterile applicator with a data sheet. The outfit is complete, neat and convenient. The hermetically sealed diphtheria culture tube preserves the sterile medium indefinitely, keeping it ready for instant use. This tube is etched for convenience in breaking.

STERILE APPLICATORS IN TUBES (B1009T)

Sterile applicators in tubes have been prepared for use in conjunction with Bacto-Diphtheria Culture Outfits, as discussed above or for use in the collection of other specimens.

These media are packaged in 100 ml. amounts in screw capped bottles. They are especially recommended for blood culture work, each bottle containing sufficient medium for up to 10 ml. of blood or other body fluid as inoculum.

BACTO

PENASE BROTH (B347B)

Bacto-Penase Broth is prepared especially for use in culturing organisms from blood and other body fluids from patients under penicillin, streptomycin, or sulfonamide treatment. It is prepared from Bacto-Brain Heart Infusion and contains sufficient Bacto-Penase and para-Aminobenzoic Acid to inactivate any penicillin or sulfonamide that might be carried over in a body fluid inoculum. One hundred ml. of this medium will inactivate 10,000 units of penicillin and up to 1000 units of streptomycin.

Each bottle of Bacto-Penase Broth contains 100 ml. of medium so as to permit the use of as much as 10 ml. of blood or other body fluid as an inoculum. Inoculation must be made under aseptic conditions. Contamination can best be avoided if the cap is held in the hand, bottom down, to avoid its contact with contaminated objects. After replacing the cap the bottle is gently agitated to distribute the inoculum uniformly throughout the medium. Incubate at 37°C. Observations for growth are made at desired intervals, preferably after 24 hours and on each succeeding day for 14 days. Material for examination may be removed with either a sterile pipette or loop using aseptic precautions.

Bacto-Penase Broth is stable when stored at refrigerator temperatures. At normal room temperatures, the Bacto-Penase in the medium deteriorates slowly and for that reason the medium must be placed in the refrigerator immediately upon receipt and kept there until used. Stability tests to date indicate that the Bacto-Penase in the medium is stable for at least a year when stored in the refrigerator. This medium must not be heated before inoculation as the Bacto-Penase is thermolabile.

Bacto-Penase Broth is supplied in packages of one-half dozen bottles of 100 ml. each.

BACTO-PENASE MEDIUM (B348B)

Bacto-Penase Medium is prepared especially for use in culturing organisms from blood and other body fluids from patients under penicillin, streptomycin, or sulfonamide treatment. It is prepared from Bacto-Brain Heart Infusion with PAB and Agar, and contains sufficient Bacto-Penase and para-Aminobenzoic Acid to inactivate any penicillin or sulfonamide that might be carried over in a body fluid inoculum. One hundred ml. of this medium will inactivate 10,000 units of penicillin and up to 1000 units of streptomycin. The presence of the small amount of agar in the medium provides a range of oxidation-reduction potentials, permitting the development of anaerobes and microaerophiles, as well as aerobes.

Each bottle of Bacto-Penase Medium contains 100 ml. of medium so as to permit the use of as much as 10 ml. of blood or other body fluid as an inoculum. Inoculation must be made under aseptic conditions. Contamination can best be avoided if the cap is held in the hand, bottom down, to avoid its contact with contaminated objects. After replacing the cap the bottle is gently agitated, to distribute the inoculum uniformly throughout the medium. Incubate at 37°C.

Observations for growth are made at desired intervals, preferably after 24 hours and on each succeeding day for 14 days.

Upon storage, and especially upon the addition of the inoculum, there may be a partial flocculation of the agar in the medium. This in no way interferes with the nutritional value of the medium.

Bacto-Penase Medium is stable when stored at refrigerator temperatures. At normal room temperatures, the Bacto-Penase in the medium deteriorates slowly and for that reason the medium must be placed in the refrigerator immediately upon receipt and kept there until used. Stability tests to date indicate that the Bacto-Penase in the medium is stable for at least a year when stored in the refrigerator. This medium must not be heated before inoculation as the Bacto-Penase is thermolabile.

Bacto-Penase Medium is supplied in packages of one-half dozen bottles of 100 ml. each.

BACTO-FLUID THIOGLYCOLLATE (B256B) MEDIUM

Bacto-Fluid Thioglycollate Medium conforms to the formula specified by the National Institute of Health for the sterility testing of biologicals, and for the sterility testing of antibiotics according to the method of the Food and Drug Administration, as well as the specifications given in the U. S. Pharmacopeia and the National Formulary. Bacto-Fluid Thioglycollate Medium is especially recommended for culturing organisms from inocula containing mercurial preservatives. This medium has been used for the cultivation of anaerobes from blood and other body fluids since the small concentration of agar present in the medium prevents reaeration of the medium after sterilization by convection currents and thus maintains a low oxidation-reduction potential. Brain Heart Infusion with PAB and Agar or Bacto-Penase Medium not containing thioglycollate, have proven more satisfactory for the cultivation of some anaerobes and aerobes from materials not containing mercurials.

Each bottle of Bacto-Fluid Thioglycollate Medium contains 100 ml. of medium so as to permit the use of as much as 10 ml. of blood or other body fluid as an inoculum. To test sterility use 1–2 ml. of the solution under assay. Inoculation must be made under aseptic conditions. Contamination can best be avoided if the cap is held in the hand, bottom down, to avoid its contact with contaminated objects. After replacing the cap the bottle is gently agitated to distribute the inoculum uniformly throughout the medium and then incubated at 37°C. Observations for growth are made at desired intervals, preferably after 24 hours and on each succeeding day for 14 days.

Upon storage, and especially upon the addition of the inoculum, there may be a partial flocculation of the agar in the medium. This in no way interferes with the nutritional value of the medium.

Just prior to inoculation the bottles of the medium should be heated in a boiling water bath or flowing steam at 100°C. for 10 minutes to drive out dissolved gases, and then cooled to below 40°C. without excessive agitation.

Bacto-Fluid Thioglycollate Medium is supplied in packages of one-half dozen bottles of 100 ml. each.

Index

343